LINER

In the great tradition of HOTEL, AIRPORT . . .
The SS *Areopagus* is as much an individual as any of her flesh-and-blood cargo which includes an Italian procurer on the run from the Mafia, a retired Australian school-teacher dying of cancer, a disgruntled migrant family returning to Wolverhampton, a nymphomaniac who makes a play for the ship's exuberant Irish doctor – among others, stewards, barmen, cabaret artistes, engineers, hairdressers, good girls and bad boys, fleeing, searching, loving . . .

'Officers and crew have problems too; they explode in a *deus ex marina* from which the author squeezes every stormy possibility'
New York Times

'A great story, full of life, character and adventure'
Birmingham Evening Mail

'James Barlow has been compared with Nevil Shute; and like him he is a splendid, extrovert storyteller'
The Daily Telegraph

Born in Birmingham in 1921, James Barlow became a gunnery instructor in the RAF at the age of 19. A year later, he was found to be suffering from tuberculosis and spent several years undergoing treatment. His writing was confined to articles for *Flight* and *Aeroplane* until 1946 when he decided to become a novelist and his first book to be published was *The Protagonists* (1956). Then followed *One Half Of The World*, *The Man With Good Intentions* and *The Patriots*, which was so successful that Barlow decided to give up his job with the Birmingham Corporation so as to devote himself to writing. His next novel, *Term Of Trial* (1961), was filmed with Lord Olivier, Simone Signoret and Sarah Miles. He has since written several more novels, including *The Burden of Proof* (filmed as 'Villain' with Richard Burton) and *Both Your Houses*.

LINER

James Barlow

Pan Books Ltd London and Sydney

All the characters in this book are fictitious and are not intended to represent any actual persons living or dead

First published 1970 by Hamish Hamilton Ltd
This edition published 1972 by Pan Books Ltd,
Cavaye Place, London SW10 9PG
7th Printing 1975
ISBN 0 330 23227 4

Made and printed in Great Britain by
Cox & Wyman Ltd, London, Reading and Fakenham

To
Jamie Hamilton
who laid the keel

Acknowledgements

For certain technical advice I am grateful to the following: Sperry Gyroscope Division, Sperry Rand Ltd; Copes Regulators Ltd; Decca Radar Ltd; Chadburns (Liverpool) Ltd; P & O Lines; Shaw Savill Line; and the Royal Embassy of Greece, Canberra.

I would like to thank the owners, agents, captains and crews for allowing me to look round various vessels, either at sea or in harbour. I am also grateful to my friends Geoffrey Boughey, Norman Siberry and Captain Leslie Balliol Scott, whose imaginations were at times way ahead of my own.

Part One

ANTIPODES

'new, powerful, large and splendidly fitted up steamships, carrying mail from His Majesty's Post Office.'

—*advertisement, 1837*

Men ... full of activity, stirrers abroad, and searchers of the remote parts of the world.

—*Hakluyt*

I

'WE'LL talk about it,' the man's voice had postulated over the telephone.

He had spoken in Italian, and Bartolomeo Tornetta had been dyspeptic in uneasiness. It, the subject of the telephone call, was, of course, money. His money, earned by work and organization, his skill in the peculiarly twentieth-century trade of titillation. The Italian might simply mean a knowledge of *him*, but it might indicate Mafia. Tornetta lived on girls, gave orders that weren't questioned, but had to cope with trouble quite often : drunken fools who presumed the girls were slot machines for pleasure . . .

'Listen !' he had urged. 'Last week I went to the dentist. Two small fillings. Today the postman brings the account. Eighteen dollars. It is crazy. What kind of a country is this for the poor ?'

He said 'poor' like someone in the preliminary skirmishes of a battle with income-tax inspectors.

It was indeed a strange country.

Tornetta had been in Australia for five years; all of them in Sydney; he was still within walking distance of the docks where he had disembarked.

The Australian manner of life suited him, although he observed its many aspects with perplexity. Much of it was nothing to do with him. He fitted his profession into its vulgar segment and eventually thrived.

The rest meant nothing to him, although it was noticeable, even exploitable. There were two Australias. At first he found both so inelegant and *gauche* that he had considered returning to Italy. There was the old Australia, dying with anger : Victorian trees, high and mighty by the side of the ubiquitous gums; colonial public buildings with tin roofs; Temperance; social conformity, middle-class gentility; the Returned Servicemen's League, and its corollaries, beer drinking and patriotism; Gallipoli's disaster celebrated as a sort of Antipodean Dunkirk by men and their sons who crept annually out of sprawling suburbia.

Then there was the new Australia : articulate academics; consumer goods; the beaches littered with beer cans and rubbish, while well-built youths asserted their qualities on the surfboards; and tall supple girls toasted their breasts brown on sand too hot for the feet, ready to prove their equality, and transistors blared pop from station waggons.

Tornetta had never belonged to this or any of Australia except Kings Cross, even though he spoke good English now and had not been called 'dago' for over three years. He adapted the world to what he was capable of; he never offered himself to an environment; he was essentially there to exploit it . . . He had climbed quickly in Sydney's hedonistic atmosphere. The hot, matey, vulgar city could be exploited. It wanted what he had the gift of supplying. He had found the city so close to frontier crudity that anything was an improvement. The first time he'd been in a big bar of suburbia he'd been astonished that men who had good wages should stand around bare footed, rancid in sweaty vests or shirt sleeves, in this cube which was tiled like a public lavatory and smelled like one. They stunned their senses with beer and listened to the gabbled radio shouting about dogs or horses. It was so aggressively masculine that it suggested a need.

Now Tornetta supplied girls for this brash masculinity to look at. Sydney's Kings Cross area boasted a school for strippers. There were discothèques and book shops, pop art, pastry shops, delicatessens, pizza parlours, and girls . . .

The voice on the telephone had suggested a few days' consideration. There was no need to be alarmed; this was something you needed, like insurance. The terms could be discussed. They – Zito and Attolico – would call on Friday at nine o'clock . . .

In the three days Tornetta had experienced terror in anticipation. He could not pay. A day later anger asserted itself, fury boiled up. He would not pay. He was aware that they would hurt him, smash the place up, slash a girl or two.

Death was a possibility. It was a city proportionately four times as violent as London.

He had thought and thought and in the end decided on escape. If they were Mafia they'd bleed him white anyway. If they were not, so much the better . . . No one in Sydney was sure if the Mafia operated or not. Some journalists felt it would add spice to the night life if it did . . .

Tornetta moved quietly behind the small crowd who were watching 'Prudence Peeler' – a big long-limbed Australian girl with black hair parted in the middle. She had a wild beautiful face. Tornetta had had her on his shabby bed upstairs twice. On a sultry day with a temperature of 106° she'd lain there naked and allowed him to do what he liked – and what Tornetta cared to do was very crude – and after pawing every part of her and then grinding his weight on top of her, he had been filmed with sweat. It had even saturated his hair. 'That was good,' he'd told her, and she'd commented in a devastating drawl which belonged to Brisbane or somewhere : 'Ar, get your breath back and do it properly !'

She was peculiar, far gone, and disturbed her audience who sensed that she despised them.

Four long-haired youths were giggling, drunk. One had his fly unfastened. Kids from some suburb with only an isolated milk bar or Continental fruit shop open after six o'clock. Nearby a taxi driver, his forehead glistening with sweat, and a man who looked like a lifesaver, pickled in brine, with his teak-tan body bolt upright. There was a man there whose wife was a hundred yards away, sipping beer in a sedan. And an old wharfie with a belly like a balloon, tattooed arms folded, police and fireman braces over his singlet, who was actually asleep . . .

Tornetta ran up brick steps to the entrance and advised the hustler, 'There are two men coming at nine o'clock. Get a girl to bring them to the kitchen . . .'

He went to the kitchen and waited, fright accumulating in lumps in his belly, and wishing he'd fled without discussion. He was not new to violence, but it had been some years now since he'd last experienced it. Two of them, Zito and Attolico. He didn't know what size of men they were, if they carried knives or guns or something peculiar to the Australian scene. Or just thumped with fists and kicked with fancy shoes.

Tornetta laid the rough table for one, and put the metal jug full of soup on to the stove behind this position. At ten minutes to nine he poured himself a plate of soup and sat staring at it, while his knees trembled under the table. Behind him eight pints of soup bubbled in the jug. For one man? For the girls? Would the two notice? He placed two chairs more or less opposite himself, so that in one arc of the jug . . .

He heard the jangle of the band at the discothèque in another street. If necessary he would pay. If they were reasonable . . .

A stripper brought them into the kitchen, without knocking, their approach unheard, so that he was caught napping.

The stripper was 'Anatomical Anne' and Tornetta knew at once that the two men were Mafia because in the light of the kitchen they did not take opportunity to scrutinize with rapacity while she was there. Anne was in something like a bikini, was tall and voluptuous, but they didn't even look; nor did they indulge in trivial expressions like 'Thank you'. It implied that strippers and suchlike were available, two a cent, where they came from.

They hesitated just long enough for Anne to get beyond the door and close it. Then the small slim one, neatly dressed, with a long wedge-shaped face, announced with an indicatory hand to his chest, 'Zito.'

'Attolico,' supplied the other dully.

He was middle-aged, fat, but it meant nothing, did not prove any weakness.

'Sit down,' suggested Tornetta, but they smiled at the absurdity, not likely to be put at such a disadvantage, and remained standing. This filled Tornetta with foreboding. He had lost already.

'A drink?' he invited.

They ignored the pleasantry.

'It is nice,' said Attolico. 'A good place you have here. Twenty people in there. Good for an early Friday night show.'

'Not bad,' agreed Tornetta.

'How long have you been here?'
'In Sydney?'
'Here.'
'Six months.'
'And no trouble?'
'Trouble? Why should I have trouble? It is pleasure—'
'That is good.' 'Good' seemed to be a favourite word of Attolico. 'You pay no protection?'
'Who needs protection in Australia?'
They smiled at that, too.
'A lot of gangs here,' Zito pointed out.
'The protection we offer is better than any insurance company's,' explained Attolico. 'If there is damage we repair the destruction, but we also seek out the perpetrators and a little social justice is carried out. If you are threatened we attend to that. If you have financial worries . . . And girls, we have plenty if you find them difficult to employ.'
Zito said, almost earnestly, 'What it amounts to is that we solve all your business difficulties. All we ask is a third of the profit.'
Attolico asked, 'How much is your turn-over?'
It was no use arguing 'That is none of your business.' Tornetta gave him a figure, deducting one third.
'And the profit?'
'Hard to say. I've been here only—'
'But approximately?'
Tornetta quoted a figure, again deducting a third.
'How many girls?'
'Five.'
'You pay them – how much?'
Tornetta began to sweat. They perhaps already had questioned the girls. He gave the correct figure.
'And the sidelines?'
'I do not understand.'
Zito informed him with terrifying calm : 'I explain. The girl you call Lucy Lolita is one of our girls. She says sidelines for a few good clients, up in a bedroom. Thirty per cent you collect, yes?'
'I had forgotten.'

'You remembered the turn-over, but not the profit,' Attolico said, like an accountant to a client who wished to be dishonest, which was very distasteful.

Zito suddenly sat down. 'Let's begin again,' he suggested. 'Five girls. A hustler. Four shows a night. What's the rent? You are obviously not a good businessman. We shall improve things.'

Tornetta stood up, turned, and stretched an arm. 'Here's the rent book.' He opened a drawer of the cheap wooden cupboard by the stove, and threw the book lightly to the seated Zito, who took it with his right hand, putting down a pencil.

Tornetta reached farther very quickly and grabbed the metal jug. Its handle was burning hot, but he was committed now.

The arc of scalding thick fluid caught Zito across the face and his left ear. His reaction in pain was so violent that he lifted the table into the air with his knees. He fell off his chair and writhed on the floor, screaming.

Attolico was a knife man. He backed a little because he was startled and wary of the jug. His face now was quite different. The talk was over. He was a professional and entitled now to exercise his skill. His employers would approve.

He threw a chair at Tornetta, who had to let it hit him or lose the contents of the jug in his outstretched right arm.

They closed in a corner and Tornetta poured fluid over the knife hand as it was thrust towards his stomach. The movement weakened, lost momentum, and the knife merely penetrated his jacket before dropping on to the floor.

Attolico kicked, fought for the jug, but he had lost his fighting hand, was in fact hissing with pain.

Tornetta tipped the jug's contents on to his chest.

It was too much agony to bear. Attolico pleaded surrender, for mercy, forgiveness; nothing would be said; he would go away, only *now*, please—

But Tornetta had the terror of someone attacked by a wasp, or who had trodden on a red-back spider by mistake. He had to inflict more harm, to be sure, to crush the wasp, stamp again on the spider.

The four cupfuls of scalding fluid left in the jug he threw into Attolico's nose and eyes, which doubled him up, blinded, moaning.

Tornetta was grinding his teeth, and sweating. He had to go on. He mustn't kill them or the dicks would become involved. But incapacitated – that was a private matter.

He kicked the prone Zito where it would cripple, and then, still fearful, used his shoes on the man's head.

He looked round then in desperation for a means of crippling Attolico, who was making much noise and blundering about. There was a small hammer in a drawer. He smashed the man's knuckles with it, then battered at the back of his head until, like a great wounded bull, the sixteen-stone Attolico dropped unconscious.

Tornetta could scarcely breathe. He gulped air like a jet engine.

The door of the kitchen opened and Prudence walked in. She took in the situation instantly, laughed, commented, 'Ar, Christ, what a beaut mess!' and rotated in order to leave.

In panic Tornetta grabbed her by the hair, and when the big girl struggled powerfully, he hit her hard across her nose, breaking it. She wept, howled and bled. It was very satisfying to him. She wouldn't despise him lightly again. He had a better idea – fulfilment with the jug.

The metal was still scalding hot. He pushed her big near-naked body against the door she had been anxious to use, and pressed the burning hot metal against her buttocks, branding her.

Prudence bucked and shouted, and then fell down. The blood from her nose was half choking her; she was now frightened. Tornetta realized that he had been foolish. *She* might legitimately complain to the dicks and bring the house down. He hit her twice with the small hammer ... She lay there groaning on the edges of consciousness, very sad, not likely to bother *him* ...

He in any case locked the kitchen door, put the key in his pocket, went into a shabbier laundry room, long since disused, and from a cupboard picked out his solitary suitcase, already packed. He returned to the kitchen, searched the pockets of Zito and Attolico, and found seven hundred dollars.

Outside, the darkness blinded him for a minute in the dirty yard, but the cool October air, even with its smell of garbage, restored him. He was not exhausted, not even tired, and fright only assailed him inasmuch as it insisted on movement.

He walked, breathing heavily, through a few back streets. He could smell the bread being baked, and saw the kaleidoscope of neon signs of the car salesrooms in William Street. From Lorenzini's he inhaled the odour of cauliflower au gratin, which would, he recalled, be followed by zabaglione and very black espresso.

The hired car was where he had left it two hours earlier. He put the case in the boot and drove, meaninglessly, movement being needed more at the moment than direction. The bright lights and heavy traffic for a while gave him the sensation of being followed. He concluded that he was panicking. The scent of onions drifted into the automobile at one traffic light, and girls in mini-skirts strolled about. No trouble. Flowerstalls, bookshops, boutiques, The Crest Hotel, American soldiers on R and R, on past the Pancake Parlour. Tornetta was losing his way and heading towards the docks.

He drove into hilly suburbia, hid himself among the strings of terraces with their cast-iron verandas, solitary lemon trees in the handkerchief-size back gardens, the dust-covered frangipani and fishbone ferns; and the escalating rows of shabby old wooden houses, saturated in paint of all the colours of the spectrum as the district alternated between gentility, poverty and the current kinky.

Tornetta had wasted thirty minutes before he realized that petrol was being burned up, he was tiring, and he had a long way to go. He filled up the tank and had the tyres checked and picked up the main road to Canberra two hundred miles distant.

They had been foolish to allow him a few days. He had in the time available been enabled to make a considerable number of arrangements. Perhaps they – the employers of Zito and Attolico – presumed that he, Tornetta, was some kind of cheap hustler, or a glorified ponce.

In that case they might now conclude that he had gone to ground in one of Sydney's crummier suburbs, that he would turn up in time and could then be dealt with. But if they were Mafia no suburb could hide him and he would have to exercise the utmost cunning to escape them.

This he had done in tedious detail. There was a P and O Lines vessel in Sydney, and Sitmar Line and Shaw Savill liners in Melbourne. Qantas Airlines had international flights out of Sydney and Melbourne every day; there were other flights of BOAC, Pan American and even South African Airways. They might be watching these places. They might be vigilant enough to canvass the main shipping lines, airline offices and travel agents – 'I have a friend booked out of here. His name is Tornetta, a man of about thirty-six, twelve stone, five foot nine. He doesn't even know I'm in this city. I wonder if you'd be kind enough to look up ...' And some girl would do just that. But for an internal flight within Australia Tornetta did not need to give his real name. Nevertheless, extreme caution would be needed, and he had booked an air ticket from Canberra to Hobart, the capital city of the island State of Tasmania, using the name Costello. He would have to wait ten minutes in Melbourne for the connecting jet, but if he managed that the chances were very high that he'd reach Hobart unnoticed. And in Hobart, arriving at the dawn of this day *after* he'd hurt Zito and Attolico, he could board a Greek liner. All this had been explained to him in a travel agency in an outer suburb of Sydney two days ago. The ship was scheduled to sail from Hobart *to* Sydney, and then to Melbourne, Fremantle, and, after several exotic Asian ports, to Guam, San Francisco, Panama, England and Genoa. Tornetta had a brother in San Francisco about whom 'they' would know nothing. Who, given practically no notice, could establish this complicated itinerary in time to interfere with it? Who would expect him to flee six hundred miles south to board a vessel which was coming to Sydney?

And now, with eyes so tired they could scarcely focus, as an airport bus crossed the concrete bridge over the mile-wide Derwent River, he saw beyond the oil storage tanks, the yacht clubs, the green lawns of the Governor's residence, and a curious cemetery on a promontory, conspicuous before the waterfront buildings and small skyscrapers three miles away, that there was a thick trickle of oily black smoke. It rose from the green funnels of a liner and Tornetta's pulse thumped in excitement, the fruition of words, plans, lies, the exchange of money for pieces of paper. For this was the Greek liner *Areopagus* which had arrived here in Hobart from New Zealand while he'd been pacing about Canberra airport in anxiety.

It was only ten o'clock in the morning. Tornetta didn't know what to do. The ship sailed at 10 PM, he had been told, but at what time passengers embarked he was unaware. He decided three o'clock would be a suitable hour. In the meantime, he must dump his suitcase somewhere and pass the hours at a barber's, having a good meal and reading the *Sydney Morning Herald* if it was available here.

Just before three o'clock Tornetta walked with his suitcase to the Empress Dock to board the liner. His first sight of it was comforting, for it was old, corrupt, probably inefficient. My God, he thought, what an old wreck! White paint had recently been applied to its hull and it had a rough texture-like powder on an old whore's face; and brown vertical stains like the fingers of a heavy smoker. He at once felt at ease. It was, he surmised, a ship in which money would talk, bribery, if it became necessary, would be an accepted fact of life.

He was in fact hours early, but joined a line of people near the bows, failing to notice that they did not carry suitcases. After a while an old man in a white coat, who was holding back this small crowd of about a hundred people, told them indifferently: 'The other gangway,' and the wave of an arthritic hand told them where to go.

Tornetta had a suitcase and was hot, and more than exhausted. He trailed hurriedly round a corrugated steel Customs and Excise shed, passed between scores of parked cars, trod over the thick ropes looped round bollards, and moved out of the way of fork-lift trucks. The old scaly white ship seemed impressively big. There was an atmosphere of holiday – people laughing, girls with cameras – but also of pandemonium. Round the other side of the big shed Tornetta was at once absorbed in a crowd of about a thousand people. Anger began to burn him. He was crushed by children, ladies tarted up as if for a ceremony, holding grimly on to cards – Founders Society, Member of the Visiting Ships' Club, and pass cards from shipping agents.

People were coming off the ship and into the shed. A few louts in silly shirts pushed through to a row of charabancs, asking 'Any birds?' A priest talked to two policemen, and beyond them people off the ship, bogged down with cases, prams and kids, answered Customs and Immigration officers who sat behind tables. It was as if Hobart had never received a ship before. Tornetta felt suffocated. Now there were cheers. A woman stood on tip-toes and asked him uselessly 'Who is it?' as some footballer talked before the TV cameras.

The crowd was now too big for the area in which it was confined and began to bulge forward. One of the shirt-sleeved policemen bellowed half-heartedly, 'Get back there!' When no one did so the two of them with a fat Customs man fetched a portable steel barrier and charged the crowd.

This pushed Tornetta to one side and left him near to the front of the mass. He protested, angrily, 'I want to board.'

'You'll be lucky. Another three hours,' a police officer forecast wryly.

'But I have paid—'

'They're still coming off.'

Sure enough, a handful of people disembarked two hundred feet away, out of sight, came in bewilderment through the crowd and boarded a charabanc. Several of these buses belched smoke into the crowd as an organized tour moved off.

'I am a passenger, I have paid,' claimed Tornetta bitterly, aware now that the crowd wanted to visit the ship, not travel aboard her.

'Bit early, aren't you?' the policeman suggested. 'Six o'clock's your time.'

Tornetta had no fear of him, he was so angry; stupid dumb dick. But the man unexpectedly allowed Tornetta beyond the barrier.

It didn't do him any good. There seemed to be hopeless confusion in the big shed. He was alarmed to see Italians with children, prams, food, weeping, sighing, embracing others, while the officers behind the trestle tables waited indifferently. There was no hurry – except for *him*.

He made his way to the obvious opening, beyond which was the bulk of the ship. Two hundred feet to the left was an L-shaped gangway rising to an opening in an upper deck. The same old man in white coat stood at the foot of these steps. A ship's officer stood at the junction of the 'L' and another at the opening in the ship's hull. A few persons were still coming off, in no hurry, dawdling, a word or two with the one officer, a laugh with the other.

The old man in white stopped the seething Tornetta as he approached the gangway. Rage alternated with caution, the need to be totally inconspicuous.

'I have paid. I am not standing round for hours. I have paid. Is this the way to treat a passenger?'

But the doddering old incompetent didn't belong to the ship. It meant nothing to him.

'I can't let you on until they're all off.'

'And how will you know that, you old fool?'

The old man became stubborn. Right was on his side. And Tornetta saw the officer at the junction peering down in curiosity, so he retreated to the opening in the Customs shed.

He stood there feeling conspicuous, a fool.

The two policemen and the obese Customs man stood there with him, passing the afternoon away. All of life revolved round boarding this vessel, being rid of these buffoons who were standing about exercising dull authority.

Still people were disembarking, although the *Areopagus* had been in port at least seven hours that Tornetta knew of. A lout with hair like a bush and a trilby hat jammed on sauntered along.

'Transit passenger?' the Customs man asked. 'Disembarking?' But he was totally indifferent as to which, and the three of them, two policemen and the Customs man, middle-aged, incompetent, perhaps corrupt, checked on nobody. Absurdly, it irritated Tornetta, who above all things wanted incompetence and indifference. For these fools a smile was a guarantee. They were indifferent to parcels coming ashore, even when carried by Chinese youths. 'Are you lost?' a copper asked two overpainted leggy girls, whose eyes were full of themselves, and who were eager for the stares which should have humiliated them; the old eyes running down the legs and estimating the size of breasts. Tornetta viewed them, too, but with dislike, as he stood there, exhausted, the small spots of soup stains on his trouser legs.

The crowd surged through from behind, ignoring the policemen. A woman's voice told them: 'We can board,' and they pushed forward to do so.

Tornetta went ahead of them, but the old man in the white coat had his last moment of authority: 'The other gangway.'

'You said that was for the crew.'

The crowd had turned. Tornetta was no longer first, but about two hundredth. No one else carried a case. They were all visitors. 'We thought we might try the February cruise,' a woman said to him.

There were crew members and an officer standing around, but no one stopped Tornetta. No one asked for his ticket or passport or at what time he wished to go to breakfast and had he had the anti-cholera injection.

He shoved his way through the groups who stood about blocking the way, and went down a couple of decks, and suddenly he was in silence, alone, a whole hundred cabin doors stretching away to the bows, the polished linoleum shining, unmarked by shoes.

It was easy to find A deck. This, too, was empty. The visitors were inspecting bars and ballrooms, resting their tired feet in a lounge and having a coffee, or looking doubtfully at lifeboats.

He had forgotten that the cabins would be locked, but he saw that along the passage at intervals were boxes. Twenty keys hung in each.

Tornetta selected the key to what was to be his cabin. Then he moved a hundred feet forward and snatched a key at random. No one would bother him. Not even the officers would dare to question a passenger 'Have you stolen the key to A93? Why?' The passengers in A93 would simply ask their steward for a spare.

Cabin A145 had two bunks. It was tidy and clean and at the moment absolutely quiet. Tornetta collapsed on the lower bunk and laughed.

He was that rare man: he had cheated the Mafia and escaped.

2

THE BOY came along the empty shabby street in darkness. He was scared, but needed comfort.

The place he sought was in darkness, which both relieved and frustrated him. He rang the bell and five floors up a window opened and the priest's head leaned out impatiently.

'Who is it?'

'Me,' the youth informed him absurdly.

'What's the time?'

'Six-thirty.'

'So it is. I'll come down and open up.'

Lights indicated the priest's descent. He opened the door, put milk bottles on the step, and greeted the boy: 'Wait a minute! Dimitrios, isn't it? Dimitrios Bitsios.'

'Dimitrios Retalis,' the boy corrected him, not impressed by the way the priest had remembered one name for five months. 'Bitsios is the Chief Engineer.'

The street had seemed empty, but with the open door and illumination two young slender Chinese sailors materialized, full of smiles and pleasantries. The four of them went upstairs, the priest, who was very solid, commenting, 'I have to plan each journey or I'd be worn out, up and down these all the time.'

There were hand-painted notices on the stone walls about badminton, dances, the evening service . . .

'I know what you've come for,' the priest ventured. 'The badminton.' And the one young Chinese man laughed shyly.

Now two girls climbed the steps, and on the fourth floor, in a room about eighty feet by forty, proceeded to set up the net.

They began to play badminton with the two Chinese sailors. They were nice ordinary girls. The atmosphere was slightly that of a church hall, but it was not a religious place in that sense : there was no insistence. Many sailors came here simply to find company, to hear the gossip from other ships, or to get away from the confined, frustrating atmosphere of their own. Most of the vessels which called here were merchant ships. A passenger liner was a minor event five or six times in a year. Some Japanese sailors asked the priest about golf courses, horse riding or the fauna. He had to know about local tours and bus timetables. Sailors were no longer the scum of the earth. They liked to be told which were the good restaurants. Sometimes the priest went to fetch them by boarding the ship and pinning a diagram showing the directions, or by talking to the Captain. A lot came anyway. A few never came . . .

The Greek boy stood about awkwardly on the floor polished for dancing. Metal chairs had been stacked round the edges of the room. Perhaps there was a dance tonight. He wasn't interested. There were an old gramophone and a radio available, but he did not touch them.

The badminton game was in full swing with much laughter. The boy felt embarrassed. The priest had gone into a small gloomy office which had no door. He could be seen, was available, but the boy was fearful. He stood about in the hall and looked without awareness at the flags of many shipping companies which hung on the walls or were pinned up. Most of them were the flags of small companies. One had an 'S' on it which was back to front no matter which way the flag was seen. Similarly, there were circular and horse-shoe shaped lifebelts from many ships hanging up.

He approached the office, which was also a small shop. A faded notice was stuck on its one window : 'Donations here', and, as it happened, the priest was counting dollar notes and silver.

'They are very generous,' he told the boy.

'Can I speak to you?' Dimitrios asked.

The priest identified the tone, the content of misery or guilt. Outside the office there was the click of billiard balls, the noise of tea cups, and someone had coaxed the old gramophone into making a noise. A polite Chinese voice was asking about the score.

'Of course,' the priest agreed. 'But a little quieter, Dimitrios, if it is confidential.'

Dimitrios understood the request and was not offended. He explained : 'It is the noise of the engines. I am slightly deaf for two days when we come ashore, and people tell me that I shout. It is not as bad as my previous ship,' he told the priest, conversational, talking fast, misery forgotten momentarily. 'That was a diesel, you see. I used to ask my mother to speak up, and she was offended because *she* was a little deaf too ! They brought a machine to that ship to record the sound level, you know, the number of decibels. And our ship broke the machine!' He was smiling – he had a good smile. 'It was too hot, that engine room. And the fumes, you know, cause cancer.'

The priest suggested, 'Let's go into the sitting-room if it's empty.'

He was delayed by another man, the treasurer, tall, earnest and sour. But the sitting-room was empty. Not that either of them was relaxed enough to sit in the soft armchairs.

There were photographs of ships – sail and steam – in the room, and a model on a crowded mantelpiece. A notice about divine services was going yellow. Out of the window lights gleamed on water and a mile away the *Areopagus* glittered, like a photograph in a book about the romance of the sea.

Dimitrios said, as if proving something. 'When we got to Piraeus the previous crew all signed off and they didn't sign on again.'

'An unhappy ship,' the priest acknowledged.

'So we were all new,' Dimitrios agreed, 'except the officers and a few others.'

There was a long silence after the priest had said, 'I see.'

Then the boy looked down at the carpet and said shakily, 'I've got a dose, you see, that's what it is.'

The priest was neither shocked nor critical.

'A lot of dirty places round the world,' he suggested, spreading the guilt. 'A sad, useless bunch of people out to give pleasure for money.'

'It wasn't like that.'

'A girl you know? You were very fond of?'

'Not a girl.'

The priest was still not startled, but he sighed with the uselessness of it. A thin boy, tousled brown hair, cheap clothes, cracked down-at-heel shoes, a sallow thinned-down face, and eyes rimmed pink with tiredness or shame. But only a boy despite the admission and the ports round the world and the 3000° furnaces and superheated steam which turned the first row or two of the turbine blades a dull red. And a boy who had feeling, guilt, an awareness of God . . .

'A fellow you picked up? Can you trace him? You both ought to go to hospital, at least have treatment.'

'One of the crew.'

'Ah! You'll both still have to go for treatment. It's not painful these days. Why not now?'

'We're sailing tonight.'

'Where to?'

'Sydney, Melbourne, Fremantle, Bali, Singapore—'

'And don't you go to England? Treatment would be free. Or America. San Francisco, isn't it? Then you and your friend—'

'Not my friend.'

'Why not?'

'He's not, that's all.'

Here was the crux of it, the priest knew, the misery and loathing.

'Not an enemy, surely?'

'I hate him. He laughs about everything. If only he'd *go* . . . He's worse than any of them.'

'Any of them' suggested misery indeed to the priest. In the confined and steamy hot atmosphere of long periods at sea it would be virtually impossible to fool anyone. Insincerity, unreliability, fear, laziness, sexual inclinations – these would soon be perceived. They'd all know about the boy and he would be aware with the instant perception of queers that they did. But where had the tolerance of seamen gone?

'And it's him?'

'There's been no one else in six months,' the boy said unhappily.

'How did it happen?'

Dimitrios found this easier to talk about.

'He's a barman, a steward. He's funny, you see, really caustic. You couldn't help but laugh at him. He was so cynical about the passengers . . . He attended – to – some of their – needs – before me,' the youth said, at rock bottom. He sighed in weariness and sneered in contempt of his own foolishness: 'And he's a pot polisher, a Saturday-afternoon seaman!'

He was virtuous now, indignant even, but in the silence was honest enough with himself to recall sordid hurried scenes in cabins and confined places, even the empty smoke-filled Forward Bar. Whisky to deaden the flesh and a mutual sweating in the tropical heat and his own body willing to allow anything . . . He imagined that although the priest understood, generally speaking, what happened, he was far too nice a little man to be fully aware of what occurred.

'What do you want me to do?' the priest asked frankly. 'Dimitrios, there are two sides to this – the physical and spiritual. You understand this or you wouldn't be here . . .'

'I don't know,' admitted Dimitrios.

The priest spoke gently but with conviction about the spiritual half of it. He did not reprimand or lecture, but simply pointed out the things they had in common. The boy was or had been Orthodox Greek, but this is almost parallel with Catholicism.

Then the priest turned to the physical half of degradation.

'How bad is this?'

'I don't know.'

'You can go blind or mad if it's serious. It takes time but – Listen! You must go to the surgeon on the ship. He is, I am sure, familiar with these matters.'

'There has been trouble.'

'Trouble?'

'The *Areopagus* has come from Southampton, Bremerhaven and Rotterdam. More than a thousand migrants. We came the Panama way to Wellington. We ran out of fresh water for washing and had to use salt water for showers. They ran out of baby foods and disposable things. There were eight in a cabin on Attica Deck. There was no choice of food. No flowers on the tables. Women had to wash nappies in the swimming pool. There was dysentery . . .'

'But now?' questioned the priest. 'It is all right?'

Dimitrios laughed outright.

'No. It is worse! There is water, to be sure. But two hundred people boarded in New Zealand, most of them old. They thought they were boarding an empty ship for a round-the-world cruise! They've been having rows with the Chief Purser,' he said, amused about it. 'Captain Vafiadis was dragged into it. Unwittingly, of course. He prefers to be the gentleman! They've held protest meetings which he's refused to attend. There are queues in the surgery . . .'

'I am sorry to hear this,' the priest said, 'but not surprised.'

He had heard about the *Areopagus* before. Friends had mentioned it in letters from Malta, Vancouver and Melbourne. It was a very old ship, being thrashed to death by its owners.

'And we shan't be able to keep the schedule of this ridiculous cruise,' Dimitrios told him. 'Once we're in tropical waters the heat of the sea means we can't cool the engines so performance is lowered. The owners assume we can make 19 knots all round the world, but here we can scarcely make 17. Tubes are cracking, and we have a job replacing the ones that are curved. We can't carry a mountain of spares.'

'But at least these migrants will disembark at Sydney or Melbourne.'

'I suppose so,' the boy agreed, but he clearly did not feel the medical officers would be free or inclined to deal with *his* problem.

'About this other fellow – what's his name?'

'John.'

'You do not have to see a lot of him?'

'No. We work in different parts of the ship.'

'And sleeping?'

'That, too.'

'Then he should be easy to avoid . . . Does he know that he is ill?'

'I don't know.'

'Perhaps you should tell him. If he's promiscuous—'

'I will avoid him,' affirmed Dimitrios with determination. 'And the others who mock me—'

'Do not allow yourself to be hurt by words,' advised the priest, aware of how difficult this would be, and how lonely the boy must be. 'Pass these things off with a bit of wit. Deflect the arrows.'

'All right,' Dimitrios agreed, beginning to move. 'And thank you.'

'I know it won't be easy,' acknowledged the priest. 'But I cannot believe that the whole boiler-room crew dislike you. You are not a person who arouses dislike. I will, of course, pray for you.'

The boy smiled.

'Okay. I will see the doctor when the ship empties a little . . . See you in six months,' he said in farewell, and the priest felt cold with the hopelessness. Ten minutes' difficult talk to counteract the influences of the entire world.

Seamen, the priest felt, were running away from something. Many of them didn't want to sail at all, and from the first day were in effect waiting to get back. Their tough postures often hid personal inadequacies. Many of them from Australian and British merchant ships were not all that bright. At times they became aggressive towards the priest, but he took his jacket off to them and challenged, 'Come on, then!' but they didn't. They wept sometimes, or sat in the room where the boy had stood, sat like children while he roared at them for allowing the Communists to run the unions.

He liked them. Their attitudes were human and simple, their problems the old ones of drink, unfaithfulness in their wives, and friction below decks. Engineers and seamen, like oil and water, never quite mixed. Seamen resented these men who got a certificate in some motor works ashore and came to sea for a while, but never really belonged. The bottle was a problem afloat as well as ashore. Some sailors, particularly on cargo ships, were drunk throughout the voyage. The Captain, getting rid of them, would perhaps be kind and give a 'clean' reference so that the sailor drifted successfully from ship to ship. Asian sailors did not seem to have any neuroses at all, or else hid them very well.

Sometimes the priest had to break bad news, tell a sailor that while he'd been at sea his little child had been knocked down by an automobile and killed. He knew currently of a timid little man, a cook, who had gone temperamental and finally run amok with an axe precisely for this kind of reason.

The priest felt that Dimitrios found the world too much because of his weakness and preferred the smaller, more manageable and tolerant world of a ship. But this was not so. The boy had gone to sea because it was a good job. In Athens the average annual wage was about £200. The peasants in the countryside were lucky if they got £50 each year. Greece was a beautiful country, but it was desperately poor and a job at sea meant meat to eat.

Dimitrios' parents lived in a village twice blasted by shell-fire in their lifetime. In the summer people passed through the village, foreigners in big cars which left clouds of dust, and they commented on the fragrance of herbs and wild flowers, the charm of the steep cobbled village street, or a girl in black with a tall brown jug on her head . . . They sighed with satisfaction and talked of this, the cradle of democracy and civilized discussion. They admired the cubistic architecture of the small whitewashed terraced houses and stared at the distant mountains, and accepted a drink of wine at a table of the *taverna*, bravely risking the chances of disease from glasses not too clean. They strolled back to their automobiles through a small flock of skinny goats and drove off back to Athens to see the horses racing at the Phaleron race course, or to dine out in the open on delicious seafood at Tourkolimano, and never mind the smells around the docks just this once . . .

They did not stay for the winter or observe the incidence of tuberculosis . . .

Dimitrios walked back to the ship. There was nothing else to do, or, more exactly, no one else to do it with. He boarded up the same gangway as Tornetta, but then descended two decks, went through the kitchens, and in his cabin changed.

He was back in the environment of semi-darkness, where there was no distinction between day and night, of humid atmosphere, and the ingrained smells of oil, soot, steam, particular foods, urine, dirty towels, sweat, all circulated uselessly by dull air which came out of square-sectioned metal trunking. There was an atmosphere of mild urgency now, for the *Areopagus* was due to sail in two hours. Men in shorts and stained singlets, slacks saturated in oil and dirt, tattered vests, already sweating, moved about, their feet soundless in split pumps.

Dimitrios went back to Metaxas Deck and almost at once encountered John in the kitchens, popping bits of hot food into his mouth. The boy felt embarrassed, almost ashamed, as if he had betrayed this tall angular man of thirty with the quick wit and possessiveness. It had been, perhaps still was, a strange relationship in which John caustically took it for granted that he and Dimitrios were special people, superior to these heavy headed peasants who filled the ship.

'Where've you been?'

'How did you know I'd been anywhere?'

'I searched for you,' John said simply. 'I thought we could look around this little town together.'

'I went to the doctor,' Dimitrios said evasively.

He found it hard to lie to John.

'Are you ill?'

'I think I have a dose.'

John laughed, hugely, as if this was a terrific joke. 'And what did the Australian doctor say?'

'That there wasn't time to do anything.'

'What a fool! He only has to give you some pills. I'll give you some. You look really frightened!'

'You should be, too.'

'Oh, I see. You are angry with me. You blame me.'

'Who else?'

'Who, indeed? I am touched. Have a bowl of soup. It's good.'

'I am going on duty.'

'So am I. The blasted Captain has guests . . . Shall I give you some tablets?'

'It doesn't matter.'

'I know where you've been!' cried John, amused. 'To that fat ridiculous priest. You saw him last time.'

Dimitrios argued, hot and bothered, 'What of it?'

'How delicious it must be to have a conscience and *suffer*!' teased John. 'It makes love so much more exciting. And pox! That must be like the flavour of hell fire!'

'I don't think it's funny.'

'But what tortures next time as the flesh overcomes the spirit!'

'There's not going to be a next time,' asserted Dimitrios firmly.

'Not with me?' questioned John, but with instant malice, protecting his own feelings. 'I'm prostrate with distress! But, Dimitrios, you're only eighteen. Despite the inconvenience of your little illness your flesh will become *eager* for love every few days . . .'

Dimitrios already knew this to be true: his body humiliated him, even alone. He had shuffled in the darkness of his bunk, hot, ashamed and frightened.

'Don't you want the tablets to be rid of it?' John asked.

'No. I'll go and see the surgeon.'

'You'll have to hurry,' John informed him. 'He's leaving the ship at Sydney. All that dysentery was too much for him.'

'I'll see the other one.'

'Why not the Sister? She'd be fascinated!'

Dimitrios said dully, 'I must go on duty.'

John sneered, 'I must find myself another innocent for my pleasures. What a pity! You were quite good at it.'

This was intended to hurt, and, unaccountably, it did.

'To hell with you,' Dimitrios snarled hotly, and turned to walk away.

'Ah, no! Hell is for people like *you*,' John corrected him.

He went out of the galleys forward, through the empty dining-room, while Dimitrios, shaking and with a bit of a headache, went aft. Just aft of the kitchens he opened a door, and beyond it, four feet away, was another door which he went through. Beyond this second door was the domain of the engineers. The two doors existed so that the forced draught – sent down by a turbine-driven pump on the Sun Deck – wouldn't escape. It was needed down here for, among other things, the combustion of oil.

Dimitrios descended about thirty feet down worn steps, slippery with oil. After a while his legs and then his chest and face came into atmosphere so hot, it was like entering fluid. The rails his hands steadied himself on were scorching to his touch.

He went through the workshop, which was old, reminiscent of a nineteenth-century institution: worn benches, vices, spare valves and cocks. Air from a protruding square-sectioned duct blew his hair about, giving momentary relief.

Farther down he came into the confused area of boilers, pipes, gauges, valves, piping and auxiliary equipment where the sixty men of the engine rooms worked. They worked in three shifts, or watches, so that twenty men were on duty all the time, ten on the port side fire-room and turbines and ten on the starboard. In the port engine room everything looked filthy and old, much of it coated with thick asbestos which was cracked and beginning to break. The safety rails were chest high and meaningless, for a man could roll under them without arching his body much: a heavy sea could throw him under the rail. Not that he would do more than crack his head or break an arm, for all the moving parts were encased.

It was Dimitrios' job to watch the pressure gauges in the port boiler room, but he also kept an eye on dials and gauges which were positioned on the bulkhead between the two engine rooms (for one was behind the other). The *Areopagus* was so old she had been designed before naval architecture and engineers had become neat and tidy. Ergonomics was a word not then invented. Ships designed today – warships, tankers, cargo ships, passenger liners, even vehicle ferries – have the bridge and engineering gauges and instruments arranged with logic and neatness. As on the automobile fascia, the number of instruments has increased and the speed of the eye and the human mind is considered. Much thought is given as to whether the dials on the consoles should be white with black numbering, or vice versa; and consideration is applied as to the possible tedium of reflective surfaces of the material into which the dials are set. But on the *Areopagus* it was as if instruments were resented altogether, and a variety of boxes and brass plates with ratchets and pointers were stuck all over the bulkhead where the Duty Officer or Chief Engineer stood. The telephone to the bridge was placed inconveniently and had no sound proofing, indeed no enclosed box at all.

The Chief Engineer was now standing on this 'flat' platform. He was a thickset man with cunning eyes and pale skin the texture of a lizard's. He was the only person who ever kept reasonably clean down here, dressed in the white boiler suits the engineering officers wore. He looked at Dimitrios with slight surprise, aware that the boy had come on duty twenty minutes early. Perhaps he would make a generous note about it in the engine room register. Dimitrios' eyes read the instruments which concerned or interested him : auxiliary steam 250, steering gear 210, returning water 120°.

After a while the bridge rang down and the Chief Engineer watched as Dimitrios took the telegraph through the test required. A quarter of an hour later the ship's siren blew and a quarter after that the bridge telegraphed Dead Slow Astern, which meant a mere 25 revolutions of the propellers a minute. There was no sensation of movement or direction, not even when, the pilot dropped, speed was increased from the manœuvring revolutions of Half Speed (forward) which was 45, to the full 130 or so revolutions of each propeller and the *Areopagus* began to pick up speed to about 17 knots. There was an instrument which recorded these revolutions and it flicked round at the digit end like the trip recorder in a car. It was reading 89,937 now and ticked away as Dimitrios looked.

He stood there in the tremendous heat and air already foul and thought of his position in the world sadly. He was lonely and diseased. He had taken the enormous trouble to learn English so that he could emigrate from the poverty of Greece to the wealth of Australia. But they would not be likely to allow him into the country if he was diseased, and he did not quite have the courage to go ahead anyway. He was committed to this strange life among boilers and turbines, to the sweat rolling down his neck and chest, and to this old ship which he loved just a little. He belonged here . . .

3

THE lorry came along George Street too quickly, and turned badly into the Dock so that its rear tyres screeched and skidded sideways. The lorry was loaded with low pressure tanks. One fell off and fractured its valve.

Gas was released in a glass-covered area. A Greek sailor came out of a sweet shop, smoking a cigarette. The gas exploded and fire roared and belched.

The lorry had moved five hundred feet by now and its driver didn't even know what had happened.

The area was not crowded, but there were a few screams. Very slowly, as it seemed, the fire was put out. There was a certain amount of comedy as water was used, in vain.

A taxi came to a stop and a man of about thirty-three paid its driver. He looked round and said in an accent partly Australian, but most of it Irish, 'Jesus! The Black and Tans have been here!'

But he went quickly across to the sailor who was lying unconscious in a small pool of blood.

'What happened?' the man asked.

There were now plenty of people willing to tell him, but he didn't listen once he knew what had knocked the sailor down.

'I'm a doctor,' he told the people standing around. 'Get a stretcher. We'll take him on board.'

Someone suggested, 'An ambulance?' but the doctor said impatiently, 'They'll be all blasted day and rattle him to death anyway.' Which was a little unfair to the city of Sydney . . .

The sailor's pulse was rapid, but weak and thin.

It was typical of the doctor's strong personality that he found two men and a stretcher at once, and he hurried ahead of them to the *Areopagus*.

The usual poor soul in white coat tried to stop him, but the doctor swept him aside. 'Out of the way, Thucydides, we have problems.' And then, to an officer, 'Where's the surgery?' and the officer, too, surrendered to the personality before noticing the stretcher. 'A Deck forward,' he told him. The doctor shouted this information to the two middle-aged volunteers who were sweating and staggering with the stretcher. The sailor was now groaning.

There was a Greek doctor in uniform in the surgery. He was sitting on a trolley drinking coffee. With him was a Greek Sister, a woman of about thirty with a sad, sympathetic ochry face.

The uniformed doctor stood up at the interruption and asked in English, 'Who the devil are you?'

'I'm the new boy,' the doctor told him. 'Dempsey. Daniel Dempsey. We've got a poor bastard crew member here—'

'The time for crew examinations is from eight until nine—'

The Greek doctor was picking his teeth with a matchstick. He produced a silver cigarette case.

'Not this one,' asserted Dempsey. He had a voice which was very incisive and a little loud even when, as now, he did not raise it in impatience. Jesus, he thought. He's going to light a cigarette in his surgery! I hope the blasted place blows up. 'This one is hurt.'

'He was hurt on board?' inquired the uniformed doctor conversationally.

'No. On the dockside.'

'Ah, good. He's not our pigeon. Has someone sent for an ambulance?'

Dr Dempsey said with bite: 'I'd heard this was a lousy ship and that the last Australian doctor walked off in disgust. When I was on the *Opalescent* a few years ago—'

They were to become very fed up hearing about the merits of the British ship *Opalescent* . . .

'There is nothing the matter with this ship or the surgery,' shouted the Greek doctor, red in the face. 'You will see this when you look round.'

The Sister was now weeping soundlessly.

'What's the matter with her?' asked Dempsey caustically.

'She is tired.'

'Overwork or too much dancing?'

'I am in charge here,' shouted the Greek, now furious.

The men with the stretcher kicked the surgery door open and stood, sweating and puffing, in the small area which was the waiting-room.

'Where d'you want him, mate?' one asked.

Dempsey said to the Greek doctor, taking advantage of this arrival, 'Can we discuss your importance later? Let's help this poor bastard.'

'Of course,' agreed the uniformed officer coldly. 'We will all pay attention while you demonstrate your professional skill and shout and curse.'

It was a bad start. Furthermore, the sailor had a ruptured spleen and torn guts. He was treated for shock and injected with morphine and antibiotics to stop infection, but had to be taken ashore two hours later to be operated on.

Dempsey was given a cabin on the starboard side near the surgery. He unpacked his suitcases and remained unpenitent, right on his side. He was usually right and forthright with it, annoying people as quickly as, socially, he amused or shocked them. He was a bachelor who admired women and who was liked by them because he was cheerful, confident, talkative and slightly outrageous – but 'safe'. He was prone to making risky or blood-curdling revelations, usually at mealtimes, and was fascinated by gossip. But women could identify him better than he knew, and were aware that he was not lecherous, was a very straight sort of man; indeed, when alone with just one woman he was noticeably less effervescent, being essentially a man who was a good talker at parties. He argued fiercely against Catholicism, but anyone could soon see that he belonged to it and to Ireland which he had left ten years before.

He had been walking down Leadenhall Street in London eight years ago and on impulse had stepped inside one of the palatial buildings which front for the passenger shipping companies. 'I'd like to be a ship's doctor,' he'd volunteered.

Dempsey had all the qualifications and obtained the references required. Weeks later he'd received a letter asking him if he preferred to serve on the African or Asian run. He had thought vaguely of emigrating to Australia beforehand and promptly selected Asia. Two weeks later he had reported to the *Opalescent* at Tilbury.

He had a practice in Sydney and had become an Australian citizen. He'd only made three trips on the *Opalescent*, but remembered them with pleasure. Recently circumstances had allowed him to consider travel for a few months and a friend in the Health authority had told him that the *Areopagus* had had problems and a doctor had walked off – probably to avoid being dismissed by the Company.

He took the evening surgery with the Greek officer, who was distinctly cool. The Sister looked at Dempsey now and again – and he felt she was a fraction converted by his humorous approach to passengers. He did nothing about which the Greek officer, who was First Surgeon, could complain.

Dempsey ranked as Second Surgeon. He knew from experience aboard the *Opalescent* that as a Second Officer he would be expected to behave, and drink, like a Second Officer of the bridge or engine room. On the *Opalescent* that had been embarrassing, for the officers had been much older men who drank heavily at parties in their cabins. Gin and whisky had been very cheap on board. Dempsey recalled a party which had included a cricket team on its way to Australia. He had ended that voyage owing the Company two shillings and three pence! But now he was eight years older, with very much more money in the bank, and with the aggressive confidence of experience; and he suspected that Greek ships and Greek officers would be different, socially, from the British.

After duty surgeries and cabin calls he was free to wander the ship, only having to tell the telephone operator where he would be. There were at present only two people in the ship's hospital, both sailors whom the Greek officer attended. The senior doctor would probably be the one who attended to the requirements and endless documentation of port authorities. Dempsey recalled visiting Japan with the *Opalescent.* The Japanese authorities had required a mountain of documentation, but after drinking a hell of a lot of gin had left the forms behind...

Two days later he trailed round with the Captain, the Staff Captain and the Chief Purser, who were all Greeks and walked somehow as if Dempsey wasn't there. This did not in the least daunt Dempsey.

The crew were fully aware of the impending inspection and prepared for it. The stewards and cooks, bakers and storemen, messmen, apprentices and pastry cooks all looked cheerfully villainous small dark men. None appeared to have used new razor blades for some time.

In the kitchen Dempsey said, conversationally, to no one in particular, 'Don't you have detergent dispensers and rinse line injectors for the dishwashers? On the *Opalescent* we had power sprays which scraped and rinsed. I mean, what's the good of these blasted things he referred to old dishwashing machines – 'if dirty little hands then pick things up?'

The Captain turned to examine Dempsey as if he'd just noticed him for the first time and found him an object of doubtful taste.

The Staff Captain – a formidable man with a hawk face, who thrived on trouble – also looked, but said nothing.

It was left to the Chief Steward to object mildly. 'The

ship was built and equipped a little earlier than the *Opalescent*.'

A few minutes later Dempsey commented, 'Is this all the refrigerator space? God Almighty! No wonder you've had dysentery aboard! On the *Opalescent* we had cubic miles of rigid foam for insulating the provision rooms and cold chambers.'

Again the Chief Steward countered any implication. 'This is a much smaller ship.'

Dempsey picked up an egg. 'Jesus! It's got a British lion stamped on it! They *all* have,' he said in astonishment. 'Do you mean to tell me you're still using British eggs taken on board seven weeks ago?'

Captain Vafiadis said coldly, very slowly, as if translating with difficulty, 'Do you suggest we throw away two or three thousand eggs, doctor?'

'Do what you like with them,' countered Dempsey cheerfully, 'only don't serve *me* with any!'

'I do not think anyone has been served with a bad egg on the *Areopagus* these last eight years,' said Captain Vafiadis, and the Chief Steward, who was standing there waiting to be commended, agreed without qualm, 'That is quite true.'

Dempsey decided to shut up for the day.

He took the surgery that evening. The Greek doctor had a habit of disappearing, and Dempsey refused to complain.

The Greek Sister stood around, vaguely apprehensive, and translated when required. She handed out suppositories and antibiotics and pills to cure constipation.

A Greek mother, who was well advanced in her next pregnancy, was the last of ten patients. She had brought along a small child of about two. The child had a bad cough, acute bronchitis, and Dempsey was not happy about her.

He prescribed antibiotics and said to the Sister, 'Tell her the child must have the medicine and she must stay in bed. She is pretty poorly.'

The Sister translated for him and answered the few questions of the mother.

Two days later Dempsey, doing cabin calls, decided to visit this patient. He expected to find the little girl much better.

She was lying in a crowded cabin and she was dying of pneumonia.

Dempsey was shaken.

The cabin was hot and it smelled of clothes and herbs and urine.

He asked, 'Does anyone speak English?'

They found a girl of sixteen, who listened to a babble of advice and then said to Dempsey, 'We tried to give her the medicine, but she didn't want it. She is a good little girl, very quiet. Is she better now?'

He instructed the girl: 'Tell them the child is dangerously ill and I must take her at once to the ship's hospital.'

The girl's face whitened in shock and her eyes moistened. When she translated there were tears and shouts, arms waved and faces were thrust before his, anxious peasant faces, already marked heavily with the burdens of life.

Dempsey wrapped the child up and hurried with her to the hospital, a trail of wailing relations behind him.

The Sister was in the surgery, and two nurses, who promptly disappeared.

Dempsey put the child in a hospital bed and searched through the drug store. It was in a state of chaos. The surgeon who had left the ship had ordered what he'd felt would be required, but had made little allowance for the thousand migrants.

'Aren't you bastards answerable to anyone at all?' Dempsey roared in great anxiety.

The Sister said stonily, 'No one has died, have they?'

'This one will.'

'What are you looking for?'

He told her.

'We don't have any,' she said, and then, in explanation, 'This is a Greek ship, not American.'

'I don't give a damn what it is. If they can order thirty thousand eggs and let three thousand go stale—'

She asked bitterly, 'What are you shouting about? We are

fully trained, too. Doctor Zafiropoulos and myself as well as you Australians.'

'Dublin,' he corrected.

'What?'

'I was trained in Dublin.'

'There you are, then.'

'What do you mean, here I am?'

She smiled and ventured cautiously: 'We're both on a ship with a Panamanian flag. What does it matter where we've trained?'

'Christ, women are evasive!' he bellowed, but with good humour. 'I wasn't talking about your capabilities but the shortage of drugs . . .'

'Are you expecting an epidemic?' she asked quietly.

'When I was on the *Opalescent*—'

'Oh, no!' the Sister protested. 'I couldn't bear such a perfect ship!'

'Come and have a drink when we've settled this kid?'

'Me? A dirty Greek incompetent? With you? Am I worthy? Are my fingernails and feet clean enough?'

'Oh, hell,' he said. 'Now I've trodden on your corns . . . Her mother's pregnant. About seven months. On the *Opalescent* we had a delivery room – Oh! Sorry! I'll try not to mention that ship again.'

'Very well,' the Sister said. 'In that case I will come for a drink with you.'

Her name was Eleni Kalogeropoulou. She was serious, but quite formidably witty. For three days they fought day and night for the child's life. She flickered on the edge of death several times, but they saved her. The Greek doctor said nothing, but Dempsey sensed a respect at the end of those three days, and knew they were going to be a good team. The First Surgeon's names were Panayiotis Zafiropoulos, neither of which was easy for Dempsey. After a week they were calling each other Dan and Pan.

It was never the same as the *Opalescent* in efficiency, but Dempsey began to like it. Sometimes he opened his mouth to tell them about the *Opalescent*, but desisted. Perhaps it belonged to a world that was dying: India and the British

Raj, colonialism and the journey Home. He recalled his Goan steward, Gomez, a young man of incredible loyalty. Dempsey had felt he had belonged to *him*. The Goan had inspected him before he allowed Dempsey to go to dinner. When he had laid out socks, shirt and so on, the socks on the bed had always been in line with the gleaming shoes on the linoleum. Many a time Gomez had in bare feet swept the broken glass of the previous night's party. He had done this in silence long before waking Dempsey.

Two nights later while he was dining alone Dempsey was called to the bridge with urgency. The quartermaster in fact came to fetch him.

He found the Officer of the Watch – tonight it was the Third Mate – vomiting and miserable with diarrhoea. He evidently had food poisoning. 'Rotten eggs!' suggested Dempsey, and had the young man brought to the hospital.

In the morning he was summoned to appear before the Master. Dempsey ranked as Second Officer, but it was very rare for a doctor to be sent for by the Captain, let alone put in the log book.

Captain Vafiadis was in his Day Cabin, which Dempsey at once compared with that of the Master of the *Opalescent* and found it infinitely inferior, almost scruffy. With the Master was the First Officer, Tomazos, a dumpy cheerful man of about thirty-five. They were studying a fuel chart.

The Master looked at Dempsey. He was a man whose feelings it was impossible to identify. As well, his translations blurred any emotion he may have felt. For this reason he always sounded like somebody reading a script, and his speeches to English-speaking passengers seemed flat.

Nevertheless, it was obviously a reprimand he now intended and he did not even ask the First Mate to leave.

'Dr Dempsey,' he pointed out. 'Last night you ordered an officer off the bridge because you felt he was not fit enough to continue his duties?'

'He has food poisoning,' Dempsey told him, not without satisfaction.

'The bridge,' said Captain Vafiadis, 'is the heart of the ship and its brain. It is essential that an officer always be there. Why was the First Officer not informed that the Officer of the Watch had been taken to hospital?'

Dempsey disputed : 'How should I know where the First Officer was? I had a duty to my patient which was urgent.'

He looked at the seated First Officer, expecting to see resentment, but Tomazos grinned very faintly and winked.

'You seem to be under the impression that because this is a Greek ship it is run carelessly,' complained the Captain.

'Not at all—'

'It is run as efficiently as any British battleship—'

'There aren't any British battleships any more,' Dempsey pointed out, refusing to be intimidated, and Tomazos lowered his face and hid a smile behind a hand.

'On this ship there is always an officer on the bridge,' said Captain Vafiadis.

The blighter thinks I'm going to apologize, Dempsey deduced with irritation. He countered, 'The bridge was in darkness but it seemed quite crowded to me. The First Officer might well have been there.'

'Very well,' the Captain acknowledged. 'May I now ask if you would care for a drink? And how is the Third Officer now?'

As on shore, patients seemed to have their emergencies at night. Dr Zafiropoulos decided to give a party in his cabin for any passengers on board who happened to be doctors. There were three and they came with their wives, dressed very formally, and for the first twenty minutes were careful with their dialogue. After that they realized that the Greek officer wanted them to enjoy themselves. They began to drink quite heavily and to laugh and fill the cabin with cigar smoke.

Dempsey was there with Sister Eleni and a nurse named Anna, who was very attractive but spoke not a word of English apart from certain words related to medicine and the functions of the human body.

They were very noisy when a man entered and shouted : 'My battery's failed.'

No one took any notice and the middle-aged Australian

called with some desperation, 'Where's the doctor? My battery's failed.'

Dempsey asked, 'What battery?' and the man informed him : 'The one in my heart.'

'God Almighty!' bellowed Dempsey. 'That's all we need!'

'What do we do?' asked Zafiropoulos, and not one of the four doctors knew.

Dempsey asked, 'Don't you have a spare for the thing?'

'I don't know where it is,' wailed the patient.

'My God, man!' protested Dempsey. 'Ask your wife or somebody.'

'I don't know where she's gone.'

'It's not such a big blasted ship,' suggested Dempsey. 'Find her.'

'I'm tired,' admitted the man.

A long search for the man's wife followed. She wasn't in the cabin. 'I've looked there; I told you,' complained the man.

'Christ, find the woman!' roared Dempsey. 'Get the blasted public-address system working.'

The public-address system had an unfortunate habit of breaking down. First they had to trace the Purser or one of his staff to open the office and switch the system on. The announcement was then made by a Greek girl to all parts of the ship where passengers might be : 'Will Mrs Shugg please come to—' and then the system broke down. After a while they got it going again and recommenced : 'May I have your attention, please? Will Mrs Shugg please come ...'

Mrs Shugg turned up ten minutes later. She was very indignant. 'They said the old battery'd be good for another year.'

'Well, it isn't,' said Dempsey.

'We paid for it,' Mrs Shugg argued.

'Where is the spare battery, madam?' asked Dempsey impatiently. 'Your husband is likely to drop dead soon.'

'It's in the baggage.'

'In your cabin?'

'No. In the Baggage Room.'

'It would be,' Dempsey agreed bitterly.

The Baggage Room was locked up and he had to find the officer responsible for the key. He then went with the officer and Mrs Shugg and they had to move dozens of heavy cases as these had not yet been placed in order of disembarkation . . .

In the morning Dempsey was sent for by the Staff Captain.

'Dr Dempsey,' this giant of a man said. 'You have criticized our ship—'

'I have *not*!'

'It is unfortunate that I must now complain about your own competence.'

'Competence!' shouted Dempsey. 'What the devil do you know about my competence?'

'A patient has complained that you were drunk while attending to her.'

'Nonsense! I'm never drunk while attending to patients.'

'The lady says you were shouting and your breath smelled of gin.'

'Who is this woman?'

'A Mrs Shugg on B Deck, Cabin 41.'

'I was not attending Mrs Shugg but her husband. And it was whisky, not gin.'

'You agree you'd been drinking?' the Staff Captain questioned.

'I was at a party. Dr Zafiropoulos' party. Of course I'd had a couple of drinks! This idiot came along with an emergency. I wasn't on duty. Am I not to eat and drink?'

'We are always on duty,' concluded the Staff Captain.

'Pompous ass!' said Dempsey, but he said it quietly, for the Staff Captain was six feet three inches tall and weighed about sixteen stone.

4

NIKOLAOS TOMAZOS, First Officer, leaned on the chartroom desk and said to the visitor, 'You see, I do my watch from four until eight in the morning and I fix the ship's longitude by timed observation of the sun soon after sunrise. And this is carried forward by dead reckoning – you know, on our course and speed – to noon, when latitude is determined by sextant observation of the sun at its zenith. The result is plotted on the chart and is the official departure for the navigation of the next twenty-four hours.'

Tomazos had no idea who the visitor was, apart from his name. Someone who knew someone who knew someone. He did not excuse himself on the grounds of exhaustion – although he had had a brutally busy day – nor on those of duties impending. He was a thickset man of five foot seven, fourteen stone in weight; but he was agile and tireless. He was enthusiastic about his work and would talk for hours to small children on the bridge while carrying out the most exacting duties.

'What about radar?' inquired the visitor. 'Don't you ever use it?'

Tomazos grinned. He had a scar just to one side of his mouth where ten years before two men had attacked him with a bottle. He had fought them off and jumped straight into the harbour water – it had been at Keelung – and swum half a mile in darkness.

He commented, 'Oh, those things! We have two sets – one British, one American. We use them in estuaries and rivers or in bad weather, but not much otherwise. You know,' he continued, thinking about it, 'ships could be completely automatic, like cameras, planes and cars. They could build a ship now which needed no crew and which could even take avoiding action in the crisis of a possible collision. Or it could have a crew of one man. But do you know what would happen?'

'The seamen's unions wouldn't stand for it,' suggested the visitor.

'I wouldn't know about that,' Tomazos qualified. 'But there would be so many dials, gauges, flashes and bells the man would go crazy. There would have to be two other men so that this one could eat and sleep. This,' he suggested with a characteristic wave of one arm, 'would tend to fill up the ship with people to look after the three men – a cook to feed them, a doctor . . . You comprehend?'

'Is this the log?' asked the visitor.

'Yes. The ship is crammed with documents,' Tomazos told him. 'Most of our ship's papers are in Greek. The crew list, amount and quality of water, Customs declarations, certificate of seaworthiness – all these are ready for our departure. The log has the name of the Master and the number. It shows all these times and compass errors, the draught of the ship and the amounts of fuel used and left. And the events of the day—'

'Social events, too?'

'Everything. Social, what the engineer reports, the doctor, the quarrels, complaints, members of the crew in trouble. As you see, one man was injured today. Even the dockside is not safe! "Greaser Ioannidis was badly hurt when a gas cylinder fell off a lorry belonging to Babble and Company Proprietary Limited and exploded,"' Tomazos read out. '"He was brought on board by Dr Daniel Dempsey, himself reporting for duty, but later had to be taken to the Parramatta Hospital." We're a man short,' explained Tomazos. 'I've signalled our agents in Melbourne. Maybe we'll pick up a replacement.'

The noise of singing and cheering drifted into the almost complete silence of the bridge and chartroom.

Tomazos looked as his watch. He said in shock, 'It's nearly nine o'clock.'

'Do I have to get off now?'

'No. You stay where you are, Mr Biggar,' Tomazos suggested. 'But I have to start the checks.' He lifted part of the top of the chartroom desk and examined a chronometer. 'That is correct by Greenwich,' he explained, and altered the clock in the chartroom, which was half a minute slow. 'I've already signalled for two tugs at nine-fifty. I've got the engines on stand-by, which means they can give full steam any time we require it. I've also singled up. I expect you know what that means.'

Mr Biggar did. 'It means you've reduced the number of

moorings to a minimum, so that the ship can move out as soon as you signal.'

'That's correct,' agreed Tomazos. 'I've let go the two back spring ropes and the two breast ropes. She's held by the head rope and stern rope ... We've cleared the ship for Customs and Health. In fact we're pretty well ready to sail, Mr Biggar.'

'I'd better go,' said Mr Biggar anxiously. 'My wife's waiting in the car. She can't drive ...'

'We shan't carry you away!' Tomazos assured him. 'You're all right for half an hour yet ... You know, I think the Australians are the most emotional people in the world about ships. Come and have a look.'

The two men walked to the starboard wing of the bridge. In the near darkness the scene was incredible. On the George Street dockside were hundreds of people, whistling, cheering, singing, waving, a few already weeping. So many hundreds of paper streamers had been thrown from shore to ship and vice versa that they hung upon each other in hundreds of criss-crossing layers. Children shrieked, girls ran about, old men who'd once been the Captains of merchant ships came to stare at this departure. What Tomazos said was true, and was all the more curious because of the qualifications. The Australians were not an emotional people; to some they even seemed vegetative or taciturn; but they became near hysterical when a ship sailed. It did not matter what the ship was or where it was going. They would attend the sailing of the *Empress of Australia* as it left to cover the mere six hundred miles to Tasmania. But Tomazos had never seen or heard anything quite like this. It moved him that hundreds of people should come and cheer his old ship and its passengers ...

There was faint illumination in the chartroom, but none at all on the bridge except light reflected from buildings on the quayside. This was so that the Officer of the Watch and the seamen should acquire and maintain night vision.

Tomazos moved rapidly and with confidence in the darkness, switching on the telegraph, the two radar sets, to warm them up and remove condensation, if not to use them, explaining to Mr Biggar, 'The gyro compass is never switched off, or at most once in four months. The magnetic compass is in a periscopic housing above your head. We rarely use it.'

'What's this?' asked Mr Biggar, referring to a handle and wire fixed to the deckhead, and looking rather like an enlarged railway compartment emergency chain.

'That's for the hand operation of the siren,' Tomazos told him. 'We'll blow the whistle at a quarter to ten if you like.'

Mr Biggar stood behind the wheel. Metal arrow pointers indicated the amount of turn. Indicators on the bridge structure ahead confirmed the degree of rudder. The rudder turned about 35° each way. Other indicators by the side of this one told the Officer of the Watch the degree of roll and the revolutions per minute of the propellers. Although in harbour the *Areopagus* apparently had a starboard incline of 6°. 'Oh, that thing's out of order,' qualified Tomazos.

Two telephones rang and he rushed from one to the other. Mr Biggar listened as Tomazos said into the one 'I'm ready to begin when you are' and then into the other 'I'm receiving you loud but not clear.'

Mr Biggar said, 'Don't you ever get into a flap?' but Tomazos smiled and told him 'No.' He then began the telegraph check. The telegraph positions were now illuminated in brilliant red light. Tomazos worked through them with an audible response from the engine room each time. He tested in the order Full Ahead, Half, Slow, Dead Slow, and then again with Astern, and left the telegraph on stand-by. To Mr Biggar he commented, 'The alarm bell sounds in the engine room and the buzzer up here until the engineer has replied to my order by moving his telegraph lever to the identical position which cancels the alarm system. You will notice that there is a reply pointer on my telegraph. This will move to correspond with my order lever when the engineer has cancelled the alarm ... Some ships now have a Wrong Way Alarm, so that if the engineer acknowledges the order correctly but then manœuvres the ship in a direction contrary to that signalled, immediately the propeller shaft starts to turn in the wrong direction the alarm signal screeches.'

Tomazos tested the rudder by turning the wheel, and the indicators ahead of him showed the degree of turn. He then phoned someone and asked 'Propellers clear?'

He called Sydney Harbour Authority: '*Areopagus* calling Sydney ... I am leaving at ten o'clock on schedule. Is there anything local?' and a voice told him 'The *Lindisfarne* went out half an hour ago.' 'I'll watch out for her,' acknowledged Tomazos.

He checked the engines with the engine room, the indicator on the bridge climbing to the maximum of 140 port and 138 starboard.

Mr Biggar commented: 'There's no vibration. No noise up here either.'

The radar sets were warmed up now and Tomazos let Mr Biggar play with them before he adjusted them to the ship's present heading and locked them. The two sets now corresponded and moved with the ship, and would show a full circle round her with 'ahead' at the top.

'You married?' asked Mr Biggar suddenly. 'Or a girl in every port?'

'I married an Australian girl,' Tomazos told him.

'Good for you!' enthused Mr Biggar. 'Where did you meet her?'

Tomazos laughed. 'At a Master Mariners' dinner!'

'What was she doing there?'

'You may well ask!' acknowledged Tomazos. 'Then a few months later she came on a cruise.'

'Ah, those cruises!' suggested Mr Biggar, echoing the romance of the shipping brochures – two young people holding hands, standing at the ship's rail and gazing at a lurid sunset and the churned water of the ship's wake.

This in any case never happened. The decks were too crowded and privacy had to be found elsewhere. And it certainly hadn't taken place like that for himself and Elaine. Five minutes' conversation at a dinner, and a plenitude of other ships' officers waiting to talk to *this* pretty girl. Months later she'd turned up on the bridge. It had been coincidental, not her deliberate choice of cruise. He had been on duty and Elaine had been one of several people visiting the bridge.

Tomazos had felt quite shaky when he saw her, and something in her demeanour and the nature of the few questions she had asked at least suggested that she remembered him. But he was an officer on the bridge. He could not stroll the decks looking for her. He found her in a bar one evening with others, and they, not she, had claimed him. He could not go ashore on excursions, but in the third frustrating week of that cruise had encountered her in a shop in Suva. A very earnest half-hour had followed, but he had had to visit Adelaide, and she Melbourne when his ship called (for the *Areopagus* did not often call at Adelaide) over a period of months before they really knew each other. These days Elaine sometimes came to Melbourne, but she wouldn't be doing it this time the *Areopagus* called, because of the two children. They couldn't keep missing school . . .

There had been a dream that he would take her to Greece, but it was still less than a probability, again because of the small children. Elaine now lived in a medium-sized stone house in an outer suburb of Adelaide, with a view of the Mount Lofty hills. She had in common with him a liking for Greek restaurants, swimming, sailing, and driving sports cars. She knew how to water ski. She was a tall very Australian girl, with a fine body and limbs and an honest straightforward face under the honey-coloured hair. She was very passionate and had soon conceived the first child. Elaine had quite a bit of money of her own. Tomazos had very little. He couldn't quite bring himself to become an Australian citizen. He didn't even like Australia as a place. But the *Areopagus* belonged to a Company which, while registered in Panama, operated primarily between Greece and Australia. It was in essence a Greek ship, but so many of the passengers were Australian or English that some of the crew had to be Australian – one of the doctors, some of the girls in the Purser's office, and, on the bridge, the Second Officer, Mollon, a close friend of Tomazos.

The Third Officer, Makris, came on the bridge, carrying a newspaper.

Tomazos introduced him to Mr Biggar.

Makris said, 'Guess what's happened.'

Tomazos shrugged. 'Another war?'

'Almost. There's a strike in Melbourne. The Port Emergency Division. They want "proper provision for safety". Also four dollars a week more. It affects only about a hundred men, but fourteen unions and three thousand men are coming out in support. They refuse to man tugs for ships with dangerous cargoes . . .'

Tomazos said in some irritation, 'So if they get the four dollars a week they'd be prepared to forgo the safety provisions? What kind of people are these? *Fourteen* unions! You see what happens, Mr Biggar? As if we don't have sufficient problems of our own they give us some more. We expect to disembark 473 passengers at Melbourne, to pick up 112, but also we expected to load on twenty-two brand-new automobiles, on their way from Adelaide—'

'By train?' asked Makris. 'They'll never get to Melbourne. The railways have gone on strike for twenty-four hours to show sympathy for these other people . . .'

The Second Officer, Mollon, came on the bridge. 'Tugs are coming up. Time for the whistle, Nikolaos?'

Tomazos looked at the clock he'd adjusted. 'One minute to go.'

There had been no diminution of the sounds of excitement on the quayside. When Tomazos sounded the siren – that of the *Areopagus* had an impressive, deep, melancholy wail – the hundreds of people began to cheer.

'I must go,' ventured Mr Biggar apprehensively.

'You'd like to meet the Captain?'

'He won't want to meet *me* right now.'

'He's all right,' Tomazos reassured the visitor. 'Not very good at X-chasing, but otherwise okay.'

X-chasing meant mathematics, and by implication the navigation of the ship.

Tomazos hurried into his cabin, which was opposite those of the Captain, and re-emerged struggling into his jacket. It was cool in Sydney this October evening and it was the black winter jacket Tomazos put on, with its three bands of half-inch gold lace on the cuffs.

He knocked on the door of the Captain's Day Cabin, and

Captain Vafiadis appeared at the threshold. He was in shirt-sleeves, as Tomazos had been, but it did not detract from the dignity he had. He was a little taller than any of his officers, except the Staff Captain, and had a weather-worn, expressionless face, with a touch of something in it – pride, arrogance, or confidence? – Mr Biggar couldn't be sure, but was a fraction daunted.

Tomazos said, 'Good evening, sir. I'd like to introduce Mr Edmund Biggar, who is President of the New South Wales Miniature Ships Association . . . Captain Vafiadis.'

A tiny smile altered the Captain's expression. It might have been frivolous.

They talked with difficulty about the ship, the construction of models, and Mr Biggar's service as a midshipman in the Royal Australian Navy during the war. 'Do you know Ernest Bedford?' asked Mr Biggar with minor desperation, but the Master of the *Areopagus* had to admit 'No,' although he said it kindly, as if he had been waiting for a long time to meet Mr Bedford but somehow things had worked out to prevent the contact. 'He's Master of the Lodge,' Mr Biggar explained earnestly. '*He* has a model of the *Areopagus* . . .'

Tomazos said suddenly, 'I think they're taking the forward gangway away.'

It wasn't true, but Mr Biggar departed, suddenly cheerful. 'I'd better be off or I'll be sailing with you.'

Captain Vafiadis had heard this remark many times, but smiled.

A little later he appeared on the bridge. There was no stiffening in nervousness by anyone – officers, helmsman or the stand-by sailor – as there might have been on the bridge of a warship. The captains of liners are important men, but they are not piped over the side when they go ashore or come aboard. There was no particular *esprit de vaisseau* aboard the *Areopagus*. There had been too many changes in the crew for that. In the darkness of the bridge there were three officers, two seamen and the pilot, who had just come aboard. Conversation did not cease, and no one pretended to appear intent upon his job or find it necessary to think up answers to possible questions or criticism. In a way, this was a compliment to the Captain and showed that the *Areopagus* was an easy-going ship in which the weapon of discipline didn't need to be used too often or harshly.

Captain Vafiadis was in fact a kind of vestigial relic of the original functions of a sea captain. As a master mariner he was nevertheless not as competent as Tomazos, nor as versed in radar and the gyro-pilot – although Tomazos recalled with humour that when, ten years before, radar sets had been fitted to the ships of this line, all the officers had been distinctly nervous of them and the captains had kept the first sets on board locked up when not in use! Since then officers had been trained in radar, although even now when they changed ship they wanted to be reassured that the radar sets were of the same manufacture as aboard their present ship.

In fact the Captain, although an object of some awe among passengers, was scarcely more than a final arbitrator in a floating hotel. Like an hotel manager he was almost reduced to doing a daily inspection of some parts of the ship and for the rest waiting with composure for a crisis. His legal and commercial responsibilities were numerous, but reduced nearly to a formality. The mail might bring him a thick pile of letters, and he himself had to write a report from every principal port of call. He had to interview the directors of the Company before each voyage and talk to a navigational superintendent, who could call his attention to any changes in charts, soundings, buoyed channels or harbour approaches. For the rest, he had to exist in an isolation and maintain dignity before passengers and crew, and wait for the rare emergency which he must answer with skill and courage and for which he would be answerable. It was usually a minor drama he had to sort out – a refusal to be browbeaten by foreign officials, or, as these last few days, settling a disagreeable dispute between a group of dissatisfied passengers and the Purser – in effect, the ship herself. And he had disliked this, for he knew that the thousand and more passengers, some five hundred of whom had just disembarked at Sydney, *had* lived in disagreeable conditions, and these had in effect been inflicted on them by the financial greed or ignorance of the Company.

The Third Officer was in the wheelhouse and had his hand on the telegraph, ready to hear, repeat and transmit the pilot's orders to the engines. Mollon was on the forecastle with a few deckhands and Tomazos on the poop head with others. The Engineer of the Watch was stationed at the telegraph in the engine room with other men standing by.

To move a big ship out of harbour is far more dangerous than to take her through a storm. For she cannot be steered without movement and a force of water on her rudder. And in this condition the *Areopagus*, like all liners, was entirely dependent on the engineers. The deck department could do nothing except let go ropes, handle a hawser or launch the lifeboats, unless they had the power of steam. When a fine manœuvre was called for, the ship was at the mercy of the engineer. There was always a time lag between the request from the bridge telegraph for movement and the function of the turbines, reduction gears, steam and auxiliary gear. A failure to reverse engines due to the time lag of having to put the telegraph first to Stop Engines and then to Full Astern might be the difference between going alongside perfectly or clouting the dockside and damaging the ship's steel plates.

Tomazos heard over the amplifier the signal from the bridge, 'Let go aft!' and he shouted it himself. On the bridge the Third Officer signalled Dead Slow Astern to the engine room and the *Areopagus* pulled against the one rope holding her. Her stern swung outwards as the crowd cheered frantically. 'Let go forward!' was the next signal and on the bridge Captain Vafiadis said to the pilot, 'She's yours, Mister Pilot.'

There were tugs fore and aft by which all these manœuvres were assisted. The *Areopagus* glided into cautious motion with a mild kick from her propellers, moving on the shiny still waters of Sydney Cove and out into the River Parramatta. The current was negligible, the tide was right, but the pilot had to exercise caution for there were submarine cables in the area.

The passengers watched with interest and confidence as the *Areopagus* reversed towards Sydney Harbour Bridge, over which a train thundered with a noise like a jet plane.

'Look at all the lights behind Circular Quay,' the pilot was saying conversationally to the Captain. 'Starboard ten degrees . . . It's getting like New York . . . One long blast on the siren, please . . . Damn these ferries . . .'

The *Areopagus* slid easily past Fort Denison with Rush-cutter Bay to starboard. The Third Officer said, 'The *Seaway Hawk* has just radioed harbour control that she's approach-ing the Heads.'

'Thank you,' acknowledged the pilot. 'Just give her a shout on the radio and tell her I'm coming to the turn . . . Ah, there she is,' the pilot said soon afterwards, and sure enough, they on the bridge could see the other's lights just behind South Head.

'Well,' said the pilot a few minutes later. 'That's about it. Stop the world, I want to get off . . . What about this strike? It's on for twenty-four hours.'

'It's a damned nuisance,' Captain Vafiadis said. 'We have twenty-two cars to load, passengers to disembark and about a hundred boarding.'

'It'll be over by the time you get to Fremantle,' forecast the pilot.

'We may have to forgo our vehicles,' the Captain said gloomily.

The *Areopagus* was a passenger liner, but carried a small amount of cargo. She did not, like many cargo liners on the Australia to Europe run, carry carcasses of mutton and lamb, or boxes of New Zealand butter. She could carry about twenty-two unpacked assembled automobiles or about the same volume (a greater weight) of general cargo, which tended these days to be unassembled motor cars in cases, tractors, electric lamps, clothing, furniture, cigarettes and parcel and letter mail. The wharfie gangs had been loading these this afternoon while lorries and vans had been bringing the jam, meat, vegetables, bacon, flour and fruit which the passengers would eat during the next few weeks. All day the officers had supervised these activities and kept an eye open for theft. Everything had to be packed so that it did not get chafed by the ship's motion; so that light cases were not crushed by heavier ones; so that cases of machinery which had been wrongly shipped with oil left in their sumps at least did not leak oil and ruin boxes of furnishings; so that things which had strong smells did not communicate them to things which had not; so that ventilation was consistent and yet did not allow salt air to corrode machinery or wet weather to ruin bags of flour. Things had to be loaded so that they weren't damaged by heavier goods and yet they had to be loaded so that those which were to be unloaded first could be reached easily. This might involve unloading what ought to be on the lowest tier at the first port of call. Logically, therefore, it must be at the top; in terms of textural strength it ought to be at the bottom . . .

All of this cargo had been handled on its way to the ship, and yet once it was over the rail the ship could be blamed for damage which might have been inflicted by the railways, cranes, lorries . . .

Captain Vafiadis was understandably annoyed about a twenty-four hour strike, for it would involve the day during which the *Areopagus* would enter and leave Melbourne. Every deckhand had worked hard today, just as every steward had been busy mustering passengers' luggage and changing bed linen. The ship's storage plan had been laid out in Mr Tomazos' room and there had been discussions about the arrangements for loading oil and water. The hatches had been closed, the tarpaulins replaced, the derricks run down, the wharfies and winchmen had departed. At dawn tomorrow the weary seamen would hose down the decks. A gang to load the twenty-two automobiles had been ordered by wireless. If the men turned up they would have to be paid whether the automobiles arrived or were stuck in some railway siding . . .

And it all involved paper. Paper, paper, paper, by the square mile, it seemed, and for which the *Areopagus* would be answerable. Inventories and international certificates, tallies of packages, formalities of police, Customs and Immigration, passengers' passports and tickets, crew lists, manifests . . .

It was hard work, with money involved. The quicker the turn-around the better, for ports cost money, pilots and tugs cost money; to keep the *Areopagus* in commission was costing £2,000 a day and more . . . There was little opportunity for shore leave, for even in a prolonged period in harbour there were plenty of overhauls to be carried out, and it was only when there were no passengers or cargo aboard, when the holds were completely empty, that the double bottom with its fresh water and ballast tanks could be inspected. The crew might have a few hours in some cheap uptown café to break the monotony of the ship's food. For those who wanted them, foreign beer and foreign women, but both in a hurry, for the *Areopagus* never seemed to stay still.

When the pilot had gone overboard and the *Areopagus* reached open water and the bridge signalled Full Ahead the officers and men resumed their normal stations.

Tomazos stood on the bridge with two seamen as the liner left the River Parramatta and entered the South Pacific Ocean. To pace up and down a fairly well-equipped bridge fifty feet above a calm sea was dull, and suggested that Tomazos lived a life that lacked something in seafaring experience. He was paid more than an officer on an ocean-going tramp, for his duties were more exacting and he had to have some knowledge of a variety of scientific equipment. All Greek officers had to have a reasonable knowledge of English before they qualified. The log book was in Greek, but also had parallel entries in English. The charts and the weather reports which looked like old telegrams, clipped to a hook on the bridge, the row of Pilot books in the tiny bookcase in the chartroom, which explained how to enter any harbour, large or small, in the world – these were all in English. Yet somehow the impression obtained even among passengers was that these were officers merely steering an hotel from one well-equipped port to another, while the officer of a tramp might well have to manœuvre a ship, often unhandy in an awkward sea, to some obscure roadstead whose surroundings were uncertain and whose pilot, if there was one, could be a gentleman in a loin cloth who spoke no English and viewed foreigners as people to be robbed.

In fact Tomazos, like most Greek officers, had served on a variety of ships, many of them old, a few shining new tankers. If he understood very fully the organization behind the *Areopagus* – with its special berths, particular gear, complicated stevedoring, and its ramified intelligence of brokers, agents, as well as its elaborate documentation of tallies, receipts, manifests, bills of lading and storage plans – it was because he had learned them the hard way from boyhood. He had gradually understood the system whereby in a cargo of 12,000 tons in five decks a bottle or a bicycle could be traced immediately. He had served on cargo liners and tramps, arguing with foreign officials, picking up cargo in small lots from five to fourteen ports, and alone making the calculations so that weight was properly distributed in the ship, so that there were suitable allocations of blocks of loading space, and the selection of cargoes was such that they neither contaminated nor crushed each other.

There had been sunshine, fresh air, reasonable food, some recreation aboard, but no dances or girls, no TV or football matches, no lazing in bed on Sunday mornings. Nor was there now on the *Areopagus*. The life of an officer in any merchant navy allows little privacy.

He had served on an old ship with a reciprocal engine, in which the coal had self ignited and burnt it out quite quickly, fortunately in harbour. He had seen men die of silicosis, the result of frequent handling of china clay. He had lost a friend in a ship which had exploded, its content of grain dust being the cause.

His grandfather had served as a junior officer on a full-rigged ship, rigged too heavily in fact, with stump topgallant masts and fore and main upper topgallants 80 feet long. It had been a ship which needed careful handling. She had finally run ashore on an iceberg and the top part of the ice had broken and fallen on the deck. Another berg had closed in on them. The crew got away in two lifeboats, taking a dog, parrot and the Captain's chronometer and telescope with them ... Tomazos' grandfather later, as Captain, took his wife and first child on a three-year voyage aboard a similar vessel. In Valparaiso in a storm a steamer broke away from her cables and drifted down on to the sailing vessel, broke her cables, and caused her to drift ashore. On striking the shore the impact caused her masts to go by the board on to the beach, and the Captain, his wife and Tomazos' father, then a small child, clambered over the wrecked masts to safety. That grandfather had later taken dysentery in Buenos Aires and died of it. The vessel had been repaired and Tomazos had seen it as a child before it was wrecked off the coast of south-west England in 1944. Tomazos' father had decided not to go to sea, and had become a schoolteacher.

During his training Tomazos had served for six months on a beautiful four-masted bark, originally employed in the Australian grain trade, and later the carrier of nitrates from Chile. He had climbed up to the highest spar, the main royal yard, a nerve-racking experience, and remembered even now the roll of the ship and the beauty of the near-thirty sails of that gracious vessel billowing in a moderate wind, the main royal cracking like a whip below his feet.

So if he now served on a fairly stable platform he had earned the position. And in fact handling a big ship like the *Areopagus* called for skill. The whole technique was, again, experience, and consisted of judging time and distance. The reaction to instructions from the bridge telegraph was slow – the engine had to be stopped and then re-engaged for the colossal gear teeth to mesh without destruction – so that the time the ship took to swing to a given course was often whole minutes and the distance it advanced or traversed would be as much as a mile. With a rudder which moved only to 35° and a great length and weight, obviously the *Areopagus* could not turn like a destroyer : the outwards heel would have been most disconcerting to the passengers : crockery, glasses of beer, knives and forks, cases, would all have fallen or slid away . . .

Once the ship had been committed to a turn at any speed it was not a matter of seconds, but of whole minutes before the ship's heavy swing could be checked or her way lost, no matter what orders were telegraphed to the engine room or called to the helmsman. It was worse at night, particularly in terms of other ships. A minute before a collision two ships would be perfectly safe, a thousand yards apart, but fifteen seconds later nothing would be able to save them, the massive propulsion and machinery would be so committed.

'Turn to 180°,' Tomazos instructed the helmsman, and the *Areopagus* turned in a mile or so from due east as she had left the Parramatta River to due south down the coast of New South Wales.

He was navigating by the gyroscopic compass, or, rather, one of its seven repeaters (for the main gyroscopic compass was amidships), and thus able to ignore variation (the difference between the magnetic meridian and true meridian) and deviation. Most ships are built of steel and iron and have themselves become magnetized as the result of hammering and vibration during construction. The lines of force of this magnetic field struck the needle of the magnetic compass at different angles for each course steered and caused the compass needle to deviate from the magnetic meridian. There were cards in the chartroom which gave the deviation on every heading. The gyroscopic compass, however, gave a true reading all the time and it was only in the rare case of its breakdown that the officers of the *Areopagus* used the magnetic.

Similarly, Tomazos did not follow what would have been the shortest route across the South Pacific Ocean to get to Melbourne. That would have been to use a great circle course across the earth's surface, that is, to navigate bearing in mind that the earth is a sphere. To follow a great circle course – except for a very great distance – would be an extremely tedious progress, involving a continuous alteration of course. It would gain a few miles but wouldn't be worth the effort. Tomazos used a rhumb line route, that is, the line of a Mercator map, on which the meridians of longitude did not converge towards the poles.

This was perfectly accurate for short or moderate distances providing all the motions of the sea and wind were accounted for. He could have been 'lazier' still and employed the gyro-pilot, but only did this in bad weather and heavy seas. There was an electrical connexion between the log in the water and the bridge so that the log could be read in the chartroom and Tomazos knew by deduction of the original setting what was the distance run and thus the speed.

There was no leeway, for the wind was dead astern, and the *Areopagus* made a steady 18 knots through the night.

Behind him and below him the passengers – there were now only 590 of them and 89 of these were to disembark at Melbourne – were asleep, or at the late cabaret show, or drinking at the Forward Bar which remained open until two in the morning, or playing cards, or taking a last stroll on the Parade Deck.

Tomazos thought about those twenty-two automobiles. Were they now in Melbourne? On their way there, or now stuck by the strike in some obscure siding? Where were they really from? Vehicles were made or assembled in Melbourne and Adelaide, Tomazos knew, and if they couldn't be loaded tomorrow at Melbourne, and if the strike really was only for twenty-four hours, was it possible that the owner's agents would suggest that the *Areopagus* made the extra call at Adelaide? If the cars were at or near Adelaide this was just possible. It depended, perhaps, on how the harbour charges related to the profit of transporting twenty-two vehicles which would retail at $3,500 in America and Europe. If the *Areopagus* called at Adelaide, even for three hours, he might see Elaine ...

He never asked favours. He had no need of them, being both extremely competent in his work and satisfied in his private life. But he had not seen Elaine for about fourteen weeks and wouldn't even have the opportunity for another twelve – and she would have to come to Melbourne even then, a twelve-hour train journey. Mollon, the Second Officer, often asked favours of Tomazos. Mollon was hedonistic, although tough and capable. If the ship did call at Adelaide, and he, Tomazos, was on duty, as he assuredly would be, just this once he'd ask Mollon ...

He stood staring ahead at a black horizon and beautiful stars, and rolling slightly on the balls of his feet. The click of the gyro repeater was the only sound. The port light gave off a diffused red incandescence and the starboard a green. Very distantly he heard laughter and a band. But he felt no jealousy. He belonged up here, was perfectly content, had no problems, and was the most competent officer on the ship.

5

THE BURSTON family – father, mother and three daughters of fifteen, ten and two – travelled for fourteen hours to reach Melbourne and found it windy, cold and empty on this Saturday afternoon in October.

Like Tornetta they arrived too early. The youngest, called affectionately Bumble, was weeping and the questions of the other two girls grated on Marion Burston's nerves so that she hissed, 'For God's sake, shut up! I might have known...'

This, for Mike Burston, had the current implication : 'It's your fault.' He argued at once, defensively, 'It was the only train,' to which Marion persisted '*Why* can't we board until eight o'clock?'

Burston talked to the old man in a white coat at the gangway, and he went aboard, returning with the instruction that they could board the *Areopagus* now, but would have to leave their cases ashore until the proper time – which was 8 PM – when new passengers would board via the Customs. 'What good's that?' Marion complained. 'These kids are tired out.'

She was thirty-seven, five foot four, nice-looking but thinned down a bit by some private misery. Her hair was still black and her brown eyes clear, but there was a mournful look about her as if life had defeated her here in Australia and she wanted to escape – anywhere – but had no conviction that life would be better anywhere else.

Mike was a large man of five foot ten, tough-looking, sunburnt a hard brown. He had big roughened hands, but they were agitated, and he looked both startled and dazed.

Both of them had the accent of the British working class, of somewhere in the Midlands; and five years before they had left England aware, perhaps, that with such accents they were irretrievably defeated. Money, yes, if Mike worked hard he could make money, but they'd never belong in the first-class compartments, or the quality restaurants, or to first nights at the theatre, or to concert going, or dinners given by this or that society; they were so ingrained in the status that they hadn't even *wanted* to belong. Now they were going back to what they had despised.

It was typical, Marion felt angrily, that even here they'd arrived at the wrong hour and, exhausted, had five hours to hang about, and had to stand in the Station Pier eating hot pies with their hands. 'Mind your coat,' she had to instruct repeatedly to Patricia, aged ten, and the kids' voices asked with innocence that hurt, 'Why can't we have chips?' – 'When are we going to board?' and the snot ran from Bumble's nostrils as fast as Marion cleaned them with tissues.

Nevertheless, they were allowed aboard an almost empty ship, although not in their cabin, and strolled and sat in sunlit corners and drank lemonade in a vast lounge.

The *Areopagus* had now discharged all but seventy-five of its migrants from Europe. The New Zealand and Australian passengers who had boarded at Wellington, Hobart and Sydney were out on tours.

At half past seven the Burstons went ashore, collected their cases and hung about in the Customs Hall. They were unaware that only eighty people were boarding at Melbourne and the hundreds of others now milling about were relations and visitors to the ship.

'Look!' cried Marion in disgust. 'Just look at that old woman pushing people. She's going to be first. Selfish. Typical Australian,' she said, unkindly, for she had found Australians not much different to the people in Staffordshire as far as selfishness was concerned.

'She's got a wig on,' observed Stella.

It took another hour to board. 'They could have started at seven-thirty,' deduced Marion in irritation. 'Typical.' They shuffled along with others, and the old lady with the wig held up the queue as she doubled back from one desk to another in anxiety. Twice ashore and once on deck they had to fill in forms or answer tiresome, pointless questions.

A steward tried to hurry ahead with their cases, but could scarcely move. The decks were packed with visitors to the ship who were in a more excited state than the passengers. There were some in the Burstons' cabin and Mike said loudly, 'Get out! What d'you think this is, a circus?' The middle-aged couple flinched and the husband pointed to a steward who was standing around obsequiously. 'He said we could have a look round. We were thinking of the February cruise.' Mike was tired and fed up, and he could see in misery that Marion was more so, and shaken by his outburst. 'All right, you've had a look. Now beat it,' he said, and they went, too startled to argue. And suddenly after twenty hours there was silence. Mike lay on a bunk and when Marion said tentatively, 'We ought to get something to eat before the kids go to bed,' he argued, 'I'm too tired.' Marion persisted with the pious edge in her voice that made him writhe, 'I'd take them only I'll never find the way back.'

She could always thrust the moral obligation on to him. He agreed bitterly, 'All right, I'll come.'

'I want soup and beef and ice-cream afterwards,' Stella told them.

But when they found the large dining-room it was empty, and when they entered – in the usual posture of resignation – an officer approached and informed them 'The dining-room is closed' and then, as if that wasn't enough, 'The kitchen is closed.'

They traipsed back to the cabin as a siren sounded. 'It doesn't matter,' Marion assured Mike, but he felt weakened with failure. Pies and a few sandwiches were all they'd had in twenty hours, and a bad sleep on a hot train.

In the cabin Marion struggled with Bumble, washing her, and her 'Oh, come on!' was tired and near desperation.

She called from the small bathroom, 'The water's brown and only lukewarm. Do you think it's safe for them to clean their teeth in? And it says not for drinking.'

Stella noted brightly. 'We're moving. Thank Christ for that.'

'Don't blaspheme,' Marion corrected her.

'Why not?' asked Stella. 'It doesn't mean anything any more.'

'Yes, it does.'

'You don't go to church,' Stella pointed out.

'I don't blaspheme.'

'You say "God" sometimes.'

'Will you shut up?' shouted Marion. 'I'm sick of the lot of you,' she said shakily, and Mike was disturbed, knowing it meant him. He'd caused it: all the distress and sour experiences were because of what he'd done.

'Stop being cheeky to your Mum,' he ordered heavily.

'I'm not being cheeky. I'm disputing politely.'

'Well, shut up.'

'What charm!' said Stella. 'What wit!' But she saw anger blaze in his eyes and was quiet.

Patricia, now undressed, asked, 'Mum, what would happen if the ship was sinking and you had no clothes on? I mean, like I am now.

Stella interjected, 'I'd put on everything over my pyjamas.'

Patricia considered it and concluded thoughtfully, 'I'd take my drawing books so I'd have something to do.'

'Oh, isn't it pathetic?' was Stella's view of this.

'Can we have the light on?'

'It's late, half past nine,' Marion said.

'Oh, Mum, I'm frightened,' Patricia told her.

'One, then. No reading and no talking because Bumble's asleep. Be quiet while we go for a walk.'

In the morning the steward brought them all cups of tea. At breakfast they found that they were to sit at an oval table with the old lady who had been so determined to be first aboard at Melbourne, and an old man who was so crippled he walked as if he'd been broken in several places and whose conversation was incomprehensible. He wore a deaf aid but bent his head towards whoever spoke, and didn't seem to hear even then. Talk with these two was difficult, and Marion felt that they, the family, should have been given a table to themselves, preferably in a discreet corner so that Bumble's noises and messy eating couldn't be heard and seen by other passengers. It was, she concluded, part of being ordinary people, who can be shoved around. But even as she smouldered with the resentment which was self-consciousness she was aware of her unfairness. It was obvious that the Greek stewards and officers would rush round at anyone's request.

The old lady sent her food back twice, and hours later Stella came into the cabin and said gleefully, 'You know that old idiot at our table?' – and ignored her mother's reprimand 'He's a cripple. Be glad that—' Stella was too amused to be hypocritical and told her parents: 'He's just been sick and his lower plate shot out and broke. He'll have a job eating his lunch!' She was obviously anticipating the spectacle and her mother sympathized in vain, 'It's not funny, the poor old thing.'

Later in the day Stella demanded hopelessly, 'I want a camera. They've got a kind of mini-camera in the shop, and it's only five dollars.'

'*Only*!' protested Marion.

Mike conceded, 'We'll have a look at that. We don't have a camera for all these places. Does it take colour slides?'

Stella told him with excitement, 'It even has flash.'

Patricia called out, 'I want an ice-cream.'

Mike gave them some money. 'Go and get one each. Be in the dining-room at twelve.'

Marion had been arranging things. Now she protested, 'You're too silly. You're being soft with them. We can't throw money about.'

'An ice-cream each?'

'You can't buy it back,' she reminded him with enormous misery, the crux of it all.

'Buy *what* back?' he demanded angrily.

'You know. And don't shout at me.'

'We're on holiday. They can have a bit of fun, can't they?'

'Holiday!' she sighed.

Mike lit a cigarette.

At once Marion said in tireless criticism, 'I wish you'd stop smoking so much. I know your nerves are funny, but it fills the cabin up. It's bad for the kids.'

'There's air conditioning.'

'Can you feel it?'

He put his hand up to the deckhead, and laughed. 'No! Nothing happening.'

'I told you. It's no good down here. Marvellous in the dining-room, but this is a cheap cabin . . .'

'Cheap!' he protested. 'They knocked me nearly two thousand dollars—'

'I wish,' Marion said, 'we'd gone straight home on a P and O boat instead of all this cruising about. Stella and Patricia ought to be at school.'

'You've always wanted to see Singapore and Hong Kong.'

'That was before you—'

'So we're back to that?'

'It's made a difference, hasn't it?'

'Don't let it make a difference all our lives, Marion, please.'

'I'm sorry. I'm tired.'

'This'll do you good.'

But it was the same in the evening when Mike suggested going to the ship's cinema.

'What *for*?' Marion asked, still seething with it. It was as if she despised happiness, or felt that they had no right to 'fun.' That was for other, admittedly silly, people, but people who hadn't done what he'd done.

'It's quite a good film.'

'And who's going to look after the kids?'

'They can't get run over or kidnapped on a ship!' Mike suggested to her. 'Stella will look after them.'

'She's useless, no help to anyone.'

'Thanks very much,' said Stella. 'Anyway, I wanted to go to that film.'

'You go, then, with your father,' agreed Marion. '*I'll* look after Patricia and Bumble.'

There was a heavy implication: that's my job, my duty, to be a drudge . . .

'Oh, come on, Dad,' pleaded Stella. 'It starts in ten minutes and they're sitting in hundreds already.'

'Will you be all right?' he asked Marion.

'Of course. I may do some washing . . . And no drinking,' she called as father and daughter departed.

'Do you think that's likely?' he countered.

As they hurried along the decks Stella inquired outright: 'What's the matter with Mum?'

'She's worried.'

'Does she have to take it out of everybody? She's gone *mean*,' Stella complained.

'She's worried,' he repeated uselessly. 'We've had a lot of problems. She'll be okay when we get back.'

'Were *not* going back to Wolverhampton?'

'No. I've got a job in London.'

'Hooray for you! A bit of swinging *life*! What a dreary place *that* was,' Stella said, damning South Australia with the ruthless decisions of childhood.

Marion had never really belonged to Australia, but up to three months ago hadn't consciously disliked it. She could recall quite distinctly the shabby sitting-room in Wolverhampton – a main road outside, with lorries changing gears at the lights: the appalling noise went on all night, tyres hissing in the rain – and the day in November when Mike had come home, tired, fed up, and told her: 'Fred's had his lorry-load stolen. Newcastle. And his head split open to give him something to think about. Jesus, Marion, it's been smog and rain for three whole days. Eh, what I'd give for some sunshine and a dry road. We ought to go to Australia.'

And they'd looked at each other and Mike had said in excitement, 'My God, kid, that's it.' Within a week he was telling her enthusiastically, 'They get $150 a week hauling copper. Imagine it: £67 a week driving in sunshine!'

Within four months they'd arrived, bewildered, hot, apprehensive, a bit disappointed. For they had found the job first and hoped the place suited, fulfilled the promises and evidence of the brochures. It could hardly have been more different from Wolverhampton. It was 'better,' Marion kept reminding herself, better than Wolverhampton, Sheffield, Leeds, Birmingham . . . It must be, mustn't it? There was a swimming pool, supermarket, their own bungalow, even if it did have a tin roof. The washing was dry in fifteen minutes. Everyone was consciously matey.

But it was hardly the beautiful part of Australia. It was a hick town two hundred miles from anywhere. It was so small that ten minutes' walk brought her to a horizon so flat and featureless it daunted the heart. And to get anywhere meant hours of travel over roads which had until recently been used by camels. A tree was a rarity, like a monument. The town was a mess of cream-painted bungalows with green or red iron roofs and rows of salmon-coloured doors. There were no fences, no privacy, no gardens except a few square yards of earth baked hard. Along the two roads out of town was a litter of smashed or abandoned cars, and the inevitable thousands of beer cans. The main street had a few verandaed shops, but the rest were plaster and wood. The one hotel seemed to have come out of a Western film. Women would sit in cars outside its bars on a Saturday night, not being allowed inside. The men within grew rowdier and rowdier, and spilled out on to the dirt veranda, drinking straight from stubby bottles of beer or directly out of cans. The flies buzzed tirelessly in thousands.

Marion had been acutely shy of such people – rough, honest and direct as they were. She learned very quickly that to compare this place with anything in England was unforgivable, and to complain aroused outright scorn. At first she felt acute nostalgia for cosiness, a fire in the grate on a cold Christmas Day; she ached to see rain. For a long time she felt she'd never belong here, but she was busy enough for it not to matter. There were the kids to attend to, the washing to do, half an inch of dust which she removed from the bungalow each day . . .

She recognized with amusement that women here were regarded by the men as definitely inferior. There was a different kind of relationship. Men ordered their wives about, and equally expected them to cope entirely with the domestic duties and problems. Mike was the only husband, she guessed, for a thousand miles around, who washed up for his wife or cared for the baby when it came.

Mike said that it was the same among the men. They had an old-fashioned and often admirable masculinity which they didn't dare drop for a moment. They spoke in a nasal slow indifferent taciturnity, sure of their own perfection in their own environment, brutally frank in their analyses of whether you were yet as good as them. They were very sensitive and insular: nothing quite equalled this small edge of the desert. When Mike pointed out habitual errors they still committed – actions which killed men – they weren't interested: his opinion was not yet valuable. They spoke of these pointless deaths and accidents in a sardonic self-denigrating manner.

Marion's big disadvantage was that, like so many women of her age and status in England, she could not drive a car. Even Mike had never owned an automobile until he came here. But this mattered less to her as she made friends, some of whom were Pommies, others admitted they had no intention of learning to drive. With friends it was easy to withstand the vulgarity of women who shoved her aside in the supermarket, and to laugh at the sign over the counter: 'In God We Trust – All Others Pay Cash.' There was another notice in the wooden post office for the first hours of the day: 'Don't interrupt, I'm sorting mail.' The lady who put up this notice was small, fierce and incorrigibly nosy. She knew everyone's business. 'Here's that cheque you were waiting for,' she'd tell the schoolmaster. 'Looks like your Mum's writing,' she'd say to Marion. Marion read the corny local newspaper with relish. She pushed the pram up slopes of shale in a temperature of 115°. She who couldn't swim, and was self-conscious about her body, paraded round in shorts or a swimming costume. She drank beer for the first time in her life because here you'd die if you didn't, and it had to be cooled in the fridge for an hour. She even admired a house built out of 11,000 beer bottles cemented together. Nothing cured her dislike of the big spiders and she feared snakes although Mike battered a big one to death easily enough.

Mike was away, often, driving the lorry for days on end, and he never really earned that $150 a week. The kids thrived, grew brown and lively and learned to swim and ride a horse. Marion never quite let go of England, but as the fourth year went by she had passed the point of no return and didn't want to go 'home'; rather she wanted her Mum to come out here and see how good a life they lived, contemptuous of cities and soft living . . .

Her eyes moistened now in the feeble light of a cabin of the *Areopagus*. With hands that trembled she picked up the brochures they'd received right there on the edge of the Nullarbor Desert. The answer to the very first inquiry had come in an envelope with Graeco-Australian Merchant and Passenger Line printed on it, giving the game away to the woman at the post office. 'Going back to England?' she'd asked outright, and Marion had countered, 'About time we went for a trip.' The brochure's reassurances mocked her now unaccountably : 'One of the most efficient systems of propulsion devised by man and guided largely by automatic devices . . . Captain Vafiadis knows that his vessel is virtually unsinkable . . . the elaborate communications system by which the *Areopagus* can instantly be in touch with any part of the world . . . heat sensors will automatically detect any rise in temperature and report it at once to the officers on the bridge . . . divided into watertight compartments; if the hull were punctured 23 steel doors would clang shut at the touch of a button on the bridge . . .' And what, she thought cynically, having seen this exercise carried out with creaking efficiency, if I happen to be passing through one of those watertight doors at the time?

'Leisurely days and gracious evenings,' the brochure had forecast. 'No less than three-quarters of the crew are employed with solely your comfort in mind. The finest hotels in the world are no better . . . Ten thousand bottles of wine . . . Telephones in every room . . . stewards, launderers, bootblacks . . . Nothing pleases the dining-room staff more than to learn of some trifling personal fancy, whether for Melba toast or particularly strong coffee; and once requested it is remembered for the rest of your journey . . .'

The family already had a private joke about this, for the contrast between the promise of the brochure and the reality was startling. The menu was long and in itself aroused appetite. The steward was cheerful and energetic: he had to be, he served so many tables. 'Soup, mister?' he would ask, the sweat dripping from his forehead on to plates and tablecloth. At breakfast he was hopelessly confused over eggs, tomatoes, fruit juices, and toast meant nothing to him. The sauces – apple, redcurrant and mint – were never on the table and when they were desired the steward would be rushing round the next table but two with the cheese tray...

'An electronic log ensures that the Captain and his officers know exactly what speed the ship is moving at . . . radar sweeps a radius of 48 miles . . . two ultrasonic devices measure the depth of the sea. A Navigational Radio Aid picks up signals from the shore and instantly plots the ship's position. Fog, darkness, rain and storm mean nothing to the Captain of the *Areopagus*, which always reaches its destination within minutes of its planned time of arrival...'

Such apparent perfection seemed too good for such unworthy passengers as the Burstons, Marion decided sourly. She recalled the hours taking the kids to the doctor's for their jabs, and their whimpers, tears and analyses. And the stares from other patients, the orange peel thrown on the carpet which was thick with dust. Later, in another corridor, waiting, ignored, the kids fingering through dirty copies of *Life*. 'Will you stamp these health documents?' and the Sister's face full of disapproval as she probed, 'Going one way?' Her silent criticism when Marion admitted starkly, without justification or excuses 'Yes.' 'So we Australians are not good enough for you?' the Sister's expression had challenged.

Mike had admitted it four months ago. He was on drugs. Marion was shocked and very frightened when he told her, but Mike had qualified strongly, 'We all take them. Kid, if we're on a 700-mile run and we're falling asleep at the wheel, what else can we do? It's not habitual, honestly; I could drop them tomorrow. Do I look ill? I sleep all right, don't I? What else can I do?'

'Get another job,' she said simply.

'Doing what? I'm thirty-nine, kid. And it brings in money, doesn't it? Ninety-seven dollars last week, wasn't it?'

'I don't care, Mike. Quit the job or the pep pills.'

'They don't seem to do any harm and they just see me over the hump. Some of the boys have been taking 'em for five years.'

'Mike, I'm scared. Five years! What will they look like in ten? You're using yourself too hard. And for what?'

That hurt him, she had seen. He pointed out in justification: 'All these things' – and waved a hand at the fridge, washing-machine, TV, the estate car under the car-port. 'They're paid for.'

'I don't want to be a widow.'

Mike had laughed.

'Hell, it's not that bad. A pill a week maybe. Not like these kids at college, you know, on amphetamines for kicks. You take a pill for a headache, don't you? Once in a fortnight. It's the same . . .'

'Mike, start looking for another job, will you?'

'I'll keep my ears open, kid.'

It was on that day that Marion had begun to dislike Australia, not, at first, as somewhere to flee from, but simply because Mike had had to resort to drugs to do his seventy- and eighty-hour week. She watched him to see if he looked ill or tired, or lost weight, but he didn't seem to alter.

Anxiety made her resentful and especially of the environment which was too tough and too big. She began to think of England as somewhere where they'd been happy before coming *here*. And she began to see things with a critical eye and mind and without good humour. Especially she despised the people who drove vehicles. For these people, she felt angrily, were not tough or skilful: they were stupid and selfish in their driving, and she read the paper every Monday in particular with grim satisfaction, righteous in proof: the dead youths and girls thrown against trees and poles for no reason except carelessness, stupidity and drunkenness. She began to resent being shoved out of the way by fat women with curlers still in their hair at 11 AM in the supermarket. She was habitually, even painfully polite usually, and held doors open for people heavily laden. They never thanked her. Now she began to call after them tartly, 'Don't mind me. I spend all day doing this.' When some youth threw a bottle out of a moving car she took it round to his home and told his mother : 'Wally threw this out of his car. I thought maybe it was something he wanted.' And she'd gone before the startled mother could open her mouth. Next time she saw that woman Marion was stared through and didn't give a damn.

She began to say repeatedly, 'They're *stupid*' and 'they' meant specifically Australians. 'Just horses and beer,' she said in contempt. 'That's all they think about.'

It seemed to be true. The radio had nothing to offer but pop music, advertisements and analyses, descriptions or post mortems of horse racing or trotting five hundred miles away. The small town had its annual picnic race meeting and Marion took the kids reluctantly. The first thing erected was a temporary bar, sheltered from the sun by a bulrush-covered frame. The inevitable hundreds of bottles and empty cans littered a hundred square yards before the first race. Flies buzzed by the thousand and the dust stirred as the horses paraded down the dirt track and cantered across the shimmering claypan which stretched away to a horizon which was absolutely flat and marked by only a few trees.

People had come from hundreds of miles around; a few had arrived in aeroplanes. The crowd lined the rails and there were at times ten false starts; then off the horses galloped with their jockeys of drovers, enthusiasts, even a few Abos. They returned in a cloud of dust and a nasal Australian accent announced the winner over a public address system. The men shouted and groaned and dispersed to the beer hut. The women and kids traipsed to the shelter for tea, soft drinks, hamburgers and hot dogs.

It went on for two days, and men lay dead drunk in the street amidst dust, tin cans and dogs which sniffed at them. The usual stupid youths drove their cars in their usual reckless fashion, tyres screeching on every corner of the town's streets, and girls shrieked on the back seats as they were driven off to where the town ended. Marion despised them and knew there'd soon be the usual annual crop of pregnant fifteen-year-olds. 'They're *stupid*,' she told Stella, who was hungry for some fun, a dance, admiration. 'The worst drivers in the world because they've got no imagination or feelings for other people.'

Then they came to tell her what Mike had done and this was the worst thing of all. She knew then that they had to leave Australia. You couldn't live in the same town as *this.* Not unless you were one of *them*, stupid and without conscience. It tore her to pieces to see him suffer so, and she began to snarl at him, because she couldn't help it, but also to sting some anger into him so that he would fight back.

'Singapore, instant Asia,' the brochure assured her, 'where Chinese, Malay and Eurasian live side by side in harmony in this great city of apartment blocks, temples and *kampongs* . . .' 'Hong Kong for festivals and fun . . . extends to the fifteenth day of the first moon when the Ancient Lantern Festival is celebrated . . . thousands of coloured Chinese lanterns of all shapes and sizes . . . the scent of burning joss sticks . . . Dine aboard a cruising sampan while Chinese musicians serenade you both . . . it will raise her blood pressure five points at least . . . Floor shows, hot from swinging Europe . . . Mongolian Hot-Pot . . .'

But there was no escape from yourself. Place had no relevance. She had the bitter sensation of a whole life – several lives – slightly wrong, one strategic error compounding another. Australia or Europe, what difference would it make? Love. She wanted him back the way he had been before that day, and in sorrow knew that his punishment was that he would never be that man again.

The sea was rough as the *Areopagus* went across the Great Australian Bight, but the old lady and the crippled gentleman at their table still ate heavily. Mike strolled round an empty deck and watched from the bows as the stern rose up to an angle of perhaps 40°. Marion and the kids felt sick and he was miserable with responsibility, as if he'd been buying happiness for them and wasn't getting his money's worth. He wondered in alarm if the sea would be like this for fifty days. Or was it a relatively calm sea and the *Areopagus* which wasn't a stable ship? They had come to Australia in a liner twice the size, so large that it had smashed its way heedlessly through the one bad storm and maintained its 27 knots.

Mike's spirit rather than his body was filled with a seediness. He dreaded talking to people. Anything they might ask would involve a dishonest reply. But no one bothered him. It was as if they knew and kept clear of him. Already twos and fours of old people welcomed each other in the library and lounges, and in the dining-room he heard them ask each other with concern in the morning how the other had slept and what was his or her condition now. They cheered whoever at their table had a birthday, when the ship's orchestra, a quartet, approached that particular table and played *Happy Birthday to You*, and the Chief Steward handed over an elaborately patterned cake and a photographer took a photograph with flash and the whole dining-room applauded. But it was as if the Burston family, contaminated by him, were determinedly alone. 'Are those beautiful girls yours?' a woman asked him in the lift, and Mike was startled, as if, belonging to him, they must be painted with failure.

Marion took the lifeboat drill seriously, tying useless bits of tape round the girls' stomachs and rushing them to a lounge for instruction. Mike half listened to the analyses of their own improbable survival. Women chattered to each other while a fat young officer with three stripes on his sleeve, conscious of their indifference, the disbelief that anything could happen to *them*, urged 'You must take it seriously,' as if he understood some weakness of the ship they had not been told about.

Mike knew that they'd all fail in an emergency. One only had to see them, a few days out, still hopelessly confused about directions, decks and stairways. The water-tight doors might clang shut and delay things, but water could rush up the elevator shafts. There'd be panic. Even Australians panicked in the end, Mike decided grimly. What would they do, how would they behave under stress – the Entertainments Officer, a blond queer in a pink suit; the pale attractive girls who looked after the children's games and the trips ashore; the Purser's girls who played with forms and foreign stamps and smiled disarmingly when they didn't know the answer?

Even a passenger could see that they were as new to the ship as himself. And what of the stewards who stood around in gloomy passages coughing with obvious tuberculosis? And the conceited big blonde girl at the Midships Bar, who went on reading a book and let Mike stand five minutes and be ignored rather than explain the system of this bar, which was that he bought a chit like a bus ticket from her and then moved three or four feet to the right to find the barman and repeat his order. This man was vain and often stood facing the mirror behind the bar. It was obviously an effort for him to serve people like Mike. As with the girl, smiles and attention were reserved for other, more interesting people, the heavy drinkers careless about currency, the show business people, officers, youths with muscle. All these would fail in disaster, Mike knew, as he might fail himself.

Only the stewards, who knew very little English, and to whom everyone, being superior to *them*, was important, failed in the reverse identification of Mike Burston which was so easy and instantaneous for eighteen-year-old German girl students serving as cashiers, and barmen who'd served thousands upon thousands of people and identified at once who was relatively important in these cubic few yards and who was not. The cabin stewards knew he'd paid the fares, a fortune, and so they erred in the identification of face, demeanour, British class, and offered a smile or greeting.

'Relax and Never Worry,' was the Thought for the Day. 'You have paid your fare. Enjoy yourself. There is nothing to worry about now.' But Mike couldn't unwind and become soporific. He sat in a deckchair, very alone, on the Sun Deck, while hundreds strolled and talked on the Parade Deck ten feet beneath him. Half a dozen people, young and middle-aged, ran up and down the Sun Deck behind a big young man who had been a surfer in Queensland. 'Run a Mile with Peter' – and as they came the second time, some already trailing the field, a man with glasses and a nice sort of ordinary girl grinned at him. The girl told Mike 'I'm cutting the corners' and smiled in camaraderie, the ship, thousands upon thousands of miles to travel, and he was touched, momentarily involved; but that passed and only served to emphasize the isolation, the distance he was from them, from normality. They were like people who never read newspapers nor listened to news bulletins. He, on the other hand, was like a man who listened and read too much and was too committed to the world for ordinary fun . . .

Voices assailed him, but remotely, along with the noises of movement and metals expanding in the increasing sun, people talking, desirous of doing that which Mike did not wish or intend to do, that is, talking about themselves carelessly : 'Are you a good sailor?' – 'I'm quite good, George was ill yesterday' – 'A Dutchman. I put him in charge' – 'They work awfully hard, don't they?' – 'Yes, but they get cocky' – 'Fourteen grandchildren to see us off' – 'We haven't introduced ourselves, have we? My name's Roy and this is Elizabeth—' And louder than any of them the metallic voice : 'Your attention, please. The time : 1.30. Latitude 35 South. Longitude 127 East. Speed 17.6 knots. Distance covered in 24 hours : 463 miles. Course 267°. Temperature 77°. Passengers are reminded that tonight the ship's clocks will be retarded one hour. I repeat –' But the voice didn't repeat, for the address system, as usual, broke down . . .

On the following morning the Burstons woke in a smell of oil. It was thick and hurt the throat and eyes. The cabin steward fetched an officer and there was much discussion and shouting on the telephone. The officer said to Mike, 'We are very sorry but there is an oil leak. It will involve the removal of panels. We shall give you a superior cabin on A Deck.'

'Hooray!' contributed Stella.

Cabin A73 was a fraction larger and it had a porthole.

Marion said idly, 'It's hot. We must be approaching Fremantle.'

Stella, in bare feet, commented, 'The floor's hot.'

'I hope the air conditioning works,' Marion offered grimly, but it didn't. It seemed pointless to complain since it was a better cabin than they'd started with, but Mike went to the Purser's office and a German girl noted the fault. Two men came in the afternoon, but when they departed after two hours there was still only the faintest movement of air.

In the night Marion was too hot to sleep, and someone in the cabin opposite kept coming and going, slamming a door, so that Marion said loudly, 'Don't they know how to shut a door quietly?' But at three in the morning a girl laughed outside, a transistor radio offered pop music, the girl said 'Goodnight' and then giggled, scuffling, and then she or someone knocked for whole minutes on the door opposite, in vain. The kids slept through this, but Mike echoed Marion's anxiety, saying aloud, 'I hope we're not going to have *that* the whole trip.'

Hours later Stella asked, 'Can I go to the cabaret tonight?'

'Not on your own,' Marion told her promptly.

'Not with *you* either,' Stella qualified. 'You're so miserable.'

'Then don't go at all,' snapped Marion.

'Well, Mum, you are. It's being so old, I suppose.'

'You can't go on your own.'

'With Diane.'

'Who's she?'

'You know – across the way.'

Mike said, 'Is she the one who slams doors at three in the morning?'

'How do I know? I was asleep.'

'I've seen her. She's cheeky.'

'She's not. She's very nice,' Stella argued warmly.

Marion instructed seriously, 'First cabaret, then. I want you in bed by ten.'

'Oh, Mum, this is a holiday, isn't it? She can't go then 'cause she goes to the second meal. And the second cabaret doesn't even *start* until 9.30.'

'Let her go,' suggested Mike.

Marion said loudly, 'I've just said she can't go. How do we know what this girl's like, if she wanders about at three in the morning and scuffles with youths?'

'God, Mum, you make everything sound like an orgy,' Stella protested. 'I'm sure it wasn't her anyway. And I'll come straight back afterwards, I promise.'

'That seems fair,' reasoned Mike.

'You don't *care*,' Marion said bitterly. 'If she does what

she likes tonight, what about tomorrow and next week? We *know* you don't have any sense of responsibility.'

Mike shouted back at her: 'That's a lousy thing to say. For God's sake, it wasn't my fault. How was I to know—'

'Then why are we running away from Australia?' Marion asked with crushing logic.

'The court said it wasn't my fault—'

'The court!' Marion sneered ruthlessly, ignoring the kids, who were all startled, Stella in fact was fascinated. 'Oh, yes, they'd say that to stop you going crazy.'

'Who's going crazy?' he demanded.

'I am,' she said, and ran into the bathroom, weeping.

He called after her, 'The court decided it,' but she countered, 'We had a good lawyer. The company's. It was important that you got off. Your job—'

'Do you think I feel good about it?' he shouted, utterly dejected, shaking.

'Don't shout at me,' Marion sobbed. 'Go away. Leave me alone.'

'All *right*,' he snarled. 'I'm in the bar if you want me.'

Because he had said he was going to the bar Mike in fact went to one as if he was obliged to. He hurried along the deck, elbowed his way through idle promenaders with an urgency which suggested something important to attend to. He avoided the Midships Bar because he did not wish to face the insolent big German cashier or the conceited barman, and went instead to the Forward Bar, which he had not entered before. The rise and fall of the ship was more noticeable here in the bows.

His haste seemed all the more absurd and his anguish the more out of place in the Forward Bar, for it was a place of discretion, of quiet corners, subdued lamps and soft carpeting. There was a small octagonal dance floor, empty at the moment, and the four men of the ship's 'orchestra' (as it was called) played sentimental music.

Mike sat down, shaking, hot and dejected. There weren't many people in the bar, for it was not nine o'clock and many people were still at dinner. A few couples – you could tell which were married for they had nothing to say to each other. A half-dozen smoothies were noisy at one table, bellowing amusement that froze Mike. He felt horribly alone.

A girl was leaning over the piano, stroking the head of the man playing it. The man was thirty-ish, cheap, conceited; any other man could tell this at a glance. He delighted in the girl's action, and was not at all self-conscious. Again the girl failed to recognize that what she was doing had been done before by others: it was traditional that girls aboard liners made fools of themselves over officers, stewards, lift-boys, hairdressers, entertainers . . . and romanticized the episode and the ship for the rest of their lives. This girl, stretched over the piano, was wearing a very short skirt, and this rode now as high as her buttocks. Mike could see her pants and was embarrassed, she was obviously so easy.

The girl had red hair and as she turned her head to stroke her own hair in a gesture of vanity he saw that she was Diane, the girl whom he had said Stella could accompany to the late cabaret. He had regrets and misgivings now, although every confidence in Stella, his favourite, who, although with a caustic tongue (it goes with frustrated intelligence, Mike considered generously), listened to a radio preacher twice a week and had been known to go to Sunday school without any prompting by her parents. Stella did not bother with boys at all . . .

Mike was longing for a beer. He had promised Marion weeks ago he wouldn't drink it again, but now he was terribly tempted: safe on a ship, his mouth dry, his body hot and his nerves screaming.

A steward sauntered over like a definition. A queer, Mike's mind told him, and, absurdly, he felt a fool about to order a soft drink. It did not matter to him that the man, a Greek, was a queer.

'Lemonade,' he ordered. 'And twenty fags.'

The steward said unnecessarily – and he had a voice that carried – 'You're joking. I thought you were an *Australian* . . .'

He inferred that Mike looked brown and tough, a beer drinker in fact, but no compliment was intended. Nothing was intended. The steward was justifying himself.

Mike snapped tartly, 'Just get the stuff and never mind the analysis.'

'Of course, *sir*,' the steward said with instant loathing.

He sauntered off, and the bunch of smoothies four tables away called him, 'Hey, John! Come here! You're neglecting us.'

They gave a complicated order, which the steward fulfilled. He then became purposely involved with the girl cashier. Ten minutes passed with Mike very brittle and thinking of using his fists.

There was an officer a few tables away. He was drinking on his own, and seemed to have gone some way with it. Mike recognized him as the First Officer who'd given the instructions about life-jackets.

He had observed Mike, although distantly, for he was obviously involved mentally elsewhere. Now he snapped his fingers and the queer steward came over in a hurry.

The officer spoke in Greek, but he was clearly reprimanding the steward with fury. The man positively recoiled before his anger.

Then the officer stood by Mike and said, 'You have been kept waiting by this oaf. Allow me to order you a drink.'

He said this in front of the steward, who suffered visibly.

'I only wanted a lemonade,' Mike told him.

'And why not? It is hot,' the officer said.

He wasn't drunk, but uninhibited.

The steward fetched drinks very quickly. The officer sat down and drank half a whisky.

'They are not all like that one,' he reassured Mike.

Mike agreed. 'No. They're good, bloody good.'

'On a holiday?'

'No. Going back to England.'

'Quite rightly,' the officer said unexpectedly. 'Europe is civilized. I hate Australians,' he told Mike with vehemence. 'Vulgar, crude people. Pigs. But no doubt you know that. Excuse me. I have many things to attend to. I hope you have a good trip.'

He strode out of the bar, a thickset young man upset about something.

The curious small incident improved Mike. He felt momentarily elated, even good humoured. He had a friend who was important. No. It wasn't exactly that. What it was, was that the Greek officer had failed to despise him, to identify, and had treated him like a human being.

He wanted to tell Marion about it, as if it had a bearing on *them*. Her face was surprised to see him back so quickly, but at once returned to solemnity, something not far away from misery.

'I didn't drink beer,' he announced. 'An officer bought me a lemonade.'

It had no significance for Marion. 'Where's Stella?' he asked.

She snarled at once, 'Where d'you think? Gone off with that tarty thing you regard as good company for her.'

'Maybe I was mistaken,' he admitted.

But Marion conceded nothing. She was genuinely worried. 'It's a bit late to be mistaken.'

'Christ, kid, I wish you didn't take everything so damn seriously,' he protested.

'I wish you *did*,' she answered shakily.

'Hi!' said Diane, her invariable greeting.

She stood by the open door of her cabin. Inside Stella could see a chaos of underwear hanging on string, and an old woman half sitting, half lying on the lower bunk of the two.

'Gee, what a tiny cabin!' Stella couldn't resist observing. 'Is that your grandmother you're travelling with?' she asked as they strolled away.

'That old wowser!' Diane objected. 'I wouldn't have *her* for my fairy godmother. She thinks the world's going to end next April! Honestly. The lousy shipping company does it. They stick a girl in with an old woman so she can look after the old thing when she's crook and the old dear can complain if the girl shows any signs of enjoying herself! You know what she did last night? She locked me out!'

Diane wasn't quite as tall as Stella, but was lithe, full of awareness. She wore a mini-dress. Stella was taller, but awkward. She had a nose which was slightly hawked and she was pale with mild anaemia. Diane was nearly two years older and had a far stronger personality. Already Stella felt weakened before it.

'Where are you from?' Diane asked.

Stella told her, and added, 'It was so boring.'

'Jesus, I'll bet! Hey, and you know what that old crumb said to me this morning! "I don't object to your swearing," she told me. "That's your business. But I will not tolerate the Name of Our Lord being blasphemed." '

Stella couldn't help but giggle. It felt like a betrayal to do so. Of Dr de Haan perhaps? He would have said the old lady was quite right. Dr de Haan spoke on the radio, half an hour, Wednesdays and Fridays. He was terrific. She couldn't fault him. And he wasn't *dreary*. He made the Bible and God and all those things pretty smart. Still, maybe this was entirely physical, a reflex action like blushing when you weren't guilty or shaking with the giggles at atrocities you recognized as dreadful.

'When we stopped at Adelaide you know what she thought?' Diane asked. 'She said "Is this Singapore?" and I said "No, it's a bonus port they've given us: Adelaide." And you know what she said? "Isn't Adelaide the capital of Singapore?" She ought to be in an institution or something.

Stella laughed, then asked, 'What did you do?'

'About what?'

'When she locked you out?'

'Roy took me to his cabin.'

Stella was shocked.

'You mean—?'

'Oh, it was all right. Barry was there, but he didn't mind.'

Stella felt hot with discomfort. She wanted to ask 'Didn't mind *what*?' but hadn't the nerve.

'I'm from Sydney,' Diane informed her. 'I was engaged. I've still got the ring. Beautiful, isn't it?'

'It certainly is,' said Stella in awe. 'You didn't give it back?'

'What, to that rat-bag?'

Just to walk with Diane was an experience. People looked at her in a curious way. Stewards tried to pretend they were staring at something else, but Stella could see that they were bothered by the high skirt and legs already sunburnt. Three times on the way to the cabaret they met youths, who greeted Diane by name and examined Stella with interest. Two of them had to paw Diane a little while they talked, as if they couldn't keep their hands off her. She objected 'Stop messing about' but they didn't.

Stella asked, probing an area about which she knew nothing, 'What's it like, being engaged?'

Diane said quickly, 'Jesus, you must have had a dull time in the outback! It was the same as usual, only the necking was more potent.'

Stella was fascinated, but didn't dare inquire further in case she revealed her ignorance. Dr de Haan was very against necking of any sort. He interviewed students and asked them if they felt it was healthy, and then analysed their recorded answers. Always what they said he found shallow and in the long run evil. They were usually pretty articulate students, who qualified, 'Necking's all right if you don't go too far' or 'if you know when to stop' or, as one girl said, 'If you're seriously in love with someone you've got to show it somehow, reveal affection and so on.' But none of them ever said outright what necking *was*, and what 'too far' meant. Dr de Haan seemed to imply that it was sex of some degree.

She ventured, 'Dr de Haan says necking is dangerous to health.'

Diane shrieked with amusement. 'Who's he?'

'Oh, just someone we know,' Stella said, defensively, betraying the radio voice she had heeded scores of times.

'Sounds like a real wowser.'

'He's kind of nice.'

'Watch him,' advised Diane. 'They're the really repressed ones. He'd probably beat you with his fists while he laid you.'

This was so crude that Stella blushed hotly.

'All the stewards come in the cabin when I'm changing,' complained Diane. 'Honestly, I don't see how they *know* ... Are you dancing after the show?'

'They say I've got to go straight back,' Stella told her, and was glad that her parents had indeed said this. Diane scared her. If she wasn't careful she'd be hustled into some ghastly situation.

Roy sat with them watching the cabaret. He was a chunky bearded youth with pale shiny skin. He pawed Diane throughout the performance, as if he couldn't believe his luck and must keep touching to confirm it. He said almost nothing to Stella, even regarding her with faint hostility, as if he identified disapproval.

The cabaret was performed in the Aegean Lounge, and the place was already hot and smoke stung the eyes, the left-over from the first performance. It was very professional, Stella felt: dancers who moved with sensual precision, two comedians who were witty about events of this very day, pop singers, a ventriloquist, a couple who did ballroom dancing ... 'They've brought three thousand costumes for this trip,' Diane whispered.

Afterwards Diane suggested, 'Let's get a drink. It's so hot in there,' and she over-ruled Stella's objections, arguing, 'They won't know to within a quarter of an hour will they? They weren't *there*, were they?'

'No,' Stella agreed. 'Just one, then, Diane, and better make it lemonade,' she qualified, apprehensively, 'so they don't smell my breath.'

Diane hurried her, with a bad-tempered Roy – he, too, was overcome by Diane's personality and just followed her around – to the Forward Bar. 'We'll go in the Labyrinth Club,' Diane said decisively.

This was a gallery forward of the Bar, and with an excellent view out to sea forward. But it had become a sort of rendezvous for particular groups of people – drinkers, card players (in the daytime), lovers and some of the cabaret folk who didn't want to be stared at.

Diane identified a group of half a dozen males in the deliberate gloom. They welcomed her like an old friend, which perplexed Stella. How could she know so many people, in a matter of a week or so? They weren't even boys, some of them, but men of thirty, one even forty.

They were boisterous, with eighteen empty beer cans, six

upon six upon six, on the table, and they welcomed Stella effusively, with genuine eagerness, as if the female voice in the darkness had a particular property, completed the party. They made a joke of everything anyone said, especially of what Diane said, and Stella sensed Roy's tension, an angry proprietorial silence, as if he was brooding: this is my girl; I had her company all night, she came to my cabin; now I see she is available to everyone...

Stella, too, was stiff with agitation, aware of how difficult it would be to get away from such company so soon after arrival.

The steward was cooperative, part of a conspiracy.

'John, John!' the men called, and he came, part of *them*; the other people, under illumination in the Bar, fools to attend to, defraud of coins. 'What is it, my darlings?' – 'Diane's arrived' – 'Well! Now the party really gets going! Seven cans of Victoria bitter?' – 'No, John. Listen. Don't go away. This is Stella. What do you want, Stella?' And John said 'What we all want, eh?' which aroused mirth. 'Don't be so sexy,' a man said, and Stella felt a wowser, damping this down with a dull plea for 'Lemonade.' 'You stick to it, darling, and keep your honour intact among these gentlemen,' urged John, but, of course, Stella felt, flushing, stung, he thinks that would be silly.

Diane said 'He's a marvel, John is. He'll go on serving us long after they've closed the bar. He'll do anything for you except hop into bed. You know what I mean?'

'No,' admitted Stella, feeling gauche.

'He's one of *them*,' Diane explained, but it still meant nothing to Stella. John was merely a voice in the darkness, a faint smell of sweat.

She sipped lemonade, worried about how to leave, and then stood up. 'They said I've got to go back straightaway,' she reminded Diane, although she was so nervous she wanted to leave anyway. A little of this sort of company would last a long time and give her plenty to analyse and think about. She changed her position to say this, embarrassed, for it was not a situation Dr de Haan had yet covered. It felt silly and immature. Dr de Haan had pointed out how evil necking was, and all that stuff, but he had never instructed on how to get out of a room, léave a party once you were in it . . .

Diane argued 'We'll have to do something about your people' and Stella agreed 'Yes' meaninglessly.

It was as if she had accepted that her parents were people she wanted to deceive, and once that condition of deception had been obtained, the whole wide world of dancing, drinking, necking and other, unknown pleasures would be hers to enjoy.

6

Miss Irene Wearne, sixty-six, weight seven stone, height five feet, had been a schoolteacher in an outer suburb of Melbourne. She had a long horsy face, rough textured, blue eyes and, until the operation on the side of her head to relieve the pressure, she'd had grey hair which in certain lights had appeared green. She seemed weightless, with arms like pale twigs in the sun, and her flesh the colour and texture of suet. Her small blue eyes were humorous and her glasses magnified the exhaustions of the illness so much that people meeting her flinched slightly.

She had been very realistic. They'd shaved her hair off before the operation and afterwards Miss Wearne had purchased a wig. She had been very practical, quite without vanity, and had sought a wig of exactly the same grey and white texture as the hair she had lost.

Miss Wearne lived a life of aching loneliness. No one came to see her. The school at which she had taught for thirty years had been glad to see her go. 'Too old; too conservative,' had been the headmaster's bigoted view. He was both right and wrong. For Miss Wearne had been a teacher for many years and belonged to a generation which, according to the new fast thinking, had been incredibly ignorant and almost limited to the three Rs. She belonged to the Australia which had been part of the vast red areas on maps of the world: the British Empire.

Not that it seemed to make any difference. Generation after generation of youths and girls had come to the school. She had seen them grow up and fail. One or two went to Canberra and a few won medals in various wars. But most of the male faces could be seen later in local stores, second-hand car sales rooms, or, worse, in local headlines : six years for rape pack; two killed in head-on collision; girl stripped in telephone box ... They looked at Miss Wearne, and if they identified her at all, sneered in superiority. For they had left her behind and discovered the world of vulgarity and money and learned to worship it.

It was as if all life was a failure and a waste of time ... The suburb was a conviction of failure. Litter, broken glass, men dead drunk on the pavements, even the taxi drivers' cars wobbled on Saturday nights. Mongrel dogs ran about the streets. A gutter Press told of rape and nudity at parties, and a small army of wowsers tried to put the world right, to what it had been in 1914, or 1939, or 1947, and their defeat was bitter before the pressures of the world outside, which flooded the bookstalls and beat at the retina of the eyes in the square box in the gloom of suburban rooms ...

She lived in a dull avenue half a mile from a main road, a tiny house but her own. It had been her parents'. There was no hope of living anywhere else. She could sell the house, but it would not fetch the amount of money that could transfer her to a better suburb. For this one had gone down in thirty years, from extreme middle-class respectability to a kind of place for people to drive through, very fast, on their way to somewhere better. Her house was next to a concrete yard, with only that and a brick wall five feet high between her and a boarding-house. Here half a dozen youths from tax offices, electric companies and builders' offices lived : there was the inevitable litter of beer cans in the yard, a hotted-up automobile that disturbed the night, pop records and tarty girls who came and sometimes stayed the night. There was a rumour that some of the youths had been drinking in a bedroom where a girl of fourteen lay naked on the bed and was, over an hour or two, raped (if that was the word for so willing a victim) by all of them. It was quite believable. The vicious, lean, hard woman who ran the place wouldn't be bothered, and was often away whole weekends. There had been visits by the police, but these had been about thefts of radios and complaints about noise.

Miss Wearne was a little scared of it, but had the Australian sense of humour which expects disaster and views it with sardonic acceptance as the norm.

She had never lived anywhere else but Melbourne. The clank of trams and the noise of road drills and bulldozers expanding the vast sprawl were part of life. She supposed it must be an ugly city, and certainly photographs of Paris, Rome, Cape Town, Oxford and so on made these cities seem very beautiful, always supposing you could believe the photography. (For she had seen books about a Melbourne which, for her, didn't exist.) She therefore accepted Melbourne's suburbia as a kind of dull joke to which she was superior: the houses of liverish red brick or wood and their tin roofs; concrete gnomes in arid little gardens; pieces of string where hedges should be; a dog howling in a yard; gum trees which remained half grey whatever the season; meat pies saturated in tomato sauce; the radio commercials and the platitudes of disc jockeys.

Each year she watched the bush fires a few miles away approaching to destroy this suburbia, and sometimes the flames came close enough for hot ash to set on fire a few nearby gum trees. Twice people had died in fires within half a mile, and these were days to remember, when she hated and feared Australia, the stifling atmosphere and an oppressive temperature of 106.

On these summer days a furnace wind blew from the north, from the vast overheated land mass and even breathing was laborious. Dust swirled and to teach children was ridiculous. Hours or even days past the point where it was unbearable some voice would cry 'She's turning round!' and the union jack on the school office and the Christmas or Moomba tinsel on the supermarket and city buildings would flutter and turn as the wind reversed and cooled, approaching with rain from Tasmania and the South Pole.

On Anzac Day she wept a little, for she had had a brother

who had died in that War. And she'd look out of the window, or stand before a flagpole with children as ordinary men marched unsteadily through the dull city streets and scruffy suburbia to remember a disaster, and then drank themselves stupid and laughed about it.

It was part of the Australian emphasis on ordinary people, carried too far so that extraordinary people were disliked more than elsewhere. They in any case fled from this aggressive equality, this two million square miles in which nearly everybody lived in half a dozen cities. Ugly cities of boxes up and down slopes, with the trees slaughtered, and no privacy except where fingers of bush poked into the outer suburbs. Cities of veneer, tin roofs and cardboard, hosepipes running in vain in the great heat; wrought-iron hotels and public buildings like lavatories; dull supermarkets full of aggressive shapeless women with acid tongues pushing trolleys laden with tins; miles of stinking dustbins; vehicles heading out of suburbia with surfboards and little boats strapped to overloaded estate cars, on their way to the suburbias of the beaches, scores of thousands of sweaty bodies and eyes staring out to sea.

Until recently Miss Wearne had been to church regularly – tarted up and scented with the best of them – and had never doubted that God was an Australian.

And so it now seemed.

A God with a malicious humour could only be Australian, and Miss Wearne accepted the joke in sardonic resignation, Australian style.

Miss Wearne had taught geography for nearly forty years, but had never been anywhere except around the State of Victoria with parties of schoolkids, or to Tasmania's mountains. She belonged to a generation which, when young, had been poor and not in receipt of hand-outs . . .

She had always wanted to go, by ship (planes did it too quickly) round the Asia she had told children about, to Singapore, Hong Kong, and to North America, England, Italy, Paris . . .

Now, at 66, she could go, for she had won a competition in a woman's magazine and the prize was a ticket on a round-the-world trip aboard the liner *Areopagus* – Bali, Singapore, Hong Kong, Guam, San Francisco, Panama, London, Italy...

It was a good joke, very Australian...

For Miss Wearne was going to die, and knew it...

She had about two or, with luck, three months to live. Already she had the occasional dizzy turns which were very frightening, but these, they assured her, had no significance in regard to the position. The headaches? Well, even those were only a result of her condition, not the aggravation of it...

Two days after they told her she was going to die the letter came informing her that she'd won the ticket for a world cruise.

Miss Wearne thought about it and decided to go. She even worked up an enthusiasm and decided it could be a good joke.

She wanted to die at sea. She wished for a few hundred people aboard to be shaken and to know of her existence. The persons she encountered in the Melbourne suburb never really saw her. She knew, because she was too intelligent not to know, that she was a kind of nothing. People exchanged postage stamps if she handed them coins or notes. They gave her a newspaper for five cents and acknowledged 'Good morning' providing she said it first. But really they didn't see her at all except as a customer, a nuisance, a nothing... And she wanted a few score people to stand nervously and witness her remains being tipped into the sea.

She wanted a small feature in the ship's newspaper and a slightly larger one on the women's pages of the Melbourne newspapers amongst the news of the smart people dining and the descriptions of what Mrs Ogilvy-Daylight was wearing for her daughter Beryl's engagement party at the skyscraper hotel where a room for two hundred guests cost at least $1,000 before anyone sat down to eat or lifted a glass... And the radio officer aboard the *Areopagus* would have to tap it out, the news of her death, in Morse code, or did he talk into a microphone? There would be another grim small very Australian joke when the woman's magazine had to admit that the winner of their prize ticket had died between Panama and Southampton . . .

All her life Miss Wearne had been nothing – for she'd never been beautiful – in the suburbia of tin roofs, slanting telegraph poles, aggressive youths and promiscuous barefoot big girls, too vain to learn from books; the dull men from Masonic Lodges and the Returned Servicemen's League, and the great army of people who could do things she was unable to do – drive big automobiles, water ski, surf, drink . . . She had never had the money to get away from them. Her escape now from suburbia was a bitter one, but she savoured it. She bought six new dresses and a camera – the latter so that she could send back colour slides to her one friend, a Mrs Boyd, Eileen Boyd, a widow, an aggressive sour woman who lived half a mile away.

These two women knew they had nothing but each other, and at times they resented it. Miss Wearne was glad that she would die first. That'd give the old hag something to worry about. She'd be missed and the cakes she cooked and the bottle of wine shared in front of the TV set.

Miss Wearne guessed that geography lessons didn't convey the reality, the smells, the humidity or the beauty of foreign places, and she presumed that the travel brochures were far too optimistic. She decided that there would be unpleasant moments for anyone as weak as she now was.

She hadn't anticipated that they would begin before and with the arrival of the taxi at the door. For it was impossible to be calm. She hadn't moved out of the State of Victoria for eleven years, nor outside the Melbourne suburb for three. So she slept badly and was tired before the taxi came.

This, too, was worrying and tiresome. Melbourne taxi drivers are cheerful souls : they do not expect tips; they like passengers to sit in the front seat beside them and will thereupon discuss the merits of certain horses, boxers and footballers. But they do not come to a house to carry the cases out. Some even remain seated and open the automobile boot automatically from inside the taxi. Miss Wearne had two heavy cases. She struggled out with one. The driver asked, 'That the lot, missus?' and Miss Wearne had to plead, 'No. There's another one. I wonder if you'd mind—?'

It was worse at the Victoria Pier because she had to carry the two cases to that end of the Customs Hall where the passengers would have to pass through. If she stood with her cases she could be first aboard, but there was an hour to pass and she was horribly tired and wished to sit down.

After a while the cases were taken away, to her great relief. She stumbled a few yards to sit down, but the benches had all been occupied and faces stared at her with indifference or hostility, or avoided her exhausted eyes altogether. A lady with an English accent took pity on her and instructed a child, 'Patricia, stand up so this lady can sit down.'

For this Miss Wearne was grateful, and would have talked to the lady, but something about her expression suggested that Miss Wearne's dialogue wouldn't be wanted.

After a while Miss Wearne felt a little better and went to stand in a position which would allow her to be first in the queue. It would be a very long queue, she decided in trepidation, for hundreds of people hovered about. Somewhere people were cheering and singing.

A few Customs officers strolled on duty, in no hurry; they just didn't see the milling people. They went to the kiosk and stood sipping tea and talked to other uniformed people. They never looked at the big clocks, and it was five past eight before they began to do something about the queue. 'Typical,' she heard the English woman complain. 'They could have let us on at half past seven. Stupid, they are.'

Miss Wearne didn't understand why she had to stand in front of two desks before she was allowed on board. She became confused and doubled back from the second desk to the first. And then a few officers sat at a trestle on the deck itself and *they* wanted to ask questions. A crowd already seethed on board, shoving her out of the way; youths shouted and threw empty beer cans; a girl put a garland of flowers round Miss Wearne's neck; men bellowed with laughter; everybody seemed to know what they were doing except herself; she felt deadly tired. Four hours had passed since the taxi had called and taken her away from suburbia. She had the wretched sensation that suburbia was coming with her : the passengers seemed just the same rude, aggressive sort of people she'd encountered in supermarkets.

The woman's magazine had not mentioned this tediousness. And when a boy steward at last conducted her to a cabin she had another shock. She should have expected it, but the wording of the competition, the letters which had come from the magazine and the shipping company had implied, somehow, that she was to have a cabin to herself. There had even been a faint suggestion that she would be waited on hand and foot.

But she was taken to a cabin in which were three middle-aged women. They were standing in a dull light, likely to be the permanent condition of the cabin, for there was no porthole, and they were not pleased to see her.

They were Sydney loud-mouths, she saw at once in dejection, and every citizen of Melbourne despises these.

They stood around as if she wasn't there, and as they were women of bulk Miss Wearne couldn't move. As soon as she sat wearily on a lower bunk they noticed her quickly enough.

'Not there, missus,' one told her, and not expecting any discussion about it. 'Up there's yours.'

Miss Wearne was at once terrified of sleeping in an upper bunk. She said, 'I don't think I can climb up there.'

'You'll have to,' they told her pitilessly. 'There's clean sheets up there.'

'I can't stand heights,' another said, conversationally, but not to Miss Wearne. 'You know, Harry used to take me . . .' A pointless anecdote followed, and the woman addressed said, as if proving her own commonsense, 'Anyway, there's no light up there. I like to have a read in bed.'

Someone knocked at the door, and came in without pause. A man in shirt-sleeves and braces; a square face, glasses, stubble, and breath touched with stale alcohol.

'Hello, hello, hello !' he said. 'No one topless ! What a pity ! Hey, are you girls coming to see the ship sail ? The lights of beautiful Melbourne and the delicious aroma of the Yarra River ?'

They made noises of disgust with their mouths. 'Another hour, more likely,' one suggested.

'No,' claimed Harry. 'The gangways are up and Captain Vafiadis is up there with his pocket compass.'

They laughed obligingly.

'Aren't you going to introduce me?' asked Harry.

'What?' they asked dully. 'Oh, her.' And they condescended to identify themselves : Ada, Muriel and Iris.

'My name's Irene Wearne.'

'All alone, are you?'

'How are you, Irene?' Harry inquired, to pass the time, Miss Wearne could see, or acquire obligations.

She didn't want to admit weakness to such vulgar people, but was very far in exhaustion and a bit dizzy, and not at all enjoying herself.

'I'm not very well,' she admitted.

It meant nothing to them, was a pivot to manœuvre their own humour on.

'You look a bit crook,' said Harry frankly.

'What y'come for then,' asked Muriel with cruel indifference, 'if you're sick?'

'I won a competition,' Miss Wearne told her. At this moment she despised *The Australian Woman and Wife* more than any other journal in the world. The cheap fraud! Just to promote sales!

'Y'getting a free trip, are you?' Muriel persisted, implying 'we've *paid* for ours'.

She had sandy hair and a heavy nose and on her fingers were three ostentatious rings.

'Wait until you're out on the Bight!' sneered Ada. 'You'll have something to worry about.'

Another man came in the cabin after the briefest tap on the door. He was heavy, thick-necked, had a brick-red face, and the heartiness of Sydney's vast suburbia. Miss Wearne knew he would be a regular at the greyhound racing, would be able to play cards, would go to the ship's bingo and wouldn't be sick often or until ten or twelve cans of beer had gone down anyway. She had nothing in common with such people and was frightened of their acid tongues.

'I might have known,' bellowed this man, as if he had surprised them in an orgy, and was only disappointed that they'd been unkind enough to start without him. 'At it again. Hurry up and fix your zips and all them things. The great ship is sailing soon.'

He said this, like the other man, in a tone of deep bitterness, a contempt of the *Areopagus*, as if the ship had failed him many times.

Muriel asked 'Y'coming Ada?' and Ada answered her, 'Course I'm coming. What's on afterwards?' she inquired as if she had an appetite which the ship must satisfy: there must never be a dull moment: they'd paid...

A steward brought Miss Wearne's second case. Muriel informed Miss Wearne malevolently, 'You'll have a job finding room for that lot,' and out they all went.

The steward followed them and left the door open, and so Miss Wearne overheard what they were saying.

'A bloody old fusspot,' Ada was complaining.

'We're lumbered,' Muriel agreed. 'Never mind. As long as she's not got religion! It's all experience, isn't it, Harry, love?'

Miss Wearne was a little hot in the face at this analysis, but not wounded. She expected such gross people to despise her, to fail to understand anything outside the experiences of their own flesh. But her spirit was low at the prospect of spending week after week in contact with them. She was too tired and agitated to sleep at once, but dropped off before they returned, clutching with one hand at the wooden rim of the upper bunk, her last waking thought being an anxiety about how to get down the ladder in the morning . . .

In the morning the steward brought her a cup of tea, and he helped her down. The three women stirred in protest. 'What d'you wake us up for?' Iris complained, but in vain, for Miss Wearne had chosen to go to first breakfast.

The *Areopagus* was pitching a little, but Miss Wearne felt as normal as she was ever likely to. The stewards conducted her to a table where she found the English lady and her family. All of them were oddly self-conscious and made no attempt to talk to Miss Wearne. The mother snapped at her children whenever they were all restive. They've got something on their minds, decided Miss Wearne, catching the father staring, lost, his thoughts perhaps thousands of miles away.

She liked the dining-room. It was large, but not overwhelming, and there were tall columns in the Ionic style and a small semi-circular balcony for the orchestra. Miss Wearne had no great appetite and when the steward – a cheerful young man who appeared not to have shaved today – came to take their orders she asked for stewed fruit.

She was facing astern and just happened to see him using his fingers to transfer prunes and apricots from a bowl to a plate. He placed it before her with a smile, but Miss Wearne, feeling a little queasy, refused it. 'No. I don't like that kind of fruit. Can I have bacon and tomato?'

Now she watched the steward with misgiving, and sure enough, to speed things up, he looked cautiously round to see where the officer was and surreptitiously transferred a tomato and sausage from the debris of an earlier breakfast.

'This is cold,' Miss Wearne told him. 'Go and get something hot from the kitchen.'

The boy smiled, aware that he'd been witnessed, and he disappeared into the galley. The Englishwoman was frowning disapproval at Miss Wearne's apparent fussiness. Her turn may come, thought Miss Wearne charitably.

It was a cold, dull day which passed very slowly for Miss Wearne. She did not wish to go into either of the bars. Bars, for her generation of Australians, were exclusively for men. She did not swim or dance or play bingo. It was lonely in a strange sort of way, for she walked about in crowds; drank hot soup at eleven; lunched with people who said nothing beyond 'Hello; isn't it cold?'; slept a little in the afternoon; sat in lounges; chose a library book; dined; bought some stamps; read the ship's newspaper; and followed the crowd to lifeboat drill. But in the whole day she spoke only about two hundred words and most of these to the dining-room steward.

The three women in the cabin dressed, undressed, cleaned their teeth, yawned cavernously, cut their toenails, put their hair in curlers, smoked, talked to each other, slammed the door, lost the key, found it – all without a word to Miss Wearne. It was as if she didn't exist : was a nothing.

Their husbands entered the cabin at any time of the day or night. They knocked the door, but it meant nothing : they came in anyway.

Miss Wearne sat in the cinema and watched a film about a divorce. It was funny, presumably, for the audience laughed now and again. It meant nothing to Miss Wearne – smartly dressed tireless people opening and closing doors in a luxury flat the size of a stadium, making cracks on the telephone, talking about adultery as if it was no more than kissing. It ended 'happily'.

What Miss Wearne wished and waited for were sunny days and a calm sea, when she could sit in a deckchair and watch other people stroll by, talk to someone, and reserve her energies for the foreign ports. But several days passed in which it was too stormy and cold to sit on deck and in the lounges no one spoke to her. She had to keep on the move and she found it desperately tiresome. There was no peace even in the cabin. The women seemed to be there whenever Miss Wearne would have liked to be quiet, or to rest. All the time there seemed to be noise, the scratching of the key and the monotonous bonhomie of Harry : 'Hello, hello, hello. And how are we tonight?' It was no use. Miss Wearne disliked them and they were going to spoil her trip.

She came back to the cabin from dinner the day before they were due in Fremantle, and found the three women, Harry and a steward standing around helplessly. The women were very hot and bothered. 'It's ruined my sandals and my yellow frock,' complained Muriel. Harry said, 'It's not good enough. We've had a bellyful this trip already.' The steward picked up the telephone in a gesture of hopelessness. 'I talk to the Purser.'

'Don't waste your time,' advised Harry. 'He's no bloody good.'

Ada grumbled, 'We might all be ill. Dirty people, these dagoes.'

An officer entered the cabin, looked around and wrung

his hands. 'What is the trouble?' he asked, and they all poured out their grievances – 'Look at my yellow dress. Just look at it' – and finally identified the complaint. 'There's a leak somewhere. It's flooded the bathroom as well, and ruined my brown bag.'

Nobody took the slightest notice of Miss Wearne. The steward was now shouting over the telephone, so angry that he thumped the cheap dressing-table; boxes flew off.

Miss Wearne blew her nose and immediately understood that it was not just water which flooded the cabin, moving to and fro in a black stream as the *Areopagus* pitched. It was urine. She obtained a faint satisfaction at their discomfort and the inability of the steward and officer to get anybody to take any notice.

The officer went out and returned in five minutes with a plumber who took not the slightest notice of the passengers because he could speak no English . . .

'I'm afraid it is necessary to transfer you,' the officer said apologetically, and Miss Wearne's heart leaped in pleasure.

'What about me?' she asked.

The officer now considered her.

'You sleep in here?'

'Yes.'

'Everything will be arranged. The stewards will come and take your cases. A better cabin,' he forecast recklessly.

Miss Wearne decided it was time to assert herself. 'Who with?'

'Yes, with your friends.'

'They're not my friends,' said Miss Wearne frankly, hot in the face.

The three women accepted the position, the insult, without dispute, for they were just as anxious to be rid of Miss Wearne as she was to get away from them.

'We cannot offer a variety of cabins—'

Ada said, 'Why not? The ship's half empty now.'

'Ah, but many cabins are booked from Fremantle,' qualified the officer.

They didn't believe him and he knew it.

'I will see what can be done,' he assured them.

In his absence the women ignored Miss Wearne. She packed her two cases almost gleefully. In ten minutes a boy came and asked, 'Which one for A101?'

'It must be me,' Miss Wearne told him decisively.

The boy carried her cases and a hundred feet forward kicked on a door.

A girl opened it. She was about sixteen, but rather tall for her age. Her face was heart-shaped and dignified. She had long black hair tied behind her neck. There was no one else. It was a cabin for two. The girl had been writing a letter.

She greeted in a quiet American accent, 'Oh, hello. Come on in.'

Miss Wearne stumbled into her own cases. The boy grinned and suggested 'Okay, now,' and left.

'Did you have trouble with your previous cabin?' the girl asked.

She had an educated sort of voice, but Miss Wearne noticed her hands, agitated in shyness. She liked the girl at once.

'It was flooded,' Miss Wearne told her.

'Anything damaged?'

'I don't think so.'

'Where shall I put your cases?' asked the girl, lifting one of them.

'It doesn't matter.'

'I guess you'd prefer the lower bunk?'

'That's very thoughtful of you,' said Miss Wearne frankly. The whole trip suddenly seemed easier. She would, she decided, make no demands on such a nice person.

'I've been using it,' the girl said, 'but I'll change the sheets . . .'

'I'm Irene Wearne,' Miss Wearne said. 'I won a competition in a magazine.'

'Fancy!' the girl said, in pleasure. 'I've never met anyone who – I didn't think it really happened . . . My name,' she told Miss Wearne, 'is Debbie. Debbie Vertigan.'

7

IT HAD been a busy morning, with two men landing themselves in hospital. Idiots, Dempsey assessed unfairly. What next? I wonder.

One man had dived into the swimming pool when the ship was pitching and had not timed it correctly. He'd knocked himself unconscious. (But what were the blasted crew doing filling the thing anyway? Dempsey wondered.) The other man was a crew member who'd had both legs broken during lifeboat drill. The boat had dropped quickly – a pleasant surprise for *anyone*, Dempsey decided cynically, for the damn things were corroded into the davits – and the handle or whatever they called it had spun violently, breaking both legs of this fellow . . .

For the moment there was nothing to do but wait for lunch. Dempsey was already impatient for it.

He picked up a passenger list. It might be pleasant to have company. On the other hand, it might not; he had encountered some colossal bores aboard the *Opalescent*. He was entitled to invite passengers to eat with him. They never refused as they presumed it was an honour of some kind, or that the food might be more interesting.

There did not seem to be on the list anyone with whom he was acquainted. He wasn't too keen on the travelling doctors, and felt that he had done his duty by them for a week or two. There were several hundred names of people who'd embarked at Sydney. Debbie Vertigan, he read, disembarking San Francisco. The name was unusual and Dempsey recalled that someone had mentioned it. After a while he recollected that a patient with another surname had said idly, "Going on the *Areopagus*? Wish I was coming with you! You'll probably see a niece of mine. She's a very nice girl . . .'

'A very nice girl' was exactly what Dempsey felt like

lunching with. He sent a steward to her cabin with an invitation. At the back of his mind a pleasant prospect of eating with an attractive highly articulate college type girl or stenographer lingered for the next hour.

He was a little disconcerted when the Chief Steward conducted her to his table, for she turned out to be a girl of sixteen, and nervous at that. She had the attitude of someone who was carrying out a duty which was alarming.

'Have a drink?' he suggested.

'I feel a bit sick,' she told him uncompromisingly.

'It's purely nerves,' Dempsey asserted. 'This blasted ship couldn't sink anyway. Have a gin? One small gin and you'll sing!'

'I don't drink,' Miss Vertigan told him with finality.

'I'm going to,' Dempsey told her. 'I've worked like a dog this morning. I *deserve* a drink. What about a lemonade or Coke?'

'Oh, all right,' she agreed.

'Well, thank God we got that settled!' Dempsey declared in his forthright manner. 'Do sit down. And cheer up. This is supposed to be enjoyable.'

She smiled carefully and sat down.

'I never met your father. I just happened to talk to your uncle.'

'That'd be difficult,' the girl said. 'All my uncles are dead.'

'That's a bit much, isn't it? A massacre of uncles! Then who was it I met?'

'Perhaps you've made a mistake.'

'No, no, I met somebody. *And* he said "My niece is going on that trip." '

The girl shrugged. 'I don't know. I'm not even an Australian.' Dempsey thought: she's shy, that's what it is. All these people, and I have a loud voice which embarrasses her.

'What do you do?' he inquired in a softer voice.

'Do? I went to grammar school in Canberra. My father's in politics.'

'Why didn't your parents come on the *Areopagus*?'

'Urgency. You know.' She smiled the careful smile again.

'They let me finish the term and I wanted to see Singapore and Hong Kong. I have a friend in Hong Kong.'

'Oh,' he said, unaccountably disappointed: she wasn't so helpless.

'A pen friend,' the girl continued. 'One of my hobbies.'

'You're going to see what this person is like?'

'Yes – and the city.'

'You'll be disenchanted. People who write to pen friends are idiots. Oh, sorry! What I meant was that they're usually lonely people, and that means something wrong with their nasty little personalities.'

'They write charming letters—'

'You have a point there,' Dempsey admitted. 'What I meant was that the average pen friend isn't as pretty as you are ...'

She blushed and moved about uncomfortably.

'What are you going to have now?'

'I'm not hungry,' she told him.

'What, already?' Dempsey questioned callously. He was ravenously hungry. 'I'll get you something. It's not really imaginary, seasickness, although some people do think themselves into it. It's to do with your ears. Where are you? Which cabin?'

'Right down on A Deck, A101. But it doesn't matter. I'm fine. I'll try the lamb,' she said, to prove it.

'How are you getting on?'

'With what?'

'Aboard the ship.'

'Oh, fine,' she defined doubtfully, and he felt sorry for her, suspecting the truth: lonely in a chair in a vast lounge, pretending to read a book; too young to go into the bars; not fitting in with the muscular extroverts round the pool.

'I'm learning Greek dancing,' she informed him.

'My God, how heroic! Meeting many people?'

'They all gamble,' she said like a complaint.

'Why not?' Dempsey countered. 'They've got to pass the time.' But she didn't argue. He could see that she wasn't quite happy.

'Vulgar boys?' he queried frankly.

'Some of them.'

'Come to a bit of a party?' he invited, and half hoped she'd refuse.

She questioned, 'Who with?'

'Second Officers, mostly. Maybe Tomazos, the First. A nurse or two, the Purser's ladies. They'll drink rather a lot, but it's cheerful.'

'Yes, but *where?*'

'My cabin. It's permitted,' he explained, seeing some disapproval. 'God, girl, we'd all go mad if we couldn't even have a drink together.'

She was giggling, hiding her head.

'Share the joke,' he requested.

'It's funny, the way you call me "girl". Like a schoolteacher.'

'I'll call you Debbie. I think it's a ghastly name,' he said frankly.

She did not ask what she should call him, but said, 'All right. Thank you. What time?'

'Any old time after 8.30 tonight.'

'Yes, but I don't want to drink.'

'God, girl, you worry too much! You *need* to drink!'

'I like to be courteous,' she reprimanded coolly.

'Wasted on the Second Officer,' he told her.

He took the anti-seasickness pills down half an hour after lunch to her cabin, burping gin, the sun in his face. He hoped, unaccountably, that she wouldn't be there.

She was asleep. Dempsey looked at her and wondered whether to wake her. He thought: how very beautiful she will be in a few years, and just then Debbie woke up. She was startled, shy and a little shocked as if she'd caught him ogling.

'I'm all right now,' she told him.

'Well, in case you need them.'

'How much are they?'

'Nothing. It is part of the Graeco-Australian Company's policy that you shouldn't be sick . . .'

Dempsey took evening surgery while Dr Zafiropoulos did

the cabin calls in order that they both might then prepare for the party.

Typically, when Dempsey wished to finish quickly, there were quite a lot of passengers who waited for treatment. Sister Eleni worked with him, almost without a word.

The last one of the evening was a young woman of about twenty-three and she was, Dempsey knew with exasperation and foreboding, going to be difficult. She had the look in her eyes and the tension in her posture. She was one of those in whom carnality cannot be hidden, a girl who exuded electricity without in any way being vulgarly dressed or made-up. She was in fact in a modest pale-blue dress, the hem of which was unfashionably close to the knees. But he identified her intense awareness. It was as if danger signals sounded in his mind : this one wasn't ill : at the very least she wanted an argument : she was hungry with self-pity but it wasn't anything he could cure.

She stared round the small surgery with interest, and asked without preamble, 'Does *she* have to stay?'

Dempsey said, 'Sister Kalogeropoulou is as competent as I am.'

The girl insisted without a qualm, 'I just don't want her around. Hell, isn't anything private?'

'Sister Kalogeropoulou doesn't know all that much English,' Dempsey said, which untruth caused Eleni to open her mouth in surprise, then remain silent.

'She's got eyes, hasn't she?'

Dempsey supposed he might oblige the young woman thus far, although to do so made him uneasy.

'Would you mind, Sister? There's no one else, is there? You might as well go. See you in forty minutes.'

'All right,' conceded Eleni.

Dempsey asked wearily when she had departed, 'What's the matter with you?'

The girl almost turned on him. 'What d'you mean, what's the matter with me? You *know* what's the matter. I could see you did as I came in. And you disapprove because it's emotional.'

Many people, perhaps women especially, talked like this

to Dempsey. Strangers plunged straight into absolute details of their own lives, their sex difficulties, sparing him nothing. It was, he believed, an indicator of the breakdown of society, its rejection of God. They wanted help desperately, not physical but spiritual, conscience problems solved. At times it was funny, not tragic, manœuvring so that he should not be seduced by a woman, a good wife perhaps, who wasn't getting the sex she needed and was too scared, socially conscious and so on to go on the street and claim a man, or too nice to seduce a friend's husband. But the doctor – well, he understood these things; it would remain confidential; he was clean, free from disease, and generally, *nice* ... It was sad, an appalling reflection of the knife-edge on which society stood. Often they were frank to the point of casualness, stripping as soon as they'd got him in a bedroom. They took no offence when he refused them, and he invariably advised with honesty and sympathy.

He qualified now, 'Let's say, then, what can I do to help you?'

'God only knows,' the girl said candidly. 'I'm going to strip off. Any objections? It's so damn hot,' she said, oddly.

She had a superb body, but it meant nothing to him. He had seen so much flesh, and examined it entirely as a series of problems. She left a very brief pair of pants on. 'You can take those off if you want to,' she remarked.

'Let's drop the nonsense,' Dempsey said sharply. 'You're not ill, so what do you want?'

'Don't be like that,' she requested. 'Be human.'

'Humans are like *that*,' Dempsey said. 'What's your story?' he asked in the same angry tone. 'The hard smart story that is so unusual you're still playing the part. Shall I tell *you?*'

'Do,' she challenged.

'You were sixteen or seventeen, smart, cool, superior, aware of your power of attraction, and you hated somebody or something – your parents, society, school, a friend who'd pinched your boy. So you took up this man very publicly, for all the world to know, the dreary moral conventional tired world you despised. An older man, probably, with a pretty wife, kids, big car, good clothes, knowledgeable about restaurants, theatre, sex, whatever it was. It was no problem for him to con you into dropping your pants. You felt that would smash his wife when she found out. It was *love*, of course,' said Dempsey in contempt. 'And maybe he did love you enough to smash his life to bits. He loved you so much in fact he had to have you raw, and you and society hadn't heard of the pill then. So you had a bun in the oven and you hated his guts because he went back to his wife, who gave him a big hello. Society didn't stink quite so high those six or seven years ago. To have an abortion was something for rich people, not grammar school tarts. So you had the kid. What happened to it?'

He knew by her nipples that she had had a child—

She had paled a little in shock, and then laughed shakily. 'I underestimated you. I'm sorry. I see you know what it's all about.'

'Christ, girl, I'm a doctor, but who doesn't know? They watch it on TV from the age of seven. What you think is that it's important, it's superior to what poor old housewives do, it's significant, strictly for cool twentieth-century people. It isn't. It's happened since people began.'

'You looked like a smug suburban doctor on a cruise ... Instead, you talk straight ... I like you ...'

'Oh, get burned,' protested Dempsey. 'You poor fools pithering about with sex like it's something invented by *Time* magazine or some English radical bishop ... People have had your problem since Biblical times. I used to see them in Ireland, nice Catholic girls from the farm who'd been put in the pudding club. They had God to contend with as well. They didn't whine like you people. They married the boy and lived happily ever after.'

'Bovine,' she said in contempt. 'What do you mean, my problem?'

'An agitated fanny,' Dempsey told her crudely. 'Well, what about it? What's your version?'

The young woman said : 'I was married at sixteen. Yes, to an older man. It was strictly love for me. I was brought up on *Gone With the Wind*, not Kinsey. I had two kids. By eighteen he rejected me. I had a woman friend who helped me. So I went to live with her. She had this curious habit of pawing me and lying on top of me. Sweet otherwise. I got to like it. But she was bitchy and I had to leave her. They took the kids away. I've never decided which I like better since then. *That's* my problem. I've got a butch friend with me now. Even she hates me. I'm paying the stewards and others to screw me ... It annoys her ... I was thinking of quitting ... You know ... Over the side ... So I came to you ...'

He didn't believe all this, although there was some truth in it. It was probably worse, even more unpleasant than her version.

'You're only about twenty-three,' Dempsey pointed out. 'And you're nice. Somewhere in that mix-up is someone nice.'

'Oh, wrap it up!' she protested, rejecting this solution. 'If I need the priest I'll send for him. They all tell me I'm *nice*, but if I pull my pants down they don't complain. Neither do I. I'm not nice.'

'You've got a fine body and excellent physical health ...'

'Everything a girl needs.'

'Exactly. So why do anything silly?'

She shrugged. 'I never do anything else.'

'What's your name, anyway?'

'Pauline. It doesn't matter about the other names.'

'What do you want? Can a temporary ship's doctor really cure you? Can I do anything, even talk, advise? Frankly, I want to go to a party.'

'Take me,' she pleaded. 'One way or the other,' she begged outright.

'Sorry, Pauline. It's not that kind of party and I'm not that kind of man.'

'I'd behave ... It doesn't matter,' she said, suddenly decisive. 'I'm a fool on heat.' She began to dress. 'How about some pills?'

'We don't carry that sort.'

'Oh, come off it.'

'They wouldn't help you.'

'You weren't always so fussy,' she said suddenly.

Dempsey was startled, and uneasy.

'What's that supposed to mean?'

'Exactly what I said. You weren't always so high minded about girls in trouble.'

'You're not in trouble.'

'Oh, but I am, darling, and I love it.'

'I see.'

'I'll repeat that,' the girl said. 'I love trouble. I love making it.'

Dempsey was silent.

'Aren't you worried, Daniel Dempsey?'

'I was wondering,' he told her, 'whether to charge you for a consultation. I think I will. It's fifty cents. And now will you get out of here?'

Surprising him, she went.

'I'll be back,' she threatened.

'I know that,' he answered.

Dempsey went to his cabin and prepared it for his small party. He had only invited people he liked, not people with the relevant status. After a while he forgot the young woman, Pauline.

The two nurses, Anna and Sophia – who were rather the same in appearance, with round ochry good-natured faces; Sophia had a small black fringe – sat shyly on the battered small sofa in Dempsey's cabin, crossed their knees carefully and waited politely – to laugh, when someone translated, and be shocked by this new Australian doctor who was so cheerful and good-looking, to eat nuts, to sip wine ... Kristina from the Purser's office sat on the arm of the sofa with a deliberate fragility as if the arm might break. She was a tall, slender, attractive, honest sort of girl in her late twenties, who paid close attention to anything Tomazos said when he finally turned up. Sister Eleni rested in a basket chair looking rather maternal and satisfied. Mollon, the tall tough Australian Second Officer was helping himself and others to beer. Zafiropoulos handed out glasses of sherry and whisky. Dempsey downed a quick one and commented, 'What a day!'

Sister Eleni asked, 'What did she want?'

'What makes you think she *wanted* anything?'

'I am thirty-two years old and a woman. I want things too.'

Everybody laughed, but Dempsey said, 'I hope you don't want what she wants. She's crazy, that one.'

'That was my impression,' agreed Sister Eleni.

Tomazos came late, in uniform and with an attitude of duties still to be attended to, and announced, pleased about it, 'We're calling at Adelaide after all.'

Kristina blushed, looked daunted, even downcast, but pointed out with a laugh : 'Nikolaos, what do you do on the bridge?'

'Play cards,' he assured her promptly.

'Believe it or not,' Kristina told him, 'we have already organized tours tomorrow for 290 passengers ...'

Someone knocked on the cabin door. 'Come in,' Dempsey shouted.

It was the girl, Debbie. He was a fraction startled, for she was attired with such elegance. A rich family, Dempsey deduced. No problems. Blasted Americans.

They stared at her, a child still, but obviously soon to be something very special. Dempsey tried, in vain, not to swear. I've no blasted lemonade,' he had to admit at the top of his voice. 'How about sherry or beer?' and the girl decided upon sherry.

She sat on the other arm of the sofa – the two nurses giggled then because it squeaked alarmingly – and talked to Tomazos.

'You will like Hong Kong,' he told her. 'I've been many times, but it continues to impress me. Don't forget your money! You will get rid of that!'

'What about Bali?' Debbie inquired.

'I've never been,' the First Officer said. 'As a matter of fact I was just looking up in the Pilot about anchorages. We will have to anchor two miles out ...'

Kristina leaned a little and with her long right arm touched Tomazos' sleeve. 'Nikolaos, I must tell you my news – good or bad. I am leaving the *Areopagus* at Singapore.'

Tomazos was startled.

'What! Kristina, what will we do without you? Chaos in the Purser's office,' he forecast in an aside to Debbie. 'Are you so fed up with Demetropoulos?'

'No, of course not. There has been much unpleasantness with the passengers, but that is all over.'

'Kristina, I am sorry. No gracious lady to sit with me at the Captain's table.'

'Thank you,' she said quickly. 'I just had to, Nikolaos.' She did not say why. 'It is a job in an airline.'

'An airline!' Tomazos protested with humour. 'This is treason!'

Dempsey said, interrupting, and addressing all of them, 'Talking of the Captain's table, he sent the blasted soup and wine back last night. Both tasted well to me. These damn Captains think they're tin gods,' he concluded. 'He told me off, just like a schoolmaster, because I proved the eggs were mouldy.'

Seeing Debbie giggle at this, Dempsey said to her, 'But have you seen the strong-arm boy, the master-at-arms? An amiable idiot, eighteen stone, but nothing between the ears! A little steward threw an ashtray at him and knocked him cold! Mind you, it was a solid brass ashtray! On the *Opalescent* we had—'

'Oh, no!' objected Eleni.

Dempsey said to Debbie, 'You see? I cannot open my mouth! Sister Eleni is in charge! Still,' he conceded, 'she's better than what we did have on the *Opalescent!* Carefully selected, fully experienced, completely sexless battle-axes, out to see the world before they dropped dead!'

'And just as well,' suggested Sister Eleni.

'I am going to sing,' announced Tomazos suddenly. 'Nobody must stop me!'

'My God! Have we reached that stage?' questioned Dempsey.

Tomazos sang well. He had a deep chest and thick neck, which reddened a little. They applauded when he finished his sentimental Greek song.

'Tom,' he then said to the Second Officer. 'Have I ever asked a favour of you?'

Mollon said at once, 'No. And it's about time you did. Before you say it, Nikolaos, the answer's Yes.'

'You seem to know all about it!'

'You're joking, mate. If I hadn't seen my wife for months and the ship was putting into Adelaide—'

'I did not believe,' said Tomazos with feeling, 'that the Australians knew about love! Sport, yes! Horses, yes! Driving motor-cars, a little! But *love* . . . You must excuse me now that I have deafened you. So busy. Twenty-two cars to load tomorrow and little space for them. Seventy-five people disembarking. Oil, water, tins of jam, air mail . . .'

'Just a minute, Nikolaos!' Kristina cried, and followed him outside the cabin.

A nurse said something in Greek.

Debbie said, 'What a nice man. No arrogance at all.'

Sister Eleni commented, 'She is a nice girl. A pity to lose her. He doesn't know, of course . . .'

Tomazos came back.

'Doctor, there is a passenger here—' and a man said 'There's been an attempted suicide. Girl threw herself into the swimming pool.'

Dempsey opined, 'And we know who *that* was, don't we, Sister Eleni?'

'I will go,' said Dr Zafiropoulos.

'Oh, no, it's me she wants,' acknowledged Dempsey.

He left them and hurried to the surgery. The duty nurse had attended to the victim. It was, as he had guessed, the girl Pauline. He had no option but to put her into the hospital. The passenger was quite certain that she hadn't fallen into the swimming-pool accidentally. It had to be the day they neglected to empty the thing, Dempsey thought again in irritation, for usually this pool was emptied at sunset.

Her butch friend turned up and Dempsey talked frankly to her. Her name was Miss Reidy, and she was a stocky, rather pleasant woman of about thirty, with neat blonde hair, short and straight.

'I'm on the way to San Francisco,' she told him. 'I'm taking up a nursing appointment – in Canada, actually, but I wanted this trip. Pauline is also trained for that kind of thing, but she goes to pieces. She's a bit of a nymph, frankly, and gets in a mess all the time. In confidence, she's had men in the cabin. Picked up in the bars. Very embarrassing for me. Where am I supposed to go? And I paid her fare ...'

'Have you had a quarrel with her?'

'It's impossible not to quarrel with Pauline. It's a kind of *situationethik*.'

'Who are her relations?'

'She has a husband somewhere.'

'Do you think I should contact him?'

'No,' said Miss Reidy with certainty. 'Waste of time. Purser's job, anyway, isn't it?'

'You think she'll do it again?'

'If it pays off.'

'That's very cynical.'

'It's me she wants to hurt . . . I'm fond of Pauline. Very fond. You know? But I'm under no misapprehension.'

He inquired carefully, 'Where did she do her nursing?'

'Somewhere in Surrey, in England.'

'The Middle Hospital?'

'That's the one,' agreed Miss Reidy.

Dempsey went back to his party, but it was breaking up anyway.

He couldn't leave it at that, just go to bed and sleep. He went to see if Pauline was conscious.

She was. She was the only patient in the female ward. Pale, bruised, blood-shot eyed, she grinned at him.

'Hello, Daniel. Worried about me?'

'I told you not to be silly.'

'It's my permanent condition. Can I have a pill now?'

'Perhaps, but only to send you to sleep.'

He gave it to her. She grabbed the hand which contained it and bit it, so that he spilled the contents of the glass in his other fist. He made no comment on her action.

'How long can I stay here?' Pauline asked.

'A day or two.'

'See? I came back. And if I do it again?'

'You'll be too ill to feel sexy.'

'I feel happy.'

'That's because you're cared for.'

'Loved? Or do you mean answerable to nothing?' she asked. She was very alert to her situation.

'More or less,' Dempsey acknowledged. 'Some people prefer to be in hospital. They can't take the world. They even creep back to mental hospitals in preference.'

'I sympathize with them. Daniel, do you think I'm crazy?'

Dempsey said, 'I just think there was little point in buying a ticket for a cruise!'

She laughed, but coughed. 'I was going to Canada. I'll never get there. I don't like *that*,' she admitted in anxiety. She seemed genuinely frightened.

'Has anyone examined you?' he asked in misgiving.

'No.'

'I'd better.'

As he did so she said wearily, 'Trust you to want to examine me when I'm too tired to care.' But he paid no attention. She turned over when requested and it was impossible not to notice that she had fine buttocks. She lifted them slightly to clear the dull pyjamas the nurse had supplied. He heard nothing in her lungs.

'You're clear. Go to sleep, Pauline,' he advised. 'You're probably suffering from some shock.'

She actually looked alarmed.

'Take the pill,' he told her, 'and go to sleep. A nurse will be around all night. Don't be a nuisance, Pauline.'

'All right,' she consented. 'You can go now,' she told him in sudden rage, and turned away from him. Then she asked, 'Did Reidy come to see you?'

'Yes,' he said.

'Was she shaken?'

'No,' Dempsey told her, and began to walk away.

'Daniel!'

'What now?'

She had turned again to see him, and her face was blank, sexless, without appetite, and it was almost child-like in apprehension.

'I was scared.'

'Not logical,' he said.

'I'm sorry I did it,' she told him penitently.

In his cabin Dempsey couldn't sleep and was uncomfortable with an erection. It annoyed him that his flesh should be insolent simply because the weather had turned humid as they neared South Australia.

He drank a large whisky. The damned slut, he thought abruptly. The ridiculous fool. What did she do it for?

8

THE *Areopagus* came alongside the tin hut which was Port Adelaide at seven in the morning. It had been over a hundred in South Australia the previous day, and the air still lay hot and moist on the land; already the thermometer had climbed to 75°.

Tomazos looked over the starboard wing of the bridge and saw that there were twenty-two shining new automobiles waiting on the quayside. Meaningless paragraphs in newspapers had achieved fruition: the strike was over. All sorts of people who had come out in 'sympathy' – cleaners, watchmen, lift attendants, and port security men who had supported the 24-hour strike of the Port Emergency Service – were back at work. Five oil tankers were anchored outside Port Adelaide; the Waterside Workers Union had refused to handle them or work any hazardous cargoes . . . Tomazos wondered if they really cared and if it would make any difference. Australian ports were notoriously offhand about safety. It was part of the Australian posture of toughness that when films on port safety were shown in the wharfies canteen they did not move five yards to the lines of chairs, but went on playing cards . . .

He was first man off the vessel. The car-hire firm official delayed him with forms, a superfluous explanation that the vehicle could not be hired for the six hours that the *Areopagus* would be here, but must be hired for the day. Tomazos paid him and relieved his frustration by driving fast along the straight narrow roads which had the appearance and texture of having been made during a war by the military and then abandoned.

The suburbs on this side of Adelaide were not beautiful. They consisted of cubes of brick and stone pitched carelessly on dull coarse yellow grass, with scarcely a tree for miles and only a handful of flowers. Most of them were ugly and none were built of wood as is the custom in Australia; Elaine had told him that here the white ant ate timber.

The city was just stirring itself. It was built on a hill and beyond its red brick banks and stone statues of George V and Colonel Light who had founded Adelaide, the Mount Lofty ranges scarred the horizon. On this morning of heat and humidity they were blue, like ribbons of cigarette smoke. Tomazos made towards them for a few more miles.

There was a vehicle near the car-port, one Tomazos hadn't seen before, a metallic steel grey sports. A little hefty for Elaine, he thought, although it looked very lively.

He put the key in the door. It was the only key he owned. The suitcases and trunks in his cabin were old, their locks long since ineffective.

It was all there for him to see, the evidence of plates, ash-trays, wine glasses, the position of chairs, but he was not looking, for he had arrived full of love, with gifts in both hands, from Southampton and Piraeus, for Elaine and the kids. The only thing conspicuously wrong was in terms of time. Where were the children? It was within half an hour of time for their departure to school.

'Elaine!' he called, full of laughter. 'Where are you, you lazy girl?'

He charged straight into it.

She was in bed and there was a man with her.

There was a half-second when she was beautiful, so much more real than the photographs in the cabin.

And then, the shock was so great it was as if Tomazos had been cut in half.

It would have been more bearable, even understood, eventually forgivable, if it had been presented to him as a pattern of words in a letter, or in a telephone call, or if she could have been *alone* . . .

But they were as surprised as he was, and hid nothing. He had it raw and flagrant. The most brutal thing of all was the movement in Elaine's eyes – there was a light in them, the shock, not of guilt but the wish for him simply not to be there, to go away, so she could continue *this*. It passed with the speed of a high-speed shutter and was replaced with alarm, embarrassment and the fear of violence and quarrels.

'Nikolaos!' Elaine cried, and she lifted herself a little, to pat her hair as if to prepare, belatedly, to meet him; and the breasts revealed above the sheet were naked. 'Why didn't you phone?' she asked with absurd logic.

The man laughed at this. He was someone Tomazos recalled having seen before somewhere; at a party, or dinner; an old school friend of hers perhaps? No, because Elaine had been to a very good school for girls only.

'Where are the children?' Tomazos asked in disgust. Were they going to run into the bedroom and see *this*?'

'At Aunt Elizabeth's,' Elaine told him.

It was as if she was a little inexperienced in what to do next, and so limited herself to answering questions.

The man said, braver now that he identified Tomazos' misery: 'Why don't you go? Can't you see you're not wanted?'

'Peter, shut up, said Elaine meaninglessly. 'What happened to the ship?'

'We called in to collect some sedans. I thought—' but Tomazos did not say what he thought.

'I'm sorry. I wish you'd phoned,' Elaine said, as if, just a little bit, this was his fault.

It was as if the man wasn't there. It was what was between Tomazos and Elaine that had been shattered. It was useless to try to repair it. Tomazos was too stunned by misery to experience the anger he might have expected to. He could have smashed the place up. He had no fear of the man, who seemed to be a big fellow, and could have smashed him up too. But his desire was to get away from this, out of the curtained room with its air boiling hot from yesterday and the smell of staleness – their breath and laughter and the sweat rolling off their bodies as they pawed each other and then copulated greasily.

'I'm going,' Tomazos said with a shake in his voice, and was hurt with brutal finality when Elaine's eyes shone with relief.

He was spared nothing even now.

She stepped out of bed in a posture somehow crude and hairy, completely naked, so that he saw the marks on her thighs and stomach where she had stretched in pain to bear his children. And beyond her the man was seen briefly to be as raw, and having much hair along the thighs and across the genitals.

Tomazos went out of the room. He heard the man's exhalation of shameless satisfaction and amusement, and a fierce conscience-inspired whisper from Elaine 'Don't be so horrid.' Later, the tone implied, later we can get back to it.

She ran down the stairs behind Tomazos, a lightweight dressing-gown trailing behind so that she was still an appalling reminder of what she had done. How often and with how many didn't matter; that she had done it at all was what lacerated; and that shutter-speed admission in the eyes.

She stood at the door, very tall and half sunburnt, someone he had married, a foreigner; a lissom Australian girl who could, he remembered very vividly, make love with long-legged frenzy . . . And now she pretended to be penitent, to say a few words to ease his pain. Did she want it both ways, the sexy fun with strangers while her husband was away and the marriage retained as well?

Elaine pleaded, abject for a moment, 'He kept bothering me. Being nice, polite, kind.'

This didn't fit the satisfied sniggers upstairs.

'And he has this way – with everyone – of touching on the arm or shoulder, so that after a while you don't notice . . . I'd been married so long,' she excused herself, oddly but with some faint logic, 'I'd forgotten there's always a motive. I didn't think I was – interesting – any more.'

Tomazos scarcely believed this when she stood there, even now very beautiful in his eyes. He told her coldly, with a mouth anaesthetized by desolation : 'People keep bothering me, too – on the bridge visits, at parties, in bars. They think its part of the entertainment. They've paid for it. The officer must be nice to them.'

But her words had a tiny truth in them, a very small area which could be forgiven.

'What do we do?' Elaine asked, as if they were both caught in some situation, equally helpless.

But this was too much for him. 'Do what the hell you like,' he said, and walked away from her.

The sweat rolled off him in the hot automobile. He didn't look back. He scarcely knew what he was doing. He wanted to cry out to God, but what was the use? It was her privilege as a human being to choose what to do, to inflict suffering . . .

Every time he ever heard a dirty joke – and Mollon tended to relate the bawdy anecdote – some respect of this morning would leap into the mind's eye and hurt. Each time he saw – on shore or at sea – some ludicrous English or Swedish film in which the naked lovers stretched languidly on a bed in a dull room and complained that the world did not understand their beautiful love, Tomazos would be reminded of the reality of adultery. The gloomy stifling room, her scars of motherhood, now neglected; her rawness as she stepped out of bed, still soiled by another man; the fibrous legs and genitals of the man; and his snigger : not a snigger that the world would care for . . . They should, Tomazos reflected bitterly, make films with smell as well as vision and sound . . . He felt just a little anxiety for her, the victim of such a venal opportunist; for a man who could snigger at such a cruel moment would sooner or later regard her as expendable, a fool who had given him what he wanted.

He drove back to Port Adelaide because there was nothing else to do. It was about nine in the morning. One of the tankers anchored outside and now moving in was Greek. A long time ago Tomazos had served on her. People aboard would see the *Areopagus* and come searching for him. He couldn't face them and squirmed at the possibility. As well, there was a 9,000-ton Greek merchant ship, already anchored. She was very old, rusted with wooden parts split with wear; her gangways were nearly vertical and he could see that her bridge was absurdly small. Oil drums were lashed on board. Australian wharfies were moving about on the working side. In the hot day the cargo in one of her open holds – thousands of sheeps' hides – stank. A line of cargo containers covered with tarpaulin waited on the dockside. Some wharfies uncovered a few while Tomazos approached, and the man using a fork-lift truck blasphemed as he failed, in his manœuvring, to place the two prongs of the truck in the appropriate slot. The other men laughed.

Tomazos asked a sailor, 'Who's her Master?'

'Captain Athanassiadis.'

'Is he aboard?'

'Yes, sir. It's his birthday,' the sailor said.

Tomazos didn't know this captain. He went aboard. He was startled by the decrepit appearance of the vessel. It had a distinct list to port, although that could be the result of the present position of the loading.

The Second Officer was on the bridge, a tall humorous man, down at heel. He saw Tomazos' quick stare at the bridge – it was very old, older than the *Areopagus*, practically falling to pieces, and was about the size of a suburban kitchen. Its brass Flinders and coloured spheres were like something in a nautical museum. The wheel was of brass and had many spokes, and there was an axe in a slot, ready for fire fighting 'or anything else that might happen!' as the Second Officer put it.

'We had a rough trip,' the Second Officer told Tomazos. 'A 75-knot wind caused some containers to break loose and caused a 30° list. This forced her to be heeled for a long time because of the way the sea was running – and so a number of steel wires snapped. There was a fire and the automatic flooding damn nearly sank her . . . Come and meet the skipper. It's his birthday.'

Captain Athanassiadis was a very young man to be captain of a 9,000-ton ship; he was a slim man of calm disposition and had a very quiet voice.

His cabin was old-fashioned but cosy, with a fridge, a bookcase full of books about navigation and ships, a cupboard loaded with bottles and packets. From the adjoining cabin came the sound of small children's voices and a woman's scolding.

'Morning, Mister Second,' he greeted. 'Who have we here?'

There were introductions and handshakes. The Third Mate came in, a very young man with a beard; he wore pull-over and grey trousers.

'Ready to sail, Mister Third?' asked Captain Athanas-siadis.

'About noon, Captain.'

'Time for a drink, then,' suggested the Captain. 'It's my birthday.'

'You've got your wife and kids here?' asked Tomazos.

'Couldn't trust 'em back in Piraeus!' the Captain said, and they all laughed.

Other officers came in and they were all very young and a little shy of Tomazos, sitting in a padded L-shaped corner seat.

The drinking began.

No one asked Tomazos why he was here. A priest came and an hour later people from the harbour authority, then the agents; and half an hour after that an officer off a tanker. All were introduced, the explanation given that it was the Captain's birthday. All had drinks. The Captain told each about the damage the storm had inflicted, about the pirated editions, purchased in Keelung, in the small book-case, about his wife and children. And they in turn said where they were going or what they were doing . . . The wife and children did not make any appearance.

All the time the voices of these good honest men and the alcohol down his throat diverted Tomazos' mind from the permutations of humiliation and despair. But they were always ready to return into the mind's eye and ear if the voices hesitated – that the man was cheap and had a ginger moustache; that his hands had pawed Elaine's legs, her but-tocks, had kneaded her breasts; that the two forests of pubic hairs had coupled and his body had pumped up and down ... (And she, how had she writhed and panted? Had she wrapped a long leg around him expressing the palpitating need for him to enter? Had her long cool fingers, so light on the steering wheel of her sports car and tennis racquet, ventured into the sweating heat between his legs?) It was unbearable and Tomazos' hands tightened in aching tension. More. More drink. If there had been nothing to remember, that would have been different, bearable, an unpleasant experience but scarcely more. But there were so many things to recall – not simply amatorial moments or appetites satiated on that same bed, but humorous moments, enormous anxiety as he'd waited in hospital while she bore the babies. Picnics, barbecues, thousands of meals together, sailing, swimming, watching the stars and explaining them to her, bouncing babies on his knees . . . And yet the shutter-speed message of her eyes had been : go away, don't embarrass my pleasure with *him*. All those other things were nothing, time passing while I waited for this . . . And perhaps the sourest aspect of the signal was 'I am like this, which is why I enjoy this other man. I am crude, hot, as vulgar as he is; I wasn't a virgin when I married you; oh, how absurd, those tender fondlings of yours! Did you believe that a woman with my capacity for speed, excitement and risk to the body was waiting around for a fat little Greek ship's officer?'

The permutations of her falseness and his humiliation were endless. They would fill many hours of the day and night. Drink helped, of course, a little. More drink then.

'Christ, it's hot,' he said, and even this had its pictorial corollary : would the sweat be running between her breasts? Would her clothes stick to her buttocks and waist so that the man – Peter, his name was, I must remember that – had to peel them off like a wet swimming costume?

How many times, in how many places? (Beds, sports cars, on the beach, hurriedly, the first time, on a chair?)

'What's the time?'

They told him. 'Eleven o'clock.'

'My God, we sail at noon !'

He shook hands; they were good fellows, had saved him a little this dreadful day—

Tomazos boarded the *Areopagus* and the world was different. The eyes and the nostrils noticed. He viewed the entire world now as an enemy; at the minimum it might snigger at him. (How many times? Her thin cool wide sexy mouth burning against this bastard's moustache, his naked shoulder, his chest. And the long procession of words – did they start with 'No' or 'I have a husband,' and what had been the pattern of oral fraud and persuasion from then to the moment when she dropped her pants and the pendulum had gone over to him : 'Hurry up, the kids'll be out of school soon . . . *Him*? Oh, hell, we all make mistakes. A fat little Greek. No, darling, not rich. Don't give it a thought. Push harder, Peter, be rough with me.')

The passengers lined the rails, it was that late, hot and limp : Adelaide's century heat had exhausted them, too. And the smells – they were old and should have been familiar, but he had not previously noticed : particular oils, foods, old wood, paint and steel. The ship. His. At least he had that.

On the bridge Mollon noticed.

'Christ, Nikolaos, you've finally discovered Australian beer!'

'What of it?'

'You're drunk, mate, that's what!'

'Who cares?'

'Not me, mate. Maybe the Captain?'

'What's our condition?'

'We're on schedule. Sail in forty minutes.'

'Good,' said Tomazos with ferocity. 'The sooner we get out of this hateful town—'

'What's up? What's the matter with Adelaide?'

'Like everything Australian, she's ugly and vulgar—'

'Oh, not that bad?'

'And stupid. Stupid, ugly and a mess.'

'Jesus, Nikolaos, you're making a noise! Don't knock poor bloody Adelaide. It was the beer that did it.'

'To hell with this ridiculous country and its dowdy coarse people . . .'

'Now wait a minute. Y'want a punch-up or something? Is it me you're bothered by?'

'Anything Australian.'

Mollon said, 'Well, you've got nearly six hundred on board.'

'Vulgar fools, drowned in beer and bingo.'

'Hey, listen mate, I don't like that—' began Mollon angrily.

Captain Vafiadis came on the bridge. They didn't know if he'd overheard this dialogue. A motor boat's engine thumped in the water and voices cheered on the quayside, although it was a very small crowd this time. There was now distinct hostility emanating from Mollon where previously there had been absolute comradeship.

The Captain asked, 'Did you get a chance to see your wife?'

'Oh, yes,' Tomazos said through his teeth. 'I saw her.'

And he could sense through the alcohol their shock and understanding. They knew, more or less, what he'd encountered.

Half an hour later they were manœuvring in the Torrens River, and Captain Vafiadis instructed, 'Officer of the Watch, take her round.'

'Very good, sir,' Tomazos acknowledged. 'Helmsman, starboard 25.'

This was to take the *Areopagus* in a half circle round to starboard.

'Not to starboard!' the Captain called loudly. 'The other way, to port.'

Tomazos, very shaken indeed by the Captain countermanding his order, nevertheless obeyed the Master. 'Helmsman, midships . . . Port 20.'

As they came round Tomazos saw why he'd been wrong. On that side of the river a tanker was still anchored. The *Areopagus* would have cleared her by thirty feet, but the awful fact was that he was so upset this day that he hadn't known of the tanker's presence.

The Third Officer, Makris, was on the bridge, too, and was startled and didn't know where to look. Such a reprimand and error had not been experienced before by Tomazos.

Captain Vafiadis said coldly, 'One would think you weren't sober, Mr Tomazos,' and walked off the bridge.

Tomazos, who never had strong feelings against the people with whom he worked, hated Captain Vafiadis at that moment. The Captain knew damn well the dejection which had caused the inattention; there had been no need to rub it in . . .

'What the hell,' he said aloud in discomfort. 'Port or starboard, what's the difference?'

But it stung, for Makris would spread the news as excited gossip. Worse than that, the helmsman was Yannopoulos, a slight man in his middle forties, with a walnut-coloured face, a very good sailor, calm, never ruffled, a man utterly reliable and very pleasant to work with.

It was *her* fault, Elaine's. Something that had been valuable and worthwhile now had its content of embarrassment and dislike. Not that Yannopoulos would gossip, but he might lose confidence fractionally. Makris, being young and bored, would prattle and from others a garbled version would get around the ship. It might even become standard commentary at specific times, perhaps when orders were resented: 'The First Officer? Oh, he was all right until the time he caught a bloke with his wife. He's been unpredictable since then, so watch it . . .'

He hid from them in his cabin a few yards aft of the bridge. It was a small neat cabin about fifteen feet by twelve, but likely now to become a prison. There were a bunk and wardrobe, a transistor radio bought in Japan, a dressing-table and wash basin. There was a door to the cabin but during the day it was normally wide open and the entrance merely curtained off. Now Tomazos shut the door. He left the whisky bottle alone because he was on duty again in a few hours. The sun had heated up the cabin and the air was stifling. Tomazos lay in his bunk waiting for the hours to pass.

A thunderstorm cracked overhead and as the ship came out of the river and into the Great Australian Bight again the sea whipped up and the *Areopagus* pitched and shuddered.

He went on duty and it was satisfying that the sea was the colour of slate and moving in small mountains . . . There was no one on the bridge except Yannopoulos, who greeted him politely. There never was much dialogue between them – it was unnecessary, they were so attuned – but now Tomazos was self-conscious. And tired. He who never wearied had been exhausted by this day, tired for ever, he felt.

'I'm putting her on the gyro-pilot,' he told the helmsman, who was spinning the wheel which operated the rudder by telemotor system.

Tomazos put the control lever to 'Off', switched on the mains switch and with the steering wheel brought the rudder amidships. He then opened the by-pass valve of the telemotor hydraulic system, leaving Yannopoulos with nothing to do. He put the control lever to 'Hand', so that the *Areopagus* was now under the control of the gyro-pilot wheel by hand. He steadied her on the course he wanted, which was 272, and put the control lever to 'Gyro'. The *Areopagus* would now cover the bulk of the 1,348 miles to Fremantle on her own, providing Tomazos made minor alterations to the 'Weather Adjustment' and 'Rudder Adjustment' – two lost-motion device controls turned anti-clockwise over a scale 0 – 6 and which allowed for the condition of the sea. It was a beam sea, and rough, and Tomazos made a rudder adjustment bearing this in mind, and the loading and trim of the ship. He allowed a certain amount of 'initial' rudder to provide a degree of 'meeting' rudder when the ship returned to her course. After a while he studied the course recorder chart which was in the chartroom to see what kind of a pattern was being made by the two ink-fed pens which were travelling horizontally across a vertical moving chart paper.

The chart was ninety feet long and provided a continuous record of the ship's course for thirty days. Down the left-hand side of the chart were four zones, each representing a course sector of 90°. The rest of the chart was divided into nine main vertical divisions, each representing 10 degrees, the figures 0 to 90 and 180 to 270 being read from left to right and 90 to 180 and 270 to 360 from right to left. Two pens were driven by the repeater motor and they traversed the area of the chart and indicated the course of the ship. The zone pens traversed the four columns on the left of the chart and indicated which row of figures was applicable to the course pen . . . The chart was lined horizontally, each line representing 10 minutes of time.

The repeater motor also drove an indicator dial which showed the heading of the ship. There was a steering repeater fitted in a swivel bracket on the top of the Bridge Control Unit (in which that part of the two-unit gyro-pilot operated by the officer on the bridge was housed). It had no part to play in the operation of the gyro-pilot, but reproduced the indications of the Master Compass card on an enlarged scale. Both these repeaters now read 272.

The zig-zag of ink on the course recorder chart was narrow and even at its edges and told Tomazos that his adjustments were correct.

There was a connexion between the Bridge Control Unit in the wheelhouse and the power unit in the steering engine flat by multi-core cable, and it was by small currents in this cable that changes at the Bridge Control Unit were passed to the power unit, which operated the valve gear of the steering engine.

If the *Areopagus* wandered off course when under her present automatic heading, a repeater motor armature turned, driving the rollers of a servo follow-up ring assembly through the 'weather' lost motion device. The servo motor armature would thereby be energized, and in rotating turn the rudder follow-up rings and also the pointer of the rudder order indicator. In addition it would turn the servo follow-up rings through the 'initial rudder' lost-motion device, thus short-circuiting its armature to arrest its motion quickly . . . The turning of the rudder follow-up rings would complete circuits which would close contacts that controlled the operation of the power unit.

Backlash was introduced into the servo system by means of the lost-motion devices which Tomazos had adjusted and which governed the responses of the gyro-pilot. The 'weather' lost motion device was in the drive between the repeater motor and the servo follow-up rollers. It prevented movements of the ship's head due to conditions of wind or sea – movements that in any case tended to be corrected by the inherent stability of the ship – from actuating the gyro-pilot.

Each time the *Areopagus* yawed several degrees the gyro-pilot indicated the movement, the transmitter operated and the repeater armature turned. This turned the servo follow-up rollers, thereby operating the servo motor. The servo motor turned the rudder follow-up rings, the rudder order indicator and its own follow-up rings. As the servo follow-up rings and rollers reached their initial relative position, the servo motor stopped . . . Meanwhile, the movement of the rudder follow-up rings operated the rudder, the amount of correction depending on the size of the yaw and the adjustment of the lost-motion devices.

As the ship's head came back towards the set course, the gyro-compass again indicated the movement and once the *Areopagus* was steady on course the reverse operation of the equipment was finished and the assemblies were in their 'rest' positions and the motors stationary.

This spared Yannopoulos many spins of the telemotor wheel, but left him with little to do.

Captain Vafiadis came on the bridge. Tomazos felt uneasy, and as if he knew it and wanted to assert himself – something he hadn't perhaps been able to do in seven years – the Captain said a little too brusquely for Tomazos' liking: 'Show me your latest fix and do stop fiddling with that silly gadget as if it could do our work for us.'

This was absurd, as the Company was not likely to buy 'silly' equipment, and in fact the gyro-pilot was an incredibly accurate and complicated assembly which was capable of doing the 'work' a fraction better than the officers did without it.

Tomazos, however, was too good a navigating officer not to have fixed the *Areopagus*' position as soon as he had come on watch.

The Captain nevertheless complained, 'We've lost a hell of a lot of time picking up those automobiles,' as if calling at Adelaide had been Tomazos' idea.

'Shall I ask for a few more knots, sir?'

'Do you think the Chief Engineer would give them to you?'

It was, Tomazos realized in relief, his own position the

Captain was worried about. He was going to be late all along the line – Fremantle, Bali, Singapore, Hong Kong . . . He had been pressed to the limit long before Adelaide. The Company would complain and, worse, so would the passengers, and this would undermine the Master's position of infallibility, his reputation of arriving with the specific tide and at the very hour forecast recklessly in the Company's brochures . . . It was known around the *Areopagus* that the Captain and Chief Engineer disliked each other. Captain Vafiadis would hate to ask a favour, particularly when he was aware that Mr Bitsios would have to turn it down.

When Tomazos came off watch at the end of his four hours Kristina was standing at the window of the radio office.

She called out 'Hello, Nikolaos' because otherwise, it was obvious, he wouldn't have noticed her or indeed anyone. And she had been there for twenty minutes conversing with some difficulty to the wireless officer whom she never saw normally more than once a month, and then only in passing. He was a Turkish man of about fifty, very capable, formal and polite, and Kristina talked to him so that she might legitimately be standing about when Tomazos' duty ended.

'What are you doing, Kristina?'

'I am cabling my mother.'

He said, 'I didn't know you had a mother.'

She chided gently, 'We all have mothers and mine has a birthday tomorrow.'

Tomazos thought about it and remarked, 'It's strange, how we know someone and yet never identify them as daughter – you know what I mean?'

'Perfectly. You see me as a part of the ship, a girl in the Purser's office . . . and to see me as something else would be somehow wrong.'

'Yes. Something like that, although you are much more than a functioning part of the *Areopagus*, Kristina . . .'

She stood there in silence, dressed very neatly in the Company's uniform of dark green skirt and pale-green blouse, in a prolonged moment of embarrassment. He said nothing because, this day, he was bereft of lightheartedness.

At last Kristina said shakily, 'We all know – well, I do – that something is wrong. And I'm so sorry.'

'It is nothing.'

'You are such a nice person.'

'It happens to sailors – and their wives.'

'I'm sorry that such a thing—'

'It can't be helped. Tough on my children,' he acknowledged.

'You will get a letter,' she forecast, 'when we reach Bali or Singapore. And the quarrel will be over.'

'It was worse than a quarrel, Kristina—'

'But it can be repaired, Nikolaos.'

'No,' he told her. 'It can never be repaired. I could not live with her again.'

'Ah, how awful,' she sighed. 'But this is what you say today, Nikolaos. Time may alter your hurt.'

'That is kind of you to believe so,' he said.

It was impossible for her to say anything further. 'Well, goodnight, Nikolaos. Remember you have friends.'

'Goodnight, Kristina.'

Tomazos went to his cabin. It was still humid and uncomfortable. He listened to a news bulletin. There were still wars and riots, people with greater troubles than his. He was aware that there would be no privacy for a distressed First Officer, friends or not. His every word, gesture, foible and mannerism would now be noted, discussed and analysed together with his habits, on the decks, in the wardrooms and bars. At meals his conversation or silence would be overheard or noted by stewards and repeated, perhaps with embellishments. If he was 'taut' it would be regarded as temper, and if he was not it might be considered that he had gone to pieces, taken to the bottle.

He did not include Kristina in this train of thought although her sympathy proved that the gossip had reached the Purser's office, which meant everywhere . . .

He was exhausted, but the oppressive heat and the kaleidoscope of his thoughts wouldn't let him sleep. Was Elaine awake, too? Was she alone tonight? Had this man, Peter, a wife? Probably, now that Tomazos thought about it, for he was over thirty. So other persons would suffer also. And Elaine? Was she scared now? No. Elaine was unusual for a woman, never frightened. But the thought must inevitably corrode her peace of mind, that her marriage was over. There was unpleasantness to go through, at the very least tedious conversations with a lawyer. The disgrace would hurt her mother, who was a snob . . .

But what hurt *him* was what he had seen, the naked sweating bodies which had coupled, the signal of indifference in the eyes which had preceded even the alarm of being caught. Go away and let us get on with it. It was in such violent contrast to everything which had gone before.

It was no use.

He had to have a drink.

The next eight hours were *his* and if he wanted to drink—

The next whisky bottle was under his bunk, unopened.

Tomazos drank deeply in his wounded desolation, and then put the bottle back out of sight so that when the stand-by came to call him at four in the morning he would not see it.

9

SEVENTY feet below Tomazos, Dimitrios Retalis was now a much happier young man.

He had a friend.

Keith Rajaratnam had come aboard at Melbourne to replace the sailor injured at Sydney by the exploding gas cylinder.

It was the policy of the Graeco-Australian Line to have a few English-speaking crew members for the benefit of Australian, New Zealand, British and South African passengers. Girls in the Purser's office, barmen, an officer or two on the bridge. But below decks the sixty crew of the Chief Engineer were all Greek and only two officers spoke some English.

Rajaratnam was from Singapore and had learned his

engineering in that great port, the fifth largest in the world. He was of Indian race, but spoke only English. Dimitrios had learned some English – quite a lot, he now realized – and by a happy coincidence was of the same technical qualifications as Rajaratnam. He was therefore chosen to show the new young man the bowels of the *Areopagus*, to instruct him on the whereabouts and correct readings of the fireroom air-pressure gauge, the oil pressures, the feed system telegraphs, the lubricating points along the port propeller shaft, the gauges and control valves to the main steam line, the superheater, the peepholes to the burners, the lubricating tanks and strainers, and whole dozens of valves, drains and vents . . .

And Dimitrios found that Rajaratnam absorbed this information rapidly and permanently. He might have been born in the port engine room of the *Areopagus*.

He was a small, neat, rather nice-looking young man, and, incredibly, always seemed clean, and never hot. He had a quick sense of humour. Best of all he accepted Dimitrios without reservations, failing in that identification which would have been instantaneous in any European, Greek speaking or otherwise.

He played draughts with Dimitrios and taught him chess. He would talk for hours, and yet be able to say, without causing offence, 'I would like to read this book now. Do you mind?' or 'I am going to write a letter to my friend, so I will not be present with you for half an hour.'

'When we get to Singapore,' he told Dimitrios, 'I will show you many places. Better than Change Alley, although we can go there and have a good barter with the traders if you wish. Do you like Madras curry or Malay satay? Chinese roast duck is very good, too, the Cantonese especially . . . My father has a shop in Serangoon Road . . . Have you seen the orchids in the Botanical Gardens?' he asked, as if it was quite natural that a merchant seaman should wish to see these flowers; and Dimitrios liked him for that.

The natural assumption that if they went ashore at all they should go together, filled Dimitrios with contentment. The days and the duties would pass quickly and pleasantly, he was aware, and his only anxiety was about when the other should leave the ship.

He wanted to pin Rajaratnam down on this, to have an unwritten contract stretching ahead for a year, fifteen months or whatever it was.

'How long will you stay with us?' he asked.

'Oh, I don't know, Dimitrios,' Rajaratnam said doubtfully.

Warmed by the use of his Christian name, Dimitrios persisted, 'But how long would you like to?'

He did not wish to be possessive; there was only the need to be reassured.

'They will throw me out at Piraeus,' Keith forecast with a laugh, 'and replace me with a Greek. That is perfectly understandable,' he pointed out, without anxiety, too reasonable, as always.

'But they can't just dump you off in Athens—'

'I hope not, indeed, but I was only able to sign for this one voyage.'

'They must let you sign on again—'

'It would be nice,' agreed Keith, and that was all Dimitrios needed in comfort: Rajaratnam spoke to no one at all except him, Dimitrios, and yet felt it would be nice to sign on for the *Areopagus*' next journey. This was comradeship indeed.

The *Areopagus* stayed in Fremantle only three hours – much to the irritation of some passengers who had been informed that she would remain for sixteen – but for Dimitrios it was like a holiday.

He strolled around the vast area of the Ocean Terminal with his friend. No one sneered at them. The stewards filled the Terminal with laughter as they crowded round, sat on chairs and drank coffee; but Dimitrios did not see John. A few played football with the Entertainments Officer (who was not an officer, but a civilian), who was dressed in his tight pink suit . . . Keith made no observations about this. He picked up a postcard with a photograph of a British liner on one side: 'I served on her. Very well run. The officers spoke through their noses. I used to wonder what they employed their mouths for!'

The priest was right, Dimitrios thought in exultation. He has prayed for me.

There has been an answer.

He makes no demands. He has no needs. And I have none of him. I like him tremendously. He is charming and even cultured. He should be an engineering officer. And this hateful body of mine does not overwhelm me and shame me with need. I respect him too much to even think of bodily contact. I have not even touched his shoulder or his clothes. We make no claims on each other, and yet I would die for him.

There was the air of excitement in the Terminal; it spread from passengers to crew. For they, the passengers, were leaving their own land, the white society of law and order, banks, newspapers, telephones and suburbs, for the moist green forests of unknown Asia. There was a strong galvanism and an unmistakeable sensation of departing from law and order of a dull kind, orthodox morality and convention, and moving into areas where their behaviour wouldn't be identified in quality by foreigners nor observed by any other white persons except themselves. It was like a conspiracy in which five hundred and fifty people wanted to escape for some weeks and be beholden to no one . . .

Hours later Dimitrios and Keith stood on that small portion of B Deck which was allocated to the engine room crew.

The sea was scarcely five feet from their feet. They stared unashamedly at the water and the sky. A band could be heard distantly and the smells of Greek cooking drifted to them. Life was suddenly beautiful for Dimitrios, even life in the confined space of the *Areopagus*' port engine room, a crowded crews' messroom, the cabin for four filled with human smells, and too hot for good health, and these few square yards of the B Deck.

'You see, *that* is the star Alpherat,' Keith pointed out. 'No. You cannot see. Look. Give me your hand and I will aim your fingers.'

And this touch of the small fragile brown hand had electricity in it for Dimitrios, but aroused no lust. There was no need of whisky and the anaesthetized flesh and sordid postures in ludicrous corners of the bar with Keith. He had a real friend and no demands of that sort need ever be made by either side.

In the cabin they undressed in darkness so as not to disturb the other two engineers, but were reluctant to give up the conversation. There was the whole world to talk about and it could be done in English; there would never be any embarrassment in being overheard.

'Will you ever get married?' Dimitrios asked.

'Me? Goodness, that will be a disaster!' Keith said with vigour. 'I suppose we shall come to it. Many children, I shall have! About eight!'

Dimitrios laughed because this seemed absurd and unlikely, and, perhaps, not intended. A sailor stirred and suggested 'Be quiet; we want to sleep.' And Dimitrios, having translated this for Keith, was content to lie there awaiting sleep.

He has no unkindness in him at all, he thought. His whole nature is charitable. He has no hardness in him whatever. Violence and filth would simply astonish him. It is impossible not to love him.

10

THE *Areopagus* had been built in an American shipping yard in the early 1930s. She now had about her a touch of the great days of the sea, a solidity of design and style which almost belonged to 1914, most noticeably her straight bows and 'cruiser-spoon' stern and near-vertical funnels. Her hull and main structural components, whose composite working stresses defied precise calculation, had been riveted, not with powered tools but by hand with white-hot rivets. The welding of a ship's hull, an unfamiliar process at that time, offered economies in weight, time and labour, and a smooth form with resultant reduction in propulsive effort, but could never equal the strength of old-fashioned individual riveting. Only now over thirty years later did the *Areopagus* begin to feel her age.

She was built bearing in mind the regulations of the American shipping industry and international conventions which covered basic design, radio, lifeboats, sanitation, fire fighting, structural materials and overhauls. Her boilers, although of an older style, were at least sufficiently forward of the 1914 era to use oil, not coal. She was modern enough to have her battery of tubes for the water to pass through. It had until shortly before her construction been the feature of boiler tube batteries that *they* should contain the hot gases which heated tons of static water. In the *Areopagus*, as in all modern turbine-driven ships, the main vessel contained the flames and gases while tubes passed the water through them. This saved an enormous amount of weight and volume. In addition, metallurgy was greatly improving at the time *Areopagus* was constructed and allowed safely a substantial rise in the pressure of the steam raised, which in fact meant the capacity for work. The rise in pressure in turn allowed a reduction in the consumption of fuel for the shaft horse-power produced.

It was always intended that the *Areopagus* should operate in tropical waters, and she was built with an open promenade deck (called the Parade Deck) in contrast to the liners operating on the North Atlantic run. She served her original American owners in the Caribbean until 1948. She then served in the Mediterranean under the flag of the Dutch company which purchased her. In 1961 she was bought for £3,000,000 by the Graeco-Australian Passenger and Cargo Line, registered in Panama, but primarily a Greek line and operating between Piraeus and Australian ports, with cruises in Asian waters during the 'off' season.

Her gross tonnage was 23,191 and net 12,463. She had a length of 643 feet 7 inches and a breadth of 84 feet 10 inches (85 feet 3 inches at the overhang). Her draught was 31 feet 0¼ inches. Her twin screw turbines had a total thrust of 22,000 shaft horse-power, which had given her a service speed of 20 knots (time and wear had reduced this). She stood rather high out of the water and was uncompromisingly of her time, with her centres of buoyancy and gravity (the forces acting on her from below and above) rather far apart so that her metacentre was below her centre of gravity. This inclined her to 'stiffness' and a tendency to jerk out of a roll to an upright position.

Her two funnels stood high above the hull and sloped only a little, another indication of her 'middle age'. These two funnels were of riveted aluminium construction, 41 feet high, 32 feet long, 23 in breadth and each weighed 29 tons.

There was a cynical tendency by some passengers to list what the *Areopagus* did *not* have. She did not have stabilizers, was without bow thrusts, her radar was not transistorized and did not include the latest anti-collision relative motion markers which were so useful in crowded waters . . . She did not have ergonomic cutlery or built-in cabin furniture of pale African mahogany for the crew. Although she had been built in America she had had no air conditioning on three of her decks and even now that this situation had been improved the crew as well as many passengers, while theoretically having air conditioning, awoke saturated in sweat. Nor did the crew have single or two-berth cabins fitted with washbasins and running hot water or chairs of natural beech bentwood, or wardrobes lined with washable plastic-faced fabric, or spaces for pin-ups. Nor were there in the crews' quarters any special cast aluminium berth lights or fluorescent strip lighting or bedspreads of specially woven heavy duty check seersucker. These things and many other comforts were supplied to the merchant ships of the rich countries which were finding it difficult to entice men to come to sea and work the big tankers and container ships . . . The *Areopagus* had been built at a time when 'comfort' was a word despised by society and by sailors themselves who had been regarded as of the lowest status in society.

The *Areopagus* had an unbalanced double-plate streamlined rudder. Her steering gear was operated by telemotor, but also, if desired, by gyro-pilot equipment. Her anchors and chains were to the original American requirements, that is, three stockless bower anchors each weighing 133 hundredweight, with 310 fathoms of 2¾ inch diameter stud link special steel chain cable.

There were two radar sets in the wheelhouse, and she had

mechanical sounding equipment. An electrically operated sounding machine was fitted on the bridge. In addition she had an echometer. A high power dry paper recorder was fitted in the chartroom. It operated in conjunction with two internal projectors, one fitted forward and the other aft. She had a gyro-compass with seven repeaters and two magnetic compasses.

Her sixteen lifeboats, eight of fibreglass construction, eight of wood, had a total capacity for 1,873 persons. Six of the boats had motors, the remaining ten were hand propelled. Most of them had ineffective davits, which were solid with corrosion and overpainting.

She had an emergency dynamo supply in the event of a generator failure. Her wireless office contained a transmitter incorporating MF and HF W/T facilities, emergency transmitter, main and emergency receivers and also IF radio telephone facilities. A portable wireless equipment set was provided for use on any lifeboat. Someone had to wind a handle to provide power . . . If the ship was ever in distress and sinking a signal would automatically be sent without the operator's presence to shipping within a radius of two hundred miles. The same set flashed a red light and sounded a klaxon if it received an alarm signal from another ship.

There were 670 deck chairs and 104 teak deck seats sited round the various open decks.

For the *Areopagus* was not just a ship, but an hotel.

And the problems of taking an hotel to sea were very much of a designer's headache. An hotel on shore was connected to a large underground drainage system provided and paid for primarily by other people. The waste water and drainpipes of the hotel on land were simply, if not very beautifully, led to an outside wall and conducted down its outer surface to the ground and below. The water supply was limited only by the weather and the hotel merely needed a reservoir on the roof and the pressure of a city's supply to fill it. There could be a limitless and complicated electric supply connected to a local mains, and not likely to be torn out of it. On the *Areopagus*, as on any liner, the requirements of the passenger might be the same as the hotel's client, but there was a limit to how much water could be carried or distilled. The ship could not have elastic plumbing nor could the pipes run up and down its outside surfaces, for there they would be smashed. To run them, or electric cables, out of sight would be costly and difficult for inspection and repairs. Yet there must be no failures and when the passengers turned on a switch or shower or tap or operated the toilet, these things had to function. Any function they did in this hotel which pitched, rolled, twisted and shuddered, and which moved from the cold of Europe's winter to the heat of Australia's summer in a few weeks. The drainage problem was not easy, for the *Areopagus* could not have an unlimited number of outlets; for every outlet was a potential inlet and thus a possible source of disaster.

The engine room took care of many of these problems. It not only contained the massive but relatively simple boilers and turbines which propelled the ship, but had a host of auxiliary engines and pumps to operate the domestic requirements. And these soon swamped the simple design of a functioning ship and turned the main deck and engine rooms into a chaos of noise and machinery. The ship herself, her cargo (if any) and passengers all required machinery: a heavy windlass for her anchor, winches on her poop and forecastle so that seamen could operate her mooring lines, all powered remotely from the engine room a hundred yards away. A complicated plumbing installation was vital, for the double-bottom throughout her whole length was divided into separate sections and it had to be possible to fill these through long pipelines with fuel or fresh or salt water, the sea water as ballast to maintain the trim. In every hold water collected from condensed moisture and weeping rivets, drained down to the sump or bilge, and again had to be pumped away perhaps several hundred feet through pipes and then overboard. In reverse the system had to be able to flood specific holds to douse a fire which had proved too much for steam or chemical extinguishing.

There had to be a battery of frozen piping mounted with fans if refrigerated cargo was carried, or an equal capacity to preserve the meats and other foods used during the weeks the passengers travelled. For the *Areopagus* did not wish to stop frequently to buy jars of cream or receive milk deliveries. That would have been a housekeeping nightmare and involved frequent stops, which meant port charges. The *Areopagus* had a capacity for 1,382 passengers and even though she was carrying only 550 at present (and a crew of 452) the requirements were enormous. Like her counterpart hotel on land, the ship had a butcher's shop, a bakery and confectionery area, a platewashing area, a silver room and a fruit and salad area. Four conveyors operated from the dry and refrigerated storerooms and there were lifts to the pantries in the passenger accommodation and public rooms.

On a 12,000-mile journey – and many of the *Areopagus'* journeys were of about that distance – if she was fully accommodated (and on the Europe to Australia run she always was full with a load of migrants) the bakers made 300,000 rolls, 20,000 loaves and 400,000 cakes. The butchers cooked 130,000 pounds of meat and poultry, representing a thousand animals and 4,500 birds; and the passengers ate 40,000 pounds of fish. They also ate 100,000 eggs, 15,000 pounds of butter and consumed ice-cream at the rate of twenty gallons a day. They got through a ton of tea, seven tons of coffee, a hundred tons of potatoes and nineteen tons of flour; 2,500 packets of lavatory paper, and they stared at 25,000 menu cards, printed on board. They soiled their fingers on six thousand table napkins and dropped food on two thousand tablecloths. Their children broke some of the *Areopagus'* 20,000 glasses, 25,000 pieces of crockery, 12,000 cups and saucers and 1,150 tea pots. They used 33,100 pieces of cutlery and switched on and off 4,600 light fittings, and complained through 400 telephones if anything went wrong. To cheer themselves up they made inroads on 15,000 bottles of wine, 100,000 tins of ale and puffed at one million cigarettes. They looked at some of the thirty electric clocks of the impulse type, all controlled from a master clock on the bridge, itself governed by an eight-day chronometer. If exhausted they threw off their clothes (350,000 articles were laundered on each west to east journey) and climbed between some of the 8,000 sheets carried aboard...

They were accommodated in cabins and looked after by stewards. But the *Areopagus* had made so many trips with scarcely a pause between each that minor problems had not been attended to. Worn carpets had not been repaired or replaced. Upholsterers and needlewomen had not been enabled to do repairs to curtains, fabrics and furniture. Each day at sea Captain Vafiadis inspected a passenger deck and himself tested the fit of drawers and wardrobe doors and the operation of taps and switches; and invariably he found a dozen a day to be attended to. But these were temporary repairs and there were others which could not be corrected or even traced until the *Areopagus* stayed in a harbour long enough. Sometimes they couldn't be traced even then. Persistent squeaks at sea simply couldn't be found by a foreman joiner in harbour. The *Areopagus* was old. Things were bound to squeak after thirty years of chafing. Every section of panelling had been carefully designed and fitted so that it moved in response to the ship's working, and every joint had been permanently packed with greased felt. Otherwise the whole ship would have shrieked like ten thousand children taking their first lessons on the violin. The hardware used for fixing all furniture and fitments – screws, locks, hinges, nuts and bolts – had been of a high quality and had stood up to the hard usage and salty atmosphere for over thirty years. A million screws had been used on the *Areopagus*.

The construction of the cabins had involved 150,000 square feet of plywood and 17,000 cubic feet of solid hardwood timber and 65,000 square feet of ceiling panels. Almost every item of furniture had had to be 'tailor made' to allow for the camber and sheer of the ship, for pipe penetration and electrical work.

The wiring system of the ship led up from the generating plant in the engine room and spread with infinite ramifications through the ship. No one really knew its exact travels unless it was the third electrician, and he was a very harassed man on the *Areopagus*. Electric wires had been armoured in lead and were lasting almost as well as the wire in the equivalent hotel on land – which was hardly looked at in twenty-five years. But there were many areas where wire couldn't be protected, and it in any case could never be buried or carried between floor-boards. Inevitably, although armoured, the wire had to be led through cargo spaces, areas of dampness and corrosion, up the sides of bulkheads and along many alley-ways. How easy it was for someone fixing a bathroom cabinet, a bunk, a mirror or a wardrobe to drive a screw through a wiring conduit on the other side. How easy for a piece of cargo or even baggage to chafe against a circuit in a heavy sea. Fire was the greatest risk at sea, and the most dreadful had been due to electrical short-circuits.

The number of things which had to be borne in mind in regard to the motion of the vessel was formidable. In this respect the *Areopagus* was old-fashioned and sensible. She had hand rails in corridors and foyers, lee-rails on the tables, deck clamps to chairs and pianos. For nothing could really withstand the massive inertia of a big wave, or rolling and pitching, and the dimensions of the *Areopagus* would have otherwise allowed alarming movement of those objects furthest removed from the centre.

Like all ships, the *Areopagus* was essentially a large box-girder divided into water-tight sections. The sides and bottom of the girder were in effect the sides and bottom of the ship and the top was the main (Metaxas) deck although this was not obvious to passengers, for there were other decks and much superstructure above it. The 'girder' had to withstand the stresses of pitching, rolling and corkscrewing, and had to be strong enough to stand poised amidships on the crest of a big wave with its two ends so little supported that they were virtually hanging.

The number of water-tight compartments into which the *Areopagus* had been divided had been determined by a set of compulsory flooding regulations, designed so that she would float after a collision or heavy stranding had fractured the hull. The sub-division of the *Areopagus* was related to her skeleton of inner construction and it was into this that the cabins had to be fitted. The hull was of steel and its skeleton was a series of ribs about three feet apart which formed the sides and were called frames. These were joined transversely by similar ribs known as floors at the bottom and beams at the top. Outside, the skeleton was covered with flesh of steel plates tacked together by millions of rivets. Inside there were two bottoms, one secured to the underside of the floor framing – this being the real bottom of the vessel – and the second the false bottom laid along the top. The space between the two was divided into sections and used for housing fuel oil, drinking water or water ballast. The tapered ends of the *Areopagus*, like every modern liner or merchant ship, were cut short inside with strengthened water-tight partitions, being collision bulkheads, which gave the ship a good chance of surviving a collision with something ahead or astern without serious flooding.

All the bulkheads and cabins had been permissibly pierced by pipes and wiring, and lower down the bulkheads were pierced by the propulsion shafting; but in the former case they could be protected by the closing of water-tight doors at intervals along those decks likely to be flooded. The propulsion shafting was protected as it passed through water-tight bulkheads by a surrounding of stuffing boxes and glands, so that there would be no leakage round the shaft from a flooded compartment to its adjacent compartment, nor any interference with the work of the propulsion shafting itself.

It all seemed easy enough to the passengers. They rarely considered these aspects of the *Areopagus*. They were more concerned with bars and swimming-pools and the ports of call. It seemed to them that all they had to do was buy a ticket and arrange passports, visas and tickets with a travel agency or direct with the Company.

But even this apparently simple basis of sale had a permutation which was almost a computer problem. For the booking of a berth on a liner had a parallel with the purchase of a ticket at a theatre. No travel agent could be pinned down for some time, for the scores and hundreds of agencies had at some stage to refer to someone who had a master plan.

Letters, cables and phone calls converged on the Company. Some were inquiries, some definite bookings or provisional bookings – the most frustrating of all.

There was the man who wished to book a cabin on the *Areopagus* for himself and his family from Singapore to Europe. He had every right to book it, and had done so in plenty of time. But it meant the cabin would stay empty from New Zealand to Singapore unless someone booked it to Singapore from Wellington, Hobart, Sydney, Melbourne or Perth, and no one had. An old lady wanted to make the cruise in exactly the same cabin as she'd once made a shorter journey. She was booked into it. Another traveller wrote for that particular cabin or none at all. He had had to be refused. The old lady had then written to say she'd got the date wrong and it was next February's cruise she had in mind . . . The other intending passenger was contacted, but refused to have anything to do with the Company. He had not, he declared, been given much consideration in the first place.

A number of single girls had booked for all or part of the voyage. There were fifty-six single-berth cabins on the *Areopagus*, but none of them had portholes or 'facilities', that is, showers, hip bath or toilet. And all of these single persons wanted facilities and in most cases a porthole as well despite the few score extra dollars it cost. This meant that they had to be given one each of the 248 two-berth cabins. This automatically barred these cabins from any male travelling alone who also wanted these kind of facilities. It had been too much to hope that the requisite number of single men and girls would make bookings to fill all those empty berths in the two-berth cabins. Often the Company had late bookings by people who could only afford A Deck, but A Deck was full – not really full because of this permutation of the sexes, but in theory 'fully booked' – and so were given berths on a better deck but at A Deck prices.

There were last-minute cancellations and bookings, letters, telegrams and items of luggage to cope with just before the ship sailed, and for pop singers, actresses and suchlike, whole sheafs of telegrams and bunches of flowers.

As well, the Company had to make a profit when the passengers insisted on moving in seasonal herds. Australians liked to go to Europe for the spring and summer, and when they came back the ship was crowded with them and with Europeans emigrating or getting away from their own winter. The *Areopagus* was usually crammed with migrants when she came south-east to Australia, but likely to be near empty travelling to Europe in the 'off' season. And this was apart from the loss because of the cabin permutations.

To mitigate this seasonal effect and avoid raising the fares to the level of jet travel, the Graeco-Australian Company, like many others, had to lure people abroad during the 'off season,' and they did this by 'off-season' reduced fares, or by travelling to Europe or around Asia on cruises. Thus the passenger who had to go to Europe anyway had a reduced fare and the Company couldn't differentiate between him and exclude the gratuitous discount which he'd be quite prepared to pay anyway.

For the passengers, the cruise now became more comfortable. The *Areopagus* functioned, it seemed to them, smoothly, and after several cool rather stormy days they were now on an Ocean which was so calm that the bows of the ship cut through it as if it was a beautiful blue pond. And it was warm. At last Miss Wearne could sit in a deck chair for soporific hours. Marion Burston couldn't entirely maintain an attitude of despair. Dempsey had his first case of heatstroke – a man in an engine room whose body had stopped adjusting itself to the temperature and wouldn't sweat. Dempsey had him in the hospital and packed him in ice . . . The officers changed from their dark winter uniforms into the white for the tropics. Passengers strolled round in bathing costumes, shorts and faded Hawaiian shirts bought on other cruises. There were picnic lunches on the aft of the Parade Deck, interesting fish and pickles, salads and delicious Greek pastries. The news items printed each day in the ship's paper began to seem absurd, not tragic.

The *Areopagus* moved across the sea – that great surface of 141,000,000 square miles which occupied seven-tenths of the surface of the world but which had a comparatively slight depth despite its volume of 324,000,000 cubic miles. It was calm and the passengers were grateful. But they never thought of how incredible it was that a great mass of water like the Indian Ocean should be calm. For here the earth was rotating at nearly a thousand miles an hour. The moon pulled at the sea and so did the sun. The earth itself had an attraction millions of times greater than either. Yet there was a pull which was enough to cause a wave in the open Ocean to follow beneath the revolving moon. The wave was twelve hours and twenty minutes long – just half the time the moon took to circle the earth. The height of this 'tide' was about three feet in the Indian Ocean and 'travelled' at about five hundred miles an hour.

The sea looked still and harmless, the waves small and without strength, an insignificant result of a slow breeze whose frictional drag created ripples. The breeze pushed against the sloping surface of the ripples but was not strong enough to thrash them even into wavelets . . . It would need a stronger wind to create a cumulative and increasing effect in the waves and even then it needed the big space of the ocean to obtain momentum.

The waves of the Indian Ocean were irregular, of many small wave trains, from hundreds of different points of origin, many speeds, now merging, dying out, some surviving, others being overwhelmed. Each wave was formed by the movement of the millions of water particles which revolved in circles at and below the sea's surface. It was possible now for a man in an office thousands of miles away, by consulting formulae and tables and making mathematical calculations, to tell the condition of the sea, providing he was told what the local wind and weather conditions had been for several hours. Or he could give reliable meteorological forecasts, predict what the sea *would* be like . . .

This kind of information – about the sea itself – was not supplied to the *Areopagus.* But she did receive weather forecasts, which was almost the same thing. The weather around the world was watched by some eight thousand land stations, three thousand aircraft and four thousand merchant ships. There was, however, a deficiency inasmuch as the Southern Hemisphere, three-quarters of which was covered by oceans, had an insufficient proportion of those observations. This was understandable as the land mass of the world – especially the civilized world which was crowded with movement and wanted to know about weather – was largely in the Northern Hemisphere. There were also delays in communications in the Southern Hemisphere and scant information regarding the upper atmosphere of the world. A recent development for shipping was the observation of ocean currents by virtue of the temperature difference by infra-red observations from satellites. Computers were now ready to handle data for the whole world.

But the *Areopagus* did not receive this sophisticated sort of information. She simply had weather forecasts from Perth, Singapore, Manila and elsewhere, and the most recent assured her officers that the Indian Ocean was bathed in sunshine and there was practically no wind. Not that the *Areopagus* would have changed course anyway. As she set sail the more than two thousand miles from Fremantle to Bali and Singapore she was twenty-seven hours behind schedule.

Part Two

ASIA

The 17th day wee were right under
the line, which is the most fervent
place of the burnt Zone : where in
the middest of February wee susteined
such heat, with often thunder and
lightenings, that wee did sweate for
the most part continually, as though
wee had bene in a stove or hote-house.

– *John Winter*

Dancing and promenading on the poop
from 7 till 9 PM, when all
passengers may enjoy themselves,
but not abaft the mizen mast.
The promenaders are not in any way
to interrupt the dancers.

– *Extract from*
Rules of the ship
Lightning, *No II: 1855*

11

IT HAD not occurred to Tornetta that there would be – have to be by virtue of sheer confined space – some kind of human relationships during this journey aboard the *Areopagus.* He was the one passenger who had come on the voyage neither for fun nor spectacle. In his mental stress and near panic the cruise had not made any impact on his imagination, which had leaped from Hobart and Sydney straight to San Francisco where Ignazio, his brother, waited. But there was in fact a 'distance' of about fifty days between the two. He was the only occupant of cabin A 145 from Hobart to Sydney, and he stayed in the cabin for long, anxious hours while the other passengers went ashore. He ate no food nor went to any bar (they were not serving alcohol anyway), but sweated time away in the gloom of the cabin with curtains drawn.

The excitement of departure was, for him, that of relief. He cursed angrily as darkness came and the time for sailing, but still the Greek ship didn't leave.

He was startled and resentful when the steward – a small quiet man who, if he observed anything, made no comment – entered, loaded with two suitcases and preceding a man of about thirty-five who was himself carrying ciné camera, still camera, tripod and a smaller case.

This man wore heavy brown tweed suit and a cap and looked ridiculous. He blinked through powerful glasses and walked with a twisted gait: there was something the matter with his right leg.

Tornetta was unsympathetic and wished him elsewhere.

The man had ginger hair, thin on the top, and his green eyes were meaningless, those of a fool, Tornetta decided. Like many people with handicaps he was something of an extrovert; later he became known as 'the Joker' round the ship, but it was not a term of endearment. It was difficult to pity him, impossible to like him, because he was so offensively hearty. He was to receive many silent and some crushing snubs on this voyage – some people were frank enough to get out of their deckchairs and walk away if he sat down alongside them. It was impossible to know if he had a skin as thick as a rhinoceros or harboured under his heartiness a deep loathing of other humans.

At any rate he never ceased to try contacts with them.

He greeted the silent Tornetta, who exuded indifference, 'How do? My name's Ron. Ron Squibb. I go bang bang!' He laughed, but Tornetta's face did not crease in amusement. 'We're going to be together for quite a time, eh? So you'd better call me Ron. Shall we be eating at the same table? It's nice to meet people isn't it? There's a lot of things to learn, aren't there? I see there's a lecture on Greek traditions and history tomorrow. That should be interesting, eh?'

When Tornetta replied to none of these questions, Squibb persisted, 'What's your name?'

Tornetta admitted his name reluctantly. Having this fool in the cabin was about the same as putting in a public address system.

Squibb said, 'Italian, eh? Not fed up with Australia, are you? I'm a Pom myself, but I like it. This should be interesting, eh? See the world and you learn things, don't you?'

Still the condemnatory silence from Tornetta. Squibb tried a different approach. 'A sea cruise will do us good. I'm a bachelor. What I need is a widow with a bad cough.' He tittered, but Tornetta only yawned.

'Tired, are you? Eh, which bunk do you have?'

'The bottom one.'

'Where are you from?'

'Sydney,' Tornetta told him, and could have bitten his tongue off. That kind of information in the possession of this garrulous clown –

'But you were already on board,' Squibb pointed out, too observant for Tornetta's liking.

'I have been in Hobart for a few months.'

'I've been there,' Squibb asserted. 'Not the same as Sydney, but pretty. Hey, she's sailing. I'm going to have a look. Come on!'

'I shall stay here.'

'What for?' Squibb asked frankly.

'I've got a lot on my mind.'

'A lot on your mind!'

Squibb laughed; Tornetta seethed with dislike; he was going to have a job avoiding trouble with this nosy idiot... 'Forget that,' instructed Squibb, who was obviously a man who had to be crushed or he would become unbearably dominant in a petty way. 'You're on holiday.'

'Business,' corrected Tornetta.

'Forget business.'

'In my business you don't forget business.'

'And what is your business?'

'None of yours, crumb,' snapped Tornetta.

But Squibb was not offended; he laughed in admiration of the twisted dialogue, said, 'I'm going to have a look' and went out of the cabin.

Tornetta avoided Squibb the next day as far as that was possible in a ship a few hundred feet long where there were only two decks to walk about on if one wanted fresh air. He saw Squibb from a distance, all noise and bonhomie, the life and soul of the cruise in his own estimation, stopping strangers – Asians, Greeks, old New Zealand couples, young seamen polishing the brass rail – and even from a hundred feet away Tornetta could see them recoil, whether from the sheer ugliness of Squibb or his noisy buoyancy. Sometimes they seemed to stand and talk with him because he was a partial cripple and they pitied him.

Whenever Tornetta saw him from a sufficient distance he retreated, went to a different deck, or into a bar, or even, in frustration, back to the cabin.

But inevitably he made an error and almost collided with him by the stern swimming-pool.

'Eh, watch this,' Squibb requested, and there was no escape, for what could he pretend to be doing?

Squibb was weighed down with the ciné camera and tripod, but he also had a pair of binoculars.

He looked out to sea, squinted and peered, and then took

the binoculars out of the case. He focused them on the same spot for a whole minute.

Tornetta sensed that people on chairs and standing about were beginning to look in the same direction.

'What can you see?' he asked.

Squibb whispered, 'Nothing, but you wait.'

Sure enough, a middle-aged man inquired, 'What is it? Flying fish?'

'Can't you see it?' Squibb asked.

'See what?'

'The seaplane.'

'No, it must be too far—'

'Have a look,' Squibb offered.

The man said, 'Oh, thank you,' and took the binoculars from Squibb. He soon admitted, 'I still can't see . . .'

'A little to the left,' Squibb prompted.

'I've got her,' the man said. 'What's she doing, I wonder?'

He strolled on and a woman reclining in a chair asked him, 'What are they all looking at?'

'A seaplane.'

'Oh, I must have a look at that. Has it come down in the sea?'

'Yes.'

'I wonder why.'

'Out of fuel perhaps.'

Squibb overheard this with great satisfaction, and Tornetta realized that this was how he got his own back on the world for the snubs and stares of pity . . . He understood, too, that for him Squibb was a man with very dangerous potential.

For this reason he suppressed his irritation when he found Squibb at the lunch table. Tornetta was eating his meals in a satisfactorily discreet corner of the large dining-room. Columns and sheer distance limited the number of persons who could inspect him from twenty or thirty feet, and he could see that these few dozen were 'harmless' anyway. Likewise the two old ladies at his table, whose dialogue was about their health, the weather, the possibilities of seasickness and the behaviour of the stewards.

It meant now that Squibb's noisy laughter and probing questions – if not Tornetta's guarded, quiet answers – could be overheard by perhaps ten people, and, worse, drew attention to the table.

He understood Squibb's motives perhaps better than Squibb did himself. For Tornetta was answerable; he could not escape. Being in the same cabin he *had* to spend some hours of the day and night with Squibb. Others might evade Squibb, make a brief reply and move on, or, if cornered, snub him or crush him, but Tornetta was like a relation in the same house : one might go out to work, to the races with friends, but always one had to come back to the unloved : one was lumbered ...

Nevertheless, Tornetta developed something of a technique, and Squibb often fell into his own trap. For, when he asked 'Are you going to the deck games?' Tornetta could counter 'Are you?' And if Squibb said 'Yes' he could say frankly 'I'm not.' But he did it with greater subtlety. If Squibb said 'Are you entering the quoits competition?' Tornetta would sneer 'What the hell for?' and Squibb's nature caused him to defend the competition : 'I think they're a very good way of passing the time and keeping us all fit.' To which Tornetta would comment, 'You go if you like that sort of thing.' And Squibb *did* like 'that sort of thing' because it forced people to have contact with him. Part of his extrovert nature was an attempt to make other people live with him ...

Despite his claim that what he needed was a 'widow with a cough' Tornetta observed that women and even girls of fourteen were indifferent to Squibb. He had nothing they wanted; they were not likely to be obliged to him, and it amused Tornetta to see them snub him, stare blankly at his jokes, even turn their backs on him outright if he stopped to try to insert himself into a conversation going on on deck. Only older people had a little pity and passed the time of day. He was kept waiting by the Purser's girls and didn't even get the smiles Tornetta did.

Women in fact looked at Tornetta. Even tall long-limbed Australian kids of nineteen identified some aggressive and interesting property he had. He stared frankly at their faces and long legs and not always did they flinch or look resentful.

He was thirty-six, tough, and no woman who saw him and learned that he was unmarried had any doubts even so that he'd had passionate experiences with women. He had that slight facial pallor and appearance of exhaustion which is alleged to interest women.

He could sit by a woman and engage her in conversation effortlessly, and even if she rejected him in the end she would feel complimented, if a little corrupted. It was something Squibb would never be able to do . . .

A little of his anxiety had left him now that they'd sailed from Sydney. His situation began to have a remoteness. Soon he would look round for things of possible interest.

He wanted to be alone, but it was impossible. There were hundreds of people, most of them talkative.

He sat in the Forward Bar, by the bar itself rather than noticeably alone at a table, and in seconds a young woman sat by him. Tornetta was a man who understood animal instincts and knew before she even spoke that this one was almost throbbing with sexual appetite. He met her eyes in the mirror and was astonished. She was very young and beautiful and burning hot. Not a call girl or prostitute or chick on drugs, just a young woman shifting about slightly on her stool she was so bothered by body appetite. Lust stirred him and overcame the anxiety of the last few days.

'There's a rumour that we're stopping at Adelaide,' he said.

She laughed. Her fingers crawled up and down her glass. It was beer she was drinking. 'I can take or leave Adelaide,' she said.

She had an English voice. 'You're a Pom,' he said.

'Oh, don't remind me. Did you ever get to Surrey?'

'I got as far as Oxford once.'

'Not bad. Where are you going now?'

'San Francisco. And you?'

'Canada, I think. But I'm getting off at San Francisco too.'

'It's a small word,' he suggested.

'Too damn small,' she countered bitterly.

'Why "Canada, I think"? Don't you know yet?'

'It depends,' she qualified.

An idea came to him. 'Are you looking for work?' He could find her plenty of work, dancing, or on her back, or stripping . . .

She looked in the mirror and protested, 'Oh, hell,' and leaned towards Tornetta. 'Please help me,' she whispered earnestly. 'Pretend to be my husband. I've enemies on board. I'll pay,' she claimed oddly.

A man said, 'Ah, there you are, Pauline. I thought you said—'

But the girl slid off her stool and said coldly, 'We were just going.'

Her 'we' included Tornetta. 'Come on, we're late,' he contributed.

He was fully aware that the girl, Pauline, was talking nonsense. She had simply got herself involved too soon with the wrong man and had now dumped him. Tornetta would be the right man. She was hungry for physical coupling. He would give it to her. She was, he knew in pleasurable anticipation, the sort who needed pain as well. He would make her writhe and sigh first, then twist her arms, perhaps thrash her. He planned her future in the five hundred strides to her cabin: violent, secret pleasure for him during this voyage and then, just when he'd tired of her, she would become remunerative, an employee . . .

It turned out differently. In her cabin she rejected him for a long time, kept looking at her watch. Then, suddenly, she gave him five dollars, began to strip and very soon they were copulating in the unsatisfactory area of the bunk.

A key scratched the cabin door as Tornetta reached climax. He couldn't stop, Pauline was so frenetic and erotic.

It might have been a man, even a husband, but was not. Behind him Tornetta heard a woman's voice protest in hurt more than shock: 'Oh, Pauline, how could you?' and he identified the situation at once. This Pauline was a nut case, her friend was a butch. And this white-hot performance, for which he had been *paid*, was to wound and anger the butch.

Pauline suggested breathlessly, 'Go away, Reidy. You shouldn't have come back just yet.'

Reidy said, suitably annoyed, 'You bloody crazy whore, I hate your filthy guts.' She went out and slammed the cabin door.

Pauline yawned.

'Thanks. You can go now if you want to.'

'Not just yet,' said Tornetta. 'I haven't had my money's worth.' And he began to hurt her.

Tornetta went down to dinner. It was easy to go ahead of Squibb, because Squibb had many things to do. For a 'Joker' he was a very earnest man. He took many pills – to avoid enteritis, to cure constipation, to anticipate and eliminate seasickness. In a stifling hot cabin in which the air conditioning was so poor it might be said to have failed, Squibb had many rituals involving his body. But the shower bath and deodorants on his feet were in vain, and filled the cabin with the all-too-human smells and Tornetta with loathing.

There were in the cabin the mutual, unavoidable smells of sweat, vests, socks and soap, and there were hairs in the wash basin.

And despite his bonhomie Squibb was petulant and complaintive. 'I'd like the lights off,' he'd said last night. 'It *is* after midnight.' And the night before it had been 'I wish you didn't smoke in the cabin. There's a great risk of fire on a ship, you know. And there's little enough air in here at night . . .'

To both these objections Tornetta had restrained himself and merely suggested, 'Change your cabin, then.' This was more than a hint and would have been enough to drive anyone else to the Purser's office; but Squibb merely blinked, virtuous and offended, but immovable, and whined : 'I paid for my half of this cabin. It's a good one and I've every right to be here.'

The dining-room was on Metaxas Deck, one deck above Tornetta's cabin on A Deck. Opposite its entrances were the Purser's office, a few shops, a barber and the telephone centre. As Tornetta came now into this area it was crowded, not with people going in to dinner – although some were – but with angry passengers.

They were having a noisy argument with the Chief Purser. Demetropoulos was a moderately tall man, slim, with a waist-line accentuated by a tightened belt. He was a man of about forty with an interesting head. It had a classical skull-like shape, with deepset large eyes. He had thick black eye-brows and black hair which might have been polished. It was quite impossible to anger him or even amuse him. He did have a slight smile at times – although it was not there now – but it was detached, nothing to do with his inter-locutor. In fact detachment was the key characteristic of Demetropoulos. Some passengers claimed that he was obtuse, others that he was impenetrably stupid and unable to speak any English except when he was seducing a woman. He had another characteristic, which was to look slightly above and well beyond any anxious or (more frequently) angry pas-senger, as if a great man's mind was surrendering part of its capabilities to this trivial nonsense of the passenger, but the bulk of the machinery was still cogitating the greater matters which had been interrupted.

The offended passengers had not found themselves a very impressive spokesman. His name was Pybus and he was supposed to be a barrister, but this seemed impossible, for he was gross, red faced with drinking, he swore, and in the Antipodean manner wore thick grey trousers up to his middle chest, supported by a thick leather belt.

He was shouting at the Chief Purser.

The two girls of the Purser's staff, one Kristina, the other a blonde German girl, stared blankly ahead. They had become acclimatized to these public arguments on the last two voyages.

Pybus was shouting, 'We've paid our fares and the Cap-tain is obliged to fulfil his half of the contract. It says speci-fically that we were to stay in Sydney twenty-seven hours – and how long did we stay? Seven hours. I'm from New Zea-land and I wanted to have a good look at Sydney—'

'Hear, hear!' supported the other passengers.

'And now you tell us we'll only be in Fremantle and Perth

three hours. It says in the literature sent by your Company twelve to sixteen hours. I didn't come on this bloody ship to stare at the sea. I came—'

'Hear, hear!' chorused the passengers again.

Demetropoulos said, quite loud but not with anger: 'We have a schedule—'

'Alter the bloody schedule!' bellowed Pybus.

'We were delayed by a storm,' the Chief Purser argued.

'There's always a storm in the Bight. You ought to know *that*...'

The crowd applauded.

Pybus said loudly, with vulgar virtue, 'I've been very frank with you and these other people and we want equal frankness. We want to know—'

Demetropoulos reminded them all: 'We gave you a bonus port, several hours in Adelaide.'

'You only called there for your own purposes,' bellowed Pybus. 'You loaded up with automobiles.'

The Chief Purser said imperturbably, 'There are many places to call at. We must maintain our schedule – we shall do so for your sake and our own, for other passengers await this ship, and berthing is dependent on the tides. All this is arranged. If you will allow us to leave Fremantle on schedule we shall regain the lost time.'

'That's all very well,' disputed Pybus, but weaker, losing now, and passengers restless, and desirous of going in to eat, 'but it will be dark when we reach Fremantle.'

'Tours of the city lights of Perth have been arranged,' Demetropoulos told him, still imperturbable – they'd bought their tickets: the Company had won on that day. 'All previous tours have been cancelled and passengers who do not wish to see Perth by night can have their money refunded.'

'It's not good enough,' Squibb said into Tornetta's ear.

But it was good. It was the way Tornetta wanted things to be. He had sweated in fear in his cabin as the long hours had crawled by in Sydney, Melbourne and Adelaide. The less time the *Areopagus* spent in Fremantle, and the sooner she sailed for Bali, the better. For even now 'they' might have suspicions, and earnest vehement persons could at this moment be crossing Australia in jet planes to ask questions. And if corruption existed one way on this ship it would exist the other, and who knew what form of unpleasantness might materialize. Tornetta might be asked to leave the ship. Passengers might join the ship for the sole purpose of seeing what could be done about Mr Tornetta in Cabin A 145. Cables might be sent to Sydney: yes, the man here answers the descriptions given, the photograph carried; and he has an air of great alarm about him. What are your instructions? So the sooner the *Areopagus* left Australia the better . . . His body and whole nervous system was in sympathy with the Chief Purser and he hoped that the Captain would not be influenced by any report of this disturbance. Go, his mind cried. For God's sake, go, move, escape . . .

In the dining-room he poured himself a glass of water, but it was not strong enough. He sent the wine waiter for a bottle of beer.

The wine waiter brought the beer and was about to pour it into Tornetta's glass when he saw that this was half full of water. He poured this water back into the jug and filled Tornetta's glass with the beer.

'That's a dirty thing to do,' complained Squibb, and Tornetta's nerves screamed as the two old ladies joined his protest: 'Yes, very unhygienic.' People at other tables stared as the waiter, puzzled, nevertheless gratified the whims of these peculiar Australians and fetched 'another' jug of water. In fact he merely topped up the water already in the jug, but the old ladies and Squibb weren't to know that. They did not care to drink water which had been in contact with Tornetta's mouth, but in his anxiety he was not quick enough to appreciate that . . .

The next afternoon the entire ship had lifeboat drill. This was painfully slow and the passengers stood in lines along the Parade Deck facing the crew, not just seamen and stewards, but cooks, engineers, telephone operators, nurses and the members of the cabaret and ship's orchestra. Half an hour passed with jokes thrown about and the Greek crew examining the passengers with as much curiosity as they were themselves scrutinized. Very few Australians felt anything but cheerfully and cynically critical of the crew. It was assumed, unkindly, that the Greeks would panic in a disaster, that lifeboats would tip over or be dropped upside down.

Captain Vafiadis, the Staff Captain and First Officer walked by, seemingly confirming this cynicism, for they were merely concerned with posture and appearance, it seemed. They had scarcely dismissed the drill when half a dozen small Greek engineers recommenced lugging oxygen cylinders about. They lit their oxy-acetylene welders with supreme recklessness from the lighted ends of their cigarettes. Tarpaulin was laid on deck under a lifeboat and hammering and burning began, with the obvious purpose of freeing the particular lifeboat from its embolism in corrosion and paint. This work went on for two hours and was left for the day, still unfinished.

Two days out from Fremantle Tornetta tried to open his cabin door but couldn't. He had the wrong key, that of cabin A 93, the one which he'd stolen. He had almost forgotten about it.

Tornetta considered his position. He had taken the money from the pockets of Zito and Attolico after crippling them with the scalding soup. He had sold his car. He had taken every cent he owned out of the bank and from his own safe, and had left without paying his strippers. All this had amounted to $4,000, but the air fare to Canberra and Hobart and the ticket on the *Areopagus* to Genoa (he was disembarking at San Francisco but had in caution booked to Italy) had absorbed nearly $1,500. The balance of $2,500 was a good sum to start with in San Francisco, but Tornetta needed a lot more if he was going to run a business, buy an automobile, bribe people, wear fine clothes, indulge women . . .

It seemed logical to him that he should use the key to enter the cabin and steal. There was no reason in his moral stance why a number of other passengers should not be fleeced during the voyage. He worked up a grievance rapidly to justify it. He had lost a good business; he had in his first years in Australia been called a 'dago'. There had been many insults since.

Cabin A 93 was only a hundred feet from his own A 145, a little too near for his liking. On the other hand it was easy to be legitimately in the area, coming and going. He watched the area until he had identified its two occupants. He was relieved that there were only two : the permutation of meals, changing of clothes, loading of cameras, washing, resting and so on of four persons would have made it dangerous to enter that cabin. But two people, that was a lot easier.

They were man and wife, in their sixties, and Tornetta now began very carefully to watch, not the cabin but *them*. He was amused to notice that they were sprightly and garrulous parading about the Metaxas Deck, but tired and petulant in the last few strides to their cabin, throwing sour remarks at each other : 'Oh, for heaven's sake, George, you're like an old woman' – 'And you *are* an old woman' – 'He only wanted us to –' 'Well, you've got a tongue in your head, haven't you?' – 'You certainly have' – and Tornetta even heard the woman snap, 'What have you done with it? Good Lord, George, you haven't lost *another* key?'

It was not difficult to learn their habits, but these tended to be protective without intention. Tornetta didn't dare go too near their cabin in the morning, for the stewards were active and between eleven and midday the Captain sometimes inspected that Deck, or, if he didn't, they themselves came back singly and stayed a whole quarter of an hour. In the afternoon they slept in the cabin until four.

Between four and half past in the afternoon seemed a good time to Tornetta, for they never missed the cup of tea and cakes served in the dining-room at that time. He would attempt it tomorrow . . .

That evening there was the first of several cocktail parties given by the Captain. This one was given the label 'The Captain's Carnival Party'. Tornetta went in order that he might see if Mr and Mrs Bewglass – the passengers in A 93 – were there, in which case he'd leave the party and go to their cabin.

The party was held in the Aegean Lounge, a large comfortable lounge with elegant pillars and a good floor for dancing, and a raised platform at its forward end for the band – not the men of the ship's orchestra but a quartet of bearded youths who were part of the cabaret. The cabaret was also performed in this lounge, which was amidships on the Parade Deck.

Tornetta managed to avoid Squibb by going early, but even so he was not as early as most.

A long queue stretched into the lounge from its forward entrance, the aft doors being closed. The passengers had tarted themselves up out of proportion to the ship and the Captain, in Tornetta's view. The men wore dark suits, stiff collars, regimental and college ties, but it was the women who had really decided to make an impression, whether on the Captain or his officers or each other even Tornetta didn't feel certain about. They wore hostess gowns, beaded, lamé and gold dresses, silks and satins, some covered with lace. The weather was now above subtropical but many had fur stoles around their necks. They almost clanked with ornamentation, paste necklaces and silver bangles and fingers loaded with the weight of rings like expensive knuckle-dusters. Their faces were different from what they had been at lunch time, creamed and rouged until they were like actresses between Acts; and the hair framing the over-painted faces had received hours of attention since lunch time and was now swept up, tinted blue or pink, and decorated with flowers or bows. In vain, as far as Tornetta was concerned. He infinitely preferred their daughters, scrubbed now, but long-legged in mini-dresses, superb physical specimens of the next Australia.

Tornetta found himself standing by Mr Pybus. There was no one with Pybus; evidently he was not married. He was very drunk now, and examining him Tornetta saw that Pybus was gross, and sweating under the eyes. He breathed with difficulty.

People were beginning to avoid Pybus despite whatever gratitude they felt because he had protested on their behalf. Right now he was startling, for he was in khaki shorts and open-neck shirt and had sandals on his feet.

He had become a bore on the subject of the *Areopagus*' timetable, and asked Tornetta : 'Are you a betting man?'

'Yes.'

'I'll give you a hundred dollars to five that we're late at every damn port along the route.'

'You'd win so I can't take your bet.'

'Bloody Greeks,' Pybus muttered.

As they approached the Captain and Staff Captain, the Chief Steward noticed Pybus in his shorts. He pulled him to one side of the queue. 'I wonder if you'd mind, sir, waiting a while?'

Pybus was argumentative. The tarted-up passengers were embarrassed and affected not to notice his presence at all. He pleaded to them, like one who says, 'I did something for you; now you speak up on my behalf.' But they didn't and as Tornetta moved on he heard Pybus' angry shout : 'I hate bloody Greeks. I hate them.'

Tornetta shook hands with Captain Vafiadis. The ship's photographer, a youth of nineteen, took a flash photograph. It was to be pinned on a noticeboard the next afternoon with scores of others, to Tornetta's alarm. And then Tornetta was half hustled into the Aegean Lounge and an attractive girl shook his hand.

She said in an English voice, but not the sort of snobbish English Tornetta had at times encountered, 'I'm Barbara. I'm in the cabaret here. Welcome. Would you like a drink?'

He stared at her, and she identified his attitudes within the morality of society immediately and did not despise him. He saw that at once as quickly as he noticed her attractive vulgarity and dancer's physique – although she was not so tall as many Australian girls aboard.

He said 'How are you doing?' in the Australian manner and she grimaced slightly. 'My feet!' And then two old people joined them simply because they were standing in the way.

The two people were Mr and Mrs Bewglass. Tornetta enjoyed the irony of being polite to them, subservient to their suburban snobbery. For they had been on many cruises and were dull with authenticity : 'Where was that, George,

Pago Pago?' – 'No, it was Suva' – 'It couldn't have been because—' and, slightly more interesting: 'We had six deaths on the *Omnifarious*. One man was too tall to put in the freezer so they put him in a bath and showered him with ice cubes every few hours.'

The girl, Barbara, grabbed a steward with a tray and asked with outright unrefined desire, 'What about us? I want a gin and lime.'

'Don't have lime, dearie,' said Mrs Bewglass. 'It'll depress you.'

Nothing, evidently, had the capacity of depressing *her*, for she and her husband took a drink off every tray carried past them. They gulped down whiskies, sherries, gins and cocktails. 'Get it down,' she urged her husband. 'It's on the house.'

Tornetta asked the girl with unconcealed interest, 'Are you from England?'

'Not really. Wales. Aberystwyth. You're Italian? I've been to Naples and Genoa. They're beautiful . . . I've been everywhere dancing my feet off! Kuwait, Aden, Germany, Iraq and Cairo.'

'How long have you been with the Graeco-Australian?'

'Our first trip,' the girl from Aberystwyth said sourly. 'And we're lumbered with a six-months' contract.'

'Don't you like it?'

'You're joking. Oh, it's all right now we've dumped all those migrants, but when we boarded – Southampton – it was crowded. We were given berths right down on B Deck and the air conditioning was lousy. It got so hot we used to sleep raw and leave the doors open and to hell with it—'

Mrs Bewglass began to offer her views on the air conditioning in Cabin A 93.

The girl said, and said it to Tornetta, who was warmed by possibilities, 'Listen. I'm supposed to circulate. The Staff Captain's looking. I'll see you.' And her hot frank stare into Tornetta's face promised that, crowded though the ship was with men who watched her dancing legs and considered that this gave her the status of call girl, part of the ticket for which they'd paid, despite many minor attentions, he, Tornetta, would be remembered and considered.

'What a vulgar girl,' claimed Mrs Bewglass and Tornetta felt it would be a pleasure to rob such a malicious suburban snob . . .

Barbara was certainly dressed in a slightly shocking costume. It was a black mini-dress of silk overlaid with black lace. The band began to play half-heartedly and she danced with a member of the cabaret, and the dress was so high she had to hold it down with one hand.

The old women sat round the edges of the lounge, too tired to stand, but still active with dislike of this spectacle.

Everybody was watchful at the first cocktail party of the trip, even anxious, as they rehearsed phrases for the Captain, should he approach their group. The entertainers stood around and attempted with difficulty to liven the conversations. A few officers appeared. Demetropoulos stood talking to two young women, quite happy, unaffected by the arguments of some days earlier, but still staring at something a few feet above the passengers, and with the same detached smile.

Squibb, inevitably, materialized, and resumed his role of Joker.

He said loudly, 'When the Captain shook hands with me, or I did with him, he started on a lot of Greek. He was still at it when I was a hundred feet away. I don't know if he was saying a quick Hail Mary or a bit of Greek Orthodox . . . Are you coming to the cabaret tonight?'

Tornetta surprised him with an outright 'Yes.' He wanted to stare at the girl from Aberystwyth, to sweat a little in anticipation . . .

Captain Vafiadis now appeared and moved from group to group, smiling woodenly and offering stilted titbits of dialogue.

He then made a speech of welcome to the passengers, equally full of trite phrases, but delivered with apparent sincerity, and a New Zealand passenger suddenly stood forward and began to sing 'For he's a jolly good fellow,' which the other passengers joined in vigorously. It was almost possible to read the perplexity in the Captain's mind. One minute these people are holding mass protest meetings and the next expressing their pleasure at being here. How can one take such persons seriously?

A special dinner followed the Carnival Party, with shrimps, turkey and champagne. The stewards were dressed up in red livery and the sweat boiled out of their foreheads and hair and at times dripped on to plates.

Squibb said it was necessary to be in the same Aegean Lounge forty minutes before the cabaret began if they were to sit in the front row. He arrived fully armed with camera and flash, much to Tornetta's embarrassment. Not, Tornetta saw, that this was unusual. Several people were similarly equipped.

The cabaret was much better than Tornetta had expected; in fact, although too noisy, it was good. It was run by a very tough middle-aged queer called Edgar. He was something of a masochist about his own middle age, offering stories involving his mother and loaded with questions like 'Did you see *Hell's Angels*? Remember that girl, what was her name? You *know* . . .' and this as inexplicably as the goodwill offered to the Captain in song raised howls of coarse laughter. Equally, Edgar was grossly suggestive about his own sexual position.

But if anyone in the audience was cocky Edgar was very tough indeed. He was a cheeky Cockney at heart, with that quick razor sharp dialogue. People who tiptoed in late were asked, 'Had a good dinner, dears?' or 'Is the baby asleep now?' or 'Shall we begin again for you?' or even 'Give 'em a big hand for bothering to come at all.' And the persons concerned withered before him and said nothing.

His humour was too fast for some of the old passengers and too English for an Australian and New Zealand audience. But he was adaptable and made up jokes about the day. 'Have you brushed all those black spots off your dresses? Isn't it *awful*? They tell me the Chief Engineer's got measles . . .' He obtained the most response when he was frankly suggestive: 'If you want anything in the night ring for the steward. He'll give it to you.'

Edgar's company included another two men who did their best to be funny; a ventriloquist who was obviously drunk, but very competent; a young man who sang sentimental ballads and a couple who did exhibition dancing. These two had won ballroom championships in the provinces and colonial towns, but never quite made the top. Their life was now ships and holiday camps with old-age in the middle distance. They considered themselves rather superior to the other entertainers, not to mention the passengers. But they quarrelled furiously and the Company got its own back through Edgar, who sometimes announced them: 'The two love birds. Well, one, anyway, because the other's not speaking to him ...'

But Tornetta would not have been interested in any of this if the girl from Aberystwyth hadn't been there. She was one of six dancers, who were all very professional as well as shapely. They came on in the first number, very leggy, heads held high, and danced with tremendous energy and precision on a night when it was very hot and many of the audience were sorry for themselves, with tired feet, discomfort from sweating and general weariness. The girls all stared straight out at the audience with smiles on their faces; that of Barbara held a little vanity.

They were disconcerted very slightly when Squibb crouched practically below their stomachs and blinded them with flash.

Edgar, standing behind them, shouted caustically, 'Want to take dirty pictures, do you? Wait until we get to Singapore, sonny ...'

This did not daunt Squibb, who was immune to snubs, and he stumbled into explanation: 'If the ship's photographer can use flash—' but Edgar had the advantage of the microphone and a hundred times the volume Squibb could achieve. 'Where do you come from, sonny? Sydney? My Mum sent a Meccano set there so they could build a bridge!' he told the audience, and there were boos and cheers and cries of 'Melbourne's better ...'

The show finished with all the performers dancing in a crescendo of noise, and then the lights were dimmed and they ran among the audience shaking hands before going off stage. Barbara squeezed Tornetta's hand, whispered, 'Hi!'

and even touched Squibb's sweating fingers and gave him a smile.

On the way out Tornetta saw that a few people were already waiting to obtain seats for the second cabaret, and they included the Bewglass couple.

Pybus was lying in a chair, snoring, very drunk, and Tornetta decided he would be an easy victim some time . . .

His heart was thumping but he knew now was the time to rob Cabin A 93. He went into the darkness of the Parade Deck to be rid of Squibb and came down at the forward end of the *Areopagus*. It was very silent and empty, the noises of music and conversation in the distance confirming that most people were at the cabaret, the cinema or in the bars.

He came into the corridor on the port side of A Deck and a long way off saw Squibb, camera in hand, turn into their own cabin. There was a steward about the same distance away, who was turning as Tornetta branched off into the opening with doors to four cabins. There was silence from all these cabins.

Tornetta knocked on the door of A 93 very lightly, then inserted the key carefully so that it made no scratching noise. He went inside quickly and closed the door silently.

The cabin was in darkness. There was a displeasing smell compounded of scent and old breath, oil, soap, and vests. Tornetta rubbed his hand along the steel by the door until he found the light switch.

He looked on the dresser, pocketed some silver and a woman's gold watch. He pulled out the bottom of the three drawers of the dresser. Clothes. The middle contained maps, tickets, pullovers and a few books. In the top drawer were more clothes. He was sweating in panic now, breathing quietly but heavily through his mouth.

There were three suitcases under the bunks. Tornetta was pulling the first one out when someone knocked on the door. It petrified him. Again the knock and a voice said 'Change water?'

Tornetta rushed into the bathroom and pulled the chain; the noise terrified him. But he knew what the steward wanted : the metal jug clamped just above the wash basin.

The steward was now in the cabin. Tornetta opened the bathroom door a little and put out one arm with the jug in that hand. The steward took it. A whole two minutes passed and then again the alarming knock. The steward called out, 'It is here, sir.' Tornetta did not answer, and after a few seconds' hesitation the steward left.

Tornetta was limp with fright. His inclination was to flee, but he might well rush straight into the steward. In fact he heard him now knocking at the three other nearby cabins, obtaining no answers, and his key scraping. Doors slammed for whole minutes while the steward changed the water jugs for the night.

In panic Tornetta re-examined the first suitcase. It was not locked, but held no money.

A second suitcase was not locked, but also had nothing inside except clothes. The third was heavier and was locked. Tornetta worked at it with a knife. He did not bother with the locks but dug at the back of the case where the hinges were held by a mere three studs each side.

Time passed with terrifying speed, but now he had the thing open.

Inside were a camera, more clothes, two passports, a travellers' cheque book and a wad of Australian currency. Tornetta pocketed this and pushed the case back under the bunk.

He waited, his chest heaving and his heart beating so excitedly that it worried him : just how fast could the thing go without damage?

It was completely silent now, but he had to struggle to find the courage to open the door. Again he closed it silently.

There was no way of knowing if anyone was in the main corridor. He had no option but to step into it.

He did this half hunched in terror, and turned the way he had come, the shorter distance to elsewhere, other decks, crowds. Before he finally left the corridor he couldn't resist turning to see if anyone had been behind him. But there was no one. Tornetta hurried up steps into the darkness of the Parade Deck. There were a few lovers pressed against each other in the darkest corners, and eyes gleamed as they viewed him with resentment.

Tornetta went into a lavatory and counted the money. It amounted to two hundred and seventy dollars. He considered what to do. It would be best to change all the money he could acquire into American dollars. He would be able to do this legitimately in a crowd as the *Areopagus* neared each port of call. For instance, it was, he knew already, possible to change Australian currency into either Singaporean or American before going ashore at Singapore. At Hong Kong anything was possible with currency, and Guam was American anyway.

The theft would of course be discovered within days, perhaps within hours. But there were no police officers on board, nor any facilities for taking fingerprints. And he was not the only one aboard with light fingers. Squibb had told him about the theft of a transistor radio.

In the morning Tornetta was tired and late getting up. He missed breakfast and went up on the Parade Deck to laze in the sun at about 10.30. The *Areopagus* was by no means crowded, but he was irritated to see that, on the sunny side, the deckchairs were nearly all occupied. Only a chair by Pybus was vacant, and Tornetta was disinclined to occupy it. Mr Pybus was snoring, sprawled so vulgarly in his khaki shorts that his genitals were visible to those who passed by. If he woke he would expect Tornetta to be talkative and sympathetic. Tornetta wasn't and did not wish to be involved with anyone who was conspicuous, apart from the girl in the chorus.

He went to the shaded side of the Parade Deck. It was still pleasantly warm, for most passengers it was in fact soporific. But Tornetta was hard, different to the middle-aged people who had come to relax. He was alert, waiting, and couldn't go into a sleepy trance as they did. He was in fact more conspicuous than he knew, for he was an Italian among Australians and New Zealanders; he was alone where most of them were accompanied; he wore a lounge suit when other men wore slacks and a cardigan; and slacks when they were in shorts or swimming trunks; he did not seem relaxed.

Thus he did not merge into the crowd as easily as he supposed.

Nevertheless, he was now drowsy and wanted to relax. He flopped full length on to an empty deckchair and looked out to sea.

Minutes passed and he became conscious that he was being examined. He turned and encountered the frank and neutral stare of a tall woman of severe countenance, just beyond middle age.

Some way off two stewards were pushing a trolley loaded with a silver urn full of hot soup.

The woman said, 'This is the biggest ship I've been on. Very stable. The food's too rich here. At home I only have All Bran for my breakfast. And on the New Zealand ships we had *cold* drinks in the warm weather. Mind you, I *like* bouillon. I wonder if you'd mind getting me a cup? You're younger than I am and a good Christian, I'm sure. I'm Seven Principles myself...'

'Get it yourself, you old gut-bag,' Tornetta snarled, and got up and walked away.

He decided to go into the Midships Bar and relax there with a cool drink.

This meant passing through the Aegean Lounge, going through the library and through an area full of fruit machines.

Already a few obsessives spent hours a day feeding five cent pieces into these one-armed bandits, but at the moment there was only a small boy at one end of the row of eight machines and a man in a lightweight grey suit at the other. Both had their backs to Tornetta.

The little boy ran out of five cent pieces and admitted frankly, 'I wish I had another one.'

The man in the grey suit said in a gentle admonition, 'You will always lose in the end. But here, try this machine.'

He gave the boy a coin and the lad, scarcely tall enough to reach the handle, nevertheless tugged it.

A few coins rattled and the boy cried, 'I've won! I've won! Here you are, mister, it's yours.'

'No, you keep it!'

'Gee! Thanks.'

The man turned, smiling, aware of a witness, and something altered in his eyes. The smile died, or was replaced, as he saw Tornetta.

He said, in Italian, 'That was nice, eh? A good-mannered boy? I came aboard at Fremantle,' he observed in a friendly manner which was nevertheless devastating. 'But I have been ill. Very sick. Now the weather and the sea are good and I walk about.'

Tornetta's hands sweated. He tried not to show the massive fear that at once occupied him, filled his bowels and fluttered his heart and caused confusion in his brain.

The man had not the appearance of recent illness or exhaustion. He was heavy and very much at ease.

They had found Tornetta and this was their emissary who would kill him.

12

THE *Areopagus'* propellers and propulsion shafts and the great weight of the massive double-reduction gears lost momentum and finally stopped. The forward anchor chain clattered and suddenly there was an absolute silence.

Tomazos fixed the position of the ship by use of the station pointer, a kind of protractor whereby if two horizontal angles between three fixed marks were known the ship's exact position could be ascertained.

It was just after dawn and the *Areopagus* was anchored in an estuary of the Indonesian island of Bali. The water glittered like polished metal and the sky was pale blue – it seemed lazy and warm, with tissues of milky cloud. Green volcanic cones sloped down to the misty water and already people were at work in terraced green and yellow ricefields. Fragile fishing boats lay on the shore by the villages which were within thick green bush. Half a dozen of these small craft were lying in the water at intervals of half a mile.

There was no sign of any quay, for it was round a bend in the river and two and a half miles distant.

Miss Wearne leaned on the rail, and was thrilled by this impressive landscape of forests and mountains, fishing boats, huts and buffalo seen in the distance, and by the hand waved in acknowledgement by a fisherman. In seconds she had seen at least thirty things of interest not mentioned in any geography book used in the school.

There was a tendency among elderly people to be slightly aggressive in anxiety, to be first in activities, to insist on being there, taking part, obtaining the best seat, a good table, a porthole. It was a form of apprehension : I'm still here, take notice of me, I am not deaf or incapacitated yet. Miss Wearne had been as guilty as the next in this, in terms of her illness, but today she was up and about because the sea was calm and she was excited by sheer pleasure. Her keenness was shared by most passengers, although they had groaned at Miss Wearne's table when a steward officer at dinner last night had said breakfast would be at six, but now Miss Wearne was hungry and ate with appetite.

It was surprising how much confusion could arise if the ship's routine was interrupted or altered. Breakfast was chaos, something approaching panic, a rather shameful exhibition of haste, greed and selfishness by passengers sitting at unfamiliar tables. (It was what was called 'an open sitting' and Miss Wearne learned to dread them.) And then those passengers going ashore were told to assemble in the Aegean Lounge and at every junction Miss Wearne found ship's crew or the cabaret entertainers directing her to it. A metal shutter now inexplicably blocked the way she normally returned from the dining-room to her cabin, and so she had to walk to the other end of Metaxas Deck to descend and fetch her camera.

Then, in the Aegean Lounge, there was some confusion as to whether she was going on Tour A, B or C; she didn't know; a lot of passengers didn't know, and she had to identify it was 'the three-dollar one.' She was thereupon issued with a triangular green sticker. 'Just like a lot of merino sheep,' a woman said to her. And certainly there seemed to be more chaos and pandemonium at this holiday island than at a major port.

Miss Wearne did not wish to burden herself on to Debbie Vertigan. The girl had been very kind. She had walked up and down the Parade Deck with Miss Wearne. She had fetched library books and bouillon. On any day when Miss Wearne felt like eating lunch on deck, Debbie had insisted on queueing for it while Miss Wearne sat in a deck chair. She had bought stamps to save Miss Wearne becoming exhausted waiting at the Purser's office and lemonade to spare Miss Wearne the unfamiliar terror of entering a bar. And scarcely one of these favours had been requested; nor did the girl know of her illness. Debbie was simply thoughtful and benignant. 'What a very charming girl your companion is,' a lady had observed to Miss Wearne only yesterday, and quite some minutes had passed before Miss Wearne realized in shock that the lady had presumed Debbie was a paid companion.

But in a crowd of four hundred Debbie now waved and called out, 'I've saved you a seat,' and Miss Wearne was glad of a little rest before venturing ashore.

She noticed with relief that Debbie also wore a green sticker. The girl in fact made no attempt to seek out anyone else and Miss Wearne, while not attaching herself to Debbie, couldn't resist staying near.

'Do you know how to load a camera?' she asked.

It was something that had been worrying her since the day she'd bought the camera. She knew absolutely nothing about lenses or focusing; she'd never owned a camera before in her life. But Debbie knew . . .

Edgar stood on the stage and called for silence.

'We're going to sing,' he announced.

Someone shouted, 'When do we go ashore?'

'There's a little old Indonesian custom which says Never go ashore until your stomach is empty.'

The passengers groaned.

There was much consultation, coming and going, and then Edgar told them all, 'The Indonesians are checking. Only another hour and a half. We set the clocks wrong,' he admitted.

Behind him a ship's clock was behaving oddly and had begun to accelerate. It went round until it showed five past six.

The passengers laughed until the Entertainments Officer said, 'It shouldn't happen to a dog, but it has. It's now six in the morning. You poor things got up at *four*!'

He sat down at a piano. Edgar and some of the cabaret company began to sing.

'What shall I play next?' he then asked.

Like the English, the Australians and New Zealanders in times of crisis dismissed all the current pop music and reverted to the old tunes belonging to war. They sang 'Lily of Laguna' and 'Pack up your troubles' as if another conflict had begun.

Forty minutes passed and then they were asked to assemble on the port side of Metaxas Deck, the ones with green stickers leaving the lounge first.

The passengers ignored this instruction and stampeded. Miss Wearne was crushed and alarmed.

Alongside the *Areopagus* were two small Indonesian gunboats, packed already with passengers and villainous, perplexed sailors.

Miss Wearne was pushed across to the first gunboat and sat precariously on the swivel seat of a 20mm canon. This gunboat filled up until it was so crowded that people were likely to fall overboard if they moved a foot.

It was hot.

Miss Wearne realized that it was more than just hot. It was like a furnace, and already the Australians, who lived in high average temperatures, wilted under this, and began to sweat as they'd never sweated before in their lives. The moisture poured down their faces, their ears and necks; it soaked their armpits and chests and saturated their hair. Clean shirts and frocks crumpled, showed great wet stains. It was all very embarrassing and uncomfortable, and this was before seven in the morning, local time...

Miss Wearne felt it a little less than others who were

fatter or had thicker blood. As the gunboat moved away from the *Areopagus* she took photographs of the liner and the volcanic mountains. Eileen would be impressed. They were a long way from the suburbia of Melbourne now.

The gunboat chugged round the bend of the estuary to a small harbour. Crowds awaited its passengers, for the town of Den Pâsar had been given the day off for this occasion. Miss Wearne heard strange tinny music and voices speaking through public address systems. She saw crowds of children and traders waiting, a line of small buses, and young men in military and para-military uniforms rushing to and fro, more excited than their visitors.

It was quite difficult for her to get ashore, down a series of planks, but ship's crew and Indonesians, knee deep in water, assisted her. She was conscious, as she stood in the tremendous heat among girls, children and old men who wanted to sell her baskets, batik cloth and ornaments, of how shapeless her fellow passengers were in comparison with the people here. As white as slugs and sweating and stumbling and already more concerned about heat. She saw Muriel, Ada, Iris and their husbands, with straw hats on, saturated around their shoulders and breasts in sweat, vulgar and red-faced, coarse and ungracious in their behaviour towards these people, and was for a moment ashamed of Australia.

There were twenty dancers to greet them – beautiful girls dressed in glittering gold leaf and with crowns of fresh frangipani flowers. They leaned and gyrated and used their hands and elbows in the ritual of the dance; and their expressionless, rather solemn pretty faces did not sweat. The passengers stood awkwardly, not knowing what to do, photographed them and walked on to the buses.

One of the officials striding round with a hand-carried megaphone was a small attractive Indonesian girl. She wore a dark green military uniform and hat, but did not seem bothered by the heat. She was ruthlessly efficient on behalf of the passengers.

They had travelled only a few miles from the harbour when the small bus broke down. The twenty passengers cheered doubtfully. Miss Wearne was now hot and had a great urge to take off her wig and scratch her head before immersing it in cold water. She felt sleepy and some of the desire to see temples and dancing had worn off.

This proved to be true of the other passengers, with the possible exception of Debbie. The efficient Indonesian guide produced another bus within five minutes and they continued the round of old temples, museums and an art gallery on the beach. But the priorities were altered. First priority was now given to obtaining a cold drink, preferably beer. Some way after that came greed for bargains, and last of all the desire to see mountains and buildings and photograph them.

As fast as the passengers poured liquid into their mouths it burst out of their pores. They saw with interest wood carvings, sacred monkeys, buffalo and temples; they haggled with street traders who were surprisingly inoffensive and not particularly insistent. They closed their eyes as the bus was driven in a manner reckless even by Australian standards.

They sat in the full glare of the late morning sun – the passengers in earlier buses had taken all the covered area – and watched a dance that apparently went on for hours. The Legong dance was performed by individual girls, dressed in dazzling gold and vivid colours, accompanied by a complete gamelan orchestra playing at once vigorously and then suddenly languorous. The girls were totally absorbed in the dance, the slow but complicated movements of hands, fingers and ankles, the turn of the head and sway of the body, all of which had meaning in terms of giants and marital fidelity and the eternal struggle between good and evil. The musicians, however, stared with frank interest at the tourists and some grinned.

It was impossible to break away; it would have been offensive, so the twenty of them watched with decreasing artistic enthusiasm and increasing thirst and discomfort. Their visible discomposure and sweating was scarcely alleviated by the flapping of newspapers and fans.

After forty minutes they began to trickle ignominiously away and stood in a cemetery in the shade of trees, not able to care whether they'd been churlish or not, or if they had been offensive towards a ceremonial *divertissement* rehearsed for many hours – as it obviously would have to be – on their behalf. Australians were the world's worst adherents of the theory of tipping, but now they looked guiltily for someone to tip. Surprisingly, there was no one.

The young Indonesian woman announced, 'We will go to the famous hotel' – there were sighs of relief – 'but *first* we will visit the art gallery and shop.'

The gallery was cool and the carvings and pictures excellent. The passengers haggled and enjoyed themselves.

Miss Wearne wandered round the large air-conditioned hotel until she found a bathroom. She then took off her wig and scratched her head shamelessly and bathed it in cold water and felt cooler.

She sat under an immense tree and was brought a bottle of cold orange liquid from the freezer.

'Locally bottled,' the waiter informed her.

She didn't know what it was, but couldn't bear not to drink it instantly. It had a strange taste, rather bitter, but was cold and satisfying. Further, it took away tiredness. Miss Wearne had a second bottle of this remarkable fluid, which in fact was beer . . .

They returned to the *Areopagus* in a small motor boat so crowded that it was necessary for everyone to stand still and cling to the rail. The water was choppy and some people felt rather ill. The smell of engine oil and smoke discomforted others.

Miss Wearne stood facing Ada, Muriel, Iris, Harry and the other two men. They had been on a different tour and were grumbling. Ada looked very pale and had a headache.

If they were to be believed, they had been swindled. They discussed earnestly the exact amounts spent. They all had faces glistening with sweat and clothes dark with the fluid of themselves.

'Aren't you enjoying yourselves?' Miss Wearne asked loudly.

They were devastated. Nothing could have been so humiliating as to have been seen not enjoying themselves.

'Oh, sure,' Iris said, modifying their mortification. 'You've got to be smart, though, to outwit these beggars. Ada got clipped ten dollars for this wooden pig and it's split.'

Miss Wearne claimed recklessly, 'You didn't do very well. I got this camera for fifteen dollars.'

She had in fact paid forty dollars for it in Melbourne.

'Is that *all*?' asked Iris in shock, ruining Harry's observation that 'Hong Kong's the place for cameras.'

Miss Wearne had the satisfaction of hearing one of them whisper, 'She's not as daft as she looks' and another hiss in envy, 'Fifteen dollars! I wonder where?'

The boat went round the stern of the *Areopagus*. 'Oh, look at that,' said Debbie.

There was haggling going on at the stern of the *Areopagus*, and the crew were paying in kind, throwing out food for the men and women on the frail catamarans. Tins of jam, chickens, jars of pickle. Miss Wearne saw a fisherman stare at a triangular piece of cheese wrapped in tinfoil and then take a bite at it with the metal foil still on . . .

The boat bobbed up and down by the *Areopagus*' gangway and some of the passengers were nervous about leaping across the gap despite the two sailors standing ready to catch them, who shouted 'Jump!'

Iris jumped and fell on the gangway screeching. Her mouth was seen to be bleeding when she stood up.

Miss Wearne was contemptuous. Debbie asked anxiously 'What are you going to do?'

'Jump, of course,' answered Miss Wearne, and when she did she was saved from toppling backwards by the two sailors.

She would normally have been terrified and had to be lifted bodily. But today, for the first time in her life, Miss Wearne was unashamedly tight.

13

MARION BURSTON relaxed full length in a deck chair not long after eight-thirty in the morning. She knew that if she did not occupy a chair very soon after breakfast the people who went to the second breakfast sitting would fill every chair until noon.

It still felt very slightly wrong to be lazy straight after breakfast, and to let the kids run about. She ought to be washing or ironing. But this consciousness of duties to attend to was not now so strong as it had been. Laziness, even dopiness, had overtaken her, and a 'holiday' forgetfulness. 'I'm always half asleep and tired,' she'd complained to a passenger yesterday, and he'd assured her 'Your cruise is doing you good then.' And it was true that Marion forgot problems and family miseries for whole hours, or as much as half a day. She had even laughed outright yesterday.

A woman sat down in the next deckchair. She was armed with a library book, knitting, stationery, and a large handbag, but Marion was aware that she wanted to talk.

The woman was older than Marion, and carried herself with a slight attitude of gravity, of personage: she would not, her posture suggested, tell you who she was because on this voyage she wanted to meet all sorts of people not normally encountered.

She had silver-grey hair and a face that suggested kindness and sympathy, and she wore tortoise-shell glasses. She was well but not ostentatiously dressed; it was only if one looked at anything she wore or carried rather closely that wealth and good taste were automatically suggested.

'It's so hot,' she commented. 'Even this early in the day I'm glad to put my feet up.'

Marion responded, 'So am I' and felt self-consciously that she had been clumsy.

'You're English, aren't you?' the woman said. 'I can tell.

Those lovely children. So polite, I've noticed. Artistic. You've got artistic children, I feel sure. Different faces from the Australians. The English have integrity,' she affirmed, probably out of date by thirty years, but using the word deliberately. 'I find my fellow Australians so vulgar. I was so embarrassed in Bali yesterday, so coarse and ungracious, they were, and talking to the – coloured – people as if they'd been to Australia...'

'I thought the dancers were beautiful,' said Marion, not to be drawn into discussion about the Australians. 'It was such an unspoilt place. And people were saying to my husband that it ought to be developed. Leave it alone, I say.'

'Oh, I couldn't agree more,' the older woman said. 'It reminded me a little of India. I was there for ten years before Tom, my husband, died. We women used to go into the hills for the hot weather. Poor Tom had to stay down there, so hot and tiresome, and he looked so ill each time he came... I remember we went by horse to see Kanchenjunga at sunrise. Very dangerous tracks and old emaciated horses. We stood there, about eight of us, and there was nothing but cloud. And suddenly it all lifted and there was Everest, so fantastically beautiful, my dear, that one wanted to die. There was in fact a plaque with the names of people who'd thrown themselves over the cliff edge, overcome by such a spectacle. Unspoilt, undeveloped, as you so rightly say... My companion in the cabin felt Bali ought to have *facilities*, whatever they may be...'

The old lady laughed, chiding herself gently, and proceeded: 'It's really so amusing. I suppose I shouldn't gossip. I don't really know her, you see – I've no idea where she comes from – but as we'd been introduced some months ago I took enormous trouble to get into the same cabin and sit at the same table. And it's very disappointing because she's so rude to the staff and so complaintive; and I can't see how to get away from her at all... But it's fun, isn't it? And nice to get away. You must be glad to have the children with you – so educational for them. To be honest, I've come away because I think my children – who are grown up, of course –

take me for granted. It will make me appreciated when I get back . . . Besides, why should they have *all* my money?'

There was a brief silence and then the lady concluded, 'I've had such lovely letters since I left so it shows I may be right, don't you feel? But I'm talking too much. Do tell me about yourself. Where are you going? Back to England, I fear. Well, I don't blame you. Such a nice *green* country . . .'

And suddenly, shakily, Marion began to unburden and confess, to share misery with this warm-hearted stranger.

'We're going home. It's not that we don't like Australia, although I suppose the edge of the Nullarbor Desert isn't exactly Kew Gardens! Only . . . you see . . . Mike . . . nearly killed someone. And it's got on our nerves.'

'You poor girl, of course it has. Sensitive people suffer most. In a motor accident, I suppose?'

Marion said quickly – it wasn't so difficult after all – 'Sort of . . . A child was injured.'

She waited, looked into the older eyes in the kind, leathery unknowing face, waited for the condemnation and the form it would take : the deterioration of the posture of admiration into shock, the change of expression and the polite excuses to get away – 'I think the library must be open now' – 'There's my friend looking for me; do excuse me' – 'The shop's open now' – 'My cabin' – 'Coffee.'

But the lady was undisturbed, lost none of her charm and sympathy.

'My dear, how terrible for you.'

'It was getting on his nerves so we had to do something. We decided on a cruise home.'

Tears trickled down Marion's face. She felt a fool, but relieved, unburdened, the other was so understanding. But she couldn't dare to tell the rest, the worst of it.

'They really are very bad drivers,' the lady observed. She sighed. 'Do you know, my son-in-law has had three minor accidents in two months.'

Marion realized in enormous shock that what she had told the other woman had had no impact. The woman wasn't likely to be shocked because she had no feelings at all. Her sympathy and charm were related entirely to the time of day and inquisitiveness and what *she* wanted. This was just a little chat with someone before the eleven o'clock bouillon, lunch, a game of cards, the ship's daily tote. Getting to meet people.

'Mike was drunk,' she said with contempt.

There was a woman whom Marion grew to dislike. She was about thirty and not unattractive. As the days increased to tropical heat this woman was seen more frequently. She strode the Parade Deck in a mauve two-piece swim suit which seemed phosphorescent and herself coruscated a sour quick wit. She came from the Northern Territories and Marion never learned her name, always referring to her as 'that woman from Darwin'.

When she strutted the Parade Deck the woman oscillated her buttocks in a manner pleasing to the old men who watched for this kind of display, but the swagger was not an indication of sexiness. It wasn't quite ostentation either, but rather a manifestation of self-assurance. For the young woman had after watching and experiencing these last few days found that it was possible for her to achieve a kind of prominence, become a passenger of significance. Many of the others, she could see, were small beer, or were wowsers, or shy, or not to be involved. But she came into an environment where she could in effect make an impact and throw her weight about. It hadn't quite gone to her head, but simply given opportunity for her to enjoy herself in an extrovert manner. Thus if there was a noise to be made, she would help to make it. If there was fun, she wanted to be there. If in the evening cabaret Edgar shouted 'Are we all happy?' she shouted 'Yes'. If anyone was asked to make a fool of themselves she was a volunteer.

Her husband was reputed to be a buffalo hunter, vulgarly rich. He was a small man with a sun-scorched skin who remained rather quiet.

They had three children and the woman from Darwin neglected them in favour of her own pleasures. She was not secretive about it, but just left them on deck or by a pool while she entered some deck competition, played bingo or had a try in a beauty competition. This was what attracted Marion's attention and caused the dislike. But whole days went by and the two never spoke, although they looked at each other in analysis, conscious of something antagonistic, a dozen times a day. There was no reason to suppose they would clash openly in a crowd of nearly six hundred, except that they both had cabins on A Deck.

They first bandied words in the ironing room of that deck. The *Areopagus* had no washing machines for passengers, although there was a ship's laundry. But this was expensive and in many cases the stewards starched everything as stiff as cardboard. So Marion did a bit of washing in the cabin now and again and ironed in the ironing room fifty feet forward.

The woman from Darwin was in another two-piece swim suit. This one was navy blue, but seemed iridescent as she moved her buttocks about. She was barefoot. Marion, perhaps illogically, found it vulgar that the woman should be ironing so attired. The woman's flesh was burning under the sun and Marion fancied she could smell flesh and sweat.

Marion said nothing, but the woman acknowledged 'Hi'. Marion began her ironing and did it in a silence which was condemnatory: those small kids left on decks or seen wandering around, dirty, sticky mouthed, wretched and tearful, pale from insufficient sleep . . .

After a while the iron Marion was using blew with a bang and blue sparks.

'Aren't you gonna fix it?' the woman from Darwin asked.

'I don't know how,' Marion admitted, startled, and could have bitten her tongue off for giving an advantage to this brash younger woman, who promptly took it.

'You Poms are all the same,' she suggested, not quite maliciously but flatly, stating what was for her a truth. 'Or are you scared of getting an electrical shock?'

This was offensive enough, and Marion countered, red in the face, 'It should be fixed properly, not Australian style.'

The young woman had an acid tongue, but before she could use it the iron she was using also blew in the same manner.

'Never a dull moment,' she commented cheerfully.

'I'll leave you to it,' Marion said coldly.

The woman flashed back : 'I'll bet you couldn't even fix a puncture.'

'I don't need to,' Marion said. 'My husband never buys cheap second-hand cars.'

'You stuck-up bastard!' the younger woman shouted loudly. 'My husband makes twenty thousand dollars a year. He has seventy men under him—'

But Marion had gone, and although she heard this, the woman from the Northern Territories couldn't be sure that she had, so the skirmishing was Marion's victory. But Marion knew that she had been lucky, for the most noticeable characteristic of the swaggering young woman was that she was tough.

She told Mike about it.

'Oh, that tart,' he said sympathetically. 'I've seen her parading her arse around. I'd thought about putting my boot to it.'

The woman's husband was a small wiry man with blond hair which accentuated his scorched pink skin. It was difficult to imagine him confronting a buffalo.

Mike saw him on deck the next morning. He was strolling very slowly, at Bumble's pace, passing time, and he saw the hunter participating in a quoits competition. Some old men who knew the man called to him facetiously now and again. At times the man from Darwin slapped his arms round his chest like someone in a snowstorm. The gesture irritated Mike, for it was intended to show these old men that the man was used to higher temperatures than this. Why doesn't he put on a pullover, Mike thought sourly, if he's so cold? Mike had been to Alice Springs and Darwin and certainly they'd been hot, but scarcely hotter than this day and assuredly not so humid. Like his wife the man was a show-off, although he had a curious technique of being one without dialogue. He rarely spoke and not at all if it was possible to convey the same meaning with a gesture.

Mike walked slowly by, almost shuffling, Bumble's pace

was so slow. It took five minutes to get to the other end of the Parade Deck.

Here two sailors and an officer were considering the immovability of a davit and lifeboat despite their work with oxy-acetylene welders and hammers.

They continued at it until there was slight movement from the davit.

'Not very encouraging for *us*!' remarked an old man to Mike. 'Have you noticed the bottom of that lifeboat?'

Mike had not. He looked at it and saw that white paint covered some kind of repair.

'The bottom's rotted away and they've replaced it,' the old man suggested, and this seemed to be so.

Mike said, 'It won't make any difference since they can't launch it anyway!'

A child was coming along the deck, bedraggled and weeping. It was one of the three kids of the couple from Darwin. There was no sign of the mother.

The three sailors had finished their work here and looped a bit of rope round the oxygen cylinder and dragged it towards steps ascending to the Sun Deck.

A few people moved apprehensively in wider circles to be out of the way, and they were wise to do so. For halfway up to the Sun Deck the cylinder escaped from its loop and clattered down to the Parade Deck.

Mike's reactions were slow, or so he thought. He picked Bumble up and moved a few feet hastily.

The cylinder hit the deck and rolled about wildly. It went round in a crazy circle and Mike saw that it was going to hit the weeping child.

He ran to her, lifted her up bodily (she howled in protest), and jumped in the air as the cylinder rolled up to him. He cleared it and then landed clumsily so that both little girls were planted hurriedly on the deck.

The cylinder rolled on down the Parade Deck towards the game with the Greek sailors chasing it. The little girl followed it, and ran to her father, who ignored her, concentrating on his game.

The old men laughed as the sailors caught the cylinder and took it away. Mike turned and strolled on with Bumble. 'Want a lemonade?' he asked.

Mike went down in the lift to get changed for the Captain's Carnival Party. There were thunderstorms on two horizons and the humidity was stifling. The lift was packed with at least three persons more than it was intended to carry and was a sweatshop in itself. The boy who operated it presumably had to breathe this stale wet air all day.

There was silence in the lift except for the information given to the boy as to which deck each passenger wished to descend to, and most of them stared with condemnation at a rather tall Greek man of about thirty.

He was a member of the ship's orchestra, in fact he was the man who played the piano and whom Mike had seen once being pawed by the red-haired girl, Diane. He was obviously cheap and vain, and had the seedy facial texture of one who stays too long in a stale atmosphere and does not get enough sleep, and possibly one who has too much sexual intercourse.

He stood in the very small lift, a couple of square yards packed with eight people, and examined himself in the long cracked mirror which surfaced one side of the lift. Then he produced a comb and ran it frequently through his black shiny hair, either oblivious of or indifferent to the silent disapproval of others.

When he shoved his way through the other passengers someone said, 'Pretty, isn't he?'

In the cabin Marion and Stella were struggling into dresses and stockings and high-heel shoes. Marion had worn this dress several times already and Mike knew it was a minor humiliation before women who were changing dresses all the time. He said so. Marion disputed 'It doesn't matter,' but he felt he had failed her again. It was an irony of their family destiny that though they'd come to Australia among other reasons to make money, and that, having to some extent made it, they'd had to sell house, car, fridge and what money had bought, for a loss, and to pay two thousand dollars for this journey . . . They returned to England as they had come, with little money.

In the Aegean Lounge they stood awkwardly, not experienced in cocktail parties, while Stella and Diane drifted away to talk to the comedians of the cabaret.

Mike, uncomfortable in a dark suit on this tropical thundery evening, stood talking to the radio officer of the *Areopagus*. This officer was a Turk, about fifty, who seemed neglected. He was a considerate man and willing to converse with Mike, but it was hard going. A small fat woman, who wore big glasses so that she looked like an owl, also stood there, a reject, of no interest to anyone.

This woman brought the conversation round to the subject of pain, for she had a headache. She refused a drink and Mike wondered why she'd come to a cocktail party at all. He sipped from a small glass himself, but had no idea what it was he swallowed. Whatever it was, it had no effect, took away no sorrow, promoted no joy.

'It was tea,' the woman explained earnestly, as they swayed very slightly at the knees and on the balls of the feet. 'Tea makes me ill at once. And chocolate. That gives me an instant headache. But all I have to do is find a barley sugar or castor sugar.'

'That is very strange,' said the radio officer. 'For I have spoken to many passengers who have what you call migraine, and this they all say, that chocolate is the beginning.'

Marion came up to Mike from somewhere and whispered fiercely, 'You might have kept an eye on those two. Stella's drinking. She's had a beer.'

'It's hot, kid. A beer won't hurt her.'

'Mike, she isn't even sixteen yet.'

'She's a big girl. Kids are big these days.'

'Is that all you've got to say?'

'What else is there to say? She couldn't stand around here and have *nothing*.'

'You don't care.'

'Please, Marion, don't make such a thing of it.'

'You spoil her.'

'I don't.'

'You take her side; she knows she can insult me and get away with it. She just told me to get burned.'

'That doesn't mean anything.'

'Oh, really, Mike.'

Marion moved away and Mike felt wretched and frustrated.

The radio officer was saying, 'Pains in the back. All the time. I love Australia. You know why? Because my ship called in the port of Tasmania, what you call it? Hobart. And there I took this, what you call apple vinegar—'

'Cider,' prompted the woman.

'Cider, ah, yes. I take it every day. Two years. No pain. Funny.'

'Excuse me,' said Mike.

He went over to where Stella and Diane stood rocking with amusement at one of the comedians.

'It's just like playing to a morgue!' this young man said, and brayed with laughter himself.

Mike said, 'Take it easy, kid. What's that you're swilling down?'

'Oh, Dad, don't be a wowser. Mum came round with a face like a thunderstorm. She's gonna murder me!'

'Let me drink it,' suggested Mike.

The comedian was saying, 'The first lot are such a ghastly audience we regard them as a rehearsal for the second,' and Mike was conscious that Diane was viewing him surreptitiously, with interest, a woman's interest. It was a little disconcerting, or had he a mind too ready to jump to that kind of conclusion? The beer mixed with whatever it was he'd had before and Mike glowed a little. He looked frankly at Diane and with a truck-driver's experience of people identified her as a hot little slut. It alarmed him.

He cautioned, 'No more boozing, Stella. Stick to heavy water' and got a laugh from the two girls. He heard Diane say 'He's all right' as he moved away.

Demetropoulos, the Chief Purser, was holding the attention of a few people. Mike circulated and joined them, the drink giving him confidence. Someone asked Demetropoulos

'Don't you get fed up with this sort of thing?' and Demetropoulos, the vague smile still there, and his eyes examining that something above their heads which never ceased to amuse him, said woodenly, 'No. I enjoy it, and it is my job.'

A small frail woman, old but with humour in her creased face, touched Mike's arm.

'Aren't you Stella's father?'

'That's right.'

'She's a nice girl, you know.'

'I'm glad you think so.'

'She listens to Dr de Haan on the radio. He's interesting, de Haan, except that he feels there's hope. This is not so, although prayer shouldn't be abandoned. I'm not saying that. But *we* feel – indeed, we *know*, for isn't it obvious from the signs? – that the end is not far away.'

'The end of what?' Mike asked with humour.

'Everything, of course. We deserve it. We were warned. The Scriptures give warning in chapter and verse – divorce, adultery, wars, decadence, men attired as women as they were during Rome's decadence, it's all there . . .'

'So you came on a cruise?' Mike suggested frivolously.

'Not to escape the end.'

'And what about the Africans and Asians?' Mike asked. He was slightly drunk, no longer a pariah who accepted the status.

'Ignorance is an excuse,' agreed the old woman promptly. 'And there's always mercy. I'm not saying God despises us, although that would be understandable . . . I came because the doctor said a complete change. My son and a grandchild were killed just before this trip. In Canada. I hadn't seen them for three years. He was doing well. A lovely boy. I went to pieces so I had to get away. You won't laugh at me, will you, Mr Burston, for being upset when I know it's all going to end soon anyway?'

'No,' said Mike. 'I won't laugh.'

– and his mind's-eye was behind the wheel, hour after hour. There were corrugations in the road, absolutely unavoidable, whatever the throttle adjustment. Kangaroos leaped from one side of the road and loped off back into the bush.

Dead animals on the roadside had appalled him at first. Cattle, sheep, kangaroos, wallabies, even horses and, strangely, a litter of magpies. Some had been hit by vehicles, others by drought. Mike recalled the large circle of the bones of many cattle bleached white. And buzzards circulating over an animal which had stood in a dry stream, motionless in confusion, his ribs sticking out like scaffolding and his skin draped loosely.

And, all over the outback, the carcasses of old cars disintegrating, some burnt out, some upside down, having gone off the road, some on their sides; all had been stripped long since of useful spares. Three times he had come upon saloons burning, apparently spontaneously just because of sheer heat. And in one the driver had been trapped and screaming. It didn't upset him too much except the smell of flesh burning.

Duststorms in the Northern Territories, followed, to his astonishment, by rain. Huge clouds of red dust enveloping the vast loneliness, whipped by wind and then mixed with rain. Driving with a broken windscreen – this along a stretch known as 'crystal highway' because of the broken glass which covered it – and rain flying into his face, turning to hail so that he couldn't see at all and just groped ahead. Soaked to the skin for once. And rain turned the bulldust into red mud. Deep slippery ruts and even his big lorry slithering from chuck-hole to chuck-hole. Skids. Once it could have killed him when his semi-trailer jack-knifed, but he'd been lucky. Mud as tough as cement had collected on the lorry that trip so that he'd had to stop every few miles for two hundred miles and scrape it off. He'd been saturated and filthy and exhausted by the time he'd reached the next town, where he learned that if the mud wasn't cleaned off at once it'd harden and never come off. Two Italian truckies had materialized and helped him. How nice next day to see the burning sun and Queensland's fields of sugar cane, tobacco, bananas and bottle trees!

Across the Nullarbor the endless dusty road of 1,700 miles from Adelaide to Perth, and temperatures of 114°. Shattered windscreens and frequent punctures, especially among saloons. Stop to help the baked traveller with two punctures, a shattered screen and an engine boiling its guts out.

Dusty salt bush stretching to every horizon, parched and desolate sheep stations, the occasional half-dozen trees twisted and bent down to the ground before the winds which howled off the Bight.

Old towns buried under creeping sand-dunes. A solitary road-house still there, with pictures and newspapers of yester-year fading on its walls like an abandoned museum.

Rough road-houses and clapboard 'hotels'. Iron bedsteads and paper-thin walls, powdered milk and lukewarm showers, if any. No screens to the windows (sometimes no windows). Matches used to light up the pitch-black washroom, so even this attracted all the winged insects of the area. Floors of hard earth covered with linoleum and doors without locks or handles. Flies hovering round the mouth and eyes and tickling the back.

Classless Australia. He'd left England with this in mind, and here at every road-house he met men who drove the huge Macks with double-bogeys fore-and-aft, loaded with sheep or cattle; massive Peterbilts with refrigerated trailers full of beef, pork and fowl; Leyland, Mercedes, Foden, Reo, Dodge, Commer . . . Italians, Germans, Dutch, English, Australians . . . All driving vehicles covered with different dusts that bespoke thousands of miles. All talk was shop, but it was a very long time before Mike had realized that many of these tough men were so strained that they took drugs . . .

He'd done the lot, from the Eyre Highway to the Stuart Highway – known simply as The Bitumen, a forty-foot-wide ribbon of pinky tan tar stretching the 954 miles from Alice Springs to Darwin through a wilderness. Straight stretches of thirty and forty miles. It was easy to average 60 mph.

He preferred the roads across the outback. In the Eastern States there were some good highways and he had often done 80 mph, so that saloons had found it impossible to overtake. He never told Marion. There were plenty of fools, especially near cities. He'd seen quite a few smashes.

Like the youths in two cars playing hide-and-seek in the

Victorian countryside, the sports car being sought doing seventy without lights. A car with headlights had shot across the main road in front of Mike's semi-trailer, followed by a bump. He'd driven a few miles with a scraping noise, remote but worrying, so that he'd stopped to see what had come loose. And embedded in the semi-trailer was a sports car with three youths inside. All dead. All decapitated. He had vomited, but it hadn't really shaken him because he was not in error. If they drove across a main highway without lights . . .

And the small sedan with driver and passenger, sandwiched between himself and another lorry a hundred feet ahead. Everyone doing seventy. The sedan pulled out anxiously, its driver saw a lorry racing towards him, waited until it had passed and then pulled out at 75 mph – and went straight into the saloon hidden by the bulk of the lorry and right behind it. The passenger was hurled straight through the windscreen a hundred and fifty feet. The drivers of both cars were very dead, but it was the passenger's face, sliced to ribbons, which had made Mike sick. The other truck driver had shrugged. 'Dumb bastards' was his comment.

No one had ever been hurt by Mike, and he'd never been in any collisions. There were times when he'd been stupid with exhaustion and it could have happened, but he'd overcome that with the occasional pill. Quite safe. Harmless. Once a fortnight maybe . . .

A few beers with two men, laughs, talk about horses, safe, a thousand yards from home, not drunk, it couldn't happen, he knew he was warm with the booze, but this was no highway. A thousand yards of rough road – a track they'd call it in England – admittedly without street lights. If there were three thousand men in the outback town for the two days' horse racing then now, now, at 10.30 at night, two thousand of them were drunk or drinking.

It had to be him, the careful one, the serious one, not the youths who drove with elbows out of the window and bottles to their lips and girls leaned across the left arm or kissing their necks. It had to be him, not drunken farmers in vehicles so old they shouldn't be out on the road, even *this* road; Mike

Burston, who had driven hundreds of thousands of miles. Nothing on his mind except to go home and get into bed. No distractions, no girl to heat his mind and body, no quarrel or problem to take away concentration.

A thousand yards to drive in his own estate car, slowly, nothing on the road. Two corners, eighteen houses.

The child ran out straight in front of him. Half past ten at night and a child of four runs straight into your headlights. Right foot stamped on brake, but the kid's already done it herself, and God only knows what damage the skidding vehicle has added.

He didn't know what speed he'd been doing, but it was slow, thirty probably, because to speed you had to consciously do it, nerves and muscles tightened.

But the condition of his body? Yes, two or three cans of beer inside it on a sweltering hot night.

Get out, go and see.

He knew that one half of his life was over. He'd reached the end of something and the beginning of something else.

She appeared intact. Her face was unmarked except, so far as he could see in the available light, puzzled, confused, wondering what had thrown her so violently.

And then she began to scream.

It had torn the flesh off him. He'd started to shake and sweat and pray and gabble : 'No. Stop. Listen, kid. It'll be all right. I'll go and fetch. *Please* stop—'

He'd run aimlessly in horror and solicitude. If physical effort, pain, speed, anything on his part, could make a difference—

The first bungalow. Five startled people, never seen before. Crinkly hair, creased sweating faces, shirt-sleeves, vulgar crockery, bottles of beer, no cloth on the table, two kids on the floor, should be in bed, Christ, what if it's *theirs*?

'Have you got a phone?'

'What's up, mate?'

Words, delays, the suction of words and explanations to draw them into it. Rough practical words when they understood : 'Doc Harvey's at the club' – 'How did it happen?' – 'Must be Beryl's kid; they oughta fetch her in, Chrise, mate, this is gonna knock them outa business.' And the long sweating moments, ludicrous dialogue on the phone, fools at the other end, and voices in the club making it difficult for whoever-it-was to talk anyway—

'Doc Harvey? Who wants him?'

'There's been an accident—'

They'd all gone to stand there and wait, and the kid had gone on screaming.

'Shall I fetch Beryl?'

'Chrise, no, she couldn't take this. Wait till Doc's given her a jab or something.'

Screams turned to sobs and groans.

Doc Harvey, not pleased. 'Why the hell didn't you get the ambulance? Her back's broken.'

Discussion and decisions, rough and ready, outback style; and the kid had been put into Mike's estate car and he'd driven to the hospital, drained of strength.

'How did it happen?'

The doc was the second of many to ask that.

Explanations to a girl at the hospital, agitation, people coming and going.

I'd give anything, anything in the world – my health, money, house, car, my sight and hearing if only—

They took the kid away, but the screaming would go on for ever—

A policeman, shirt-sleeved, hot but calm. Begin again. Explanations, from and for his perspective. 'Yeah, yeah, I see. I'll take a look at the car in daylight. Can you leave it here?'

I'm so tired I just want to die.

The parents, hers, agitated as he'd never seen faces before.

I'd give anything in the world, only let me go now—

They did, and he stumbled home to Marion. She was frightened, didn't understand his utter exhaustion. It had to be analysed, discussed. He just wanted to sit still and stare. And the tiny fissures of dislike had widened into open cracks and burst into visible wounds. It all came boiling out, another agony, theirs.

'Why you? Why did it have to be you? Why not one of

those dim, coarse, stupid, dull people out there? We can't stay here, Mike. I hate them. And they'll hate *you*...'

'What do you mean?' he'd asked.

He was numbed, incapable of feeling anything outside the area of screams, the panic and horror, the beginnings of appalling shame and recriminations. What else mattered?

'What'll they do?' she wailed.

'Who?' he'd asked, drunk with tiredness and confusion.

'If she dies you could go to prison.'

Even this hadn't penetrated.

'Mike, were you drunk?'

'I don't think so.'

'What did you *say*?'

'Nothing special.'

'God, Mike, wake up. It's serious.'

'I'm tired,' he said.

'I hope she's all right. My God, I hope it's not serious.'

There was no sleep. They just lay on a bed, sweating, tossing and turning; every quarter of an hour Marion thought of some other aspect, some way *they* could destroy him. Mike didn't understand the need to prepare any defence. He had destroyed himself.

In the morning people came; it had to be talked about. No one could really prove anything because only Mike had been there; he'd been the only witness, so to speak. It was too late now to determine if he'd been drunk. Only his conscience could prosecute him on that account. The marks on the vehicle told little. In the end it boiled down to words, talking about it.

The rest was up to his conscience and nerves.

Twelve hours later he'd stumbled again into his own bungalow. A neighbour was in there with Marion, who was pale and strained.

He was far too broken to hide it or indulge in care. Only Marion was capable of pride or the slightest discretion.

Even she couldn't bear to let him just stand there with some new and greater burden. She was aware that he'd been to the police station.

'What did they say?' she asked.

'Her back's broken.'

The neighbour inhaled with pity. 'Oh, poor kid. Did she die?'

'No,' Mike told her. 'She'll live, I suppose.'

They looked at him and Marion knew that wasn't the end of it.

He said, 'She's become a paraplegic' and Marion had begun to sob.

I'd give anything at all, everything I have—

The old lady said, the long procession of days later, 'I think I ought to tell you, because she's a nice girl, Stella. She's going about with Diane. It worries me. Diane's in my cabin. She's a very coarse girl, who swears and blasphemes and reads dirty magazines. Youths keep coming to fetch her.'

'I'll talk to her,' promised Mike, but was weary beyond measure. Who was he to talk to anyone?

Stella sat on Ken Beltz's knees in the dim light of the Labyrinth Club. She was a big girl and he shuffled about a bit to adjust her weight and move her into a position suitable for exploitation. On two beers this sheila had lost some inner rigidity. He estimated that on three she'd be crawling over him and on four shrieking for what he had to offer big girls.

They had been dancing, but it was too hot. She couldn't keep it up.

The beers hadn't cooled her and she was aware of the anaesthetic effect, the subjugation of her self-consciousness. She talked rapidly and with unaccustomed impertinence with a mouth slightly numbed. Sweat filmed her thighs and stomach and trickled between her breasts, saturating her light dress. It wasn't embarrassing, for no one could escape the heat, and Ken's shirt was wet and his armpits had the animal smell of hairs.

She shifted about a little too, so that she could lean over his face and get at his mouth. He recommended the necking. It was too hot for it, but Stella didn't wish to stop. It was a situation she wished to exploit, too. It was what she had hoped for – love of some kind, pleasure of a sort, excitement in a tropical evening. It gave tactile delectation to her hands to trace the fingertips across his face and have him bite them. Her situation was corny and the posture clumsy, but it satisfied. He was a quiet passive boy, it seemed. He didn't throw compliments about, but his response to Diane's 'Hey, do you want to meet Stella?' had been crudely eloquent those two days ago. A frank examination from head to toes and an outright 'This voyage at last becomes interesting.'

A feeling she reciprocated, although not aloud. Because he was touched with timidity despite the apparent self-assurance. Left with her, he had almost nothing to say. They got going very slowly on the superfluous inquiries: 'Where are you from?' – 'Where are you going?' – 'Who are you with?' This made Stella less constrained. The other youths scared her. They were too noisy and got too drunk and were then openly vulgar, monopolizing the pool and the ballroom, and if they were attracted to a girl their demonstration of it was too assumptive for Stella. She was grateful to Diane for the introduction to Ken. Diane was talking to some of the loud-mouths now, and she was twice as fast mentally . . .

'Come for a walk?' Ken suggested.

She was hurting his genitals as well as arousing them with the unintentional friction of movement.

'Round the park?' she countered idly.

'It's too hot in here. We could,' he whispered, 'get a bit of privacy out there.'

'You're about as subtle as the American Marines—'

'Anything they can do I can do better. We could go in the pool,' he suggested.

'They've emptied it.'

'So what?'

'You need water to swim in.'

'Who said anything about swimming? Come on, anyway,' he insisted.

He was through with the preliminaries. Two hours was more than enough. She presumed there was to be an increase in the tempo of the necking. Her heart boomed with excitement, but her legs were jelly scared. It was the first time the boy, any boy on this ship, had attempted to isolate her. The implication was warming: that she was what he wanted more than anybody else on the *Areopagus*. She walked with slightly drunken pride because of it. Previously they'd been invariably part of a crowd – and she had been glad of it.

Ken was a tall, thin youth with curly blond hair. His half-humorous face revealed nothing. Another girl might have considered it a vacuous face, and a third decided it was cunning and with possibilities of vulgarity and bounce. He didn't look like a boy who sat around reading Spinoza.

'We'll take a couple of cans,' he affirmed. The two tins of beer suggested to her that he was a little in awe of her, scared, and needed the help of alcohol.

There were quite a number of people – old and middle-aged – walking about with pillows and blankets.

'An orgy,' suggested Ken, and sniggered – an acoustic smirk which sounded alarm bells in Stella's mind.

The Promenade Deck was quite crowded with these people. They had come on deck to sleep because it was too hot to do so in their cabins. 'Hell,' complained Ken. 'The place is as crowded as the Domain.'

They strolled about and at the stern found a party in progress. There had already been a lot of drinking and the sheer volume of singing and coarse shouting frightened Stella. She didn't want a noisy party. She wanted romance, hands touching and the moon reflected in an ocean like ink. Here twenty people were making a noise like a riot. She saw that some kids were in deck chairs, necking, ignoring these others. Their postures suggested that it was the kind of necking Dr de Haan viewed with anxiety – kids in swim suits with arms and legs locked, shrieks, giggles, murmurs of enjoyment, total indifference to witnesses.

Others were dancing to a record player. These, too, were sufficiently frenzied for Stella to freeze in inhibition, even dislike.

There were stewards rushing in and out with trays of beer. Glass shattered, a youth laughed and a girl shouted 'You stupid bastard, I've cut my feet.' To this the youth responded indifferently 'To hell with your feet. It's not them I'm interested in.'

'Let's dance,' Ken suggested.

'I'm not sure—'

'Ah, come on, Stella, It's cooler here.'

'I've got to go soon—'

She advanced the proposal hopelessly; she'd never get away; she was committed and it scared her.

'Have a can?'

She took it but didn't drink.

As they danced Ken swallowed out of his can. Other kids threw cans over the side. They were barefoot, intense, totally concentrated, here for ever, it seemed, vibrant with energy.

Stella asked, 'What's the time?'

'Who cares?'

'They'll murder me.'

'Another can and you won't care. Hey, you haven't drunk that one!'

The music ended and a few youths and girls wandered off. A murmur of complaint could be heard from those who had settled down with blankets further along the deck.

'I'll have to go,' she said decisively.

'Jesus, already?'

'Soon,' she qualified.

'That's better.'

Ken sprawled on a deck chair. 'Come on! There's room for two.'

They lay side by side and the thing creaked as if it would break. She could smell the sweat as it poured from him. He recommenced the necking, but with the violence promoted by the cans of beer and her anxiety about time.

But she'd made a mistake and knew it. Struggles pleased him, were part of the game. She had to wrestle to get him off.

'What's the matter with you?' he asked, whining.

'There's too many people.'

She made this excuse because she didn't want to appear a fool, a wowser. But now his hands were everywhere, between her legs, on her buttocks, and she jumped straight off the chair.

'I've got to go,' she said, and began to run.

He didn't follow.

It had a dream-like property. Was he real at all?

In the cabin her mother greeted her with violent irritation.

'Where have you been?'

'Dancing.'

'Who said you could wander around till midnight?'

'Is it midnight?' Stella asked, startled. They'd only just got going up there; what time would they finish?

Her father said in a calmer reprimand, 'You're still going around with that vulgar Diane.'

'I'm not.'

'The lady she's with says you are.'

'That silly old thing.'

'Are you crazy?' shouted her mother. 'Who do you think you are to decide if old people are silly?'

'She thinks the world's going to end next April.'

'And you know it isn't?'

'Oh, Mum, don't be crazy.'

'You'd better not stay out until four in the morning like that girl does.'

Stella complained, heavy with virtue, 'I don't, do I? There's no chance of that with you as parents.'

'Don't be stupid,' hissed her mother.

'What's stupid about it?'

'And stop this insolent answering back. We're responsible for you.'

'I suppose you'll tell me next that you *love* me,' Stella sneered thoughtlessly.

'Why don't you talk to that nice American girl who walks round the deck? She's a sensible girl and she's on her own.'

'Nice?' questioned Stella, repeating one of Diane's opinions. 'Nice? Her? She's a snob. Imagine it! An American and a snob!'

'Oh, get in to bed.'

After a few minutes Stella commented, 'Whew! It's hot in here. Did you know they're all sleeping on deck?'

She lay in the bunk, frustrated, everything wrong, not happy about anybody. And after a while she thought about the boy's hand. He'd actually pawed her buttocks like someone who'd been married for years. No wonder Dr de Haan frowned on necking. You could hardly be more personal than that, especially when it was so hot and his hands were sweating.

Away from the fright of the experience and the noise of others, she thought about it and fell asleep considering that it could be exciting with the right person. In her dreams the right person faceless, but with tenderness, touched her, and her limbs stirred and responded in acceptance.

'You look tired,' her mother said with concern the next morning.

'I'm all right. Stop bothering me,' Stella protested petulantly.

Marion inhaled to argue and correct her, but let it go.

Stella lazed on a deck chair all morning. She saw no one who'd been on deck or in the Labyrinth Club last night. They didn't emerge until nearly noon. It was like a Continental city – Paris, say – in which the same boulevards were crowded by day with tourists of a different kind to those who filled them at night, people with a dissimilar perspective of the world. Stella's mother and father were day people – they had small children to look after and were committed to them by day and to being near them by night, and they were willing and glad to go to sleep long before midnight. Stella was desirous of the things of the night, but within the orbit of her parents.

She didn't see Diane until nearly four o'clock in the afternoon, when the girl was encountered striding along the Parade Deck in a bikini, eating a banana.

'Hi.'

'Hello,' greeted Stella awkwardly.

'How did y'get on with Ken?'

'Oh, all right.'

Diane propounded her own philosophy: 'No one should go on a cruise unless they can swim, dance, play bingo, drink heavily or make love frequently.'

'I don't like doing things in public,' Stella qualified.

'You don't do 'em at all—'

It was like an accusation of cowardice, and Stella looked uncomfortable.

'And have you ever—?' probed Diane.

'God, no, I'm not quite sixteen—'

'But you want—'

'I don't know,' Stella admitted, confused, the words of Dr de Haan still loud in her mind, the qualities of her parents known perfectly well. It was just restlessness. If she had a boyfriend, however dull...

'Not even a touch? When I'm at school—' Diane told her what the girls did to each other at the school she'd been to. It wasn't anything Stella had encountered or even heard about. Diane's strong personality defied Dr de Haan, mocked him, considered him a fool.

'But *where*?' Stella asked frankly, her pulse beating in great hammer blows. This, she knew, was enticing her into something : an arrangement would be made...

'You're scared,' Diane said.

'Honestly, no,' Stella disputed. 'I didn't really like him.'

'You're itching only you're scared,' Diane insisted, and Stella stood by the ship's rail, abject in admission.

Diane whispered, 'Come to my cabin.'

'When? What for?' asked Stella shakily, but she guessed what for.

'The old fool's gone to tea.'

'What for?'

'We'll have a bit of fun, private.'

Stella was trembling, shaking with timidity, and shame; but a more powerful lust disturbed her, fluttered her legs and she justified herself; it wouldn't be the same; it would be an experiment, an initiation; it would be a molestation without consequence. It would satisfy curiosity and that would be that. She'd be aware of the emotions of depravity without being committed to them by love . . . She would then calm down, go to the cinema with Patricia, be more considerate towards her parents, take Bumble for walks and stand by the kids' pool while she splashed about. And this disgraceful sickness would be gone...

But she emerged from Diane's cabin coarsened and obdurate, unashamed, not even embarrassed by Diane having been witness to her moral dissolution. She had not known her body could be capable of this prurience.

'I'm going for some tea,' said Diane, oddly, as if nothing of particular moment had taken place.

'See you, then.'

Stella wanted to be alone, to consider what had been aroused and how to experience it again. She hid many things from her parents and had a degree of cunning. But these previous deceptions had been almost accidental and of no great moral importance. The significance lay in the failure of submitting an account of them to her parents so that they could make a decision or criticism. But now and for ever she would have to look them in the eye and talk of trivial things and all the time remember the secrets her body now carried.

Stella could also deceive herself, and she did so now, persuading herself that nothing *wrong* had happened. Dr de Haan had certainly been proved right. Petting carried to extreme certainly would be wrong. But there had been no boy here and so it didn't matter: it had been like a rehearsal and the actual performance would never take place.

The air conditioning broke down altogether now and in the Burston's cabin the temperature was 106°. Stella had a shower – very distantly she recognized that there was a motive even in this – and it was impossible to dry herself. The sweat rolled.

Her mother and father were grumbling, and she told them again: 'Lots of people go on deck.' Her pulse thundered at the possibilities now in view...

But it took a quarter of an hour and howls from Bumble and Patricia before the whole family moved self-consciously on deck.

It was nearly midnight and the Parade Deck was quite crowded with people asleep in deck chairs or even on the hard deck.

Blasts of steam now and again startled them, unaccountable, until someone said 'It's the safety valve.' The *Areopagus* was moving through the night at 19 knots.

Stella was restless. 'I'm too hot. I'm going for a walk.'

A hundred yards away, on the other side of the deck, towards the stern, the record player wailed, enticing her. She was scared, hot with fright, but the great physical itch was there, demanding completion...

'Stay where you are,' Marion commanded.

Stella was still awake an hour later, when her father was snoring and the two kids were silent. The music was still touching her senses and still her body made her writhe. Her hair was damp with sweat.

She couldn't make out if her mother was asleep or not. She justified herself: well, I'd have to go to the lavatory...

She was at the end of the row of prone figures, and she just had to move. She even hoped *they* would frighten her so badly she'd run back, desires eliminated. Just a touch of a hand to satisfy, to finish what Diane had started.

They'd never find her now, she was a hundred feet away in a dark corner...

Who? she now wondered in alarm. Everybody would have a friend. She'd look a fool.

She was barefoot and had no bra on, but was otherwise dressed.

The stewards were still rushing about, and there was a party of older men, drinking solidly. And there, alone with a can of beer, was Roy, bearded Roy, to whose cabin Diane had once retreated.

He looked at her and recognized the availability, but hesitated.

'Hi,' Stella greeted, and went towards him.

14

THEY were playing chess when John entered the cabin. Dimitrios hadn't spoken to John for ten days and had not seen him for five.

Rajaratnam usually won these games, and he was winning now. This did not disturb Dimitrios, because Keith had only recently taught him how to play; and he never corrected Dimitrios with anything but kindness.

Dimitrios was immediately full of misgivings. He metamorphosed from pleasure to sulkiness. The emotion was so powerful and unreasonable he could not control himself, and, shakily, he asked :

'What do you want?'

John was at his most affable, loose limbed, at ease. He carried a bottle of whisky. Dimitrios knew he'd been a fool to give himself away in four words. Where emotion existed John could exploit it, cause pain. And there were no secrets on board. He would find out, if he cared to, and with little effort, that Dimitrios played chess with Rajaratnam in the afternoons sometimes, stood with him looking at the stars, showered with him, ate talking to him; he might even be subtle enough to identify the relationship as innocent, even tender and beautiful. That would be sufficient for him to become interested, to wish to soil it. Seduction of the normal was John's defiance of the world which identified him and sniggered. Thirty-two years old, this could still flay him. His nature was good humoured and indifferent, normally, but too often circumstances aroused the abnormality and the years had taught him how to be cruel. And Dimitrios' rejection of him in favour of a fat priest, the dogma of God, this had stung, promoted hatred. To hurt what had been loved was satisfying, for one knew the weaknesses, and it had parallels with the original emotions...

John answered in English. It was Dimitrios' bad luck that John could speak English as well, if not better, than he could : he had had much practice among the passengers.

'That's a welcome! What do I want? Hello, young man. How is the world with you?'

'Not bad at all,' Keith said, seeing no viciousness because he contained none himself. 'I think I might win.'

'Let me see. Ah, yes. Check mate in three moves, yes?'

'Do you play?' Keith asked.

'Of course. We must have a game some time.'

This offer was made in genuine intention, but it was also intended to worry Dimitrios. And it did. He was now hot in the belly in apprehension, knowing the power of John's charm. John recognized the fear and was delighted. So that was the way it was! The fool! The dull ignorant peasant. He'd have him weeping soon.

'I've acquired a bottle of whisky.'

'Stolen it,' translated Dimitrios.

'Not quite, not quite. Honest John, they call me. You know that the First Officer is drinking? Did you know that?' he asked Keith conversationally. 'His wife's shacked up with some muscle-bound Australian. He's upset. Poor man,' John said with savage indifference. The bastard had chewed him up in front of a great dumb English navvy. That was unforgivable. There was a technique for such fools; they withered if kept waiting. And Tomazos had on another day pulled him up during lifeboat drill. The dumb oaf, clowning about with bits of tape and inflated stomachs! He was suffering now because of *love*. What a fool, marrying an Australian tart!

His face conveyed none of this vitriolic resentment. It was a droll item of gossip: the First Officer was drinking. 'Perhaps he'll run the *Areopagus* aground,' John forecast. 'And there's this passenger, a New Zealander, supposed to be a barrister. He's on the bottle the whole day. I have to water it down a little, he'd be so ill otherwise.'

'We don't drink,' affirmed Dimitrios.

'*We?*' queried John.

'Keith is a Hindu.'

'Don't they drink?'

Keith laughed gently and admitted, 'In Singapore I am a good Hindu. But when I am with Christians I am a good Christian! I then drink! It makes me silly, but this is good Christianity, to be friends, to loosen the Anglo-Saxon inhibitions.'

'My God, you're a bit of a boy, you are,' chided John.

The words had isolated Dimitrios. It was *their* conversation now, which he could join if he was capable. He was so full of foreboding and sulky anger that he couldn't. He recalled the lure of words which had seduced *him* a long time ago.

'Finish the game,' suggested John.
'It does not matter,' Dimitrios qualified.
'You don't like to lose?'
'How do you know I will lose?' Dimitrios demanded angrily.
'Let me see.'
'I cannot concentrate.'
'I will be quiet.'
'That is not enough.'
'Oh, well,' John sneered, shrugging, and smiling at Keith.
They began to drink in the stifling hot small cabin. Dimitrios was silent and endured the careful taunts of John, apparently harmless, but which, in view of the previous relationship, stung.
'I must go,' John said after half an hour.
'You are on duty?' asked Keith.
'No, but I mustn't outstay my welcome.'
'Have a game of chess?'
'You will want to play with Dimitrios.'
'Afterwards.'
'But he has nothing to do.'
'It doesn't matter,' said Dimitrios bitterly.
As they played John extracted information, took interest, asked questions about Keith's experiences, his life in Singapore, his training in the Singapore dockyard, and questions which probed tenderly at racial problems in a manner which Dimitrios couldn't achieve.
'We'll have another game some time,' Keith suggested.
'Very well. That would be pleasant.'
Keith had won the game but with effort, and was inevitably satisfied at beating a player of skill.
'A return match,' he said, laughing. His eyes were bloodshot. There was an alteration in facial expression, something Dimitrios had not previously seen. Why, he's a fool, he thought miserably, but his emotions were in tumult. Happiness and calm were going to be taken away.
'—in my cabin then,' John was saying. 'I'll lay on some booze. How about you, Dimitrios?'

'How about me?' asked Dimitrios sullenly.

'Want to watch? We're having the return match tonight.'

It was unbearable. Dimitrios qualified, 'I'll see' and John said as if planning kindness, a party for intelligent friends, chess players, 'I'll get some nice food, too.'

Dimitrios did not go.

He waited for the two hours during which Keith was away. He suffered and knew it was absurd; Keith was not answerable to *him*. He was permitted to have other friends, a game of chess; to stick to Dimitrios' company day after day would become tiresome and eventually end in silence, nothing to be said. Unless it materialized into love. This was something Dimitrios did not think about. Keith had assuaged pain and despair, delivered Dimitrios from unbearable loneliness. Keith was delightful because he was different, so incorruptible, almost naïve: in many hours of talk he, a boy of eighteen like Dimitrios, had not offered one coarse remark about girls or women. His perspective of life was so free from European and shipboard sophistication that to talk to him was like being cleansed, beginning again with innocence.

He had an honest, forthright, silently humorous face. When they stood under the faulty showers together Dimitrios saw that he, who looked slight and even frail, had a well-made body, with chestnut gleaming skin, taut stomach and muscles across his shoulders that rippled in movement. He was beautiful, but Dimitrios felt no physical yearning. It was sufficient that this boy was his friend. Nothing further was claimed.

And yet he waited now nearly two hours, doing nothing but seethe in fear and jealousy, and genuine anxiety for his friend.

Keith came back, red-eyed again from alcohol, ready to laugh, but Dimitrios couldn't bear it. He knew he'd suffer, that suffering was what John intended and that silence and care would be the way to defeat it.

'Where did you go?'

'We played chess.'

'Is that all?'

'Ah, you should have been there, Dimitrios. John had brought some jumbo shrimps and meat balls.'

'You must be careful, Keith.'

'Careful?'

'John is an evil man.'

'He is cynical, to be sure, but amusing. He meets strange people.'

'No. He is evil. I know.'

'But a game of chess?'

'Listen. You are my friend?'

'Yes, I am your friend, Dimitrios.'

'I tell you in sincerity that this man is vile.'

'I do not understand that.'

'Can you not believe without understanding?'

'I am a religious person, so I have beliefs without mathematical proof.'

'This is the same thing in reverse.'

'You feel he will harm me?'

'Yes.'

'In what way?'

'He will, for instance, teach you to despise me.'

'He said kind things about you.'

'You do not believe me?'

'It would be wrong to despise someone for no reason.'

'I should not have spoken about it.'

'I will repeat nothing, assuredly. You have been too long at sea, Dimitrios.'

'Perhaps,' admitted Dimitrios.

The *Areopagus* reached Singapore only fourteen hours behind schedule. She was kept waiting by pilots and for a berth, and passengers were informed the night before arrival that the ship would only be in the great port from dawn until nine at night. This meant about eleven hours ashore instead of the twenty-five promised in the brochures.

Mr Pybus, in pyjamas open at a sweating hairy chest, not quite sober from last night, looking very ill now, stood up in the dining-room and began to bellow protest. But there was no response; the passengers had weighed him up now and considered him a vulgar loud-mouth and grumbler. Further, they thought the *Areopagus* had done well. And experience at Bali had conditioned them to an affection for the old ship. Eleven hours walking about and they knew perfectly well they'd be glad to be back on board.

For Dimitrios the brief stay at Singapore meant no shore leave at all. He would be lucky to even come out of the gloomy bowels of the vessel and *look* at the city. Keith, however, was allowed ashore for two hours because he was supernumerary and in his home city. The Chief Engineer, Bitsios, was a tough man, but by no means thoughtless in such matters.

It was disappointing, for Dimitrios had regarded the call at Singapore as a sort of bond, an impletion of his new comradeship.

Keith returned into the port engine room full of joy, refreshed.

'How did you get on?'

'Oh, splendid, Dimitrios. It was good to see my family. My mother has a new baby, ten months old, a bouncer. John thought—'

Dimitrios was so shocked he couldn't hide alarm.

'*John?*'

His heart jumped in jealousy, his mind was full of the crawling worms of fear.

'John came along. It was such a pity you could not also, Dimitrios.'

'But why did John come?'

'*Why?* There he was, standing about; he seemed lonely ...'

'You asked him?' Dimitrios inquired in dismay. It had the hurt of a betrayal.

'But why not? I wanted my mother to meet at least one of my friends.'

Dimitrios could scarcely breathe for unhappiness. His *friend*. John, the insolent, ruthless, tainted Saturday-afternoon sailor, had achieved a position of friendship with Keith! He ranked equal to Dimitrios before Keith's mother. This frightened Dimitrios as well as hurt him. If there was to be competition – who could amuse Keith the more, play chess as an equal, admire and advise him, inform him – he knew in despair and jealousy that John would win it.

'Where did you go to?'

'Not far, assuredly!'

'What did you do?'

'Oh, talk. By the time we'd had an hour with my family it was necessary for me to hurry back...'

'I wish you had not taken him.'

'Why do you say that? Is he not your friend, too?'

'He despises me.'

'I feel sure he does not.'

'If he could hurt me—'

'Have you had a difference with him?'

'We had a quarrel. He cannot bear that I should have a friend.'

'But he speaks kindly of you, Dimitrios.'

'He is not a fool. He is thirty-two, subtle, has great experience of people.'

'You are upset. I wish you could have come. My mother has this new baby and you should have seen it! John was very funny. You would have laughed. Is he married? He seems fond of kids.'

'Of course he's not married.'

'What's the matter, Dimitrios?'

'He's vile.'

'I am sorry that you quarrelled. He can be so funny and cheerful. And it doesn't matter. No one will influence me in regard to you, my friend.'

'He might hurt you.'

'*Hurt* me?'

'And thus alienate you.'

'But how could he hurt me? And why should he wish to do so?'

'He's peculiar. He gets satisfaction from doing things like that.'

'You have been hurt in the quarrel.'

'You are my friend?'

'I am indeed.'

'Promise me that you will avoid him.'

'But, Dimitrios, this is absurd.'

How could he warn Keith without admitting his own base behaviour?

'Don't you have a girlfriend?'

'Ah, girls!' Keith said, with surprising vigour. 'One day I find a girl and get married. But here in the engine room of the *Areopagus*? I think not!'

Dimitrios had to let the matter drop or become too persistent and thus arouse suspicion or embarrassment.

But he couldn't let it rest. He had to be active, settle the matter, probe the wound. The unsettled condition of what had been calm and beautiful couldn't be tolerated. At the very least he had to discuss it, and since he couldn't talk about it with Keith, it had to be with John. It was foolish, he admitted, to approach John. If what he feared was true John would exacerbate his misery, crucify him, mock him with affected ignorance: 'What are you talking about? Who do you mean? Oh, that boy who played chess with me. Leave him alone? But if the poor fool wants to follow me about?'

But there was the other half of John, and no one aboard the *Areopagus* knew it better than Dimitrios – the sincere, thoughtful, affectionate man who should be doing something better than serving beer to tourists. Had he really aroused an intense loathing in that half of John? Was a visit to a priest and a fear of disease so unforgivable? Could they not have a sensible, kindly but calm relationship?

He was very nervous about the encounter. Whatever he did or said, he would be the one who abased himself and had to plead.

They had always met in Dimitrios' cabin when other men were on duty, or in the bar late at night, or in secret corners of Metaxas and B Decks. Never in John's cabin because there were five other stewards there.

Dimitrios approached the Forward Bar after midnight. Only a few lights were on and the place was emptying.

'Where's John?' he asked the girl cashier.

'On the Parade Deck.'

Dimitrios was not supposed to be in any bar, nor to mix with passengers. But he couldn't bear to withdraw now that he had nerved himself up.

The ship was very quiet, but on the Parade Deck there was confusion, a surprising number of people asleep in the deck chairs. And at the stern, by the big pool, a dance for the kids. It meant nothing to Dimitrios except that this was where John would be, serving beer, swindling these drunken fools out of small change in the dark.

He was very young, trembling with agitation, and tired. He was due back on duty in four hours.

There was John, inevitably successful, acquiring equality and friendship with these muscular Australians he said he despised. He was drunk, to, and very hot in the steamy night, his face wet and shining with sweat, the armpits of his white linen jacket stained by the mere exertion of fetching trayfuls of booze. Dimitrios was startled by the violence and energy of the passengers. Eleven hours ashore and these big youths and long-legged girls were still like people in a frenzy. They shrieked and laughed and ran about, almost bare, and wrestled, male and female, shouting obscenities, in a coarse equality. A few seemed to be coupling, indifferent to witness, scarcely ten yards away.

Dimitrios touched John on the arm as he approached the storeroom in use as a bar.

'My God, you!' said John in surprise.

'How long does this go on?'

'Until the fools drop dead or they've screwed each other or the booze runs out.'

'I want to talk to you.'

'The conditions are hardly propitious!'

This was obviously true.

The voices called him, indifferent to his tiredness, his working hours, 'John! John! Come on, you idle bastard! Bring the bloody stuff!' – 'Leave him alone, he's gone for a pee.'

'Wait a minute while I satisfy this menagerie,' John said. 'All right, you lovely colonial bastards! Have your money at the ready!'

He came back to stand in shadow with an empty tray. 'They're crazy, these people,' he told Dimitrios with feeling.

'I wouldn't mind a beer.'

'Help yourself.'

Dimitrios did so.

'Something on your mind?' John asked. He shook his head and beads of sweat rained on to the deck.

Dimitrios said it with a confused paroxysm of words: 'Leave him alone! He's my friend.'

'Who the hell are you talking about?'

'You know very well.'

'I don't know what you're raving about.'

'I hate you when you pretend not to know.'

'Dimitrios, I am so busy serving this scum I'm stupefied.'

'You stood about today so he would notice you—'

'Ah, you mean that little fellow!'

'You have plenty of friends up here in the bars—'

'What, *these*?' John laughed caustically. 'These lovely people and their mums and dads! Transitory friendships, Dimitrios. They leave after twenty or fifty days, full of love and bonhomie, but never write. They even forget to tip. Just a barman. I have to steal it from them. How degrading.'

'There are other stewards.'

'They do not understand me. They do not have the same tastes. My tastes are specialized, as you know, Dimitrios. A barman aspiring to culture! Ridiculous! Naturally they despise me. It's a traumatic experience, every trip.'

'You didn't have to hurt me—'

'I wouldn't do that.'

'What's he to you?'

'Who? This little man? Nothing, Dimitrios. Not like you.'

'Then leave him alone.'

'I'm a lonely man, Dimitrios. I need friends.'

'Everybody knows what you are.'

'And what is that?'

'A perverted goat.'

John laughed.

'You are getting quite juicy in your phraseology.'

'Keith should not be corrupted.'

John considered this for a moment and then said in derision:

'You love him.'

'It is friendship.'

'You *love* him,' mocked John. 'Your stomach is warm with cheap tawdry romance ... You don't know what it's all about. Under the shower you see the lovely golden body, and you are flattered by his smile and earnest talk ... I'll show you what trash your romance is. I'll take him away from you and prove how cheap and temporary it all is. And I won't denigrate you. I will always declare that you are my dear friend. But in a month or less you will be so boring to him that he will have a job to be polite and conceal it. He'll shrink at the sight of you and seek out me in preference, and one day he'll tell me what a dull thing you are. *Love!*' sneered John. 'A bit of a fright about the pox, a pat on the arm from the priest and love for ever withers, turns to fright and dislike. How second-rate is that? Does he know you have the pox? It will be something to talk about.'

'I'll kill you!' snarled Dimitrios.

'Cheap opera!' derided John. 'As cheap as your emotion when your body needed satisfaction. A month ago you whined that you loved me. It was the biggest thing of your life. I was wise and sensual and compassionate. I understood you. I do!' he hissed.

'I'll smash your face in!' shouted Dimitrios, losing all control.

John tittered.

'What vulgarity! What guttersnipe promises! You *are* running hot bearings!'

Dimitrios swung his arm in an arc and the nearly-full beer can caught John across the mouth, smashing a few teeth and splitting the skin round the derisory lips.

John recovered very quickly. He rammed the tray he was holding into Dimitrios' crutch, kicked and moved about with the speed of a ballet dancer.

Dimitrios was totally out of control and would have killed him. He seized a wine bottle and ran at the steward. It shattered on John's arm and white wine ran down his clothes.

John seized the hand that still held the shattered bottle and turned it towards Dimitrios' face. It cut into Dimitrios' hair and left ear before, with a scream of rage and the last vestige of energy, Dimitrios wrenched his arm free and rammed the jagged slender bottle into John's throat. The man began to bleed heavily down his neck.

Dimitrios hung his head and sobbed.

The Australian passengers, while interested in this violence, now stopped it. An officer appeared and was very angry indeed; but had no option but to send them to the ship's hospital.

The Australian doctor attended to both of them. He was cheerfully blasphemous. 'Why in the name of God you have to start something on the one night I decide to go to bed at a reasonable hour—!'

John received twenty-seven stitches and Dimitrios needed eight.

They both lay in hospital bunks ten feet apart, saying nothing. John couldn't speak much anyway because of his injuries.

Dimitrios was terribly tired and in pain. But most of all he was unhappy. He had very probably done what he set out to do, that is, ended any relationship between John and Keith. For John's mockery had backfired on him, and he would not care to continue it. But what about the relationship between Dimitrios and Keith? All night Dimitrios lay in the bunk, sadly aware that Keith would hear about this fight. He would seek explanation and someone would tell him. An older man or even an officer might advise him for his own good. Then what would his reaction be? Go on playing chess? Talk about the stars? Throw the soap under the shower?

The Staff Chief Engineer came to see him in the morning. He was not as big as the Staff Captain, whose functions he matched, but was more unpleasant, having no association with passengers to soften his outlook.

'What were you doing on the Parade Deck?'

'I was looking for *him*.'

'Why?'

'It was urgent.'

'What the hell do you mean, urgent? Your business is in the engine room. Do you find stewards *there*?'

'No, sir.'

'Do you realize the impression you've given the passengers?'

'I'm sorry about it, sir.'

'I am tempted to kick you out of the Company.'

'It won't happen again, sir.'

'You're damn right it won't. I'll be logging you. You'll lose a month's pay for sure. I'll think about whether this ship and Company need you.'

'Thank you, sir.'

'Don't thank me.'

Half an hour later, like the Second Act of a comedy, Dimitrios had to lie there and listen to the Staff Captain putting similar questions to John.

'With a face like that I'm not sure I can have you attending to the needs of passengers. Maybe you should be cleaning lavatories.'

John hissed, 'It wasn't my fault, sir.'

'There was a reason, I suppose?'

'We'd had a difference of opinion.'

'I shall log you. I can't demote you, since you're the lowest of the low anyway, so you'll lose pay. Any more fights and you're out on your ear.'

'If you say so, sir.'

'And no damn insolence to me.'

'I was simply standing there when this aggressive lout attacked me—'

'We know all about that,' said the Staff Captain. 'We're not blind. Take better care of your sex life in future.'

He stamped out, giving Dimitrios a long fierce stare in which there might have been the trace of a grin.

Dimitrios was heartened. At least he'd not see John in the engineer's half of the *Areopagus* again!

Thirty-six hours later, still a little weakened, he returned to duty. The men all stared at him, and a few grinned outright. One even said, 'That's a lovely scar you've got there, boy.'

But Keith didn't stare or smile or come forward to welcome him back; nor did he ask about his health ... He wouldn't meet Dimitrios' eye at all, and when he did at last, his own eyes had a new, unwelcome expression which withered all hope of any resumption or progress in their *rapprochement*. For in Keith's eyes were shame and embarrassment.

He *knew* ...

The *Areopagus* had in her lifetime steamed something like 4,300,000 miles. It was not surprising then that she had a formidable collection of minor faults caused by her age, or that she no longer made the 20 knots she had thirty years earlier. She had to strain to make 17. The high temperatures of steam passing year after year through the rows of high-speed rotor blades had resulted in the first rows in a very slight distortion, lack of strength and rigidity and minute misalignments. There was windage loss caused by fluid friction as the turbine wheel and rotor blades turned in the surrounding steam, and diaphragm packing loss caused by leakage of steam from one stage to another through the diaphragm packing.

She was a very old liner, but like the steam-driven railway engines of yesteryear there was in theory no reason why she should not steam on for ever. Perhaps the fundamental difference between the two was that a railway engine didn't need to use its pure water over and over again. It could fill up with new. A ship did, and in addition to this returned 'condensate' used desalinated sea water. Only corrosion and breakages and the increasing cost of repairing them should ever make her uneconomical to operate. But where the entire ship floated in a corrosive fluid and the very air was so salt-laden that a razor left on a cabin dresser turned brown in a day, all the care taken with water passing through tubes and boilers couldn't keep it entirely pure all the time. The *Areopagus*' boilers were over thirty years old and of an outdated design, and many of the scores of tubes –

most of them two inches in diameter – reached 'end point' and cracked prematurely, or because of age and corrosion on each voyage. They were, however, easily replaceable.

The boilers were secured in position in the ship by means of saddles and supports. Each enormous boiler steam drum was supported by the tubes which in turn were supported by the water drums and the water headers. The boiler casings were supported by steel framework built up from the water drums and water headers. The webbed beam construction, riveted to its various members, rested upon huge rigid beam structures built up from and a part of the rigid longitudinal structural members of the ship's framework. These rigid boiler supports were braced both fore and aft and athwartships.

Underneath the tubes and brick and metal baffles was the furnace. The steel casing was lined with insulating blocks, high-temperature insulation bricks, refractory firebricks and plastic refractory. The insulating blocks were made of uncalcined diatomaceous earth, which in its best form was pure silica, white, light in weight and insulated up to 1,500°F.The refractory (or 'dense') firebricks were a compound of silica, alumina and calcined flint clay, and could withstand temperatures of 3,000°F and had excellent flame resistance.

It could hardly be expected that with over thirty years at sea the *Areopagus* would not show her age. The very nature of the sea had a compressive strength about which little was known. The buckling load of stiffened panels and the effects of residual stress and temperature factors were still theoretical considerations, papers read to learned societies, as were the lateral load and in-plane axial movement of the edges of the panels, which were free to slide inward but clamped against rotation. Loading might have a bearing as well as external forces. Price had a relevance; merchant ship designers had to use simple and sturdy construction, seven times cheaper than the elaborate structures of warships. Isolated extreme loading could cause local cracks or hasten the metal fatigue caused by years at sea. The pressures of the sea in the storms encountered over thirty years caused the *Areopagus* to creak at the joints and make odd noises in the night. The vibratory stresses and very high transient local pressures in longitudinal bending caused by slamming and riding the crests of huge waves with the enormous weight of the bows and stern in mid-air had loosened very slightly many parts of or within the main hull of the entire ship.

In a liner so old sea water leaks, corrosion, lubrication leaks, dissolved oxygen all took their toll. The *Areopagus* had desalinating apparatus and Dimitrios had at times cleaned this, breaking lumps of salt as hard and big as rocks. But salt water leaks were inescapable, to be fought continuously. The liner creaked and groaned; things were loosened, and impurities found their way into the boilers if the struggle was neglected for a moment.

Boiler compounds were used to defeat these corrosive processes and the dissolved oxygen in the boiler feed water was controlled by heating and mechanical de-aeration. But the old piping of the ship had to be cared for like the stomach of a duodenal case. Any impurities, such as oil, in boiler water promoted foaming and priming which caused carry-over of moisture in the steam from the saturated steam drums to the superheater or even the machinery. Baked sludge still reduced heat transfer so much that blistering occurred and this sludge was not disintegrated by boiler compound. The exact condition of the boiler feed water was checked very occasionally for alkalinity, salinity, soap hardness and dissolved oxygen, but there was an understandable, possibly Greek tendency to let something happen and then repair it.

The whole purpose of the boilers, superheaters and other equipment was to generate steam – dry superheated steam of a temperature of 900°F at the superheater outlet and a working pressure of 600 psig – which would convey thermal or heat energy to the turbines; the exhaust steam being converted into water and returned to the boiler for repetition of the cycle.

The *Areopagus* had two old-fashioned large boilers – one placed athwartships in each engine room – of the type called sectional header boilers because the front and rear headers (square sectional tubes) were built up in sections.

The normal water level in these boilers was near the middle of the steam drum – a huge construction high above the furnace and tubes – at the lower lip of the return circulating tubes. Feed water entered through the feed stop-and-check valves and was distributed throughout the steam drum by means of the internal feed pipe, which was a large pipe having holes along its sides and extending the length of the drum near the bottom. The relatively cool and heavier water descended from the drum through the downtake nipples and front headers to the front end of the scores of two-inch tubes, that is, at the lower end of their 18° incline, via the cross-box, and then went into the tubes and to the rear headers and up them. The hot gases of the furnace, passing over the tubes, transferred heat to and through them to the water, which, when heated, became lighter and therefore rose up the incline of the scores of tubes and vertically up the rear headers. As steam bubbles formed in the heated water they rose also and tended to accelerate the circulation. The hot water and steam flowed to the tops of the rear headers and through circulating tubes to the steam drum.

The hot water flowing from the circulating tubes mixed with the relatively cooler water in the drum and recirculated, but the steam was directed downwards by a baffle over the ends of the circulating tubes, rose through the water to the top of the drum and into the dry pipe (still inside the massive boiler). From there it went through external piping to the superheater.

Steam passing through the tubes of the superheater element had its temperature raised to 900°. The superheated steam now passed to the main steam line and operated the turbines. At this temperature it was not only dangerous but difficult to handle, and did not give up its heat as readily as steam which was just at the saturation temperature.

It was desirable to use steam for the general services of the *Areopagus* – running anchor capstans, windlasses, heating accommodation and galley stoves and improving the viscosity of the heavy-grade fuel oil to make it pumpable – but it was so dangerous and unchangeable that for these purposes it had to be desuperheated. It was necessary to reduce the heat of the steam supply, where it was diverted, to a point just above the saturation temperature and at the pressure for which the auxiliary equipment was designed to operate. This was done by injecting relatively cold water into the steam so that by diminishing the temperature a larger quantity of steam at a lower temperature was obtained. The control had to be sensitive or cracking noises would come from the pipes. In fact it was done by a device which sensed the steam temperature and then introduced water by means of the de-superheater. The water was at once reduced to a fine mist so that it mixed readily with the steam and took the excess heat out of it.

The very hot dry steam entering the *Areopagus*' high pressure turbine passed through 18 wheels and turned 5,132 blades, and the rotor shaft revolved at a maximum of 5,746 turns a minute.

Turbines should operate at high speeds. Propellers, on the other hand, have their highest efficiency at low speeds. If they rotated too rapidly – each of the two propellers of the *Areopagus* weighed 10 tons 18 hundredweight – they churned the water and cavitation followed. Cavitation was the forming of cavities in the water round the low pressure sides of the blades owing to the propeller trying to discharge the water faster than it could flow into the propeller. It was capable of buckling the blades.

Therefore the high rotational speed of the turbine had to be reduced by reduction gears which themselves weighed tons. The *Areopagus* had double-reduction gears to reduce the 5,000 revolutions a minute of the rotor shaft of the turbine to the 130 of the propeller in the water. These great big main reduction gear wheels – eight feet in diameter – and the smaller pinions were of the double helical or herringbone type. In theory they were long pitch screw threads which ran very smoothly with little noise and with even distribution of pressure along the entire length of the tooth.

The whole gear assembly was installed in a housing of welded cast steel and boiler plate construction.

The design of flexible couplings permitted a small amount of misalignment to the hubs. Rigidity would have affected the meshing of pinion and gear and resulted in the breakage of teeth. In the *Areopagus* this condition was still fulfilled adequately, considering her age. But the radial alignment between the port pinions and gears was not exact and was causing uneven wear due to the driving force being concentrated on a small portion of each tooth rather than over the entire tooth contact surface.

The two engine and fire rooms of the *Areopagus* were arranged one behind the other, the port being forward of the starboard by as much as seventy feet. Thus the port propulsion shafting was also seventy feet longer than the starboard. The main propulsion shafting transmitted the torque (roughly, the power to move weight) from the main engine and reduction gears and in turn transmitted the axial thrust of the propellers to the ship's structure so that it moved. It was not a single piece of steel but several pieces, of which the actual propeller shaft had a diameter of 20 inches and the intermediate shafting one of 17½ inches. The port propulsion shafting of the *Areopagus* was 140 feet long and it consisted of several sections of single steel forgings with a smooth bored axial hole from end to end.

Due to the weight and length of the propulsion shafting it had to have bearings to support it as well as hold it in alignment.

Over the years these shafts had worn minutely but sufficiently for them to be fractionally out of alignment. This caused a variation in the wake stream (in the sea) of the propellers, and in turn aggravated the propeller blade angle section of incidence which occurred twice per revolution with reduced, or misdirected thrust and torque through the 360° rotation of each propeller, particularly the *Areopagus*' port screw. Because of this wake variation and asymmetrical nature of the flow the centre of thrust was markedly off the original shaft axis and was as much as 12 inches away from the shaft centreline as it now was. The severe cyclic forces induced in the propellers were causing fatigue, although the bronze propellers could be expected to last the life of the vessel... The propellers were, even in normal alignment, a source of shafting vibration, and more so after thirty years of wear with the gradual shifting of position...

Propeller blades are approximately helicoidal surfaces. When rotated about their axes they shove aside the sea water in which they are immersed in a general fore-and-aft direction providing the alignment of shafting is normal. The slight misalignment in the *Areopagus* was only noticeable in wasted effort, reduced performance and increased vibration. The solid-built propellers – each made in a single casting and then finished to final dimensions by hand – turned 'inwards', that is, the port propeller revolved clockwise when viewed looking forward, and the starboard rotated anti-clockwise.

The owners of the *Areopagus* used the cheapest possible fuel and lubrication oils. The selection of oil for a turbine lubricating system was always a compromise, for it had to lubricate under several conditions. In theory selection should have been based on the most arduous conditions likely to be met. In fact price was the main factor, and the turbine reduction gears, high speed bearings and gears having heavy tooth pressures were all lubricated from the same system and the viscosity of the oil used was lower than desirable for the bearings.

The oil line to the reduction gears of the port side was part of the main engine lubrication system. The oil was sprayed through nozzles upon the meshing teeth and it fell to the bottom of the casing. The oil level there was neglected. It was still below the lower level of the teeth of the main gear. No oil excluding pan was fitted. If the oil rose any higher the main gears would be immersed in it and would churn the oil into foam or emulsion, which would cause the lubricating oil pumps to lose suction. Further, the oil would have become oxidized and cause harm to metals.

Much of the lubricating oil had to be used over and over again and it had to be clean and at a proper temperature.

This was very nearly hopeless on the *Areopagus* for it was impossible to eliminate the scale and sand from various castings or prevent dirt entering during overhauls. These substances were picked up by the oil and, despite strainers and centrifugal oil purifiers, and even magnets within the strainers, they scratched the bearings and gears minutely...

One of Keith's tasks was to look through the peepholes of the furnaces, inside which the temperature had to be 3,000°F. But it did not need technical training to know that something was wrong. Any passenger on board could see the thick black smoke pouring out of the funnels. Female passengers complained to the Chief Purser (in vain) that their clothes or their bodies had been spotted with black smuts when the ship's siren blew at every noon or for alarm practices or when the wind happened to blow the stack smoke downwards. Men in the bars said knowledgeably 'They're using the wrong oil' or 'They're really thrashing her'. But the thick smoke trailed round the world in all conditions and speeds. It could be seen from miles away and from aircraft and was a joke among other passenger liners. When Keith walked on mats saturated in oil he sometimes thought one day there'll be a stack fire and my God, it'll start something down here...

Through the peepholes he could see that the flames were dark red or orange, which indicated dirty atomizers. With insufficient air the fuel oil was broken down into its constituents and the unburned carbon carried up the stack.

The fuel oil used in the *Areopagus* was cheap. Distillation was incomplete and not carried out at high temperatures. The 'uncracked' fuel had a higher pouring point and had to be heated in the ship to 110°F. When not working in the tropics there was difficulty in pumping it. The small percentage of ash had a salt content which over the years had caused a surface decomposition of the furnace brickwork. Water and sediment, still present in the oil, caused wear on pump valves and burners and tended to clog the burner orifices. It caused some emulsification and interfered with proper combustion. Because the oil had to be heated to facilitate pumping from storage tanks through pipe lines and heaters a little carbonization was unavoidable.

The oil was, however, stable in storage and the movements of the ship caused no problems. It was difficult to ignite in bulk and not capable of spontaneous combustion. But the vapours which it gave off formed an explosive mixture with the oxygen in the atmosphere. This vapour, being heavier than air, tended to accumulate in low levels such as bilges and the bottoms of tanks, where its presence might not be detected until it was ignited by a spark. There was a sailor (from the deck, not engine room) on patrol all the time. He had to go round the ship every forty minutes and turn keys in 39 positions to prove he'd been to them. But if an oil fire ever got going even this patrol would be in vain...

The metals in contact with seawater had been subject for a very long time to its galvanic and velocity effects. Stress corrosion, cracking, dezincification and graphitization were all at work on the *Aeropagus*' exterior.

In addition the very paint which was slapped on whenever the vessel stayed still for a few days was giving no protection at all, as it should have been. Here again, hurry and price consideration and possibly the prestige desire to have the hull always a bright white for the passengers to admire and photograph, was corroding the old ship. Localized corrosion was removed, revealing pits in the steel and a rough surface profile for coating. The paint was applied with an apparent coating film thickness, but isolated high spots of corrosion protruded above the mean plane of the profile and were immediate potential sources of future and worse corrosion. And the paint itself was not really protecting the steel hull, for sodium phosphates were deposited *underneath* it. The sodium came from the seawater and the phosphate from the phosphoric acid in the wash primer. The water-soluble phosphates were thus a built-in source of failure, promoting lack of adhesion due to an osmotic process.

But all these faults were spread over a large ship which had a crew to keep an eye open for them. The *Areopagus* was like a luxury hotel, now gone a little seedy and catering for people of a different class to those who had dined and danced aboard thirty years ago. The new guests didn't complain with so much arrogance as the old. They put up with the hotel because they'd never known it to be better. And the Greek staff were so cheerful and obliging, why bother to grumble? The faults of the old liner were widely spread and, for the most part, the passengers were unaware of them. They were put right as quickly as they were encountered. It would need a disaster of unimaginable stresses to show up every weakness at one and the same time.

15

TOMAZOS came on duty at four o'clock and ten minutes later a party of visitors was conducted by a seaman on the bridge.

It was a typical group. There was a company director (who managed to proffer this status as information with his first question) and his wife, a plump little woman who was overcome by awe. (She thought Tomazos was the Captain.) Also a New Zealand sheep farmer, a small wiry sunburnt man who had made four trips to England and now monopolized the dialogue to the irritation of the other passengers. Then there was the myopic gangling idiot, loaded with ciné camera and malicious barbs who endeavoured to prove that the job of being a ship's officer was nothing important really; any fool, including himself, could do it. (This was Squibb at his maximum *grossièreté*.) There was the inevitable man who wished to air a grievance and simply followed words until they could be seized upon and exploited with this in view. This was Pybus, who was offensively drunk, almost past coherence, blinking rapidly, and sweating what smelled like pure alcohol. He had, incredibly, put on a shirt and tie and a jacket with an emphatic badge on it. His breathing was so heavy it was audible like an engine, and his face was ravaged by beer and heat... There was a family which included the small boy who was allowed to stand at the wheel, but had to be watched subsequently because of his tendency to press buttons, depress switches and talk into voice whistles to the radio room and the Captain... There were also two girls, unaccompanied, pleasantly self-conscious in the afternoon sun. One of these Tomazos recognized as Debbie Vertigan.

He always wore dark glasses at the start of these visits. It was to achieve anonymity or overcome slight nervousness until he'd established a relationship with the visitors. Then he would take them off and rub his eyes and be willing to see them in sharper focus and be stared at himself. But even with dark glasses on he could see that the second girl, older than Debbie, was agitated in consciousness of her own eroticism, and this with some justification.

Yannopoulos was at the wheel and smiled obligingly as people took photographs.

Tomazos was in white, without jacket, and the whole atmosphere was equally informal. He did not hurry them; they could stay for an hour if they wished. He answered their questions, avoided their snobberies, and was quite frank about the age of the *Areopagus*.

'How long do you reckon she'll last?' someone asked.

'Five more years,' forecast Tomazos. 'You see, people like new things, and speed.'

'New ships seem to catch fire or run aground or have trouble with their turbines,' suggested the company director amiably. 'I prefer the old ones.'

'She's stable, I'll say that for her,' agreed the New Zealand sheep farmer, patronizing the *Areopagus*.

'Why does she leave all that black smoke?' Squibb inquired.

Unexpectedly, he obtained a laugh, as if, for once, he had said something truly funny.

Tomazos answered, 'She's probably using too much oil or has a clogged burner—'

'Why isn't it cleaned then?' Squibb persisted, but obtained no camaraderie this time.

'Well, she is old, you see,' Tomazos said. 'Or maybe the Chief Engineer doesn't like to lose steam.'

He explained to them what were the functions of the bridge, how it was the heart of the ship and its brain. He showed them the radar sets and gyro-compass; he pulled down the periscopic magnetic compass for them to look into. He pointed out the inclinometer which showed the attitude of the ship in a roll. The instrument had a maximum of 30° to port or starboard. 'But we can't stop her if she rolls more,' he concluded with a smile.

'She hasn't got stabilizers,' said Squibb in accusation.

'That is true.'

'She's stable,' reiterated the New Zealand farmer. 'When we once came out of Sydney harbour aboard the *Opalescent*, which is 34,000 tons and had *everything*, she rolled like a rowing boat.'

A woman asked, 'Have you ever been in a bad storm?'

'On the *Areopagus*?'

'Well, yes.'

'I like her in rough weather,' admitted Tomazos. 'It gives me something to handle.'

'Suppose we hit a typhoon,' Pybus said. 'She'd go down like a stone.'

'Oh, no,' disputed Tomazos. 'The Captain, in the war, served on a concrete American ship. In the Caribbean he went through a typhoon, and it was quite stable—'

'Have *you* ever been in one?'

'Certainly.'

'What was it like?'

'The nastiest was off South America,' Tomazos recalled. 'We were off a lee shore and the sea was so strong the ship couldn't even be turned to meet it.'

'What happened?'

'We turned into the sea, with it, and reversed engines for fourteen hours.'

'God!'

'It was calm at the centre,' Tomazos recollected. 'In another ship of this Line I was right in the centre of a typhoon once. The water was moderate but confused. The air was calm but we were gasping. There were birds circling. Then the other half – a quarter really – of the storm hit us ... It took thirteen hours to get out of it. It was unpleasant but not all that dangerous ...'

Mr Pybus said in interruption, 'I bet this bloody ship doesn't get to Singapore on time. I bet you a hundred dollars it doesn't.'

Tomazos could see that the other visitors were rendered uncomfortable by this accusation; they had come here in a spirit of interest and friendliness.

'We haven't quite caught up the schedule,' he admitted. 'But you will undoubtedly have a day ashore there.'

Debbie Vertigan diverted the direction of the questions and asked about radar and collisions, and why wasn't radar switched on now?

'Ah, well, *look*!' Tomazos requested, and pointed forward to a clear sea and sky and a horizon empty fifteen miles away. 'You understand: although collisions are the greatest hazard these days this has nothing to do with radar. It is a matter of speed. There were no collisions in the days of sail ... We are approaching Singapore now, a crowded area, but there is no fog. What happens in fog or darkness is that two vessels on reciprocal courses see each other on radar. But they do not know each other's size or aspect or speed, nor can they for some time identify any change of the other's course. So maybe they've both altered course. Minutes pass and they see the next heading of the other vessel. It is again reciprocal to their own new course. They alter again, but so does the other. And suddenly they are no longer ten or five miles apart, but too near. Quite safe in a visual encounter where the aspect of the other can be seen, but here, in fog, maintaining rather high speeds because no captain likes to actually *stop*, they are in great danger because there is no concerted action. So. At the last moment one turns to starboard – this is the correct thing to do – and the other to port because that is theoretically safer in view of the available information. But his information is one step out of date. So they swerve and might miss even now. But do you know the length of a tanker? A thousand feet! How much better not to swing to one side, *not* to present that thousand feet! For the angle of aspect, as it is called, would then – in a head-on position – be one breadth of the tanker instead of nearly eight. So that tanker gets rammed side on, which is very bad...'

They laughed nervously at this understatement.

Debbie persisted: 'But radar is better than the eye, surely, in such a situation?'

Tomazos thought about it and then said, 'No. Radar is not better than the eye. Yes, maybe in fog and darkness if we all follow the same rules. If there is no echo on the screen there may still be a wooden small boat in our way, giving no echo. The weather can influence performance. Atmospheric conditions – usually exactly when we need great accuracy! – affect the propagation of radio waves... Then, you see, there is a shadow sector, mostly astern. Now we can move our eyes with our bodies and go and have a look. But radar stays fixed so if we are worried on this score we must zig-zag the ship, and this may be in an area where we should not do so... We also have to change from one distance scale to another, but the eye sees all scales at the same time...'

'But I can't see why if you can now see a ship coming towards you in fog there should ever be a collision,' Debbie commented, perplexed.

'You only see it as a dot,' Tomazos told her. 'At first you don't even know if it's coming towards you or moving away ... It takes at least twenty minutes in fog and using radar to be sure of what you're both doing and to manoeuvre accordingly... One is fumbling a bit, at first, for in fifteen seconds the other fellow might alter course a mere 4°. This is not even noticeable on radar, but it may have placed the other ship from a port to a starboard aspect. Even an alteration of 30° may not be noticeable for several minutes after its execution...'

'Gee!' said Debbie. 'Maybe my parents were right to go by plane!'

The passengers and Tomazos were amused by this.

Tomazos said, 'Well, we are in an area of the world pretty

free from fog. And the typhoon season is just over. Perhaps we shall survive!'

'Is this the roughest sea?'

'Oh, no,' Tomazos said decisively. 'The North Atlantic is the rough one. Fog and icebergs too. No deckchairs on that trip! The seas in these parts of the world are usually very calm. The Pacific Ocean was named so for exactly that reason.'

The attractive woman spoke for the first time, and created a noticeable tension even with a harmless question.

'What,' she asked, 'does the Captain do?'

Tomazos had to look at her to answer, and her eyes mocked him, gleamed in awareness of her own capabilities of disturbing him. She had the ability to make him slightly uncomfortable.

'The Captain is always on duty and always responsible, asleep or awake,' he told her. 'Even on leave or when he's gone ashore. Or when a local pilot is on the bridge...'

'Yes, but what does he *do*?' she persisted.

'He has the power of a magistrate although it is not true that he can perform the marriage ceremony—'

'That's a relief!'

They laughed with her.

'The owner can signal a change of port or to take a load or some passengers somewhere, but it is the Master who says how or if it can be done...'

'It doesn't sound very masterful,' the woman suggested. 'We still don't know what he *does*.'

Tomazos was unruffled.

He informed her: 'There are staff conferences, ship inspections, interviewing heads of departments, dealing with correspondence from head office and officials at ports of call. He has the final responsibility for navigation, and expects to be called to the bridge in fog or storm or unusual circumstances. Each voyage he entertains a few people in his Day Cabin and meets every passenger in a number of cocktail parties. He judges competitions and gives prizes. There are occasional problems – stowaways, thefts, irregularities and emergencies. As you may have noticed, he sometimes takes the non-denominational morning service on Sunday...'

'Oh, this is pathetic,' said the woman. 'You read it in a brochure! I mean, honestly, what does he do? Right now, what's he doing?'

Tomazos suspected that Captain Vafiadis was in his Day Cabin reading a paperback, but he assured her loyally, 'I expect he's working on documents relating to our arrival in Singapore, or on official letters, to be posted there to the Company.'

She let it go at that, but smiled slightly in the knowledge that she had made him a little uncomfortable and could by persistence have stung him out of his gravity.

Someone offered the comment, 'It's hot today' in a tone of slight weariness, and at once Pybus took up his cue. He tried to trap Tomazos into an admission by asking, 'What temperature's the ship supposed to be at?'

Tomazos was puzzled.

'The temperature? At the moment the air temperature is 93 and the sea 86. Did you mean the furnaces? They are burning at 3,000°.'

'No. The ship,' said Pybus. He sucked in air laboriously and went on brusquely. 'The cabins, how hot are they supposed to be?'

'Mine is *very* hot,' laughed Tomazos. 'The sun beats on it all day.'

'The bloody air conditioning isn't working,' complained Pybus. 'People have had to come up on deck to sleep.'

'The coolest places on the ship are the lounges,' advised Tomazos, 'and the dining-room. I don't really know what temperatures the cabins are supposed to be at.'

'They don't bloody care either,' growled Pybus.

He staggered away, sniffling noisily, gasping the humid air.

The company director said in what seemed to be apology: 'A gross man. Very embarrassing. Never sober. And he's one of *us*, alas. The same Lodge.'

The visitors began to drift away. A few who had not managed to ask any questions now came up and had a brief conversation with Tomazos. But soon they'd gone and he went for a minute to see Yannopoulos.

He then returned to the chartroom to continue the

plotting which the visitors had interrupted, and found the sybaritic young woman leaning on the chartroom table. He was a little ruffled, but said politely, 'Can I help you?'

'What are these?'

He knew she wasn't interested. She referred to two plan views of the *Areopagus* with coloured markers which could be moved.

'Those are to show the position regarding water and oil. It shows them in tons, as you see – the blue indicating water and the red oil. Some are empty, some are carrying ballast, a few are now only half full. I need this information, not only for the obvious reason but to know the trim of the ship.'

'You give a good lecture.'

'I don't know about *that*!'

'Oh, but you do. You're happy in your work.'

Tomazos coloured very slightly and responded, 'One must be happy in something.'

'You are unhappy in others, then? How interesting! You looked so calm, so impenetrable!'

Tomazos said, 'You must excuse me, I have to plot our next position.'

The woman smiled at his discomposure. 'Not to be alarmed. I am unhappy, too. My only happiness is in sex.'

Tomazos asked frankly, 'Have you had your money's worth?'

She bristled at once. 'What do you mean?'

'Of mocking an officer who you know cannot answer back.'

'You are a stubborn little man. But you've got it wrong. You fascinate me.'

Her fingers touched his on the chart of the approaches to Singapore, and crawled across his one hand. The tactile sensation was surprisingly sensual.

She urged, 'Oh, come on! Don't be unhappy. Where's that stuffy old cabin of yours?'

She was certainly bolder than her predecessors who had been in search of the same result.

He said coolly, 'I am not so unhappy that I need to cheapen myself.'

She wasn't visibly upset, but instead sniffed and commented, 'My God, darling, you *have* been hitting the bottle!'

He was shaken; it was his turn to demand quickly, 'What do you mean?'

'Your breath, pigeon. Neat Scotch is coming straight off the roof of your mouth!'

She was tremendously sensual, but inevitably he thought about Elaine who was equally cheap.

'I must ask you to leave the bridge now,' he said. 'You should not be here. There are plenty of passengers surely to enjoy yourself with.'

'Pathetic,' she said. 'You pompous pathetic little fat man. I'd have given you the time of your life... You damn well stop that!' she shouted suddenly, and left, rapidly, so that the action puzzled him as much as the raised voice.

Yannopoulos had been screened from view and if he had overheard anything, even the shout, it would have meant little to him, for he spoke scarcely any English.

The explanation of her raised voice came when the Staff Captain came to see Tomazos an hour later.

The Staff Captain ranked superior to Tomazos, but only fractionally so. He liked to throw his weight about, and was not liked even among his fellow officers. It was, perhaps, inevitable, since his whole business was discipline.

Nevertheless, his approach was friendly, perhaps to trap Tomazos if he was guilty.

'Someone doesn't love you any more,' he said when he came into the chartroom.

It meant nothing to Tomazos.

'There's been a complaint about you,' the Staff Captain continued. 'Lady named Mrs Pauline Triffett. She says that here on the bridge, on duty, you made certain suggestions to her, offered coarse remarks, pinched her backside. She says you were drunk and shouldn't have been in charge of the *Areopagus* at all.'

Tomazos asked with rage, 'Who the hell is Mrs Pauline Triffett?'

'Oh, come now, Nikolaos. That won't do.'

'Describe her.'

The Staff Captain did so, and suggested, 'Not a young lady you'd fail to notice.'

'She came with the bridge visitors?'

'You're dragging this out, Nikolaos. Of course she did.'

'So they will tell you I made no coarse remarks.'

'She says after they'd gone.'

'No one asked her to linger. Yannopoulos will tell you that I went straight to him when the visitors had left. *Then*, when I returned here, this female was leaning where you are.'

'That sounds fair enough and can be confirmed by Yannopoulos,' agreed the Staff Captain. 'If she was waiting, I accept the reversal of intentions... She's a very lively looking young lady. Why didn't you take up her offer?'

'I have troubles of my own.'

'So has she, it seems. They tell me she's tried to commit suicide a while back—'

'I didn't know that.'

'Would it have made any difference?'

'No. I am not the answer to her problems. *She* is.'

'How about the drinking?'

'I would dispute that I was intoxicated.'

The Staff Captain eyed Tomazos cynically, but made no comment.

Tomazos asked, 'What are you going to do about her complaint?'

'Nothing if Yannopoulos confirms what you say... I'll put her in irons if she starts whoring round among the crew...'

Tomazos was a little irritated to find that this woman turned up at a party given by the Second Officer.

The discord between Tom Mollon and himself had not lasted more than a few hours. Mollon understood all too clearly the cause of Tomazos' misery, and their previous amicable relationship had been resumed. Tomazos went along to his cabin because Mollon was not the man to raise an eyebrow at the amount of drinking. He could put away a fair amount of beer himself.

Dr Dempsey was there, and the American girl, Debbie,

who exuded a very slight air of disapproval. Sister Eleni and a nurse sat on a rug. Kristina sat near to Tomazos, but there were long silences between them. Eleftheriadis, the Deputy Purser, was there, a suave young man who was learning to become as impenetrable as Demetropoulos.

They were talking when the young woman, Mrs Pauline Triffett, knocked and walked into the cabin.

Dempsey protested at once, 'Oh, God, no! Can't you go and be ill somewhere else?'

She responded buoyantly, 'Not ill, Daniel, darling. I'm in rude health.'

Dempsey asked frankly, 'Then what the devil are you doing here?'

'Didn't you ask—?'

'No, I did *not*,' roared Dempsey.

Mollon, who knew nothing about Pauline, but could identify a pretty girl instantly, said, 'I'm having a party. Care to join it?'

'A beautiful idea,' Pauline accepted.

She was introduced. Sister Eleni was decidedly cool; Dempsey said frankly 'You'd talk your way into anything'. When she faced Tomazos, Pauline was a little shaken; or was this, Tomazos wondered, affected? Kristina, behind him, didn't even acknowledge the woman.

'I'm sorry about all that impeachment earlier,' Pauline said meekly and without a qualm. 'I didn't realize you really had problems.'

Her apology was so unabashed and her personality so outrageous he forgave her at once. He was too good-natured a man to bear resentment.

He grinned for the first time in more than a week and said, 'Think nothing of it. Have a drink? At least we have that in common! What sort of a trip are you having?'

Their relationship was reversed in that immediate adjustment which is one of the twentieth-century's few improvements in personal and social behaviour.

It seemed to Tomazos that the Staff Captain had been talking in confidence to this young woman. He might even have given her a hint of this party. She was certainly dressed for it.

'What *does* the Captain really do?' she asked.

Tomazos laughed.

'God only knows. I've never dared to ask him!'

Dempsey claimed, 'He's getting liverish. He doesn't get enough exercise.'

A little later, a little drunker, Tomazos asked Pauline, 'And what did you do to Mr Triffett?'

'Oh, he got fed up with me and went off with an intellectual girl. I was left holding the baby – two of them. How about the First Officer's wife?'

'She took a fancy to someone else.'

'She was a fool.'

'Thank you. You've made my day!'

Tomazos was aware that Kristina had been listening intently to this. He pinched the back of her neck and informed Mrs Triffett, 'Here's a young lady who's marrying an airline tomorrow. Or is it the day after?'

'I am not divorcing the ship to do so, Nikolaos. You know that. I don't really want to leave her.'

Pauline asked, 'Then why do so?'

Kristina said, 'It's a good thing to leave a ship when you're happy. If you wait until you're unhappy ...'

'That's too profound for me,' admitted Tomazos.

'Yes,' agreed Kristina quietly.

Two hours after this Pauline called to Dempsey: 'Come on! Time to take me home!'

'Take yourself home,' bellowed Dempsey. 'I'm not your blasted keeper!'

He looked rather worried, Tomazos thought. He went to his own cabin, at ease for the first time since leaving Adelaide.

Night after night he had been building up a mental file, examining it, staying awake. For he had remembered who 'Peter' was, and to recall where he had previously seen the man was to squirm, to feel a fool, to be hot in humiliation and the certainty that he should have been violent that day, damaged the man, kicked him in the fibrous genitals. For Peter had sold him his sailing boat, and Elaine had bought two of her sports cars from the distributors of which Peter was sales director. Tomazos recalled having found the man in the house once before, at a normal hour, and that Elaine had been very enthusiastic about 'the demonstration' – too enthusiastic, Tomazos now recognized.

But tonight it didn't hurt so much. The ridiculous encounters with Mrs Triffett had reduced Elaine to an equal absurdity. Perhaps, thought Tomazos with his more customary charity, Pauline had been more accurate on the bridge than she had known. Possibly he was a sensual man who was a mild hypocrite who pretended not to be. Had he married Elaine because of an emotional love and things in common – sailing, swimming, eating certain foods, hoping for the same kids? Or had it been because of a fat man's delight when a tall voluptuous foreign girl responded to his admiration? Had he married as a prerequisite to sexual indulgence with that body or had he been in *love*? Why hadn't he married a nice Greek girl – like Kristina, for instance? (Why wasn't Kristina married anyway?) She, too, was tall, but graceful rather than sensual, slim at the hips and with no impertinence in the buttocks; she had an arched long graceful neck and a demure classical face. She would be utterly loyal to whoever she loved – loyalty was one of her properties . . .

He slept soundly, and no one mocked him; Elaine's body did not writhe, greasy with exertion, in another's grasp . . .

The stand-by shook him awake before four o'clock in the morning and in minutes he was on the bridge.

The *Areopagus* was entering the Straat Durian about eighty miles south of Singapore. On one horizon lightning flickered thirty miles away. Ahead a light flashed eight or nine miles distant.

It was ferociously hot, like steam. The sea was completely calm.

There was heavy traffic in these approaches to Singapore and many islands and headlands. But Tomazos had no need to reduce speed yet. Soon he would have to do so and to exercise extreme caution because even the most prudent manoeuvring might not be possible.

He switched both radar sets on, the one at short range and

the other on the maximum scale. Nevertheless, he did not consult them often for he wished to maintain night vision.

Radar on the open sea, with plenty of sea-room, and where traffic was less dense, allowed high speed. The busiest shipping routes in the world had plenty of sea-room; ships were not crossing each other at a distance of a few hundred yards. But there was a point where persistence in speed was taking definite risk, and Tomazos, torn between a delayed schedule and safety, would soon have to choose one. Excuses after a collision were useless to dead passengers. A ship's log which showed that the Officer of the Watch had varied his speed might prejudice an inquiry in his favour, but not his own conscience.

In the approaches to a large port risk was unavoidable and was at its greatest where all routes converged, or the direct route between two points which had to be passed through, and when looking for a pilot vessel or anchorage. Here, Tomazos was close to land now and again and he saw the lights of several ships.

In clear weather he watched the approaching lights of several vessels. Entering thick mist he turned to the radar to observe the next oncoming vessel. Radar could not in fact tell him the aspect of the vessel, but it told him the range. From a combination of time, bearing and this range he worked out its speed and course and deemed that no risk applied unless it altered course violently. He watched the relative speed closely, for not only was it needed for him to resolve the triangle of velocities, but it had a fundamental consideration should manoeuvring action become necessary.

In such waters communication by radio between ships might have seemed a good idea, but would have been frustrated by the congestion of traffic on the wave-length, although some ships of the same company on cross-channel routes did employ bridge radio telephones. Tomazos was aware that even so two had collided. It was the same old business of contradiction – the need for speed and that for safety, and the in-built optimism in every sailor : it happens to the other fellow, not to me.

There was another factor, psychological and cunning,

among some navigators and captains. This was to take the risks but to manoeuvre accordingly. But again this had contradictions. The preference for the active rather than the passive role in a collision – wherein the active nearly always suffered the least damage – was countered by the knowledge that the ship rammed often came to be regarded by the inquiry and even the insurance companies as the victim and therefore eligible for the benefits. Old captains, versed in cunning, also had a tendency to manoeuvre in such a way that if a collision took place it did so on his own ship's port side. He did this on the basis that the other ship would bear the main blame, for a ship was not obliged to alter her course to avoid another which was on her port side. But this semi-legality applied only to clear weather and with a considerable distance between ships.

Tomazos could not indulge in any risky philosophies. His first duty was always to the safety of the passengers.

He was, for instance, rounding a headland now. It was safe to do so at a distance of three miles and ships approached from different directions at an angle of 30°. The routes of different ships were spaced out from that three miles to about eleven. Most of them 'cut the corner' and the concentration was even greater than that which mathematics indicated in the smaller area. Tomazos kept eleven miles out. If any difficulty arose, not only was the concentration of traffic less but he had the open sea available...

Soon, free of mist, he took the *Areopagus* through a narrow channel where ships did not exercise the discipline of those which followed the 'traffic lanes' down the parallel shores of, say, the Strait of Gibraltar. Here, there was heavy traffic and considerable danger even from vessels travelling in the same direction. There was no limit to the width of the channel followed by traffic in each direction, no 'neutral zone', and consequently the risk was quite high.

Nevertheless, Tomazos was not as anxious as when he took the *Areopagus* through the English Channel in fog or darkness. The density of traffic in that Channel was the most formidable in the world – with dozens of collisions each year. The bulk of traffic passed between Dover and the

Varne, where the available width was just over five miles. Tomazos used the less crowded route between the Colbart and Cape Gris-Nez, where the width was seven miles and the navigation no more difficult. There was in this Channel the additional hazard of high-speed ferries crossing from England to France across the main shipping route. This other traffic informed the North Foreland station by radio of their departures and arrivals, and other ships, by listening to these transmissions, could identify the chances of an encounter... If he looked at his radar an Officer of the Watch in the English Channel was likely to be unnerved by seeing fifty vessels on his screen...

Dawn came with a great blast of pink light. There were a surprising number of small vessels, sampans and junks in view. A two-masted junk was passing close by, sailing on the wind. She was a beautiful awkward shape. Her grass-mat sails were stiffened horizontally across their entire width with flexible split-bamboo battens. She was rigged so simply that one man could have taken in her sails in seconds if a storm had whipped up quickly.

Sailors were hosing down the *Areopagus*' deck and there were a few passengers up and about early. They waved to the junk.

The liner approached Singapore with her signal flags flying where they could be read without obstruction from masts or stays.

The flags were made of bunting, which was a strong woollen cloth woven in Yorkshire. The *Areopagus* was wearing her merchant flag at the stern. At the mainmast she was wearing the house flag of the Graeco-Australian Line and hoisted at the fore was the courtesy flag, in this case that of Singapore. She also wore the four flags which were her identification as a ship, and a signal requesting a pilot. Tomazos did not feel she would be in port long enough to merit being ceremonially dressed. That would have to wait until she reached Hong Kong. Then she would be 'dressed all over' – with masthead flags as well as ensigns and jacks, and with decorative lines of signalling flags from bow and stern to the mastheads and also 'rainbow fashion' between the mastheads, and from the mastheads to the deck. At night there would be lines of electric light bulbs...

They had to wait an hour for a pilot while hundreds of passengers, having finished their breakfasts, lined the rails and noted with caustic commentary the comings and goings of small boats.

But at last the *Areopagus* inched her way through channels and for the fifty-third time Tomazos scrutinized the City of Lions, which had a population of eight thousand people in each square mile and saw the arrivals and departures of thirty thousand million tons of shipping each year.

The Somerset Maugham landscape of green cricket pitch, grey stone harbour buildings and red-tiled bungalows was still here, but it was broken and dominated now by the smog-encrusted high-rise hotels, office blocks, department stores and flats.

Anchored in the roadsteads were merchant ships from all over the world, and around the harbour scuttled overladen Chinese tong-kangs ferrying goods from ships to shore, Indonesian barter boats, Chinese sailing junks, Singapore River bumboats with magic painted eyes as big as plates on their bows to ward off evil spirits. From the shore drifted the pungent smells of spices and rotten fish.

Captain Vafiadis and other officers were now on the bridge, and half a dozen Singaporean officials, in good humour.

And now Kristina rushed on.

'Ah!' greeted Tomazos. 'I'm so glad you came because it will be hours—'

'There is some mail for you! You *see*, I did say there would be!'

Tomazos was disturbed; his pulse hastened as he saw that the postmark of one letter was Adelaide.

Kristina made no move.

Tomazos muttered, 'Excuse me,' and read the letter from Adelaide.

It was not from Elaine. He did not know who it was from. There was no address or signature. The first words were 'Somebody ought to tell you that your wife is whoring round...' The words swam a little before his examination. 'Disgraceful ... I know you Greeks don't believe in morals ... not a thought for the children...'

'Something wrong?' Kristina asked, absurdly.

'Something unexpected. Read it...'

She did so, unabashed.

'My God! How sordid! How mean!'

'It is a sordid business.'

'Not your half of it, Nikolaos, I am sure.'

'Ah, well, I am feeling a little better. It is so horrible it can but be a nightmare. Listen! I am glad you came, although I see Captain Vafiadis will have some rude remarks for me later! Because I shall be fiddling about here for hours, and I did want indeed to wish you well.'

'That is kind of you.'

'It is an interesting city. You'll be happy.'

'I hope you will be, Nikolaos.'

'I have plenty to do, that is the thing.'

'Look me up next time you come here, won't you?'

'Oh, I shall do that all right, Kristina! Will you ever come back to Greece?'

'I just don't know at present. When I get lonely...'

'That won't be for a very long time.'

'I must leave you now, Nikolaos. I see the car from the airline.'

'I am sorry. I wish you weren't going. We shall miss you.'

'We?' she pleaded.

'Me.'

They shook hands. It felt insufficient to him after knowing her for three years. He touched her under the chin.

'Cheer up. You look a little daunted.'

She was as awkward as he was, and said 'Nothing of the sort.'

She turned and left. He called out 'Goodbye, Kristina,' but she didn't seem to hear.

A few moments later he went to the wing of the bridge in a curious anxiety, and happened to see her at the foot of the gangway, with cases. She turned her face and looked up.

Tomazos felt oddly guilty and he saw in alarm that she was crying.

He was filled with compassion and at last understood.

He waved, but the airline's automobile had blocked his view, and now it drove away and she had gone.

16

'DEAR friend,' Debbie Vertigan wrote. 'Here I am writing to you, when I am on my way to Hong Kong and hoping to see you within a week. I wonder if my letter will reach Hong Kong before I do?'

It was too hot and she could obtain no reality in the words. The writing room of the *Areopagus* was merely space filled in at a junction of Metaxas Deck, and consisted of a few tables and chairs. All the chairs had been occupied and one lady was even energetic enough to type. Debbie's table was by a porthole and the sun burned her with ferocious retardation. Her neck was moist with sweat, and her dress stuck to her waist and to the leather of the chair. It was impossible to concentrate on anything.

She looked at her watch. It was ten o'clock in the morning. But she was reluctant to move now. She was too self-conscious to sit in a deck chair to pass time away; it would have been an admission that she had nothing to do. Sometimes she sat for nearly an hour in the Aegean Lounge when it was fairly empty, looking at a book but never turning a page. But finally some dull conceited youth would come along and try to persuade her that *he* was what was missing in her life.

Ten o'clock and boiling hot so that she was in a torpor. Ah, well, she reflected, I'd sooner be here than there, in school – Alfie telling us the obvious. He's so *laborious*. Now if Daniel was a teacher he'd be terrific! He's so *alive* compared with other people. Outrageous, but never vulgar. A small smile altered her face as she day-dreamed. I like the smell of tobacco. Not so keen on the whisky. Why does a doctor drink whisky? He must know it's harmful. I wish they didn't all smoke. I feel so silly coughing. I feel absurd, anyway, inhibited, a child, I still rank as a child, even *he* identifies me so and just doesn't interpret the message even if he intercepts it. He thinks it amusing if I drink a sherry and pull a face doing so. What do I have to do to shock him into understanding? Nothing disconcerts him. I suppose doctors get like that. I ought to behave as they did when we crossed the Line – throw sausages at him, pour tomato sauce over his hair, hurl great wet lumps of liver about. Or maybe I should shock him with words: 'You're an amusing bastard, and you monopolize my hopes, dreams and wishful thinking. So will you please do something about it? Kick me, pull my hair, smack me, kiss me, but stop circling around up there in that empyrean orbit and satisfy my adolescent silly penchant for middle-aged doctors of Irish extraction ...'

Anyway, I've written enough of this, so let's go and post it.

Debbie wrote to six pen friends regularly. It was her hobby and even aboard the *Areopagus* she had informed them of the ship's schedule; and at each port there had been a satisfying small stack of mail for her. But something was causing a loss of interest, a remoteness; *he* had said only silly people did it. At Hong Kong one friend was to meet her. It was funny because Debbie didn't know if her correspondent was male or female.

At eleven Draco took six of them through the same steps as yesterday and the day before and the day before that. He used the same record day after day. But slowly they were learning the Greek dance. Sooner or later, Debbie anticipated in trepidation, the six of them would have to put on a public performance. However, it was too late to back out now.

At twelve she went to lunch. There was a young officer who teased her. 'We must feed you,' was his theme. It was an amiable relationship which would never alter. She knew that there was no other intention but to bait her tenderly. How crude and without charm in comparison were the boys round the pool or staring in the lounges in selfish demand.

But today the Chief Steward also came to her table. 'Miss Vertigan?' he inquired. 'You are Miss Vertigan?' She agreed that she was and he gave her an envelope. Inside was an invitation to dine with the Captain. The Chief Steward was waiting for an answer and Debbie said 'Well, thanks. What do I do?'

The other passengers at her table viewed her with slight envy and regarded Debbie anew: she must be someone important. But she presumed that the invitation was because she was her father's daughter. Or perhaps *he* had engineered it.

The young officer again teased her: 'Oh, he'll feed you! You'll groan!'

It was Debbie's habit to walk round the Parade Deck from about four o'clock to five in the afternoon. It was a time when many people had gone to have a drink of tea, and, having had it, they proceeded to the Ionic Lounge for an hour's bingo session.

Today the sea and sky were so flawless that Debbie did not understand how people could sit in a stuffy lounge in a herd for any silly gambling game.

There were only a dozen people on the port and starboard sides of the Parade Deck. At some time in the day most people exercised by walking round it. Some did it after breakfast, some late at night. Many wouldn't stroll alone. They felt, correctly, that they would be stared at, and so went round with husband or friend. Debbie had to walk alone. Sometimes in the morning she proceeded with Miss Wearne at that lady's snail's pace, two or three times up and down, by when Miss Wearne had had enough and flopped into a deck chair. But Debbie had young energy to burn and went round and round the deck – sixteen or twenty times. Each time she was baited gently by three old men who sat together, and acknowledged by a few solitary elderly women. She smiled self-consciously back at them.

There was another female who did this at the same time. She was a thin hatchet-faced woman of about thirty, sexless, of grim countenance, always in an orange dress so that women tittered maliciously and joked about her meagre wardrobe. She didn't even look at the old men and they, having been snubbed long since, made loud and caustic remarks almost every time she came round. If she heard, the woman ignored them. There was a rumour that she was on her way to San Francisco to take up an important scientific appointment. But this was contradicted by the fifth-hand information that someone on board (no one knew who) had worked in the same government office, and she had been loathed there and finally dismissed for stealing. Each day the woman went into the pool and swam fifteen times round in grim exercise, in a clockwise direction, in a costume the same drab colour as a dishcloth.

Debbie had smiled and said 'Hello' ten days ago, the first time she took up the four o'clock routine, but the woman had stared through her spectacles and ignored the greeting. Now it was slightly embarrassing to meet her and it required a little determination to exercise at all . . .

There was a cat miaowing. Debbie stopped perambulating in her long careful nervous stride. She liked cats and was astonished that there was one on board. But she couldn't see it. There was a steward making a noise as he stacked deck chairs, sliding them violently into each other. Debbie hesitated and then walked on. As she came round once more she again heard the cat. She was worried now, feeling it might be trapped, and began to look for it.

She called to the steward, 'There's a cat.'

He was the steward who served the bouillon each morning and stacked chairs at dusk. That was all she or any passenger knew about him. He was about thirty and of medium height. His handsome good humoured peasant's face was traced by lines of sweat.

'Pleeze, Miss, a cat? You've lost a cat?'

'I heard one.'

'Listen. You like cats?'

'I love them.'

'She doesn't like cats. She doesn't like anything.'

He referred to the grim woman just striding round by the aft pool for the fourteenth time.

'Listen,' the steward repeated. 'I am a Greek, yes? I am a

simple sailor. Now tell me, why does a woman like that come on a cruise?'

'I don't know,' said Debbie frankly.

'She has wheels in her head,' the steward observed.

Debbie giggled and he grinned.

'You know that in the night she goes round looking at the rubbish bins? Crazy, that one. She tells the crew how to run the ship. She shouts at the librarian "How dare you close the library at half past five?" Listen. Why do you travel on the *Areopagus*?'

'I'm on my way to Washington.'

'Ah, you are not Australian?'

'I'm American.'

'That is nice. Everyone wants to be American and rich. But what does it matter. A cat is happy without any nationality.'

The cat made a noise.

Debbie said in shock, 'You've got it in your pocket! A kitten!'

The steward smiled. 'Listen! He's very lively, this cat. He scratches.'

'Let me see him.'

'You like cats?'

'I told you.'

The steward brought out of his pocket a small thing which looked like a concertina. He squeezed it and it gave forth a noise like a cat.

Debbie exhaled in disappointment.

'Listen, Miss. You won't tell anyone? Sometimes I get the old ladies very worried. They search and search for the cat. You are not married?'

'Not at my age.'

'Listen. I am – what-you-call-it? – not married, but—'

'Engaged?'

'That is it. To an English girl. Very beautiful. She comes to Athens on holiday. We fall in love. She sends me letters and cards. Every port. Next April we get married. High Wycombe. She doesn't speak much Greek, but I speak a little English.'

'That's romantic,' acknowledged Debbie.

'It is romantic, yes. But you are a nice girl. It will happen to you. You will marry an American who is an attorney or great aviator or doctor – Ah, you blush!'

'I shall stay single and run a home for cats,' Debbie said decisively.

It was still hot at eight o'clock at night. The Captain had picked a sultry evening for his guests. Debbie felt it must be the hottest night she had ever experienced; the temperature stood only at 93 but the humidity was that of a glasshouse. The men looked uncomfortable in their dark suits and as they ate and drank the sweat boiled out of them and they mopped red faces.

The Chief Steward – who had an extraordinary memory for names, even foreign names – introduced the ten guests to each other before they entered the dining-room, but Debbie at once forgot the names and re-introduced herself to the two men between whom she sat. One was an Englishman named Mr Burston, who seemed very shy. 'I don't know why he asked *me*,' he confessed to her, 'I'm only a truck driver.' His odd nervousness made him likeable, human. Debbie's other neighbour was an Italian, a seedy, rakish-looking man of about thirty, named Tornetta. He viewed Debbie with outright sexual interest, and probed with questions as if he had a proposition of some kind, even a proprietorial interest; 'I can get you a job. Big money. I'm in the entertainment business' – 'I haven't been to university yet' – 'You don't need that sort of education. You've got the looks' – 'I can't sing or dance' – 'Who cares?'

That baffled her. Later this man asked about currency. 'Have you got any American dollars?'

This alarmed Debbie more than the inexplicable suggestions about a job, and she answered evasively, 'Only a little. I'm using Australian currency.'

At the far end of the table Dempsey's voice preceded frequent loud laughter, and Captain Vafiadis stared with apparent disapproval. The Chief Engineer smiled thinly. Between courses he was bored and silent and employed a toothpick. Debbie used the opportunity to stare at Dempsey, examine him affectionately, collect details for the mind's eye. She did not believe that he had noticed her, but during the meat course he suddenly called out loudly: 'I remembered about your uncle, Debbie. His name was Toogood. Damn silly name. Is he dead as well?'

She was very embarrassed, because they all stared at her, but delighted that he had not ignored her as he could have done with four people between them, one of whom was the Captain. She shook her head. Across the table a big man, an Australian loud-mouth, drummed his fingers on the wood. He had suggested, when introduced, 'My name's Ballantyne, but call me Harry.' But no one did. The women who sat on each side of him, too timid for such a man, preferred to talk to their other neighbours at the table, and Mr Ballantyne was building up a pressure of resentment likely to be inflicted on someone before the night was out ...

The Captain sent back his soup and, later, his red wine. Mr Burston, observing this, whispered to Debbie: 'I wonder why he does that? It seems okay to me. Do you think it's to irritate the Chief Steward?'

'Perhaps he's a snob.'

'It makes a change,' Mr Burston said oddly, 'to have decent cutlery and service.'

Someone had made the mistake of asking the Captain of the *Areopagus* if the ship would be late reaching Singapore. Captain Vafiadis answered in his wooden manner, slowed down by translation, 'As far as I am concerned the ship would be on schedule. But the wishes of the Company and myself cannot always be translated into steam.'

The passenger, a middle-aged lady, who was finding the Captain by her side rather heavy going, was satisfied by this adroit answer.

But it had been overheard by Mr Bitsios, the Chief Engineer, who now addressed her, without heat but as if amused.

'The heat and pressure of steam are known factors, and a specific number of propeller revolutions can be provided. The schedule could be arranged with the benefit of this information. But it rarely is. It is assumed by those who ought to know better that the *Areopagus* can always maintain maximum speed and that the sea will always be of a calm disposition. These others are perhaps not aware that the world is round ...'

'My navigating officers,' the Captain informed the lady, 'can bring the *Areopagus* to within a specific hundred square yards of the Pacific Ocean. They can do so at a given time providing their modest instructions over the telegraph are carried out.'

'I have served on this vessel since it was purchased,' Bitsios told the passenger, who was now scarlet and uncomfortable. 'We have had three Masters and it speaks well for them that for our first five years we had a reputation of arriving within a quarter of an hour of the advertised time. Of course, most captains have acquired their positions, not by birth or financial considerations, but by experience and merit.'

Mr Bitsios evidently considered the subject of no further interest and resumed activity with the toothpick.

Mr Ballantyne complained with sour animosity. 'If we ran a business the way they run this ship we'd never last a week.'

But no one took any notice of this, nor of his subsequent complaint: 'Aren't we keeping the cabaret waiting?'

They were. It was the custom of the Captain to take his guests from the dinner to the late cabaret, but he in no way hurried them or himself to do so. He led them into the Aegean Lounge twenty-five minutes late. The assembled audience was already restive. The performers were furious.

Debbie sat by Mr Burston at one side of the stage where a dozen seats had been placed for the Captain and his guests. If it had been hot before, here it was stifling, two or three hundred people crowded in for the second performance, curtains drawn, lights hot, cigarette smoke thick under the coloured bulbs. Debbie could see the sweat shining on scores of faces.

The six girls danced with their usual precision and nimbleness, and then Edgar confronted the audience.

'Are you hot?' he asked. They sniggered. 'Have you taken

your shoes off? And your shirts and ... other things? *Well!*' They laughed. 'That's right. Make yourself at home. Tired? Are you sticky? Did you have a good dinner? The Captain did! Three extra courses.' They tittered now. Edgar continued: 'Are you looking forward to seeing Singapore? Do you think we'll be allowed ashore? Do you think we'll ever get there?' There were cries of 'No!' Edgar said 'Never mind. They're *trying*. Do you know, to make sure we get there on time, they've hired a hundred tugs and they're pulling Singapore Island to meet us! Isn't that nice of them? There'll be a small charge, of course ...'

The Captain and Chief Engineer were used to being the butt in concerts and other entertainments. It went with their jobs. And the satisfying truth was that, late or not, decrepit or not, the passengers remembered the *Areopagus* with affection. Perhaps it was because she and her crew were fallible, as they were. They came back for second journeys or visited her like an old friend when she was in port.

Now Edgar and the other comedian, with the dancers in support began to sing:

'Bless this ship, O Lord we pray,
Keep it moving night and day.
Bless the turbines and the steam,
Make them better than they seem ...'

The audience loved this and bellowed. Some of them were already drunk and empty beer cans were rolling about. The sweating stewards hurried about with trays. One placed a small glass of green liquid in front of Debbie, but she left it alone.

Edgar now sang:

'Bless the Captain, tall and proud,
Far above the common crowd.
Teach us him to fairly trust,
And not because we simply must ...'

Bitsios smiled carefully in satisfaction at this and lit a cigar. Captain Vafiadis stared woodenly at nothing.

The other comedian sang caustically:

'Bless the funnels pouring smoke,
Dropping spots on reckless folk.
Send some experts down below
To make the air conditioning blow.'

Mr Ballantyne stood up and shouted, 'Hear, hear! This isn't a Greek ship! It's a Turkish bath!' He received a laugh and a flutter of applause and was satisfied.

Twenty-two hours later Miss Wearne inquired. 'Are you going somewhere special? You do look smart.'

Debbie, sitting near the telephone, hating the instrument, qualified, 'I don't know about that.'

It rang, and she jumped. Her agitated hand reached out. A voice said, 'Eric, listen, we'll see you in the Midships in ten minutes. Okay?'

It wasn't going to ring for *her*; the clock admitted that. A vague invitation of five days ago, and *his* promise 'I'll let you know,' not fulfilled. He had a lot to attend to; she forgave him; but was nervous about thrusting herself into a party to which the overture had been a mere 'You'll come, too, won't you?' She wasn't even sure of where Mr Mollon's cabin was or how to get to it. However, the radio officer, when encountered, told her.

They accepted her readily, Daniel even commenting, 'I wondered where you'd got to. Come and have a beer.'

This seemed promising enough, and she even drank the liquid which, to her, tasted like chilled dishwater. But the evening soon began to go wrong. She probed cautiously: 'What are you going to do in Singapore?' and he answered, yawning with enormous indifference. 'God only knows.' This hurt, proved utter unconcern. Perhaps it was a careless moment and he hadn't really ignored the hint. She selected words carefully: 'I've never been,' to which he said, typically, 'It smells and the taxi drivers are corrupt.'

Mollon, overhearing, commented, 'They're all corrupt, but the girls are beautiful.'

Sister Eleni said, 'That is not true about the corruption.

The present government is very much against corruption. It demands six signatures where others require one ...'

Mr Tomazos sighed.

'I hope not, Eleni!'

And then the evening's hopes were foiled, the pleasure was diverted. The woman Pauline barged in. Daniel shouted at her, but it was the noise of familiarity. The vulgar poise of the woman outclassed Debbie's capabilities. She was not at ease anyway at parties in which others became noisy through drinking. Even smoking discomforted her. If only there was a window to open!

It became terribly hard to bear. She was tensed with concentration, not quite understanding the relationship nor the fierce dialogue. After a time she was simply miserable and waiting for time to pass so that she could leave legitimately without being a poor sport or reminding them by her departure that she was a child.

At eleven she yawned, not quite deliberately, and Dempsey, noticing it, chided: 'I hope you're not bored.'

She was stung and said, 'I want to go to bed.'

The officers and women smiled at this.

'I'll walk you home,' suggested Dempsey.

But she was cross with him for his perfunctoriness.

'It doesn't matter,' she said tartly. 'I'm not likely to get lost on a *ship*.'

She hurried away and it was difficult not to weep in the protection of darkness.

In the morning she escorted Miss Wearne round the shopping centre of Singapore, and strolled round the Botanical Gardens. Miss Wearne would have been hopelessly lost without her. They watched the monkeys and suddenly it began to rain. Nearby was a tin-roofed shelter in which people were selling orchids. The rain was the heaviest Debbie had ever seen. Or heard. It tattooed on the tin so that conversation was impossible, and bounced on hard surfaces. Disappointment and hurt filled Debbie. When anyone asked her about Singapore it would always open a small cicatrice. Ten years hence, the journey and the people forgotten, the City of Lions would be mentioned in some conversation thousands of miles away, and she would inquire, 'Is that rain I can hear?' and some small sensation of heat and a sadness like nostalgia would touch her, re-open the scar...

17

BY NOW a number of passengers were going down with some form of influenza. They at once identified it as Asian, but Edgar suggested that it was 'air conditioning flu'. Some of the old people were flushed or very pale, and for them enjoyment faltered and became distress.

At lunch one day it happened to Squibb. He seemed to fall alseep at the meal, then recover, several times, until he finally fell forward over the table and his face dropped into the cream cake he was eating.

Tornetta found this very satisfying, and sneered to the other two at the table, 'He's joking, of course.'

But Squibb wasn't joking. He recovered a little and staggered away. 'Oughtn't you to help him?' one of the old ladies suggested in reprimand. Tornetta was contemptuous. 'He'd be humiliated,' he excused himself.

Tornetta didn't go near the cabin for hours. Squibb did not turn up for the next meal. 'How's your friend?' the same lady asked. Tornetta growled : 'I don't know. He's no friend of mine. He's a fool.'

Such frankness, however truthful, was too much for her and her companion, and they were silent in condemnation...

It was quite pleasant to have Squibb incapacitated. It allowed some freedom of action not possible before. Tornetta found Squibb pale and weak in his bunk. The cabin smelled of sickness. And it was amusing to hear Squibb, no longer an extrovert, but complaintive, anxious for consolation :

'I was sick a lot. He never examined me. Just pills. How does he know—? I ought to be in hospital.'

'Keep fit,' sneered Tornetta. 'Have a go at deck tennis! Cut your toe nails! Apply deodorant!'

The eyes stared at him wretchedly, unable to resist the mockery.

'I was sick. Five times.'

But if he expected consideration or offers to fetch glasses of water or plates of dry toast, Squibb was disappointed. For Tornetta had no sympathy. He was tough. Illness was something he didn't tolerate. It just didn't happen to him, had never been allowable in the environments in which he had matured. Pain, yes, pain inflicted and received, that was necessary for progress, social adjustment.

Squibb was a fool, one of many on board. He merited illness. And the others – how easy it was to despise and rob them! Old men and women whose skin under the tropical sun seemed to have cracked into squares like wood with dry rot. Women who exposed old big feet with lumpy toes as they sat in deck chairs waiting for the next excuse to fill their bellies. Muscle-bound bare-chested youths who queued for the picnic lunches reeking of the morning's exercise. Women with immense scabrous arms and mottled hands and faces dried out and cracked by years under the Antipodean sun long before they came here. They wore vulgar straw hats of too shiny blue or black, top heavy with ludicrous birds or fruit or silly messages of happiness. Old men who still, in sultry Asian heat, wore dark grey heavy trousers hitched high up on the chest, and carried immense stomachs before them. They sweated into brightly coloured shirts. Only Australians or Americans, Tornetta felt, could be quite so ugly, and although they were good humoured, reasonable and often polite, he despised them. Soft, vulgar provincials who had saved for years to stare at this sea. He moved among them, more conspicuous than he was aware, and it was easy to steal their money. Walk behind them as they went to lunch, see them put the key of their cabin into the box – fifth key, second row, say – and turn at the next junction and go round the other three sides of the square for it. Straight in and out. Of course, if they had forgotten something and came back for it – but so far this hadn't happened.

They were easily intimidated by social customs, clocks and gongs . . .

He stood in the right-hand of two queues of about eight persons each who waited for the shipboard branch of an Australian bank to open. He had a little Singapore money to change. Mr Pybus was in the other queue, his breath rasping, heavy with complaint. 'It's after ten o'clock. What are they messing about at?' No one answered him. Tornetta reminded himself that Pybus should be easy to rob, being half or totally drunk most of the time, and untidy, careless about jackets and, it was to be expected, about money and wallets . . .

The bank opened and the two young men who were cashiers began business. They had a routine, slow and frustrating to people like Mr Pybus. Every transaction involved dialogue, questions and answers about amounts of money, and the first two things the cashiers wanted to know were the passenger's name and his or her cabin number. Almost invariably this was followed by an outright 'How much?' and Tornetta was able to listen. It was impossible to hold all the information in the mind, but he didn't need to. The cabin number and a name were enough, and could be checked against the passenger list.

This morning a man in the adjoining queue, Mr Ballantyne, was noisy with self-importance.

'What's the best currency for Hong Kong?'

'Oh, anything, sir,' the cashier told him. 'Your Australian will do fine.'

'Okay. Can you cash these travellers' cheques? Five hundred dollars worth?'

If he thought the cashier would be impressed, Mr Ballantyne was in error, but Tornetta was interested. It was quite dull in this part of Metaxas Deck, and when Mr Ballantyne had received his money he turned away to his left, rather than to his right where the other queue waited, and thus he did not see Tornetta at all. Tornetta waited a moment and then, as if changing his mind or remembering something more urgent due at this time, moved away to the right and strode the length of the deck before ascending to the Parade

Deck. After ten minutes he went down in the lift to A Deck and to his cabin.

Squibb wasn't there, which surprised him.

Tornetta examined the passenger list, which confirmed the information Mr Ballantyne had been so ready to give in his loud voice to the cashier, namely, that he was in Cabin 37 of Attica Deck.

This was a little worrying, as Attica Deck was regarded as being unstinted, not far short of luxurious; and on such decks – Delphi was even grander – stewards buzzed like flies and steward officers collected obsequiously. There was no Mrs Ballantyne in the passenger list and Tornetta felt it was a matter of extreme haste, or not at all, and thus was too panicky to read through five hundred and fifty names and numbers to see who was in the cabin with Ballantyne, if anyone was.

He lifted the telephone. Hurry, you idle wench, his mind pleaded.

A girl's voice asked with a Continental intonation: 'Can I help you?'

'Cabin 37, Attica.'

'One moment.'

Ballantyne's voice said 'Yeah?'

The chain was flushed two yards from Tornetta, behind the partition wall, terrifying him, and Squibb's hands were clattering the door.

Tornetta's heart accelerated to pure panic. He said hastily, 'You're wanted at the Purser's office.'

Ballantyne procrastinated with irritation: 'What for?'

'I don't know,' was all Tornetta could think of.

'Well, find out.'

Squibb inquired, 'Who's that?'

'Immediately, if you please,' Tornetta pleaded furiously into the mouthpiece. Idle, lazy, arrogant loud-mouth, why didn't he do what the previous two had done, that is, agree to rush up the decks (in this case one deck) at once?

'I was told it was urgent,' he said now. 'Please come at once.'

'When I'm bloody ready,' disputed Ballantyne, and rang off.

Squibb repeated, 'Who was that? You look worried.'

'She turned me down,' said Tornetta. '*Me!*'

'Temperature's down to 99,' Squibb informed him. 'Oh, but I feel weak.'

'Back to bed then,' urged Tornetta, and rushed out of the cabin.

He hurried to Metaxas Deck and stared in the shop window. There was a lot of people trying to obtain attention at the Purser's office, itself like a post office counter, and only the German girl and Deputy Purser were attending to them. And they weren't rushing themselves. If Ballantyne came now he'd expect to be seen at once, but Australian aggressiveness in the others would delay him until they had been first attended to, and even if his sheer self-importance persuaded them to allow him before themselves, it was safe to assume that the German girl and Eleftheriadis were so dopey that some time would pass before they had convinced Ballantyne or themselves that in fact no one at the Purser's desk required to see him at all. He'd disbelieve this until he got back to his cabin...

Here came Ballantyne in haste despite his surly qualification. He had left behind the jacket he had been wearing in the queue at the bank. He hesitated, clearly irritated at the prospect of having to wait whole minutes while Eleftheriadis and the blonde girl sold stamps or attended to passport problems and tickets for excursions ashore.

Tornetta waited no longer. He hurried behind Ballantyne, ignored the vacant lift, and ran up the steps to Attica Deck. A long empty corridor stretched before him. There was no point in hesitation. A steward sauntered into view as he neared the point where Ballantyne's cabin must be. He opened the small box and with nervous fingers picked number 37 off its peg. Surely the presence of the key here proved that there was no one in the cabin...

He passed the steward and, hot with misgiving, sweating and trembling, his legs fluttering, turned off the main line of cabins into the smaller row athwartships. He had words ready on his dry lips: 'Oh, so sorry, I want 137' – 'Oh, excuse me. I was looking for Mr Croxley.' People were slow in reaction. Whole seconds would pass before they questioned 'Who gave you the key?'

Fear quietened as he pushed the door open and went in. He was committed, in action, and his glands attended to his anxieties.

It was gloomy in the cabin. His acoustic senses and his nostrils were touched before his retinae made identification. Otherwise he would have fled. Instead he had closed the door. A strong smell of spirits and something else – medicine, antiseptics – assailed his nostrils. And then he heard the rasp which was not the sea or faulty plumbing or belonging elsewhere.

A gross figure was sprawled on the carpet gasping and writhing, huge and flabby, so that in terror Tornetta moved backwards quickly, believing it was some animal.

His eyes then told him that it was Mr Pybus and he was having some kind of fit . . . He was on his face and stomach, one arm bent and the other outstretched with twitching fingers. The fist of the bent arm clutched banknotes. Other notes lay on the carpet.

Tornetta was paralyzed with funk, waiting for this animal thing, seething with its private miseries, to turn and see him. He had no interest in sympathy. If it died or went into unconsciousness, so much the better . . .

He breathed through his mouth to obtain silence, but Pybus was far beyond hearing others. Then Tornetta's eyes, examining his position for a line of escape, saw Ballantyne's jacket on the upper bunk.

Tornetta moved a step or two and reached it at the full length of his arm. It dropped and made a heavy noise on an uncarpeted part of the deck. Keys or cash. Pybus made grunting ululations, a hoarse dissonance for help. But he evidently could not move, and if he could not move then he could not see. Tornetta in the speed of panic ripped the contents out of the pockets of the fallen. It wasn't too satisfying – the bulk of those five hundred dollars had been put somewhere else, and there wasn't time—

He snatched the wad of notes from the hand of Pybus and gave his head a quick kick, to occupy it with pain while he retreated, still unidentified. He stuffed all these notes into his own trouser pocket, and fled precipitately, not caring if a steward saw him at not.

In this condition of inhibiting terror he hurried along Attica Deck, up to the Parade Deck, and, finding crowds, failed to calm himself and merge. He went higher, up on the near empty Sun Deck. The smoke from the forward funnel, without breeze or air to carry it upwards or away, was sinking as soon as it was belched out. Only the motion of the *Areopagus* kept it up long enough to prevent it falling all over the Sun Deck. Astern it sagged in an oily smoke screen on to a motionless sea.

Tornetta stood between two lifeboats; no one was near. He took out the notes and counted them. Two hundred and five Australian dollars.

He looked up and jumped guiltily. From another ship people were staring.

The other vessel seemed dangerously close, and Tornetta saw in astonishment that it was on a heading which might bring it into collision with the *Areopagus.* He joined other passengers who also were fascinated by the spectacle.

The vessel was a Soviet merchant ship, very modern, and it was on the port side of the *Areopagus.* This meant that on courses which were clearly convergent this Soviet ship was obliged to give way to turn aside. Instead she was maintaining course and trying to cross ahead of the Greek liner.

Passengers shook their fists at the Russian crew members who could be seen.

The old *Areopagus* had the edge in speed, and also held her course. Slowly she overhauled the Soviet vessel, and this crossed behind her at scarcely a ship's length.

As it did so it ran into the heavy saturation of black smoke lying on the water, and a beginning breeze, or perhaps one created by the *Areopagus*, shifted the direction of the smoke from the funnel and it continued to pour over the bridge and decks of the Soviet ship long after she'd passed to the starboard quarter. The passengers on the *Areopagus* cheered.

In the middle of the afternoon Tornetta went to the cinema simply because he felt nervous still and wanted to be out of the way.

The cinema of the *Areopagus* was an amateur affair, with a projector placed on a table in the Ionic Lounge and wooden chairs assembled in rows. The chairs were used here on Sundays for church services.

Quite a few people had turned up. The film to be shown was about their next port of call, Hong Kong.

Alone, Tornetta felt his apprehension return. Everyone else chattered with friends and relations while waiting for the performance to begin. He felt isolated and therefore conspicuous, and cursed the electrician who was, as usual, late.

Out of the corner of his eye he saw a girl looking for a seat. It was the dancer, Barbara, on her own. He turned to examine her frankly, and she recognized him and came to the adjacent seat.

'Do you mind?' she asked, but already seated, fully aware that he did not.

'Where've you been?' Tornetta asked outright. 'I haven't seen you for days.'

'Touch of the flu.'

'I've missed you.'

'That's nice.'

'I wanted to talk to you.'

'Just to talk,' she sniggered archly in a whisper.

By now Tornetta was full of confidence and his natural tastes asserted themselves. The girl was wearing a vulgarly short dress. It had risen as she had sat down and he put his hand on her knees in the darkness now and moved it slowly round into the warmth of her inner thighs. She did nothing to stop him. The outright impudicity of English girls startled Tornetta. He could remember a time only a few years ago when English girls visiting Italy had been scared to death. Now they were almost predatory.

His body was bothered by the tactile concession. He took her nearest hand in his own and crushed it to his swelling genitals. So far from being alarmed or insulted the girl from Aberystwyth explored delicately with her fingers and whispered, 'I'll see you tonight? After the show?' and he had to move the fingers which were too sensual to bear . . .

But he had to wait many frustrating hours for her and had doubts as to whether they would be able to find anywhere private.

He watched her body in its various costumes in the late cabaret, librating with impertinence. She knew he was there and put that extra ounce of oscillation into each of the three dances of the evening's entertainment. He wondered if anyone in the audience was shocked or capable of identifying the lewdness added to what was simply a vigorous and attractive dance . . .

She met him in the Midships Bar and drank quite heavily and quickly. There were now interesting pouches under her eyes. Others were dancing, but she did not want to dance. 'My feet!' she protested. 'This sultry weather is murder. I suppose it's better than a storm. I nearly broke my leg on the way out from England.'

Tornetta assured her, 'You're too beautiful for this sort of stuff. You ought to be on TV or in some important London show—'

'You're joking. Dancers are two a penny, and they have to be terrific to make it—'

'Would you like to work for me? In San Francisco to start with. Las Vegas or New York later.'

'You're giving me the chat so you can lay me,' she suggested crudely.

'No. I am entirely frank.'

'What at?'

'The game. High class. Big money. Your own automobile, clothes by the ton, a luxury flat . . .'

She wasn't upset by the suggestion.

'I dunno. You're *somebody*, see, in the dance business, even aboard the *Areopagus*. I've been to the Army and Navy camps – Aden, Malta, Germany . . . All sorts of people ask to marry me,' she claimed, as if this proved status.

'Do they put money in your bank?' he asked.

'I never asked them to.'

'Have you got money?'

'Hell, no, Bartolomeo. I spend it.'

'You'd make thousands, faster than you can spend it. No tax. No problems.'

'I might be interested,' she admitted. 'This is bloody hard work. We rehearse for three hours while everybody else is having a siesta. Then two performances at night. And touches of enteritis and flu thrown in ...'

'You'd be respectable,' he claimed ludicrously, and meant it.

They were both mildly drunk, hot with lust, unable to keep apart. Physical contact became a violent compulsion. They went to his cabin. She was drunk enough not to care about Squibb.

Squibb woke up and was most disturbed to overhear the sniggers, to listen to them writhing and giggling on the lower bunk.

'Are you crazy?' he croaked. 'What the devil are you doing?'

'Take no notice,' urged Tornetta, his hands spread on the girl's buttocks so that she wriggled and sniggered. 'He's a wowser. He's got Asian flu. He can't do what I can!' Tornetta boasted. He knew that Squibb would be a virgin, he'd look at the hot magazine photographs and his body would shuffle with heat while his mind, allegedly superior, condemned, was shocked ...

Squibb became very silent and Tornetta, his sweating buttocks heaving up and down in the confined space, knew that Squibb was intent in auscultation, identifying every sibilance of breath or snigger, and excited masochistically by every acoustic evidence of clothes and flesh ...

It was irritating to be aware that Mr Ballantyne had several hundred dollars and have no means of taking them off him; and humiliating for Tornetta to realize that fear held him back from any second attempt at robbery.

Circumstances now arose, however, whereby it might be possible to take money from this big arrogant man legitimately.

A week earlier Tornetta had read the notice in the Ship's Daily Activities which told him 'Mrs Carter will teach you bridge, 11 AM, Labyrinth Club.'

The notice was in the news sheet nearly every day, and the lady concerned probably never saw the sea, she played or taught card games for such a large proportion of the day.

Tornetta was something of a card sharp, but at other games, not the surburban game of bridge. He went along to learn how to play and to pass the time which hung so heavily on his hands. (For, even though he now was becoming intimately acquainted with Barbara, her day was a working day and fully occupied until eleven at night, with few exceptions.)

No one else on this day had come forward to learn bridge. The truth was that passengers either played cards or they did not, and those who did not were a little wary of learning aboard the *Areopagus*. Mrs Carter was not having brisk business.

She was a medium-sized woman of the middle Australian class, about forty, quite sexless in appearance, with a leathery face and hair very short and curly. In a few days and with the assistance of others she taught Tornetta how to play bridge, and she was very thorough and earnest. Tornetta learned slowly, deliberately, not wishing to frighten anyone by being too proficient, for at the back of his mind was the possibility that as well as entertainment he might at some stage play for money and make a killing...

Soon he was a regular player – one of perhaps sixteen who came daily to the Labyrinth Club and passed a couple of hours very quickly. No one played for money, it at first seemed. Tornetta watched the techniques and mannerisms of this group of people – tough gross women from Sydney suburbs, youths who thought they were smooth, businessmen for whom bridge was an addiction.

Tornetta was to some extent aware that he himself looked a little fly, so he played calmly, without passion or aggression, and his conversation and manners were exemplary, a good imitation of one who had just learnt the game and was anxious not to put a foot wrong.

After a while they played for money, and not many hours after that fate gave him Mr Ballantyne as a partner.

Mr Ballantyne's whole posture was aggressive, and he had no hesitation in telling others what fools they had been. And since he was six feet three inches, of apparent good physique, albeit about forty years of age, other men did not argue with one whose flash-point was low. A few heavy women resented his analyses and argued with him quite noisily, but generally he was allowed to get away with it . . .

He was explaining with bitterness hours later what a fool Tornetta had been at a certain stage of the game. Tornetta was undisturbed. This was his moment to tempt Mr Ballantyne.

'You take the game too seriously,' he said.

'We lost five dollars,' countered Mr Ballantyne.

'Chicken feed,' suggested Tornetta. 'A game for clergymen and old ladies and representatives of soap companies.'

Mr Ballantyne's eyebrows rose. He considered Tornetta with what he thought was care, and Tornetta could almost identify his conclusions : a cheap dago, café proprietor, maybe a gigolo or small time con man.

'You'd like to try some other game?'

Tornetta affected to hesitate. 'Some time, yes.'

'How about today?'

'Well . . .'

'Chicken already? You say this is chicken feed. What kind of money can you put up to support your big mouth?'

This was insulting, but Tornetta had to swallow it, for he could not take on Mr Ballantyne physically. The two other men at the table were shaken. One said, 'No need for that kind of talk, Charles.'

'Why not?' Ballantyne asked brutally. 'He's losing my money because he doesn't take this game seriously.'

'I'm good for a thousand dollars,' said Tornetta.

They were startled. Even Ballantyne hesitated. Then he accepted. 'All right. What game?'

'Whatever you like.'

'Know 'em all, eh?' suggested Ballantyne. 'There's a session here at four in the afternoon for money.'

Tornetta turned up that afternoon and was a little surprised at the number of men who also came. Twenty of them, all aggressive with self-confidence.

They sat down to play, and in ninety minutes Tornetta had taken six hundred dollars from Mr Ballantyne. The man was a cheap loud-mouth, filling himself with beer now and soon he'd be looking for an excuse to inflict violence. Tornetta did not know how he could escape it if the man chose to find legitimate cause...

'Mr Tornetta,' a voice said, and his confidence and skill went to pieces. 'I have been looking for you. So! This is what you do?'

It was the Italian who gave the little boy five cents, who spoke softly, in English now, who had 'been ill' but had the appearance – and the appetite, Tornetta had observed fearfully in the dining-room – of excellent health. He had the shape of a pear – but a young pear, not yet soft. His face was sallow and smooth, his eyes big and innocent, but somewhere along the line his hands had acquired the texture of newly-sawn wood.

'You were looking for me?' Tornetta commented, his own hands suddenly moist so that the cards he held became wet and slippery.

'I felt we must get together,' Mr Rossi said expansively. He continued in Italian: 'We are the only Italians aboard. Did you know that?'

'You want to play?' asked Ballantyne impatiently.

'Of course, of course. What are you playing?'

They told him.

Mr Rossi sat down delicately, his considerable weight balanced lightly on the edge of a wooden chair.

Tornetta began to lose and Ballantyne to regain some of what he'd lost. Mr Rossi also won without apparent effort. He shuffled his cards like a computer. Only the exodus of the rest of the group for a meal spared Tornetta. He strolled out on to the deck, dazed, eyes out of focus, with Mr Rossi alongside, affable, gratified, apparently, by the victory which had given him ten dollars. Mr Rossi was full of small talk.

'I won the ship's lottery today too!' he told Tornetta in

mild intoxication. 'Four dollars eighty-two cents. We steamed 432 miles in the twenty-four hours. I estimated 434 – the sea is calm, of course. So! Today I show a profit! Are you dining now? Come! Let us have a drink first.'

In the Midships Bar Mr Rossi was still garrulous. He did not seem to notice that Tornetta was almost silent. 'How much did you take that big fellow for?'

'About three hundred and fifty when we left.'

'Dollars? My goodness, he won't like that! A bit of a big mouth, wasn't he? But three hundred and fifty! And you'd been losing for an hour! You are a very good businessman, Mr Tornetta! But you must avoid that gentleman! You *are* in business, I suppose? I, too, have a business. Printing, you know. In a small way. It is very pleasant doing business in this manner. An hour, that is all I shall need in Hong Kong, and I may be richer shortly afterwards by thousands of dollars. In San Francisco it will be different, tougher. I expect trouble there . . . What did you say your line of business is?'

'Entertainment,' Tornetta told him reluctantly.

'Ah, that is good. The Australians are great extroverts. You make money at this?'

'Not bad.'

'You are on business now?'

'Holiday.'

'Your wife is not with you?'

'I am not married.'

'Ah! My wife does not like the sea,' claimed Mr Rossi. 'Nor the airplanes. A pity, for what is there to worry about? It is as calm as an automobile today. You are going far?'

'To Italy,' said Tornetta, his mind in confusion. He would leave the ship at San Francisco, that was a certainty now. His brother would be there, Barbara would come. They'd be quiet for a few months, and then explore the position.

'We must see each other more often,' proposed Mr Rossi. 'Two middle-aged Italians. We must do business, surely? Printing and entertainment. There must be something I can do for you and you for me. You know Mr Osborne?'

'No.'

'He is big in the entertainment business. I am surprised

that you did not know him ... I must introduce you to a few people here . . . You come from Sicily, Mr Tornetta?' he ventured slyly.

'Palermo,' acknowledged Tornetta.

'Ah! I thought so! A place to get away from. Although things are improving, I understand . . . I have been in Australia twelve years. Very difficult to start with. Even the British treated us like cattle on their ship. Not allowed ashore, I recall, at Aden, because of our probable infestation! Those days are over, but they were hard. I worked in a restaurant for two years, a waiter! I saved and saved. Money talks in Australia, as it does in the United States. Five years ago I started my own business. Are you a brother, Mr Tornetta?'

Tornetta was startled.

'A brother?'

'Ah! I see you are not. I joined a Masonic Lodge, and this is the brotherhood of business. You must join, I feel. One always needs help, Mr Tornetta, and friends . . . Ah! Now listen. Will you be my guest? There will be a function in a few days.'

'It is kind of you, but—'

'No excuses. You are naturally apprehensive; there are ceremonies and mysteries. But this is just a social gathering – a few speeches, drinks, introductions and some dancing.'

They separated to eat at different tables. Tornetta's appetite was diminished by fear and, later, his sexual desire attenuated, although Barbara seemed satisfied.

He had to think, but couldn't. The man had persisted in this intention of introducing Tornetta to a lot of Masons, Australian middle-aged businessmen and their wives. Why? It would make both of them conspicuous. Further social engagements and contacts would follow. It would remove anonymity for both of them, cast them under a minor limelight. From being inconspicuous passengers, known only to half a dozen people, scores of persons would now identify them daily, offer a greeting every time encountered. If it was a stratagem to humiliate him, Tornetta failed to see its subtlety. The Mafia did not work this way. The executioner did not parade his victim around a ship. Was Mr Rossi the instrument of retaliation at all? It he was not, then no one else aboard the *Areopagus* was and he, Tornetta, was safe.

But he did not feel secure. He had experienced danger before, the anticipatory days before the men came and he'd been thrashed with fists and sticks. It was why he had left Italy. And now his nerve-ends jangled in the same manner. But this time he was not in a society which accepted vengeance as inevitable. Even aboard the *Areopagus* there were rules, law and order could, if necessary, be maintained.

The invitation came, a piece of cardboard, two days later. What harm could there be in going? They would not hurt him there, only make the initial move in the stratagem which was to destroy him. He could go along and perhaps, identifying this first move, frustrate the second.

Squibb asked from his bunk – he was still there, weak and now petulant – 'What are you getting dressed up for in the afternoon?'

It was half past five.

Tornetta told him, 'I am a guest of the Masons.'

'Aren't you going to spray yourself with eau-de-Cologne?' Squibb inquired sarcastically.

'Watch your mouth,' Tornetta said angrily.

It was indeed his habit to use a little scent. The women liked it. But now he walked out of the cabin without doing so.

And it was as well that he neglected this personal habit this time. For among the forty Masons and their wives and guests was Mr Pybus. His breathing was a considerable exertion, but he was almost sober and dressed in a dark suit. He had a square of adhesive bandage on the side of his head, and he was holding forth to those four or five Brothers and their guests who had the misfortune to be near him.

'— And this swine not only robbed me when I was very ill, but kicked me when I was down. But I'd know him,' claimed Pybus. 'I didn't see him, but I'd *smell* him if I met him. Because he was scented like a bloody dago.'

Tornetta went hot with shock and turned his face away lest someone noticed his concern.

Mr Rossi introduced him to many people, and these acknowledged him politely. Only Mr Ballantyne was offensive. 'You've got a face, coming here amongst honest people,' he told Tornetta with surly humour.

Mr Rossi conducted Tornetta on, commenting sadly, 'Oh, he takes his loss badly, that one!'

Tornetta was tense with expectation, but the affair was quite dull, even tedious.

They were at last seated. Chairs had again been arranged in the Ionic Lounge, microphones installed, small tables spread about, and stewards moved slowly around with drinks on trays. Tornetta drank quickly, but it made no difference: he was scared.

There began a long list of toasts which, for him, were ludicrous – toasts to the Queen of England, the King of Greece, the Masons, the Captain and the Ladies. And each speaker insisted among his panegyrical platitudes, 'We're having a fine time' – when nothing had happened, and, in correction of this, 'I won't say much because we're running late ...'

Late with what? Tornetta wondered, moist with apprehension, baffled by this rigmarole – the tired sallow stooped man of importance who repeated, 'Brothers, ladies, guests, charge your glasses for the next toast,' and the thickset woman in a costume, sandy hair thinning and gash mouth overpainted: 'I'm not gonna say a lot 'cause—' How did it end? A secret initiation? An offer of a loan? Oaths sworn? Tornetta was sorry he had come; this would make him conspicuous, and therefore answerable, all the way to San Francisco. Was that a part of Rossi's intention?

Even comedy failed to take away uneasiness.

'Brothers, ladies, guests, I give you the next toast . . . The Captain!' But another Brother called 'Out of order!' and Captain Vafiadis looked uncomfortable.

Some volunteers from the cabaret did turns – a monologue of embarrassing eulogy; some exhibition dancing by the professional couple. This was followed by two songs.

Demetropoulos sat by Tornetta, in white uniform, slightly soiled round the tight fit at the neck. He was evidently ignorant of the masculinity of the Masons, for he believed the pretty woman next to him might be open to a proposition, and was probing her defences: 'Are you travelling alone?'

The visionary smile was on his face and his eyes, as ever, stared whimsically at a point some feet above the Captain as that gentleman went to the microphone and stumbled through a speech. 'I am very happy. I am always happy among my passengers,' Captain Vafiadis told the assembly with sepulchral enthusiasm. 'I love my work . . .' The hypocrisy was effortless, part of duty. They presented him with a gift and he again had wooden phrases at the ready: 'I am always happy when the Masons are on board. Many occasions have I attended and always I am happy to do so . . .'

Tornetta was stupefied by it. Where was the trick? When they had finished these ridiculous speeches what was going to happen?

Nothing happened. The sallow, bent, rather military toastmaster, even more mournful than the Captain, pleaded suddenly, 'Brothers, ladies, guests, charge your glasses. North, South, East, West, are they all charged? Hurry, please, this microphone is heavy. The final toast is, of course, "Hands, heart and pocket."'

He touched his chest and pockets to demonstrate the ritual to the guests, and abruptly it was all over, people were chattering, on their feet, anxious to be elsewhere.

And Tornetta knew in shock what was happening and what was intended.

It was an artifice of considerable cunning. For these introductions and the dull dialogues overlaid with charm and hypocrisy were not for Tornetta's benefit, but for Rossi's. Of this he was sure. They were to establish *his* alibi. When Tornetta fell down twenty steel steps, or over the rail, or was drowned in the pool, or killed by an unfortunate electric shock, his friend, Mr Rossi, would be distraught. He would weep, literally, and every consideration would be attended to. He would tirelessly collect coins from passengers for a wreath. Cables would be paid for. There would be a handsome wreath from the Masons aboard, perhaps even a memorial service. ('He was not yet one of us, but in his heart and intentions he had surely joined us, was a Brother.')

It had all the subtlety of an intrigue by the other brotherhood, the Mafia, when that organization cared to indulge in sardonic artfulness. Tornetta sweated and trembled in very genuine terror of death. It still occupied his thoughts when he went to bed. His legs fluttered as he lay in his bunk, for this had a brutal probability; he had no doubt that this was the way it was intended.

But they had, once again, given him a little time – a few days, perhaps as much as a fortnight. For the evidence would have to be conclusive, no doubts must arise : the tearful petition 'He was my friend, my very dear friend' had to be believed, must arouse other tears and whispers of consolation. How would it come? By scalding? Electricity? It had to have the appearance of accident, and, to be sure, the *Areopagus* must be full of places where hurt could be inflicted. But Tornetta couldn't think of them or how it would be done. Was there safety in crowds?

In two days they would arrive at Hong Kong. Would they kill him ashore? No. Not if he avoided Mr Rossi and went off with Barbara. Even then he couldn't be certain that he wouldn't be fingered and the job carried out by someone now reading an apparently innocent cable. An accident which included Barbara wouldn't matter to *them*; it might even be more convincing.

But surely it would be at sea on the long haul from Hong Kong to Guam or the subsequent journey from Guam to San Francisco? A long way from the facilities of investigation. Ah, yes, this was probable.

That gave him time to summon up courage and anger. Stay ashore at Hong Kong? No. That would be too obvious and there was nowhere to flee to, or if there was, it would burn up the large sum he now had, and the most casual inquiries would establish his destination. He couldn't book an overseas flight without his passport and so his correct name would be there on some agency's list.

He had boarded this liner because of his assumption that there would be minor corruption and carelessness. It didn't exist in the way he had hoped. But suddenly now, stretching his nerves taut, but satisfying, final, he realized what he had to do. There was an area of confusion, and it existed whenever the *Areopagus* was in port.

He would consider it for the next forty-eight hours, and decide upon details and alternatives, pursue them to perfection.

There was one way to confuse them.

He would kill Mr Rossi in Hong Kong.

18

IT WAS embarrassing to witness the conceit of the man. Mike Burston sat waiting in the small hairdressing saloon on Metaxas Deck and flicked the pages of semi-pornographic Australian magazines, but had no option but to overhear the man in the chair.

He was the worthless piano player whose vanity Mike had already observed a week before in the elevator. Now the man was hard to satisfy. The hairdresser was a thin youth from some English industrial city and he was obsequious now, snipping here, combing there.

The piano player stood up and considered himself in the long mirror. He put his head on one side, touched his sideboards, borrowed a brush and whisked it to and fro. He was in no hurry, nor was he perturbed by, even if he was aware of, Mike's condemnatory examination and the youth waiting for payment. The appearance of himself was obviously a matter to be scrutinized with the utmost care.

At last he left and after a long silence Mike couldn't resist saying, 'He likes the look of himself, that one.'

The youth motioned Mike to the chair and considered him briefly. 'Medium?' he asked: a verdict in itself: if some were too conceited others were insufficiently considerate and to attend to these latter was a bore, but necessary because of money . . . He informed Mike: 'He has to keep up appearances, I suppose.'

'To play the piano?'

'That, too.'

'As well as what?'

'You hadn't noticed?' inquired the youth, as if saying 'How unobservant you must be.'

'No. Can't say I have.'

'He gets through the women. God knows why,' complained the youth in what might have been envy. 'He's pretty old, every bit of thirty.'

Mike was thirty-nine; he smiled and said 'Yes, that's pretty ancient.'

'They call him heartbreak,' the youth told him, 'but that's not the organ he's after.'

He sniggered and Mike was silent. The youth sensed his disapproval and changed the subject. 'You goin' ashore at Hong Kong?'

Mike went up to the Parade Deck, looking for Marion, but failed to find her. Despite the haircut he was very hot. He sat in a deck chair for a while, but wanted a drink. He again strolled the port and starboard sides of the deck to find his wife, but she was not on the deck at all. He gave up and went for a cold drink.

He hadn't been in the Forward Bar since the night when the First Officer had reprimanded a steward on his behalf, and that had been the day after they'd left Adelaide. Marion had blamed *him* for not knowing that the *Areopagus* was to call at Adelaide. They'd travelled all the way to Melbourne, paying train fares, when they could have made the far shorter journey to Port Adelaide. Even the ship's newspaper, with its announcement of the 'bonus port,' hadn't quite satisfied Marion. 'Stupid,' she'd grumbled.

The Forward Bar was almost empty in the middle of the afternoon, but this did not stop the German girl cashier from ignoring Mike. She was, as usual, reading.

He waited a minute, fulmination collecting, and then leaned as far forward as he could to ask 'A good novel?'

She was unruffled.

'Philosophy,' she told him.

'Why bother with philosophy when you have learned so well the technique of indifference?'

'I beg your pardon?'

'A large lemonade, if you please.'

'Fifteen cents.'

Mike gave her the money and moved to the right to catch the eye of a barman. He saw that it was the same queer as before whom he had to attract, but was committed to doing so unless he just walked away and lost fifteen cents.

The steward, John, looked pale and tired. He had adhesive bandage across the left-hand corner of his mouth, stretching almost to his ear. Like the piano player, however, he considered his reflection worth lengthy inspection. He combed his hair and turned away from the mirror. He would have moved off altogether, but the German girl, penitent perhaps, called him : 'John, a lemonade.'

The steward put as much distaste as he could into the matter of serving Mike. He examined the ridiculous ticket. 'The ink's faint,' he told the girl.

'So what?' she said tartly. 'Is that your problem?'

Mike said, 'One large lemonade, when you've time.'

The steward affected not to hear this. He turned to find a glass. It was dirty, so he swilled it briefly under a tap. Then he picked out ice cubes from a bowl, using his fingers, and added the fizzy lemonade.

Mike was white hot with irritation. He said 'Do it again and this time with the tongs. I don't want the flavour of your dirty fingers.'

Someone sitting a few yards away called out 'Hear, hear!'

The steward claimed 'My hands are perfectly clean.'

'They've touched your filthy hair.'

Unexpectedly, the German girl supported Mike. 'Why don't you do as he asks? That's the third time someone—'

The steward lost control of himself and shouted 'Who the hell asked you to speak?'

'Don't you shout at me!'

'A cheap trollop who can read!'

Mike said loudly, 'Take this damn drink away and do your job properly.'

'I am not obliged to provide the ship's equipment. My fingers are good enough for the likes of you.'

Mike threw the contents of the glass into the man's face. Only the width of the bar stopped him throwing punches.

The steward was quick to retaliate, but with words, not action. He had great expertise in malice and animosity, and had the razor tongue of the queer who had been smiled at many times.

'Such melodrama! What arrogance from the pure of heart! The puritan trots round the world, stares at the rest of us, such vulgar dirty folk, not like him! But what about your paragon daughter? How's her virtue standing up to the voyage? Where is *she* this afternoon?'

The positiveness with which the steward hissed this scorn was equal to its malice, and Mike was shaken. The face of the steward was flushed and distorted now, but that he believed what he was saying was evident. It was a truth meant to hurt.

It caught Mike by the nerve-ends. The impetus of his anger stumbled. The man was nothing, could even be pitied – a lad who had to be a steward on a liner because fate had made him a homosexual – but the invective about 'your paragon daughter' frightened him instantly. Stella, his mind cried out in alarm. Does he mean Stella? How does this man know Stella and talk so confidently about her?

'What are you talking about?' he demanded, and the alteration in his voice was noticeable, an application for information.

The steward was now anxious to withdraw, end what could be a brawl. 'Oh, well, it's none of my business . . .'

'It can't be my child. She's only fifteen.'

'You know what they're like at fifteen these days,' sneered John. 'So *healthy* with all that milk and overfeeding . . .'

Mike turned and went out. He knew he'd obtain no information from *him*. The steward had seen him only once before, so how could he even know who were his children?

Nevertheless, as if to reassure himself, he went looking for her.

In the cabin Marion insisted, 'Quiet! Bumble's gone to sleep.'

'Have you seen Stella?'

'Not for an hour. Why? What's the matter?'

'Nothing.'

'Then what's the hurry?' she asked, but already Mike had shut the cabin door.

He searched through the lounges and went to the cinema, but there was no film showing. There was no logic in his pursuit, but his instincts prodded him. He was prepared even to look a fool.

The usual fifteen or twenty youths and girls were stretched alongside the pool, frying themselves in the tropical sun. Diane was with two youths. They were horsing around lazily, as if in slow motion.

Mike asked abruptly 'Have you seen Stella?'

Her eyes flickered in expectation, then became evasive. She knew, but wasn't going to tell him.

'I don't know.'

'Come on! It's important.'

'I just don't know.'

The youths stirred restlessly and smiled in superiority.

Mike strode away, his mind still in turmoil. They were discussing it behind him. Perhaps they would move, and thus resolve the problem. But they let it go. Wherever Stella was, it was somewhere he wouldn't learn about.

He'd been everywhere where a passenger could legitimately move or enter. It was impossible to ask anyone and he went back to talk it over with Marion, and wait.

Near the cabin their steward was leaning against a bulkhead, tired, his tuberculosis slowly killing him; cigarette ash dripped on to his jacket.

'Ambros!' said Mike hesitantly.

They had had a cautious relationship, the hesitation on the steward's side probably due to the manner in which Mike had shouted at the visitors in the cabin that first day in Melbourne. There had, on Mike's side, never been any expectation of dependence. He pitied the little man, but wanted nothing from him beyond morning tea, a change of towels, a smile. But now – if anyone knew what Mike wanted to find out, the steward would.

'Mister?'

'Ambros, you know my daughter? The big one.'

'Ah, of course. Stella.'

'Have you seen her?'

'Not for – an hour.'

'I think she's in trouble.'

The steward stared at him anxiously.

'What kind of trouble?'

'Where do they go? Where's the mickey run on the ship?'

'Oh, Mister, I am sure—'

'I'm not. So where is it?'

'There is a cabin at the stern end of B Deck, next to the laundry—'

'Thanks.'

Down a deck, in haste, because a lot of time had passed, so if it was true—

Heat rolled along B Deck as if it had been pumped out of a bellows. Mike was hot and beginning to tire, but it didn't matter . . . The smell of boiling laundry wafted out of an illuminated room, and men's voices chattered in Greek, and laughed.

He suddenly felt a fool. All these doors were numbered, and could be the cabins of passengers. If there's nothing, I stop. All I have is the malice of that bastard. It's probably somebody else's daughter anyway.

The room next to the laundry.

He opened its door and stepped in. And it was his daughter, not someone else's.

She was on a bed. It had no linen. With her was the cheap piano player. He was by her side, but leaning over, in charge. Stella's dress was unfastened all the way down to her waist and the big left hand which tapped out the music of sentiment had cupped her right breast, its fingers had aroused that nipple into an inflamed red spot. Nobody was saying anything, but the spectacle was of a girl relaxed, without opposition; it proved previous experience.

The man turned his head, shouted, 'How dare you come into my cabin?'

And in the same agitated seconds Stella was able to see

beyond his head. She screamed and leaped off the bed, and ran past her father, sobbing – a curious lamentation, as if he had been guilty of the vulgarity, not she, he was to be despised, and there could be no reconciliation.

Mike had been rushing round in pursuit of his own destruction for half the afternoon.

It hurt unbearably. That this vain, cheap peacock, swollen with self-approbation, should touch *her*, should be able to talk her into anything at all, let alone *this*—

He struck her as she fled, her dress unaccountably in order now, and the edge of a fingernail caught her, so that a line of blood crossed her face. She cried out with great bitterness, justification accumulating, and ran sobbing, as if all the sadness of the world had come to her.

Mike went for the man. He was big, but Mike was as big, and behind Mike was an accumulated fury, beginning a long time ago, given an impetus by the contempt of the German cashier and the rancour of the steward. The man was also alarmed, aware of guilt, possible repercussion, complaints to the Purser by this man. There'd be trouble. True, he hadn't got the kid's pants down. That would have merited five years in a Greek prison.

'She agreed,' he explained breathlessly. 'It was foolish, but I had her acquiescence. No harm done, nothing at all.'

But the girl's father wasn't interested in appreciating the finer points of evidence, the procession of inane dialogue and the appetites of a shallow lewdness. These could be proven: that the girl was a fool, like the rest, in search of love, self-gratification, preferably without pain, trouble or responsibility. And the most important thing for her had been to fool herself. She had not fooled him. They came and said they were different, that they had this and that condition; but this was mere fright and he smoothed it a little with soft irrational words, and then rubbed it away altogether with tactile exploration, so that they ended up like bitches on heat, senseless, heedless of what he did, aware of their predecessors but indifferent even to these. All this could be explained, given time. It could be proved conclusively that the kid – what was her name? – Stella – had been in search of *him*; every move had been hers; she had merely had to overcome herself . . .

But the parent wasn't going to extend time, discuss the matter. He was, like the kid, a moralist at heart. It was necessary for him to inflict pain.

Mike smashed the man around the face until he went on his knees as if in supplication, covering his bloody nose and mouth with the same fingers that were his profession and his gratification.

Then he hurried back to his cabin. He was breathing badly and there was almost nothing left of the impetus which had carried him through the afternoon. He was downcast.

Marion was still in the cabin. Perhaps only a few minutes had passed. To him they felt like hours.

'Where is she?' he demanded harshly.

'Mike, what did you do?'

'What did *I* do?'

'Her face is bleeding.'

'Oh, that. A scratch.'

'She's hysterical.'

'Where is she?'

'In the bathroom.'

Mike shouted, 'Come on out. Don't hide and pretend nothing's happened.'

Marion protested, 'For God's sake, what are you shouting about?'

He told her, briefly and brutally, in the language of truck drivers.

Marion went pale, but she, who was constantly reprimanding Stella, and this with an acid tongue, now pleaded for her: 'Don't be so angry. She has to live with it, too.'

'She loved it.'

'Don't take your own despair out on the kid.'

'I'm not doing that, Marion. That's unfair. I'm not like that. Doesn't it matter to you?'

Marion agreed, 'Of course it does—' but stopped.

Stella came out of the bathroom, silent, cringing, but defiant.

Mike demanded 'How many times has that happened?'

The girl said tautly, 'I don't care. He's as good as you.'

Marion bristled, but pointed out with patience: 'Listen. We are entitled to ask you what's been going on.'

'He loves me, that's all. I wouldn't expect you to understand.'

Mike waved an arm in contempt. Stella flinched and screeched: 'Don't you hit me. Big hateful beast.'

He told her: 'You're a fool. I was having my hair cut – this very afternoon. And he was there. The kid who cut my hair says he's been through five women so far this trip. Love! A bloody vain ape posturing on a tree! You don't believe me? You think you're exclusive? You know better? Ask Diane, your smart friend. He's had the lot from her. You dumb fool. You listen to that fellow – what's his name? – Dr de Haan; you believe him, but the first vulgar lout who talks butter can take your dress off.'

'Gossip,' Stella disputed, but she was trembling.

'Gossip?' Mike bellowed. 'Why, the little slut has even given *me* the eye.'

'You flatter yourself.'

'Don't give me lip. Do you think I don't know?'

'Mike, take it easy,' Marion beseeched. 'Who else?' she questioned.

'No one,' Stella said, but with defiance.

'Don't lie,' insisted Marion. 'You crept away in the night when we slept on deck.'

'I didn't.'

'Yes, you did.'

'To the lavatory.'

'For three hours?'

'What do you know about it?'

'Patricia told me.'

'She's a pig, a liar.'

'I didn't believe her at the time,' Marion said. She persisted, 'Who else? And what happened?'

'Nothing.'

'Do I have to take you to the doctor to find out?'

'You wouldn't dare.'

'Try me. What happened?'
'Nothing.'
'But there've been others?'
'A boy. He was kind.'
'What name?'
'What do you want to know for?'
'His name?'
'Roy.'
'With a beard?'
'Yes. And he's a man, not a boy. He's twenty-one.'
'What did you allow him to do?'
'Nothing. He was kind. He didn't want—'
'He got fed up with you?'
'I don't know what you're raving about.'
'About you, Stella, my own trusted daughter.'
'I didn't mean – to go that far.'
'With a man of thirty on a liner? Do you think he'd stop at holding your hand? Did you go to the privacy of a cabin to *talk*? Am I supposed to be so dumb?'
'Oh, no. You're so *clever*.'
Mike shouted, 'Stop being so damn insolent.'
Marion persisted with details of proof, like the ritual of an Inquisition, proving fault, hoping for penitence and conversion: 'So this boy, Roy, is too nice to take your willingness too far. And you therefore move on to somene else Diane suggests.'
'I did *not*. He found me in the Club.'
'Waiting,' suggested Marion.
'You're so *dull*,' cried Stella hysterically, still defiant, in a shrill voice. 'I can't do anything. What did we do in Singapore? Went to an aquarium, round the shops. We could have done that in Adelaide.'
Mike forecast grimly: 'You won't be seeing *him* again, nor that tramp in the cabin opposite. That old lady warned me about *her*—'
'She's a stupid old crow.'
Mike shook his daughter until her hair was all over her face and her teeth rattled. 'She's lost her son,' he cried, 'but she doesn't whine round the ship like you do. If you don't

stop this dumb arrogance I'll break your neck. You know the difference between right and wrong and you chose wrong. That doesn't make you superior to anyone, or turn you into an adult . . .'

Stella sobbed. 'I hate you . . . Big stupid truck driver . . . Dumb and satisfied . . . You killed someone!' she shouted. 'You broke a little girl in half and you think you're better than *me*.'

It stopped him, it hurt so much. This one hateful afternoon had revealed that the daughter he treasured most was a slut and didn't care how he felt about it: she reciprocated nothing, was deeply involved in a dirty world of her own, previously guarded behind silence. He was filled with despair and could find nothing to say.

But Marion responded with instant fury. 'That was an accident and he didn't kill her. Do you think your Dad did it deliberately, like you chose your actions? You cheap nasty vicious girl. Get out of my sight!'

Stella climbed into her bunk and lay face downwards sniffing with self pity.

The silence was suffocating.

Mike asked 'Where's Patricia?'

'In the play room.'

Two hours later they went to dinner: habit was stronger than distress.

They stood by the table. The stewards, as always, welcomed them with smiles. Did they have daughters too? The stewards didn't notice the stony silence and white faces.

Mike said with feeling, 'I don't want that pig sitting next to me. She'd better sit over that side.'

Stella suddenly wept and walked away.

'Oh, Mike,' Marion chided. 'You shouldn't have said that.'

Miss Wearne said brightly, 'They say it's Asian flu, and it comes on so quickly.'

They smiled thinly and sat down.

Later they strolled the Parade Deck in the dark and talked about it.

'What do we do?' Mike asked frankly, lost already.

'I don't know.'

'Have we lost her?'

'Of course not, Mike.'

'I didn't want to get angry.'

'I know you *care*, Mike.'

'It kind of spoils the trip.'

'She'll get over it.'

'Over it? She doesn't care! That's what worries me. She's hard.'

'No. She's frightened, so she's defiant, like a dog showing its teeth.'

'I don't know what to do. This filthy generation.'

'Oh, no, Mike. It's not a new problem.'

'She knew all about my accident.'

'I didn't tell her.'

'Kids at school.'

'She's never said a word before.'

Mike said sadly: 'She meant that to hurt; as if she hadn't done enough for one day.'

'She's growing up.'

'Into what?'

'You can't win her by shouting or violence.'

'All the same, she's not to have the freedom to run around *this* ship. There's four weeks of it yet. She comes with us.'

'I suppose so, yes.'

'Something will happen,' suggested Mike.

He stared uselessly at the immense and cloudless sky and the mocking stars. Am I to be punished for ever? he wondered.

Marion again clashed with the woman from Darwin – a minor imbroglio but unfortunate as it arose during the Children's Fancy Dress Party.

This took place in the Playroom situated aft of the Purser's office and hairdressing saloons.

It was for small children, but kids of up to ten were noticeably present, in the hope of enjoyment, chocolates and a gift, and in these they were successful.

Patricia had been preparing for this in nervous rehearsal

in the cabin, at meal times and lying in her bunk, so that it was difficult not to flinch or groan when once again she recited 'My job as a nurse is to make you less worse.' Nothing could persuade her of the misconstruction of these words. She dressed up several times a day in white and wore a hat made by Marion. She could have been mistaken as masquerading as a nun so Marion sought high and low until she found some red material and made a cross to sew on the front of the dress.

The Playroom was a pleasant room with plenty of toys and books, and a 'rocket' in which were two seats, and a miniature stage coach which could seat four small children.

Twenty children and a handful of apprehensive parents, mostly mothers, turned up, the ship's photographer was there, and Ricky, the Entertainments Officer, controlled the children together with Pamela, the English girl who was normally in charge of the room.

Ricky had a precise enunciation and could be heard above the shrieking. He was a young man who put much energy into his job, whether running the day's bingo session or helping with shore excursions. He withheld nothing now, so that the children responded equally. He had just the right balance of phraseology to extract amusing answers from a child, or to give it confidence, and yet entertain the others present, without hurting the child's feelings. The mothers stared in ferocious possession, but Ricky handled the children without arousing resentment.

They played games – musical chairs, pass the parcel, 'Simon says' – and then they did their individual performances. Some were so quiet and nervous that they could scarcely be heard, others grinning in unabashed braggadocio.

Bumble, a confident two and a half, was ready to go on all morning. She recited : 'My elephant is kind, but don't give him bread. We take him a walk every day on a piece of string. The string is fastened to a motor-bike.'

Patricia went forward in sullen determination.

Ricky asked 'What's your name?'

'Patricia.'

'That's a nice name.'

'I don't like it.'

'You don't. Why not?'

'I want to be called Ruth.'

'Where do you come from?'

Patricia told him.

'Where's that?'

'South Australia?'

'In the desert?'

'We had a tortoise.'

'What are you going to do, Patricia?'

Patricia took this as the 'Go!' signal and recited rather quickly:

'If you are ill
I give you a pill.
My job as a nurse
Is to make you less worse.'

Her audience laughed.

Patricia told them: 'It's not funny.'

Shortly afterwards Ricky said, 'We are all going to have cakes and lemonade, and guess who's coming to see us? Father Neptune himself.'

Father Neptune turned up and was rather obviously Harry, the ventriloquist. The adults recognized that he was slightly drunk, but the children shrieked in pleasure when he entertained them.

He gave them all presents from his sea chest, and then Ricky, who saw that time was passing and he had duties elsewhere, organized the parade.

'Leave your toys,' he suggested. 'Come back for them after the parade.'

The children trailed through lounges and along decks and were duly met before the Purser's office by Captain Vafiadis on return. Photographs were taken and then the party was over. The kids went back into the Playroom to collect their presents before dispersing...

'Excuse me,' said Marion, very English, to the woman from Darwin. 'That doll belongs to my little girl.'

'You're wrong,' disputed the woman promptly. 'This was given to Phoebe.'

'No, she had the book,' argued Marion. 'I saw her drop it. Bumble had the doll.'

'I want the doll,' contributed Phoebe. 'It's mine.'

'The point is,' said Marion, anger accumulating, 'that it was given to my little girl.'

'What's the matter with you anyway?' asked the other woman. 'You're always bleating and complaining.'

'Why don't we ask Harry?' suggested Marion.

'He's gone,' said the woman from Darwin. 'And I'm going too. I'm not going to be called a thief by a whining Pom.'

Marion appealed to Ricky who was about to depart. 'Did you see who received this little doll?'

Ricky identified the anger in her eyes and in the posture of the other woman.

'I'm awfully sorry. I can't help. They were all wrapped up.'

Bumble complained, 'It's my doll.'

The other small girl claimed, 'No, it's not. It's mine.'

Marion said, 'Didn't Uncle Harry give you a book?'

'I don't want it. I want the doll.'

'Yeah, all right, you've got it,' snapped her mother. 'So come on.'

Bumble screamed 'She's got my doll.'

Marion agreed : 'Yes, she's a nasty little girl, badly brought up.'

The woman from Darwin turned back angrily. She snatched the doll from her child and threw it at Marion. It missed Marion and cracked its head on a cupboard.

Phoebe began to howl. The woman said, furiously, 'Ah, shut up, you useless little bastard!' and walked away, leaving the child weeping noisily on her own.

Marion picked up the doll and gave it to her. But the child was inconsolable and protested 'It's broken so I don't want it.'

19

MR PYBUS breathed heavily. He sweated with a kind of angry insistence, the moisture rolling through a savannah of hairs down his chest. He was a very heavy man with a thick neck, massive torso and hands like uncooked sausages. He had many hairs protruding from the nostrils. His face was an interesting study in some kind of failure. He breathed now through his teeth, themselves stained and irregular and with purulent gums.

Dempsey asked – and it seemed almost frivolous – 'And what can I do for you?'

Pybus said bitterly, apparently with contempt: 'Nothing. I'm going to die.'

'Aren't we all?' suggested Dempsey wearily.

'I'm going to die before this voyage ends,' declared Mr Pybus.

'Not if I can help it.'

'I'll bet you a thousand dollars I do.'

'Don't be ridiculous,' snapped Dempsey. 'And don't waste my time. I repeat, what can I do for you? What is the matter?'

'I had a pain behind my chest bone. It went down the inside of my left arm and right up to my neck. It bloody hurt, I can tell you.'

Retro sternial agony, Dempsey knew, with pains along the inside of the left arm, were symptoms of a heart attack.

'How far down the arm?' he asked.

'I had pins and needles in my fingers.'

'All of them?'

'These.'

Pybus indicated the fourth and fifth fingers.

'Let's feel your pulse.'

It was thready, Dempsey found.

'And some bastard robbed me while I was lying on the deck in bloody agony.'

'That's tough,' sympathized Dempsey. 'Did he take a lot?'

'Enough.'

'Have you told the sergeant-at-arms?'

'What? On this bloody ship? Do you think the Greeks would do anything?'

'I don't see why not. That's what the man's aboard for . . . I'd like to listen to the music in your chest now.'

'Jesus, it's hot,' complained Pybus. 'I'm sorry it's boiling out of me.'

'It doesn't matter.'

Dempsey listened and there was no doubt. The man's heart had triple rhythm. At the base of the lungs were the moist sounds of crepitation. Mr Pybus had a heart condition all right, but not necessarily a killer.

'Do you smoke?'

'Thirty a day.'

'Too many.'

'Yes, I know.'

'And you're drinking a fair bit aboard?'

'It's so hot,' Pybus excused himself.

'Yes, that doesn't help a heavy man either,' Dempsey pointed out. 'I'm going to see what your blood pressure is.'

He thought it might be very high, but in fact it was low. But then, Pybus had had a shock of considerable impact.

'Have you had all these pains before?'

'No.'

'Good! Well, that's not so bad then.'

'Heart attack, wasn't it?'

'Yes, but that doesn't mean you're going to have another.'

'Ah, come off it, doctor. I'll be dead before this journey's ended.'

'Rubbish! It doesn't help to drink heavily and you're carrying a lot of weight. Not to mention smoking – more than thirty a day, I know.'

'I never count the bloody things . . . I'll bet you I die,' asserted Pybus.

'You won't this trip. You should last for ever if you pack in the drinking. What is it, spirits?'

'A thousand dollars,' suggested Pybus. 'I'll bet you a thousand I die before we return to Wellington.'

'And who would I give the money to, since you wouldn't be here?'

'I've got a daughter.'

'You might drink yourself to death deliberately . . . I'll take you on for a hundred,' said Dempsey in good humour. 'With a side bet of ten dollars that if you halve the boozing and smoking you don't have any more pains this trip.'

'Agreed,' said Pybus.

He was pleased about it, and Dempsey feared he would now talk of nothing else providing he could find anyone to listen.

When Pybus had left Sister Eleni said, 'You have money to throw away? That one is so unpleasant he will die just to rob you. And he has the face of one who has given up, knows he is despised and that there is no point in living.'

'This ship,' Dempsey informed her, 'is packed with philosophers . . . Anybody else or can we go and rot our livers with whisky?'

'Of course there is somebody else!' asserted Sister Eleni. 'Your most persistent lady friend.'

'Oh, no! Not *her*!'

'Yes, her. And I shall leave you to it.'

Dempsey was disturbed, but was obliged to see anyone who turned up and claimed to be ill.

Mrs Triffett came into the surgery. She looked very beautiful in a pale blue dress. Her expression seemed calm and reasonable.

'Sit down,' Dempsey invited. 'The Sister has fled in fear of you! What's your trouble?'

'Daniel, I can't swim.'

'It's not necessary to be able to swim to go on a cruise.'

'Oh, don't mock me. I could swim but now I can't.'

'So?' asked Dempsey in irritation.

'I mean I used to be *good* . . .'

'Mrs Triffett, why do you bother me with such nonsense?'

'Pauline; don't remind me of *him* . . . You've been to a party with me and should call me Pauline . . .'

'Look,' said Dempsey frankly. 'I've had two in already this very morning. "I'm off form, I can't seem to play deck tennis like I did last week." In Sydney I had them come in : "My golf's deteriorating." What the hell am I supposed to do? I want to help people who are ill, not neurotics who drank too much the night before, or over-eat, or go to bed too late and with too many persons . . .'

'I'm sorry, Daniel. I was frightened.'

'Does it matter a damn if you can swim or not?'

'It was alarming because I went in the fourteen-foot end.'

'And this time your suicide was nearly successful?'

Dempsey laughed, and Pauline smiled and agreed, 'I suppose it has a certain macabre humour. That – other – thing – was a gesture . . . Daniel, we're all horribly mixed up. My limbs didn't function that other night either: it became genuine. Do I have an in-built death wish or something?'

'No,' said Dempsey firmly. 'You have a splendid sense of melodrama which even fools you.'

'I'm damned depressed today,' she told him. 'But I wasn't lying. I very nearly drowned. A horrid taste, that water's got. I just thought maybe my muscles had taken the hint from my mind.'

'What's the matter with you, Pauline? You're perfectly fit physically, you know.'

'I don't know. Yes, I do. I want someone to *care*.'

'To care or simply to take notice? We do care, some of us.'

'Yes, but superficially, when it's necessary or convenient or part of duty or a time-table. I don't think anyone really cares. So I want to shock them and make them.'

'This is what students and agitators do. You may shock, but you also arouse resentment . . . You won't succeed that way.'

'How, then, Daniel?'

'Jesus, Pauline, I've had a bit of a day and an emergency hernia in the night . . . But it goes like this. We're all too intent and we all analyse ourselves to death. We've lost simplicity. We all know that the motive isn't what it seems – it derives from the urge to obtain or do something else. We envy supposedly simple African people who are abiding, like children, by the basic game. Jealousy, for them, is jealousy; courage is courage, and so on. We know better. The hero is a fool or a delinquent. The puritan is a repressed or impotent voluptuary. We're too damned smart. We become miserable. It serves us right.'

'What did I do wrong, Daniel, to forge the first link? God, I'm only twenty-three now.'

'You probably sought happiness like someone choosing a dress. The pursuit of happiness is absurd and should be struck off the American Bill of Rights. Look where it's got *them*! You tried on this dress, tried on that. They didn't make you consciously happy like a double whisky warming your belly . . .'

'All I ask is simple love—'

'Oh, no, Pauline! You're not that simple. You're Eve and Delilah and Scarlett O'Hara. There's nuclear fission mixed up in your motives. You *like* confusion and temperament, a degree of chaos . . .'

'But it's true, Daniel. All I want is simple pleasure, love . . . Will you take me round Hong Kong? You know the city, don't you? I'm a bit scared of it on my own, and Reidy's doing the standard tours . . .'

'I've already promised, or half promised . . .'

'I know. That kid, Debbie. Nice looking, isn't she?'

'There you go! Feline, fissionable. Do you think I've got designs on a girl not quite sixteen?'

'Don't you know she's very fond of you?'

'Nonsense.'

'I am not being a tigress. It's just true, and very tender I find it. Simplicity, like you said. And you tread on her emotions like an elephant.'

'Good God! How absurd!'

'She hinted – very delicately for one so simple! – that she'd have liked you to take her round Singapore. Yes. At Mollon's party.'

'Don't try to make an innocent relationship uncomfortable.

She's a nice girl. That's all. Someone asked me to look after her...'

'Why aren't you married, Daniel?'

'How the devil do I know?'

'Shall I tell you?'

'Can I stop you?'

'Because you're a very shy person. You were scared. You're scared now.'

'Of what?'

'We are in Hong Kong two days. All right, so you'd like to take care of Debbie one day. Delightful for both of you. But how about the second day? Why not with me? Because you're nervous.'

Dempsey asked slowly, 'Why did they boot you out of the Middle Hospital?'

'Who says they did?'

'What was it? Too friendly with the male patients?'

'I love you, Daniel. You know that, don't you?'

'You don't. You're up to something.'

'No. I'm emotional but I *respect* you . . . And that's crazy for me.'

'You threatened me.'

'I did?'

'About the Middle Hospital.'

'Oh, that.'

'Yes, that.'

'I wanted to penetrate, to shock you, to force an interest in me.'

'You're only twenty-three now. You were a child when I was there.'

'Yes, but I was a naughty child. I pinched things – pills, documents.'

The telephone rang.

Dempsey answered it. 'I'll be along.' He said to Pauline, 'A child hurt ... We'll have a day out in Hong Kong, Mrs Triffett...'

'Oh, Daniel, bless you! How sweet! That'll be fun.'

'Boring,' he suggested.

Dempsey hurried with his leather bag to the cabin on A

Deck where a child of two had fallen six feet from an upper bunk.

There was a man coming out of the cabin as Dempsey approached it – a fair-haired man of about thirty with a face burnt by sun long before he came on this voyage.

Dempsey told him : 'I'm the doctor.'

The man said indifferently, 'She's in there.'

'Where are you going?' Dempsey asked frankly, in astonishment.

'There's a meeting of the Toastmasters.'

'I thought your child had hurt herself?'

'I told you – the wife's in there.'

Dempsey asked outright : 'Aren't you interested in your child?'

The man considered this in apparent perplexity rather than offence. 'Listen. I pay you to see to the kid, don't I?'

'God Almighty!' exploded Dempsey, and went into the cabin.

The mother, dressed in a bikini, was almost equally indifferent, and obviously anxious to be elsewhere.

The little girl lay on the deck. The mother had done nothing. The child's face was very pale, she was moaning a little now and being sick.

'What happened?'

'Ah, she fell off the bunk. She looks a bit crook.'

'She was knocked unconscious?'

'Too right.'

Dempsey examined the child.

'Nothing broken,' he told the woman. 'She'll be all right if she's kept quiet for a day or two.'

'No pills or nothing?'

'No. She probably won't feel like food for a while.'

'How much, doc?'

Dempsey told her and went on his way.

Marion Burston saw this child later in the day, lying in the tropical sun on the Parade Deck near the aft swimming pool. The little girl was asleep when Marion sat down by Miss

Wearne. The sun moved in its almighty arc and soon it was beating on the child.

The girl looked very pale indeed and a trickle ran out of her mouth. It worried Marion.

Miss Wearne was teaching another daughter of the same parents how to knit. This girl was about six and seemed glad to have Miss Wearne's attention.

After a while Marion couldn't stand it. She didn't know about the girl's concussion, but regarded it as dangerous for her to lie for over an hour in the full sun. People walked round the girl, or looked and walked on. Then Debbie came by on her daily exercise around the deck and stopped to consider the girl. She hesitated and then strode on. The woman 'with wheels in her head' didn't seem to see the child, but went fixedly on her way.

Marion said to Miss Wearne tentatively, 'That kid's been lying there an hour or more.'

Miss Wearne agreed, 'They do seem to neglect their children those two.'

'They're just like little ragamuffins.'

Miss Wearne inquired of the older child : 'Where are your mother and father?'

'Mum's gone to the Fashion Parade.'

'And Daddy?'

'He's gone too. It's a joke.'

'Why haven't you gone?'

'I've got to look after *her*.'

'She looks very pale.'

'The doctor came this morning.'

'Why was that?'

'She fell off the bunk.'

'Which one?'

'The top one. She was unconscious and sick and everything.'

Marion was alarmed.

She said in anger : 'What are they thinking of, leaving her in the sun like that? I'm going to fetch them.'

Miss Wearne forecast, 'She won't thank you.'

'That child's ill. She's being sick.'

The little girl awoke and began to weep wretchedly, but as if it was an effort.

Marion was apprehensive because the child was Phoebe and her mother, the woman from Darwin, would conclude that she was trying to humiliate her. At the same time she was angry with the woman and anxious to express her contempt for such incompetent parenthood.

The Fashion Parade was being held in the Aegean Lounge. Some of the female passengers and two of the dancers were parading the clothes they had purchased in Singapore. They were surprisingly competent, and Marion, entering behind an audience of three hundred or so, was a little daunted. Ricky, the Entertainments Officer, was broadcasting a running commentary, and so far from being frivolous, he was very professional, with a knowledge of fabrics and styles at least as good as Marion's.

Marion looked along the rows of seated passengers, but could not see the woman from Darwin or her husband. Ricky's voice, enlarged by electricity, boomed across the lounge: 'Next, and understandably glad to be cooler, June models a swim suit of batik cloth. I'm not sure that batik cloth was intended to be chopped up into a bikini. But while we admire sloe-eyed Chinese girls and voluptuous Malay beauties dressed like birds of paradise in kebaya, cheongsam and saris, and those billowing baju karongs, I understand that Australians like their women raw ... Are you ready, June? I can't keep up this prolegomenon much longer.'

'Can't find my shoes,' a woman's voice said from out of sight, and the audience laughed.

The voice was that of the woman Marion was seeking.

'Never mind your shoes,' chided Ricky. 'Come just as you are. Like you do for dinner!'

Again the audience laughed.

The woman from Darwin walked into view. At first Marion didn't recognize her, for she wore a wig which changed her hair colour from dark brown to silver blonde. She strolled about confidently, oscillating her buttocks exactly as she did around the Parade Deck. She pivoted and walked to and fro, and smiled at the audience. A few men whistled.

Marion was now self-conscious because she alone was standing in the audience. She was tempted to retreat, but considered the child.

She went behind the curtains and found an area which was a chaos of garments, wigs, a litter of shoes, and mirrors hung or leaning. About fifteen women, mostly young, were getting into and out of costumes.

The woman, June, had received applause and came back into this area while Ricky was announcing the next item. Despite her self-confidence the woman was a little shaken, so that for a moment she forgot hostility, the by-now-normal condition regarding Marion, and asked, 'You gonna have a go?'

'Your kid's ill,' said Marion.

'Yeah, I know. She fell off a bunk.'

'She's being sick.'

'She ate chocolate ice. Serve her right.'

The woman was now adjusting herself and realized that Marion had come specifically to tell her about the child.

'Listen,' she commanded. 'Nice of you to tell me, but the doc has it in hand so why don't you go back to minding your own business?'

'What kind of a mother are you?' Marion asked angrily. 'That kid's lying in the sun and has been for an hour. Now she's being sick.'

'I didn't know that.'

'Well, now you do, why don't you stop parading your arse around and come to see to her?'

The woman was contemptuous.

'You miserable Pommie wowser. Rose is looking after her. Why don't you relax for half an hour and enjoy yourself?'

'I can't if a child is dangerously ill—'

'Oh, burn up. She's my kid, not yours. Haven't you got any of your own?'

'I've got three, and if they were ill I wouldn't be tarting around in a wig—'

'You're just a miserable bastard. No wonder you're going

back to England. Now get lost, will you? I've got to put my next gear on ...'

'Your other girl isn't old enough to look after Phoebe.'

'Where we live, everybody's capable—'

'I'm going to fetch the doctor.'

'You do that, Pom, and you'll be in trouble.'

'Then where's your husband? I'll talk to him.'

'You do that. He's a great conversationalist,' said the woman, and turned her back on Marion.

But the husband couldn't be seen. Marion had to give up, and as she retreated Ricky came on before the audience with the man she sought. Both wore grass skirts and began a parody of ballroom dancing. The audience shrieked with amusement.

On the Parade Deck the steward who had the toy which made a noise like a cat had carried the child Phoebe into some shade, and was giving her a drink of water.

After a while some of the people who had been watching the Fashion Parade came on deck.

The woman from Darwin ostentatiously abstained from noticing Marion, and approached the child. The steward grinned his usual good-humoured interest and said, 'She has been sick. Very sick. Not like the hot weather.'

'Yeah. She's a bit crook because she fell down. How are y'doing, Phoebe?'

'I was sick.'

'Where the hell's Rose?'

'Can I have a lemonade?'

'Sure. Why not? That's what you're here for – to enjoy yourself. Come on, kid. It's almost time to go to the pictures.'

Stella Burston lay on her stomach on her bunk. She held a book by the side of her neck so that the light from the port-hole fell on its pages. It was a dirty book which Diane had lent her. She read it with the impact of physical shock crawling like insects across her face, and then turned back to go again through the several pages which described seduction and tactile love. Her body writhed in restlessness. Her face was hot.

Her mother came in the cabin and Stella slid the book with haste under a pillow and lay in a posture of dejection.

Marion pleaded, 'Don't sulk all day, Stella.'

'I'm not sulking.'

Marion stepped nearer to talk with tenderness. It interested Stella by virtue of contrast. I've got them worried, she deduced, and the experience was one of power, fascination, a position to exploit carefully.

'Come and get some fresh air.'

'I can't go anywhere.'

Marion whispered. 'You can't expect your father to allow you the freedom of the ship.'

'I hate him.'

'That's silly.'

'It's not. He's inhuman.'

'On the contrary, he's human and bitterly disappointed.'

'I'll never speak to him again,' declared Stella.

'Would he be hurt and angry if he didn't care?'

'Care? He doesn't care. Not about me. It was an automatic reaction. It's himself he cares about, to be the boss, not to be made a fool of. I read that in a book on psychiatry – people don't know their own motives.'

'What were your motives?' Marion asked.

Stella was silent.

'What did you do?'

'Nothing, Mum. Only what he saw.'

'That was enough.'

'They laughed at me,' Stella informed her mother.

It was true, but she had been willing to pursue the pianist; she had known her probable destiny with him. Even now, reading the book, the imprudent itch weakened her between the legs so that it would have been uncomfortable to stand up.

'Who laughed at you?'

'These people, *his* friends, in the bar, you know, grown-ups. They made me feel silly, not doing anything.'

'Stella, you're old enough to know better than that. There are always people like that – on ships, in offices; surely you had some even at school?'

'There was Betty Bugg.'

'She was raped.'

'That's what the papers said,' affirmed Stella. 'She was peculiar. She used to steal and she'd go with five or six boys every lunchtime and take—'

'I don't want to know about it,' said her mother. 'Is it the way you want to be?'

'No, Mum, you know it isn't.'

'I don't know my daughter any more,' Marion pointed out. 'I thought I could trust her.'

'I was frightened,' declared Stella.

This also was true, but it had been a fear she had been eager to overcome, to abandon so that she could be like Diane. He had been very gentle so that in seconds she'd been necking, confidently, aggressively, with physical effort, out of breath, aching, and when his hands had opened her dress she'd been trembling not with fear but in haste. The touch of his fingers on her breasts had scorched her, burned away reticence and anxiety. She'd been proud to see the alteration of expression on his face, what she had aroused. Any chance of this experience coming her way again, of continuing to fruition, withered, as if she'd been damaged physically. There was practically no fright left in her now: she lay in her bunk at night hot with frustration, knowing she'd be guarded, that months must pass before any situation with possibilities came to her again...

'What about other boys?' persisted her mother.

'I don't know any.'

'You know what I mean.'

'There was one, Ken, who tried to get fresh. I stopped him.'

'And Roy?'

'He was kind.'

'There was nothing?'

'No, Mum, honestly.'

'You know what I mean?'

'I think so.'

'I mean—'

But Marion couldn't say it.

'You mean did any boy seduce me?'

'Yes.'

'They didn't.'

'I'll never understand how and why you allowed a vulgar pianist to go so far ...'

'I told you. I was scared.' Stella was very anxious to convince and obtain trust. She sensed that her mother *wanted* to have faith in her. 'I was shaking so much that I couldn't speak. But *he* doesn't believe me,' she concluded sourly.

'He was bound to conclude that if he hadn't come into the cabin the situation would have deteriorated. His view is that you were offering no resistance.'

'I was scared, Mum. My legs were shaking. And I'd been necking with him. That was nice, and this other thing was unexpected. I thought he might kill me. Not literally, but, you know, smash me up with his fists. They're peculiar, I suppose, the Greeks ...'

'They're no different from English or Australian ... It was sordid, Stella, you can't get away from it ... But don't sulk, girl, or act as if your father had no right to be angry ...'

Stella asked, still fascinated by these, which were evidently peace proposals, 'What shall I do, Mum?'

'Say you're sorry.'

Stella flared up. 'Why should I? He hit me. He was brutal and coarse.'

Marion sighed.

'It won't hurt to say you're sorry. We all do foolish things—'

'Not according to him.'

'All right,' conceded Marion. 'You don't have to actually *say* it. Just stop being sullen.'

'Nobody wants me,' cried Stella, and suddenly it was easy to weep, to pour fluid.

Marion touched her hair and head. 'Ah, come on, kid. Be honest. You said harsh cruel things to him ... Listen. We're approaching Hong Kong. Come on deck. It's something you may never see again.'

'Oh, Mum, I'm too ashamed. People will stare.'

'Nonsense. Nobody knows.'

'He'll tell Diane.'

'I don't think so. He's feeling pretty silly, with a couple of teeth missing.'

'Did Dad do that?'

'He did. Come on, kid. Let's go and see what's happening.'

'Let me wipe my face.'

On the Parade Deck hundreds of passengers crowded the rails and moved from one side of the ship to the other in excitement. Cameras were already at work.

The *Areopagus* was passing between Hong Kong Island and Tung Lung on a course of 314°. The sky was faltering a little, the brilliant clarity and heat of the day sagging. It was cool. In the Tathong Channel lights were beginning to flash. Over Dragon's Back, to the left, the sky was pinkening as the sun began to plunge.

Stella was stimulated, and forgot her dejection. It was impossible to maintain an attitude of sullenness, whether imitation or genuine. The tremendous approaches to Hong Kong – islands of rock and flashing lights and Boeings flying over with winking red lights, one a minute, it seemed – all communicated excitement.

The *Areopagus* slowed off Junk Island to pick up a pilot, and then proceeded with infinite caution. Merchant vessels, junks like swarms of butterflies, sampans, American war vessels, could be seen. As the ship turned to port into the huge area of Victoria Harbour Stella saw the skyline of tall buildings. Skyscrapers studded the hillsides like matchboxes placed on end. How on earth had they been built on such slopes?

Ahead was the remarkable promontory of Hong Kong's airport runway. Boeings descended so low over the *Areopagus* that people flinched. They took off and roared between skyscrapers, left trails of black smoke which seemed to lie at once on mountain tops.

Again the *Areopagus* came almost to a halt as the Port Authorities came alongside and boarded. Now the sun was dropping behind Lantau Island and the whole world was silhouetted islands, flashing lights, real and reflected, and noises – Boeings coming on and off that incredible platform which jutted straight out into the harbour; the subdued roar of traffic; honking junks; sirens; bells; music; and the voice over the public address system; 'May I have your attention, please?' But few passengers could be bothered to take their senses away from the traffic on the Hung Hom Fairway – the aircraft-carrier at anchor, the whole half dozen other passenger liners, Italian, British and American, and the flood of ferries, obviously packed, crossing to and from the piers of Kowloon to those of Victoria. The *Areopagus* proceeded in waters nine or ten fathoms deep, crossed over submerged gas mains and water pipes, and turned north to shuffle round until she had berthed alongside the Ocean Terminal.

Whole hours passed, very frustrating to Stella, before the excited passengers flooded ashore. She fulminated in the cabin while Bumble was put to bed, and anger accumulated while her parents simply waited for the child to go to sleep. 'Oh, come *on*!' Stella pleaded, losing patience and caution. 'She'll be all right.' But her mother wouldn't leave until Bumble was definitely asleep.

Even then her parents' decision was to go for a walk. 'Just for an hour,' qualified her mother.

'A *walk*!' complained Stella.

Her father snarled at once, 'Where d'you think you're going? To the strip clubs or a discothèque?'

She didn't dare to argue, for fear of being left behind.

But even a walk in Hong Kong took her breath away. In the Ocean Terminal alone were two hundred shops, clean, brilliantly lit, and packed with a staggering array of things. Clothes smarter than any in Australia; shoes of finer quality than it seemed possible to buy these days in England; Oriental jars and embroidered linen; fine furniture and carved chests; knitwear; jewellery; watches and cameras; superb carpets; whisky; hand-carved ivory; Irish linens; Japanese transistors; Thai jewellery; Italian silks; German motor cars. And the people selling these things were intelligent and courteous, the girls often supremely beautiful.

Her parents shook their heads, refused clumsily to negotiate with these persons, and Stella despised them. Hick people, wowsers, who didn't even know how to enjoy themselves. They walked along the exhilarating Nathan Road, but bought nothing, seemed overawed and even alarmed. And then Patricia wanted to go to the lavatory, but they couldn't cope with that. They turned back, but Patricia couldn't even control herself and she howled with temper when they suggested that she should go up a dark entry. She was too frightened to do so. Stella wanted to flee from them all, she was so humiliated. They went to bed at ten o'clock while Stella seethed, aware of the ship's empty silence, hundreds of people who weren't coming back until three in the morning—

It was the same dreariness in the morning. They'd booked on a tour of Kowloon and the New Territories. They fussed about Bumble's pram and looked tired before the little bus had started out. Her mother was obviously going to end the day with a headache. Serve her right for panicking about silly details.

Again, the very impact of the place and the strangeness and excitement took away Stella's frustration. Maybe Diane was doing something terrific with Keith and the others, but *this* had a fascination even if it was a dreary tour. Perhaps tomorrow they would cross over to Hong Kong Island and have a day there. But it still seemed exasperating to be touring areas of dull flats and fields, factory sites and packed markets when they could have been doing something glamorous – Chinese opera, eating in strange restaurants, riding in a sampan with musicians serenading them; throwing crackers in some festival; travelling on the hydrofoil to gamble at Macao. Instead they were lumbered with Bumble and righteousness and played it safe and did *this*. And it was so hot and the Czechoslovak woman's amplified voice so loud in the little bus. They flinched before the noise and were, as usual, complaintive, or sad, staring out of the window at crowds who swarmed like bees in a hive...

The woman, tough, blonde, attractive, worn out, it seemed to Stella, talked about fires sweeping squatter areas of old timber sackcloth and cardboard, of new resettlement areas. It was like being lectured at school and Stella resented it while her parents looked gloomy and responsible.

Stella's eye took it in visually, without pity, as her brain accepted the facts without interest. She sweated because it was very hot again. The Czech woman was tireless, telling them about immigrants and refugees, shanty towns without hygiene, built of scrap, spreading like a rash up boulder-strewn gullies and along hillsides. Now look at it! was her message. Torrential rain had washed suburbs away; typhoons had blown down these places; finally fire had killed scores and 50,000 had become homeless in Shek Kip Mei alone ... But the resettlement estates had gone up ... H-blocks accommodating 2,300 people each and built in sixteen weeks. And work for the people in factories close at hand ...

The bus wound its way through mountains. Stella stared at buffalo and ducks, at factory estates, at people working in the fields, at gravestones. She stood in a crowd of excited Japanese, all photographing each other, at the border and gazed with indifference over flat dull earth and a river to the mountains which were in Red China. The Czech woman talked deafeningly of the bodies washed down from there, and told the passengers that the poor people of the New Territories didn't want to find these bodies because their religion demanded that if they did they must bury them, which involved great expense.

Stella yawned in boredom. She, too, felt seedy and liable to collect a headache. The restlessness of several passengers communicated the need for refreshment and after a while the bus stopped outside a floating teashop.

To reach it they had to cross a frail wooden bridge. In the café an old woman offered face flannels, and Stella drank a Coke.

Crossing the bridge ten minutes later voices assailed her. An old crone pleaded from a sampan. There were in fact twenty of these boats, old, full of boxes and rubbish. And Stella threw a coin into the water. The old woman with a face lined like a pricked balloon missed the coin and Stella was shocked to see her at once weeping. She howled. Other faces stared in pleading, and the old woman, in black rags, got into the water, waist deep, and searched.

Stella began to shake and went pink in the face. It didn't

make sense. The poverty and the scores of faces staring at her, not in resentment, but in hope. She was rich, they were poor. A coin mattered. It had no relationship to the man in the cabin fondling her breasts and her whole body shifting about so that he could and would offer tactile fulfilment elsewhere. The poor are always with us. Dr de Haan said it often. He probably had an income twice that of her Dad. College training. He was in with the big people. The voice talked with confidence and scorn, but it came from a full belly. And yet he was right. The poor were always with us, as he quoted. But it had nothing to do with this sorrow she felt. Nothing. Her tired sad parents who were so provincial and dull. And the book that made her hot in the face and moist in the areas of agitation. Why did they seem interlaced like basketry? Why couldn't she feel sorrow for these people and nothing about the fingers pawing in the cabin and Diane's shameless penetration, a debased quarter of an hour which had altered her character for ever?

She knew why and resented it. There was no differentiation. Her parents were right. It was all or nothing.

She was ashamed.

It was the time of the year when the oppressive humidity of summer had in theory ended, and the keen north-east monsoon should have set in. But the day was hot and pleasant. Fleets of giant fishing junks swept leisurely back and forth towards Macao and the China Sea. Around the Peak the sea hawks dipped and soared. Chinese children flew their bright kites in the breeze. At the Cricketers Club's nets the men were practising under the shadow of the Communist Bank of China across the street. In the Des Voeux bearded armed Sikhs stood guard at street corners against hit-and-snatch bandits. The street was a corridor of wealth : of banks of many nations, of gold and jade shops so numerous they might have been selling vegetables. Its regulars met in the smart coffee lounges and bars twice daily, negotiating in millions over cigars. These taipans perhaps spent an afternoon in this season watching the hopefuls being put through their paces at Happy Valley race-course.

'Where,' asked Dempsey, 'would you like to go?'

But Debbie Vertigan asked in return: 'What shall I call you?' – for her a more important problem.

He suggested in his forthright manner: 'Whatever you usually call me.'

'I never call you anything,' she told him truthfully, and giggled.

'Don't you?' He thought about it. 'All your uncles, you tell me, are dead! So I don't want to be called Uncle—'

'I had no intention—'

'Nor Doctor or Mister. You'd better use my name. It seems reasonable enough even if it is a silly name. Daniel. It's no worse than Debbie,' he claimed.

'No, of course not, Daniel,' she agreed hastily.

'Let's browse round this place,' he suggested, having not much more idea of how to take in Hong Kong than she had.

Debbie was in any case more mindful of being with *him*, very aware of his sunburnt face; heedful of his contrarient nature, revealed in the very Irish wit, sometimes black, the content of apparent malice only revealed as harmless by the gleam in his eyes. She admired his choice of lightweight suit and the bow-tie. Had he thought consciously about her when selecting it for the day? And, if so, what did he *see* in the mind's eye? Her own apperception was modest, that of a tall thin girl with arms too long. At most she approved of her own eyes.

Inevitably, to begin with, they talked of the ship and those aboard her, because, at the moment, these were all they had in common.

'Is it true that Mr Tomazos is drinking a lot?' she asked in concern.

'Yes. He found when he went ashore at Adelaide that his wife was being unfaithful.'

'Ah!' she sighed, hurt on behalf of the nice officer who had chided her gently about this very city. 'How sad and hurtful. He is such a nice person. I'll never be unfaithful,' she claimed, and meant it.

'Not even with the mind?'

'Not at all.'

'There are always other people worthy of admiration.'

'Yes, but—'

'And so how far do you take it?'

'My dog is faithful to me,' Debbie claimed. 'If I cannot—'

Dempsey said in his forthright manner, 'Your dog's faithfulness is related to his dinner. It excludes his possible relationship with a bitch!'

She giggled again, and qualified, 'You know what I mean!'

'I do, but your dog probably doesn't . . . Still, it was damn tough on Tomazos . . .'

A little later she ventured inquisitively, 'Who is that Pauline person?'

'Mrs Triffett? Just a passenger. And a patient of mine . . .'

'She seemed a bit hysterical.'

'She is neurotic.'

'And a little – vulgar.'

'She has problems of a sort. Didn't you know she'd attempted suicide? It was strictly for kicks, but she might have succeeded.'

Debbie was startled.

'But she seemed so – extrovert. And capable of enjoyment . . . You must see some strange people in your work, Daniel.'

It gave her pleasure to voice his name.

'Pauline's problems are strictly for television—'

She wanted to make a remark of disapproval, but didn't dare to. The last thing she desired from him was any kind of derision.

They strolled round the main streets of Kowloon, and it had become easier to talk to him. There were many remarkable things to jest about, to comment upon lightly, with a foreigner's perception – a man carrying an elephant tusk; a coffin shop; very colourful flower stalls; clothes, exotic tropical fruits . . . They refused sugar cane from one hawker, but accepted hot chestnuts from another. The smell of burning joss touched their nostrils.

They ascended the stepped 'ladder' streets and stared in small shops which clung to the mountainside. Everywhere seethed with people, active, hurrying, talkative under the buntings, banners, flags, awnings and signs.

'He's as bad as I am' said Debbie.

'Who is?'

She pointed to the old man in a shop counting on an abacus.

'Probably a millionaire,' suggested Dempsey. 'Tiring yet?'

'Not the slightest. It's so exciting. Stand over there. I'm going to take your photograph.'

'Oh, God!' protested Dempsey. But he stood with good humour by the colourful street sign. 'Do you know what it means?' he asked when she'd taken the shot. Debbie shook her head. 'It tells of the merits of the Suzie Wong area,' he said convincingly.

'I don't believe you.'

'No one will ever know.'

'You don't mean it?'

'Of course.'

'My father might understand when he sees the slide.'

They lunched in a Chinese restaurant. It was a little disconcerting, Debbie found, for they were stared at. And it was incredibly noisy, parties of people shouting to others. She was, however, hungry, and gobbled down shark's fin soup, fried prawns with chilli sauce, diced chicken with walnuts, sweet and sour pork, crisp shrimps with rice, and Tien-Tsin cabbage with cream.

'Want to go skating?' Dempsey then asked.

'Goodness, no!'

'Skin diving?'

'No, Daniel, not for me.'

'As a doctor, my advice is violent exercise. But as a friend, I think a trip on a walla-walla.'

'Goodness, what's that? It sounds very Australian!'

'No. It's a sort of taxi boat. There are all sorts of islands around here, with caves and terrific views. You'd better re-load your camera.'

They hired the small motor boat and it chugged out into Kowloon Bay. The spectacle was staggering – the white stone skyscrapers, the Boeings coming in over her head on to the mile-long promontory of concrete, the crowded merchant shipping anchorage and typhoon shelter near which were hundreds of sampans. Across the water was the other tremendous horizon, of Victoria itself, more popularly called Hong Kong.

After a while they left behind the aircraft-carrier and white liners and the ferries scuttling to and fro and were tossed about a bit in open water.

'Where are we going?' Debbie asked.

'I'm not sure. I think it's Peng Chau Islands.'

Just then they came up behind four junks. The two youths in charge of the walla-walla turned to grin in excitement.

'Festival!' one cried. 'We follow?'

'Sure,' agreed Dempsey. 'Have your camera at the ready, Debbie.'

They saw now that the junks were being towed by motor boats. Chinese music blared from the loudspeakers lashed to the mastheads of three of them. Paper-decorated shrines were placed at the aft end of the well deck with burning candles and thick sticks of incense. The nearest junk was dressed overall with a hoist of signal flags. As they came close Debbie saw that on board were scores of men and women, and these were making as much noise as possible slamming down mahjong chips. Children ran about and pursued each other in and out of cupboard-like cabins and through a maze of spars and ropes.

Fire crackers exploded and on the fourth junk a hired band made as much noise as it could with clarinets, gongs and cymbals. Young men began to prance about and leap around the gunwales.

Dempsey said, 'If the things don't catch fire they'll fall overboard anyway ... Where are they from?' he asked the two youths.

'What's he say?' Debbie pleaded.

'From Yaumati and Causeway Bay typhoon anchorages. It's a kind of pilgrimage.'

Scores of fishing vessels and other junks were now joining the procession.

They were approaching an island, but to land seemed impossible because of rocks. But the young men from a dozen boats rushed about, waded and shouted, and very soon half a dozen gangways stretched forty yards to a beach.

The gangways consisted of planks resting on trestles and rocks.

Women and children flooded ashore, carrying whole roast pigs on ornamented biers, decorated with paper lanterns. A few pessimists carried umbrellas. Hustlers had already set up shop to sell fairings.

The fire crackers exploded, children shrieked, old women carried ashore dozens, even hundreds, of hard-boiled eggs, dyed red, chickens, banners and honorific screens. The band had set up on shore.

The launches cast off their tow and the four junks came in head on, over-riding their anchors to facilitate warping out. From these, too, long planks were put ashore and votive shrines were landed, followed by the pigs, each carried on a bier.

Hundreds of people were now ashore, milling about on a shingle beach. Their own walla-walla pulled alongside a makeshift bridge of planks.

To get ashore was not easy. Having climbed on to the planking Debbie found that the sagging of the planks had made them springy. They had thus become bouncy and it was funny to see whole families bouncing about, and funnier still when Dempsey fell into the water. After the first shock and then the relief of seeing that he was soaked only as high as his thighs, she giggled. Plenty of people helped him back on to the plank with good humour free from malice.

'The sun will dry me,' was all Dempsey said.

She admired him all the more for not complaining.

On shore she flinched as twenty-foot strings of crackers turned the air blue.

Many of the youths from the decorated junks had now dressed themselves in 'lion skins' – gaudy creations of silk and paper, and consisting of a fierce head (dragon-like, rather than leonine) and many 'back legs', pantomime style. They went through the sinuous motions of the ritual dance, surrounded by youths, themselves in white caps and bright red trousers, women with wide straw hats, and children raucous in excitment.

The youths and women with offerings of hundreds of eggs and the pigs on biers then climbed the cliffs, followed by hundreds.

'If they can't drown us they'll break our blasted necks,' growled Dempsey, but with Debbie he made the difficult ascent.

The dances were repeated before a temple shrine on a space levelled out of the hillside, fronted by a square court with a high retaining wall facing the sea. Many steps led up to the shrine and the breathless, sweating women, burdened with offerings, now entered and presented the food. Individual women carried in bundles of paper clothing and emerged with flaming packets which they consigned to a brazier already pouring black smoke. The fire crackers were still being discharged and added sulphurous fumes.

Lion dance teams of two men performed in relays before the temple, and other entertainments began.

Two hours passed and the sky began to pinken in the west.

On a ridge nearby, when the dances were over and the last junk had presented its roast pig, the young men of each *tong*, the name of which was inscribed prominently on a banner which fluttered from the junk's top mast, performed the last ceremonies.

They formed a ring round a table which was loaded with self-launching projectiles, each with a tag bearing a number.

Debbie jumped when these things fizzed thirty feet into the evening air and exploded, shedding burning debris over the spectators.

The crowd scrambled for the tags. They were fired in order of importance. The second one fell at Debbie's feet and she picked it up, although without wishing to claim it. She surrendered it willingly to a young man of the *tong*, merely asking, 'What's it mean?'

'Good luck.'

'Second class,' explained Dempsey. 'You have the second luck. In theory you could claim a trophy.'

'The luck will be enough,' she said.

Night had its own strangeness. Above the beach a bell began to toll with a deep boom and scores of voices to chant devotions and ceremonials. On the shore carnival had begun; all was noise, shouting and rushing about. Dust coated Debbie and there was the strong smell of salt from pans somewhere on this island. It was still enormously hot. Fresh discharges of rockets had determined many degrees of luck.

At last many began to embark. Each of the four ceremonial junks warped out so that its motor launch could make fast alongside. There was much shouting and laughter. It surprised Debbie that no one fell overboard.

Each of the junks, before setting course for Hong Kong, made two circles and fired off crackers in salute.

As their own walla-walla overtook the junks Debbie could see that wine bottles had been opened and a feast was beginning.

'I'm hungry,' declared Dempsey.

'How are your clothes?'

'They're dry enough except the shoes. Those feel squelchy.'

She was satisfied and would have been willing to end the day. But he took her to a floating restaurant for dinner.

This was crowded and fascinating. It was, at heart, just a restaurant where meals were being served as fast as possible, a profit being made, but everything about it was, for Debbie, uncommon. The intense noise was in such contrast to European restaurants. There were a few Europeans nearby, Germans, she thought, who called and bellowed, but for the most part ate with something like fury. It was the Chinese themselves who made the racket – merchant seamen, children, businessmen who belched and picked their teeth. Then the very surroundings were unusual. All tables were round. Advertisements hung on walls and were, by virtue of bizarrerie, works of art. Pots, jars, dishes, glasses, were all of unusual shape. The only European note was that of hygiene: the square-sectioned bone chopsticks were wrapped in cellophane. The atmosphere was that of steam and the smells foreign: sauces and the heat of soups, jasmine, ginger, fish cooked in wine. There were spittoons by every table, for the men, and jars of toothpicks for everyone.

Trays of hot damp cloths were carried round at intervals, and Dempsey used the tongs on the trays to remove the cloth and wipe away the sweat from his face. Debbie was very hot but not sweating yet.

They sipped at the jasmine-scented tea from bowls; ate the *deem-sum* with relish : small cockles dipped in sauce, prawns and pieces of ginger and other things not identifiable but delicious. Chicken with lotus seed followed. She left it to Dempsey who seemed to know what he was ordering. Meat balls came next, featherweight in dough.

Debbie had had enough now, but Dempsey tackled sucking-pig and its crackling and grinned at her as he wiped his mouth with a napkin. She had coped with the chopsticks reasonably well, and it was permissible, he told her, to use the small porcelain spoon for objects like peas.

The soup followed.

'You must try some,' he insisted, 'or they'll be offended.' He grinned again, very Irish, and informed her, 'Only the fish course after that, and the mopping up!'

The soup was birds'-nest, and she enjoyed it until Dempsey informed her cheerfully, 'It's made by boiling down the salivary excretion which binds together the mud nests of cave martins.'

Around Dempsey's dish was a frank litter of rice like a snowstorm.

He persuaded her to try the fish, a yellow garsupa. It stared at her and she felt a little queasy, but it had been cooked in wine and was of great delicacy.

She had accepted several cups of what she thought was some harmless variety of tea, but this stuff, called *shau-shing*, was a wine distilled from rice; because it was sweet and even cloying she had assumed it to be innocent. But now she was a fraction anaesthetized, and even though aware of it she became, by her standards, noisy.

'Daniel, you've got me tight!'

He stood up and toasted her. 'Yam seng!'

'What's that mean?'

'Bottoms up! Where's that man with his blasted face flannel? Have a liqueur?'

'Not on your life. I might be seasick. What will you do tomorrow?' she asked, half revealing what was in her heart.

But he was evasive.

'A surgery, I expect. How about you?'

'That pen friend is to meet me.'

'I hope he's not a disappointment.'

'I don't know if it's he or she,' Debbie admitted. 'I'm going cold on it anyway.'

It was a hint, but he missed it – as usual, she thought charitably.

'Ah, look!' she cried with pleasure. 'There's Mr Tomazos!'

The First Officer was with Mollon, another man and two very attractive Chinese girls dressed in their colourful *cheong-sams*.

They talked to him on their way out. It was obvious that the two girls were with Mollon and the civilian, but Tomazos was cheerful enough, it seemed.

He greeted them with undisguised pleasure, so that Debbie, inhibitions burned away by the wine, reciprocated the warmth. It seemed incredible that the cheerful solid man should have been betrayed.

'Look who's here!' he called.

Mollon examined Debbie with frank physical admiration, and the third man stood up for the brief introductions.

'What are you celebrating?' Tomazos asked.

'Well, nothing in particular. Have you anything in mind?'

'You seem very happy.'

'And you? What are you celebrating?'

'Ah, we are celebrating the typhoon which surely awaits us.'

Debbie said prettily, 'I am sure that you are doing no such thing. But if it was so, I would be content to have you above all men to be in charge of the *Areopagus*.'

Tomazos looked at her and knew that something kind and human was intended; that she had learned of what had happened to him and was disturbed, hurt on his behalf.

'That is a compliment I shall treasure and try to be worthy of.'

'Have a nice party,' she suggested.

'And you, too.'

'Thank you.'

The Chinese girls smiled cautiously and Mollon said, 'Too right.'

The restaurant was on an upper deck. One deck beneath it was the world, where the vulgarity of the West permeated the strangeness. Debbie could not be expected on this night to notice the intrusion – the counter stacked with American soft drinks, the postcards, films, colour slides of what had been thought a singular experience, but was evidently just a tourist attraction. Beyond was the misery of the world, the sampans crowding round in the hope of a tossed coin.

It was after midnight when they returned to the *Areopagus*, but the Parade Deck was crowded with traders, passengers and ship's crew.

Debbie was reluctant to end the day, and Dempsey, too, found it hard to unwind, switch it off.

They strolled round examining the linen and cheap *objets d'art.*

'I will buy you a pair of shoes,' Debbie said, for the pair Dempsey wore were still squelching uncomfortably.

'Not your fault I fell—'

'Ah, but I laughed and so want to pay penance—'

'If everyone who laughed—'

A cat miaowed.

Debbie turned and said, 'You don't catch me a second time.'

The steward grinned and asked, 'What you buy, eh? You have good time?'

'Marvellous,' she told him promptly.

Dempsey commented, 'This fellow says he's got some jade.'

'Ah, how beautiful!' cried Debbie, looking at it, ignoring the poor value of light.

The trader was quick to identify the situation.

'Yu din,' he explained. 'Three-legged vessel. Made in the

time of Emperor Chien Lung. And this is a miniature *Yu Shiang Lu* – that is, an incense burner. This *Hwa Shuen* – flower vase. Many rings.'

'Soapstone,' challenged Dempsey.

'No, mutton fat, good white. This Celadon, what you call olive green. This ship Spinach Green, you try to scratch you will find it is not soapstone ...'

'Would you like a trinket?' Dempsey asked clumsily.

Debbie whispered, 'I'd love the three-legged ship, but it'd cost the earth—'

'What, *here*?'

He asked, 'How much is the ship?'

'Hundred Australian dollars.'

'I'm a doctor, not a gangster.'

The steward whispered to Debbie, while Dempsey haggled badly, 'I'll fix this fellow good, eh?'

He blew a whistle and shouted, 'All traders ashore.'

Dempsey knew that this gave him the whip hand.

'Not a cent more than ten.'

'This is genuine *Yu Din* of Emperor Chien Lung. Carved and polished two hundred years ago. It is worth a thousand dollars – I give it to you for fifty. Years of toil to make it, wheels pedalled by craftsmen ...'

The traders were being herded to the gangway, and the steward put a hand behind this one's back. 'All ashore. Plenty of time for that tomorrow.'

'Forty,' suggested the trader.

The steward inserted himself into the discussion. 'Which palace you take this from?' he asked.

'Beautiful chemical impurities and oxides cause this perfection—'

'Ten,' said Dempsey with finality.

'May it bring you long life, many children and protection against pain,' proposed the trader, surrendering with grace.

He gathered together his several trays and boxes, dropped them into a sack and went ashore.

In the greater illumination of the Aegean Lounge they examined the tiny vessel. It seemed supremely beautiful.

'I shall always treasure it,' said Debbie frankly.

'And may it have the charms he suggested.'

They were conscious that they must separate and that there were things unsaid, emotions not clarified.

'Want a drink?' Dempsey asked.

'No. That would spoil it. But thank you.'

They strolled along A Deck. Her cabin was amidships, one hundred and fifty feet astern of the surgery.

She wished to convey something of her emotions as well as gratitude for an unusual day. It was impossible to talk in terms of affection; he was just too distant even now. She knew that she would have to convey what the day meant to her by writing a letter to him. Or making a phone call. A letter would be better, for it would allow care of expression, the consideration of words. But right now the day was still very much with her and, as he was not likely to do anything rash, it was up to her. He was helpless, she could see, hesitant, not aware of how to separate with grace, without inflicting pain.

Audaciously – so that her face was hot with embarrassment, considering it for an hour afterwards – she, who was as tall as he, took his head between both hands very quickly, kissed him somewhere round the left eye, and said breathlessly, 'Bless you, Daniel, for the day,' and fled, only to have to stand two yards away fumbling for a key. He said 'Good-night, my dear' and was gone. The feeling was distinctly one of anti-climax and she found that she was trembling. But the beautiful piece of jade was hard in her hand in proof of something.

Lin Yuen, pen friend for eighteen months, proved to be a young man. He was a great disappointment. Perhaps this was inevitable by virtue of comparison with the day before.

It was not that Lin Yuen was of uninteresting appearance. He was quite a handsome youth of nineteen, a college student; he was in no way vulgar. But the neuter-ness of his correspondence was explained now by his interests, which tended to be prejudiced to the point of bigotry. His dedication was not to things social or sexual. At first intimidated by his strong views expressed with vigour, Debbie gradually appreciated that his perspective of the world, particularly of Hong Kong, was bitter, not to be interrupted by argument or minor truths. He had written to her and asked questions about America and Australia, and now he inquired orally in the same outright manner, but the words, aloud, lost the quaintness and all the charm which had been presumed in the letters. He regarded Debbie as someone who was part of a greater guilt, answerable to him. He did not really want to learn, but to adopt facts to his prejudicial condition. His pursuit of knowledge, at the age of nineteen, was formed, frozen, and everything extraneous was additional evidence, not qualification, to help condemnation, not to assist estimate or temper with mercy.

She soon began to wonder if he had continued the correspondence because he had found out that she was a diplomat's daughter. In this she was a great disappointment to him. He was well versed in political semantics. To her, politics meant nothing, bloc hatreds were meaningless; human beings were what mattered. He became incredulous at first, then a little derisive, finally scornful.

They were in the vast amusement park called Lai Chi Kok, on the Kowloon side. There were many entertainments here which were unusual and would have interested her – story tellers, fortune tellers, blind minstrels, hawkers, a replica of an old Chinese palace where they could have eaten, roller coasters, Chinese opera . . . He just strolled about in the blazing sun despising everything, even her.

It was impossible even to pay compliments.

'It's so beautiful and exciting,' she said, early in the conversation.

Lin Yuen waved a hand in scorn. 'To an American, yes. Money paves the way. The best is available. And the English pay their expatriate civil servants well. They have crazy leave provision – whole weeks and months. The Chinese factory worker takes five days off in a year. Oh, yes, it is beautiful for the two per cent who are answerable to nobody.'

'It is better than life across the river,' she suggested.

'It is?' he demanded. 'How do you know?'

'Because they fled in millions here.'

'Old fools with a sense of gratitude,' he claimed. 'We who are young are not obliged to grovel before the wealthy British. We see the poverty and the cynical exploitation. It is a community in which vulgar wealth and poverty stand side by side. But you choose to see only the wealth and the glamour.'

'I have only been here a day and a half. But even I know that a million of the four million here are in newly-built Government flats . . .'

'You think a flat with a toilet and shower is justice?'

'It is better than a sleep cubicle rented on a time basis, with shared facilities.'

'It is exploitation of the poor either way,' he suggested angrily.

Stung, she said, 'Do you do anything about it except complain?'

'Oh, yes,' he said, not offended, but smiling. 'The end of the road is not independence here. The British may keep their hundreds of millions of pounds reserves in London. They and certain Chinese exploiters import their Japanese and Oriental wares or make baubles here in factories but their days are numbered . . .'

There seemed nothing else to say to one so conditioned. She stared around as they strolled aimlessly. At first she had felt humiliated, ignorant, as guilty as he meant her to feel, a political fool. But after two hours of it she was merely annoyed. And finally she was resentful, waiting to escape, and thrashing her brains to find some excuse to leave which would convince him who was not open to conviction. She would never write to him again.

Meanwhile, he persisted, whipped her with his curious prejudiced logic and expected her to respond, to be overwhelmed by it. He was, presumably, an activist of some sort. She limited herself to the minimum, to 'Yes' or 'No' or to silence which should have told him he was a bore, not mindful of his guest.

With great shock she saw two Europeans a few hundred yards off get into a taxi, and her pulse thumped so that even her head throbbed. For she identified them as Dempsey and the woman Pauline. But the sensation of shock and even faintness passed, for she was conscious that it was her imagination and that her mind, being full of him, saw Dempsey everywhere. She returned her attention to the harsh opinions pouring out of the thin mouth, so fast that it was as if he was pumping in material in a specific time period and, aware of it, must hurry, the words could be digested later; she would then be convinced . . .

Several times Debbie nerved herself to utter the dishonest genteel excuses and leave him. He would know they were courtesy only, and would despise her, but it seemed he did that already.

She was so ingrained in politeness that she could not do it without anger to assist her. But suddenly he said something of which she caught the last words, '. . . half Asia starves while the American barbarians strut round smiling and killing and working out the possible profit.'

She said angrily, 'If you believe such rubbish you are a fool.'

He was anxious to discuss it. 'No. You are foolish because —'

'—And you will not wish to have my company. Good morning.'

She crossed the street recklessly to be decisive and get away. He shouted abuse behind her : 'You are a mental and moral coward who cannot face your guilt . . .'

But she had a long stride and was round three corners before the density of traffic could have allowed him to cross the street in pursuit, if indeed he wished to. She hailed a taxi in a panic and went back to the Canton Road.

In the Ocean Terminal she saw Miss Wearne, alone, perhaps lonely, staring in a shop window. In three hours was this as far as she'd got – a few hundred yards from the *Areopagus*? By a motor showroom Mr Pybus sprawled in a seat, dead drunk, snoring, vulgarly attired.

Debbie greeted, 'I was looking for you.'

Miss Wearne said, 'My dear, I thought you'd gone off for the day.'

'Only for a couple of hours. I thought you might like to come with me to see some Chinese opera at the City Hall.'

'How kind of you! Is it very far?'

'We only have to cross in the ferry.'

'I'd be delighted,' admitted Miss Wearne frankly.

She was tired, but eager to see some more of this remarkable city. Alone, she had been afraid of getting lost. This had happened to her yesterday. She rested in the ferry and told Debbie about it.

'I got on the wrong train and went too far. It was most interesting. There were people in the compartment drinking out of saucers and eating fishy things and the women were picking things out of their children's hair. An officer told me I was on the wrong train, but I didn't believe him. He stopped it eventually at a little place with a market covered by scores of umbrellas. All sorts of officials made sure that I boarded a train back, and half a dozen more met me at Kowloon. Very thoughtful of them.'

Debbie laughed and told her about Dempsey falling off a plank . . .

They sat in the memorial gardens for an hour and then went in to see an opera. It was not Chinese, but Gilbert and Sullivan, but Miss Wearne had never seen such a thing in her life and was delighted. Further, the seats were very restful and for a while she could rest her feet and kick her shoes off.

It was experience enough for Miss Wearne, who would not have known the opera hadn't been Chinese if Debbie and the programme hadn't told her.

The girl now insisted on taking her to dinner. Miss Wearne was impressed by her confidence. Debbie turned into a restaurant which would have been too formidable for Miss Wearne had she been alone. It was packed with apprehensive Europeans from ships, restless children under the care of *amahs*, businessmen and parties of shrieking girls. All was bustle and colour and unfamiliar scents.

They were unable to have a table to themselves, but sat at a round table with six other people, four of whom were Americans.

Miss Wearne studied the menu. It was not only a very full

list of strange names, but a thing of beautiful design. She coveted it. What better proof to send to Eileen Boyd, a confirmation that she was indulging in sophisticated enjoyments? She had no idea of what the dishes were, but they had a romantic appearance just printed on a colourful piece of card . . .

She found that she could handle the chopsticks quite well, with occasional assistance from the porcelain spoon. A man came round with hot flannels, but in this restaurant they were not moist with rose water but hygienic and Occidental with disinfectant.

'Where's the menu?' an American gentleman asked.

Miss Wearne had put it under her plate. She fiddled with it as if it had fallen on her lap, and viewed the man with misgiving in case he put a greasy thumb mark on it.

'How long are you gonna be with that thing?' the man's wife asked.

'I can't figure it out,' the man admitted. 'The soup seems to come half way.'

After a while Miss Wearne recovered the menu. She dropped it on her lap and covered it with a paper napkin and looked blank when another man asked what came next. Hot and bothered, she folded it under the napkin. It dropped on the floor. Miss Wearne went a bit dizzy recovering it, but put it now with finality into her large handbag. It was the first time since childhood that she had stolen anything, but she was unrepentant. It was necessary to overawe Eileen Boyd, and if to pinch a Chinese menu helped to do so, that was that.

But she waited with apprehension for someone to ask 'What did you do with it?' or the waiter to suggest 'Can we have it back, please?'

She ate well, but was relieved when Debbie suggested that it was time to leave. The Americans offered farewells and the Chinese waiter smiled and bowed and people at tables stared with interest at the foreign girl who was very beautiful and so much taller than her grandmother.

Right by the door a young man stopped them. Miss Wearne was scared : they'd caught her.

The young man asked politely, 'Would you like to take a menu with you?' and picked two from a pile of hundreds,

The young woman was conversational. It was as if Pauline was being interviewed by a journalist. Instead of which she was having her fortune told in a bamboo hut in the gigantic fairground of Lai Chi Kok.

'It's not easy with Europeans,' the Chinese young woman told them apologetically. 'With us it's all written there on the face.'

'I wouldn't have thought that,' Dempsey said.

The young woman arranged cards on the table before her.

'What beautiful cards!' Pauline commented.

The woman smiled.

'German,' she said with a shrug. 'Did you think they were Chinese? May I see your hands? Yes, both of them,' she urged, laughing. 'Value for money, yes? Beautiful hands, if I may say so.'

'Never done any work,' suggested Dempsey, but he agreed with the opinion of the girl. Despite her incidental remark she had an attitude of seriousness, of someone who accepted the challenge of frivolousness and would prove it mistaken. There was the smell of cooking to undervalue her skill, and, outside, the noises of the acres of enjoyment.

She produced a box of small ornaments rather like chess pieces but made of jade, pearl and silver.

'Please select these as you wish and place them on the cards of your choice,' she instructed.

Pauline did so. It was not quite meaningless, for she put a horse on the king, a turret on a jack . . .

The Chinese young woman pleaded, 'Excuse me' and put her head on to her hands as if in anxious thought. Once she looked up to check the arrangement.

'I see many people dressed in white,' she informed Pauline. 'The sun is hot. The king comes. There are tears. I can smell paint burning. There seem to be endless journeys. You have received much love and yet you despair. Do not be afraid. You have great beauty, you laugh and smile, but happiness avoids you because you are in pursuit. Stand still and it will approach you. Bite the fruit that seems bitter . . . You'll never forget Hong Kong . . . I'm sorry,' she concluded. 'It's gone.'

'Not bad,' opined Pauline.

'It wasn't much.'

'I certainly shan't forget Hong Kong.'

'Are you satisfied?'

'More than satisfied; I am impressed.'

'Thank you.'

Outside, Dempsey laughed and commented, 'It wasn't paint she could smell burning; it was her blasted dinner!'

Pauline objected, 'But she was good. All that stuff about love.'

He told her frankly: 'Anyone can see you're beautiful. It's a fair deduction that you'll therefore have emotional problems rather than economic or health.'

'I think doctors are too practical. What do we do now?'

'How about an hour's Chinese opera?'

They were fortunate enough to have only a quarter of an hour to wait before one began. It was in traditional style, with much beating of gongs and clash of cymbals. The strange voices and over-acting by people with bright costumes and exaggerated make-up were fascinating for a while, but after an hour the ceremonial style had a tedium and Pauline was restless. 'I want to go on the roller coaster,' she whispered.

The roller coaster was not only nerve racking but rewarded them with superb views of the harbour. 'When I get my stomach back I want to eat,' Pauline declared. 'And then can we go up on the tram to the Peak? I like to do corny things.'

She was like a child being taken around, but Dempsey was not fooled. She was purposeful, the careless charm was part of intention. And there was within him the inclination to succumb. Why not? She was very beautiful, dressed in the pale blue dress. No ornamentation, no make-up; she didn't need them. People stared at her, indifferent to his (or her) resentment, and even in Chinese youths Dempsey saw the shock of identification: she exuded physical provocation, intentionally or otherwise, and perturbed the beholder.

It was difficult for him, even aware of this property, to refrain from touching her. She was all electricity, hands that were agitated, a face very alive, eyes never still. She had no qualms about touching him, taking his arm, leaning on him in the taxi and the ferry and clinging to him outright in the little train as it made its near-vertical ascent above Victoria.

It was the only place in Hong Kong where they'd experienced quiet. They followed a track, each corner revealing a new and magnificent panorama. It was very hot and eventually they sat down to laze. 'I'm going to sleep,' Pauline said. She lay on her stomach, absolutely relaxed, soft and sensual, and he was disturbed by the contours of her buttocks. He studied her hair and neck and grace of posture. She was magnificent, physically. But she was neurotic, cunning and predatory.

'What are you thinking about?' she asked.

'You,' he admitted.

'Well, that's nice. I like that.'

'I was thinking you're a chameleon.'

'I don't care for that.'

'You adapt to the situation.'

'Don't you?'

'A little hypocrisy for the dying, yes. I mean, what's the real Pauline Triffett like?'

'I don't know either,' she admitted.

'I'd like to meet her.'

'I think you know me now, Daniel.'

'I want to.'

'I'm glad you care that much. You heard what the woman said: "Bite the bitter fruit."'

'She was talking to you.'

'Perhaps I'm a rotten fruit. Bite and see.'

'I'm thirty-five years old.'

'Poor thing. So what?'

'I take things cautiously, with seriousness.'

'I wouldn't have thought that at first, Daniel, but I believe you. I don't like the inference.'

'Which you presume to be—'

'That I'm flighty, neurotic, don't take anything seriously.'

'What happened to Mr Triffett?'

'Like I told you.'

'It's a vague situation.'

'You want it cut and dried?'

'Doctors don't like to have relationships with other men's wives which their patients might object to.'

'To hell with your patients! What about *me*? We're on a journey. Different values apply.'

'I don't know *how* to value you, Pauline.'

'I can't do it for you. Somewhere along the line you have to believe your own judgement.'

He was afraid. That was the truth of it. He had no wish to hurt her, but was sensitive to the possibility of being hurt himself, and perhaps this was her intention. She liked sensation, quarrels, trouble; he could imagine that the mental chaos had been too much for Mr Triffett. The tantalization, mockery, violence of emotion, all preceding or following passionate love-making may well have caused him to look elsewhere, for calmer emotional pastures. But maybe Triffett was just a dirty young man who'd seen a piece he fancied more, and any brittleness in Pauline was a result, not a cause.

'My senses tell me you're a very beautiful woman.'

'Hooray for your senses.'

'But frenzied, sexy, and in many ways selfish.'

'It's your rotten old caution which gives you that message.'

'As I said, I'm thirty-five and a doctor.'

She asked in apparent anxiety, 'I'm not ill, am I, Daniel? I mean, because of Reidy . . .'

'No. Nothing more than a high moral fever.'

'She can't alter. I have.'

'Let's go and try some other Hong Kong attraction.'

'A Chinese film?'

But this, he deduced, was merely a device to rest the body and pass the hours. Later he took her into a bar and then for a meal. She ate ravenously, with frank greed, through nine or ten delicious dishes. They moved on to a floor show. It was funny and rather affected, Chinese dancers attitudinizing for the benefit of Europeans: London was far more shocking.

Later still they found a dance floor that suited their mood: a barn of a place, almost in darkness, where hundreds of youths, shrieking girls and American sailors danced with frenzy or cheek-to-cheek, whatever took them. A go-go girl danced in an illuminated cage, a voluptuous Asian, not Chinese, but probably a half-caste, sultry, insolent and tireless, pouring sweat down her thighs and arms.

Pauline crushed against Dempsey, was frankly sensual and perturbing, undulating her body against his, kissing round his neck, clawing him. He found the touch of her burning hot, the flesh moving to and fro to the music was erotic in his hands.

They kept it up for an hour or so, until they were moist with exertion and gasping the hot smoky air.

Then, as if it was a problem that had been postponed for as long as possible, they went back to the *Areopagus*. The night air was cold, and they both dithered. Dempsey froze a little, caution returning to him more urgently than to her, if indeed she ever felt caution.

It was two in the morning and he had a surgery at eight. Nobody would turn up, but he had to go through the motions. He felt all the caution of a professional person who must consider the duties of tomorrow and relinquish some of the fun of today.

But she clung to him outside his cabin door, sensing the drop in temperature.

'You can't end it there,' she asserted. 'Daniel, believe your senses.'

He hesitated and she saw the irresolution, the professional care clashing with the desires of the man.

'I'm sorry. I think I understand,' she conceded.

He was hot with care diminishing. He had lost all dialogic skill and was confronted with his own desires and had no words left to avoid them. Not unless he simply rejected her. In her naked emotional state no hypocrisy would suffice. He'd have to say he didn't want her.

She was neurotic, subtle, full of some feminine cruelties. He knew she would always be trouble. She might be diseased, she had been so casual. She had picked up men and taken them to her cabin. And she had enjoyed the physical relationship with Miss Reidy. These actions were repugnant to him.

But his emotions told him also that she really cared for him. And she was brittle, had presumably been wounded seriously by someone, probably Triffett. He just couldn't bear to hurt her. He was deeply fond of her, possibly in love, albeit scared. And he had all day watched those swingy thighs and buttocks.

'Come on then!' he urged grimly.

'Oh, Daniel, how kind!'

'Kind? You fool! I love you – with some reservations!'

'I've no reservations,' she told him.

Her eye took in the cabin instantly. It was larger than the double cabin she shared with Reidy. It had a bed, not bunks. She looked at Dempsey and grinned with outright satisfaction.

He stripped her slowly down to her pants. Her breasts were already swollen, the nipples erect and the areola circle around them was tumescent. Her torso was flushing.

He pawed her as long as it was bearable and then pushed her across the bed. She intertwined her legs round his, slippery with sweat, and gasped and writhed. She kissed him all the way down his back, and bit his ears and neck, while her fingers clawed his buttocks and then crawled round with sly insistence to stroke his genitals. When he turned her over she was groaning as if already approaching climax. He ripped the absurd pants off, and, sure enough, the folds of flesh were fluid and swollen.

She gave a brief cry of pain, oddly, at the touch of his hands on her inner thighs and then thrust her stomach up and demanded him. It had been too exciting for him, and his climax came in a couple of minutes, but so did hers, the flesh shuddering with him.

Ten minutes later he said, 'I'm sorry if I hurt your leg.'

'Don't be sorry about anything. You hurt my bruises too!'

'What bruises?'

'Some man beat me up.'

She was moving one leg very slightly, and he saw circular scars, very recent, on her inner thigh. 'What the devil are those? Why didn't you say?'

'And stop you? Don't ever stop. There was nothing like that before. I trusted you, you see, completely.'

'But these scars need attention. What the hell have you been doing?'

'A little game Reidy and I played. We stubbed cigarettes out on each other to see who was chicken. She was . . .'

Dempsey was silent.

'Now you despise me again . . .'

'No. I'll never despise you. But don't do that again. Your legs are too beautiful . . .'

'Oh, that was a lovely day you gave me, Daniel,' she sighed, and was asleep.

He fell asleep himself, too tired to take care, and the steward woke them both at half past six in the morning.

The steward was not shocked, although a bit startled. After a two-seconds' pause he inquired, 'Another cup of tea?' and Pauline whispered 'Yes.'

'Letter on floor,' the steward said.

He gave it to Dempsey. It had been pushed under the door and was a bit creased. Dempsey recognized the writing on the envelope; not that he'd seen it before, but it was the neat rounded script of a girl of fifteen.

He read it later. 'My dear Daniel,' it began, and continued in careful phrases to express gratitude for an unusual and beautiful day. It ended 'Your very dear friend, Debbie.' He knew what it meant, was aware of the weight of sentences, the balanced phraseology which she had probably written out four or five times . . . The tender day in which they'd seen the junks and the dragons, the cool hands holding his head briefly and the child's mouth touching his eye – they meant almost nothing to him.

But he felt the weight of responsibility, as if answerable to her, and was anxious.

20

AFTER much thought Tornetta decided to use a knife. He bought it in Kowloon on the way to the Macau Hydrofoil Terminal. It was a beautiful piece of Japanese steel which would certainly penetrate anything Mr Rossi wore on this hot day. It was a little difficult to know where and how to carry it without it being noticed. He eventually fixed its pigskin sheath somewhere on his left buttock. There would come a moment when he had to either take off his jacket altogether or fumble for whole seconds. It frightened him, but he was not committed. If the circumstances were not propitious he would postpone Rossi's death until later.

Mr Rossi had himself suggested the situation for his own obit. They had talked yesterday after breakfast.

'Where are you going today?' Tornetta had asked.

'Business,' Rossi had told him. 'Much business today. But tomorrow pleasure.' He grinned with cunning, his face close to Tornetta. His smile deteriorated his value, metamorphosed him most unexpectedly from the pious front of businessman and good Masonic fellow, orthodox, conservative within the Australian society he had become a particle of, to craftiness. It was as if a bishop had hinted at intended lechery, or as if he, Rossi, was, by facial expression, telling Tornetta: 'I know you. You are cheap and cunning, in the entertainment business for quick profits. I, too, am in some game, but one more lucrative ...' 'Pleasure with business tomorrow. Why don't you come?' Mr Rossi had suggested.

'Where to?'

'Macau, the Portuguese city over the mouth of the Pearl River. There is gambling, not permitted here, and business of a nature not allowed anywhere. Not in quite the same manner, anyway, eh?' His slyness was vulgar now and he nudged Tornetta. 'Gold, Bartolomeo. I have a bagful of the stuff to sell.'

'Ah!' sighed Tornetta.

'There is a hydrofoil which comes at unannounced times. Not that the Portuguese care, officially, you understand, but if the day is not known a robbery cannot be organized. I have the word. It goes to Macau tomorrow. Half an hour's discussion and I am so much richer. Why don't you come? I cannot, of course, take you where I am going, but afterwards – some gambling, a smile from a girl, a stroll round the place, eh?'

If Rossi undertook gold smuggling it also confirmed that he was Mafia. Tornetta was sick in the stomach with fear, but he had already been planning on that basis.

It might be that this was where Rossi intended to kill *him*. With effort he had 'considered it' for two or three seconds. Macau had an attraction: it was 37 miles from Hong Kong. To go there involved effort: a visit to the Portuguese Embassy in Hong Kong for a visa; many hours of the two-day stop-over. Most passengers of the *Areopagus* wouldn't bother when all they had to do was stroll from the ship into the pleasures of Kowloon or to the ferry which took them in five minutes to Victoria.

The Portuguese kept him waiting, smouldering with hot anger and fear. But by the hydrofoil Rossi waited among scores of noisy Chinese on their way for a day's gambling or to watch the Australian greyhounds at the Macau stadium – another form of betting and racing not permitted in Hong Kong.

Tornetta sat by a window, but sweated in claustrophobia. Alarm was unnecessary. There were a few Europeans aboard, but not from the *Areopagus*. Most were Portuguese from the colony. The pilot of the hydrofoil was an Australian, but even he, if he saw Tornetta with Rossi, might presume that they too were Portuguese, although a camera hung ostentatiously on Rossi's chest. He whispered with satisfaction, 'All the way from Perth I have carried this camera and not taken a photograph yet.' He tittered. 'It is loaded, but not with film. I will take your picture. It is beautiful, this place, Macau, do you know?'

Tornetta nodded affirmation, but was shaken, for was not

this further proof that Rossi was to kill him. How thorough *they* were, and how subtle! Get the victim to pose and smile before a camera when the gold had been removed, and show the colour slide back in Perth or Sydney. He could do this in full innocence, in the presence of his family: 'And this is Macau. Those are banyan trees. That's my friend.' And *they* would know that the right man had been killed.

He looked out of the window to the harsh green mountains and the scores of fishing boats. Two graceful three-masted fishing junks were passing. It was too easy to indulge in smuggling; it always had been in this area – drugs, opium, guns; so why bother with the risk of hydrofoil and Mr Rossi travelling thousands of miles on a Greek liner?

Macau had no deep-water harbour – which was why Hong Kong had surpassed it – and its shabby but beautiful port was only crowded with a forest of masts of small Chinese vessels, with the sampans and junks of the poor 'water people'.

Mr Rossi took a taxi in haste. Tornetta stayed for a while on the waterfront, affecting interest in the fishing junks with their russet sails, honking out these days under the power of a Japanese diesel engine. Passengers about to board the returning hydrofoil considered the purchase of little wicker baskets of crayfish.

After a while he walked into the town and strolled cobbled streets lined with buildings of a Mediterranean style, ornate with balconies and colourful with red pannen tiles. The main avenues were broad and shaded by banyan trees. It was surprisingly quiet – after the clangour of Kowloon – among the colonial style offices and gracious houses, the statues of forgotten Portuguese and of Marco Polo. The vertical banners and neon signs were in Chinese and Tornetta felt conspicuous and European.

Rossi met him outside one of the main hotels. They lunched together – it was unavoidable – and Rossi was most anxious to get on with the gambling. Tornetta had to remind him, 'Don't forget the *Areopagus* sails at ten tonight.'

'We won't miss her,' promised Rossi. 'Listen. The light is

good? Are you tired? No. Then let us stroll a little and afterwards we will burn up some of this money I have earned. There is a floating casino – a weird thing, ornate with balconies and decorated carved wood. There are escalators between decks, and Chinese girls who are obliging. We cannot hope to win. The main game is blackjack, but there are others with dice. It'll be fun ...'

But soon Mr Rossi's mood changed, became surprisingly nervous. (Was he, too, becoming weak with fear, preparing to kill?) He said, 'Listen, Bartolomeo. Do you have a good pocket? Will you look after half of this money for me? I might be robbed... I'm a good Catholic; I didn't mean I would bother with a woman. I like to talk, that's all.'

This suggested to Tornetta that Rossi was merely nervous of women. Given a little alcohol and some encouragement by the girl herself he'd alter, adjust the moral issues involved. A Chinese girl; the thought even warmed Tornetta, but it was useless. There was a killing to be done, then retreat, get out of Macau as fast as possible. He was baffled by Rossi's request about the money. He did indeed have a pocket with a zip, and he took the notes which Rossi passed over with such extraordinary trust. He saw that Rossi had only acquired a few hundred dollars.

They climbed the steps to the façade of the ruined St Paul's Basilica. There were a few people about; too many.

Rossi took a photograph of Tornetta standing by the massive pillars.

The view from up here was considerable: of crumbling gracious houses and streets in the style of Lisbon; office blocks amidst trees; the masts of ships; and across the muddy river the green – possibly of paddy fields – and beyond everything a harsh horizon of row upon row of mountains – ridges, it seemed, of shale.

Tornetta urged, 'Let's take the path, go higher. The view will be tremendous.'

'Is there time?'

'Three or four hours.'

'I meant the light. I am hot.'

'It will be rewarding.'

'On this cruise I am doing nothing but sweat and bet!' complained Mr Rossi lightly.

They ascended the dusty path, Tornetta repeating the plea 'Just to look over the other side of the hill. The Macau promontory is only a mile wide, so there must be another view.'

There was. Tornetta said breathlessly, 'If you include that tree you will have a beautiful picture.'

'The sun is sagging. I must see what the light meter tells me.'

Beyond was water gleaming under a sky beginning to pinken. Darkness, thought Tornetta. In six hours we will be gone. If they find him next week, who is he? I must take the passport and visa.

He touched his buttocks. The knife was there. He took it out clumsily. The click of a stud unfastening was, to him, as noisy as a pistol shot.

Mr Rossi said, 'It may not come out. The meter says—'

Tornetta thumped the knife into his back as hard as he could.

The camera leaped out of Rossi's hands and fell a few yards away, raising its own dust.

Mr Rossi went on living. 'Oh, I am hurt,' he told his friend. 'A snake—'

He stumbled and began to cough. It was a very disturbing cough even to listen to, and when he saw that he was coughing blood he was very frightened. 'Oh, my God, Bartolomeo, I am very ill . . .'

Tornetta was terrified.

Die, you fool, die.

There was no one in sight. The deed was done, in theory and practice, but the fat fool wouldn't die.

Very tense and panic stricken, Tornetta struck again and again. Mr Rossi fell on his face, but persisted in living, praying, beseeching. Tornetta stabbed him in the head and it was over. There was blood on his shoes – they must go overboard, the police, proof, he'd read it—

He ransacked the victim's pockets. Passport, two hundred dollars, a letter, a receipt, a wallet.

Tornetta rolled the body to the edge of the path. The incline towards the river on this side was of about sixty degrees. Rossi's body rolled a few yards, stirred dust, and then was halted by small trees and bushes. Tornetta rolled it more and finally had moved it about seventy feet below the path. It might never be discovered.

He kicked dust over the blood on the path and over that on his shoes. He dusted himself down, examined his clothing, breathed deeply to obtain calm and walked to the crown of the hill with terror so great that his arms and legs fluttered. He fully expected to be met by policemen, witnesses, friends of Rossi from the *Areopagus*.

Half a mile away two people examined the Basilica, but turned and descended the steps.

He felt confidence rise, although he was very brittle and had the terrible sensation of having made a mistake, that Rossi was as innocent as his prayers.

A headache hit him like hot fluid boiling up his neck, as he remembered the camera.

He dithered, paralysed, it involved so much courage to go back. Whole half-minutes passed and then he went to find it. He had covered his tracks so well he couldn't even tell whereabouts it was that Rossi had fallen. He cursed and ground his teeth and was red in the face with fury, kicking at grass and bushes. Night was coming, mocking him. He saw a tiny particle of broken glass and that guided him. He tore the back of the camera open and ripped the film out. Even now he was too scared to simply throw it away, its evidence surely destroyed by the impact of light. He had a terrible certainty that science would find a way of restoring what light had removed. *This* piece of celluloid must be dropped in the river or sea...

He had to wait forty minutes for the hydrofoil which was to take him back to Hong Kong. He paced about in terror, bit his lips until they cracked and bled, then bit his fingernails. He was able to dispose of the film, dropping it during a 'stroll' along the waterfront. He considered throwing away Rossi's passport. But he was not sure if this action might not be the worst possible thing to do. The Purser's office asked for all passports before departure from any port. Tornetta felt sure they didn't get them, but he was equally sure that if they were not received and accounted for within a day or two inquiries would be made. There would first be the general plea over the public address system – 'Will all passengers who have not yet returned their passports to the Purser's office please do so at once' – followed by the approaches to the two or three individuals who took no notice whatsoever of the ship's system and regulations.

The hydrofoil thundered through the dusk. It was not so crowded as the one which had brought Tornetta and Rossi to Macau. The sensations of relief and escape were enormous. He at once felt hungry and desperately tired.

In Kowloon the shops were still open. Tornetta bought a pair of shoes. There was discussion about size. With shock he realized that there might be blood on his socks. In panic, therefore, he refused to take off his shoes to try on the new ones. He spent more time explaining that he was in a hurry than he would have done trying the shoes on, but the Chinese trader did not persist, knowing that he was a foreigner and therefore mad. Tornetta stood in the darkness of an entry by an hotel in the Salisbury Road and put on the new shoes They were hard and uncomfortable. He would have to buy some more in Guam... He dropped the old shoes into the harbour near Number 5 Pier and strolled back to the Ocean Terminal and the *Areopagus.*

He saw Pauline walking at a leisurely pace back to the ship with a man, one of the ship's doctors. He thought about Barbara. Lust stirred faintly amidst his exhaustion.

He saw a barber's shop and a Chinese girl manicuring a man's hand caught his eye. It was irresistible, and Tornetta went inside. He throbbed with weariness and was still afraid; he felt he ought to stay ashore until the last possible moment. A man cut his hair and shaved him : the sensation was that in doing so he chopped and washed away evidence. A girl shoe-shined the new brown shoes pointlessly. Another – the one whose eye he had caught – manicured his nails and talked, aware of his interest : 'You like Hong Kong? – What have you seen? – Where do you go next? – You'll come back?' The smell of her soaps and scents and the inevitable rustle of her clothes against his legs was exhilarating. Her small hands fascinated him. When it was possible he stared with outright lust at her legs or down her throat to the beginnings of her small breasts.

There was still the passport to get rid of. And there was also the terror of guilt, of the face staring into his or the hand on his shoulder, and the voice, British or Chinese, 'Just a moment. Are you Bartolomeo Tornetta? Where have you been?' or even the milder interrogation, the plea for help: 'Mr Tornetta, have you seen Mr Rossi today?' And his guilt and lies would be identified. But if the ship sailed the burden of proof became harder for them as each day passed. A man found stabbed to death on a hillside in Macau. Obviously the work of local thieves. There would be a rumour that a hydrofoil had come on what must have been that day, and transactions in gold had taken place.

It only needed the stupid German girl, or Demetropoulos, or his deputy, Eleftheriadis, to say, 'Ah, you've brought Mr Rossi's passport, too!' to form a starting point when the investigations began. 'But I remember; his friend, Mr Tornetta, handed in the passport an hour before we sailed...' And yet he *had* to pass over that passport. If he did so, it half proved that Rossi had returned to the ship: perhaps he had gone ashore again for half an hour and missed her when she sailed.

The temptation was very great even now to drop Rossi's passport into the water. But above all things, as in Hobart, Tornetta wanted this old ship to sail. It was just possible that if the passport was not handed in she would not sail, or if it wasn't accounted for within two days radio signals would be sent to the Hong Kong police: 'We are a passenger short' – and perhaps by then the body would have been found and the counter-signal would be radioed: 'We have found an Italian, aged about fifty, whose clothes were bought in Perth...'

No. The little piece of cardboard had to be handed over.

There were traders on deck, a bustle of passengers, the hisses and mechanical noises of a ship preparing for departure. A steward was going round with a torch, shining it on the linen and metal bric-à-brac which was for sale. 'Five more minutes,' he shouted, but Tornetta knew it would be two hours before they sailed. This thing never left or arrived on time. The pithering about with ropes and gangways always went on for an unexpected half hour or more.

He went down to Metaxas Deck, just to see what was happening. Metaxas Deck was open on the port side: it was the main exit and entry. The Chief Purser and his staff were on duty. Other officers were hanging about, and a crowd of Chinese and British officials, talking like people at a cocktail party. Passengers and visitors to the ship were wandering round in excitement, complaining 'It's so hot,' or boasting, making their usual claims: 'We got it for thirty dollars' – or asserting their social superiority: 'We were taken round the whole place. He's Embassy so he knows it all. You've got to know somebody to get round and really *see*.' A tall boy was necking with a girl frantically, leaning against a bulkhead; no one stared, but it would have made no difference if anyone had. These two were racing against time. A few women were already showing off wigs they'd bought; even the mother from Darwin was parading round, a new person, with blonde straight hair... Pybus walked through the crowd, in shorts and open neck shirt, breathing through his teeth with grinding effort, his face set, alone, with his own problems.

Tornetta shook with terror, ignored his brain which told him this was good, suitable, an ambiance close to confusion.

There was a row going on, almost unnoticed, between the German girl from the Forward Bar and the Chief Purser. She stormed at him: 'I had to go on for four hours—' but Demetropoulos was as enigmatic and indifferent as ever. The slight smile and the stare at something just above the attractive angry face. 'The contract says—' The girl dismissed it with fury. 'I don't care; it's *crazy*. I didn't come on this ship to do overtime; I came to see Hong Kong' – 'You should have come as a passenger' – 'I wouldn't be so stupid!'

And on the desk were twenty or thirty passports. No one was looking after them. Typical, Tornetta thought. He edged round towards that end of the counter, his fingers hot and moist on the two passports in his coat pocket.

He put them with the others and walked away, his head and neck rigid, as if, seeing nothing himself, he therefore could not be seen. No one said anything and he went back to the Parade Deck. The siren blew in a plaintive blast of steam. Particles of oil drifted down, spotted passengers and the deck. A cat miaowed somewhere.

The passengers were crowded along the rail, staring at the activities, the movement of men, lorries, cranes, the last-minute arrival of taxis. The urge to flee or hide in a lavatory was enormous. Visitors were pouring ashore. Again the siren. Already it was an hour after the scheduled time of departure. Tornetta wanted to scream with alarm and impatience. Wouldn't the cursed thing ever sail? Even now the gangways were there. Lights flashed all round and now one flickered on a vehicle racing round Kowloon Point. The police! They'd come. But it was an ambulance. Nothing important. Someone else's pain.

The gangways had gone. Steam hissed. Beside Tornetta a girl sobbed. It was Diane. The fool, he thought, hope and arrogance returning. What is there to weep about?

Cheers. No sensation of movement; it caught him unawares, but suddenly the Ocean Terminal and the cranes and people standing on shore had receded a few feet.

The *Areopagus* reversed into the Central Fairway with agonizing caution, for this was a crowded merchant ship anchorage. There was a merchant ship directly in line with her reversal and some of her crew stood watching the discomforts of the *Areopagus* with interest as she came within seventy feet, the tugs straining. It took twenty-five minutes simply to move out and turn round. The lights of Green Island and Kau Yi Chau flashed ahead. The *Areopagus* was not leaving Hong Kong the was she had arrived.

In the cabin Squibb was indulging in the ritual of his feet – deodorants and towels. He noticed at once: 'You've got some new shoes.'

It shook Tornetta.

'Yes. I'm not sure I like them.'

'What did you do with the old ones?'

Tornetta countered: 'Why? Did you want them?' and then, more cautiously: 'Did you have a good time?'

In the morning the sky was streaked with cloud and it was as though Hong Kong had never existed.

But he was startled at breakfast, for a woman came up to him and asked, 'Where's your friend this morning?'

'My friend?'

'Mr Rossi. He never misses breakfast.'

Tornetta took the cue. 'Ah! But perhaps this time he was too late going to bed.'

And at lunch the same woman again inquired, although not with great anxiety: 'I can't think where he's got to.'

'Didn't he disembark at Hong Kong?'

'He's listed to go to Melbourne.'

'He had business; he told me that.'

'What a pity,' she complained. 'Such a nice man to talk to. Did you buy anything?'

'Not much,' said Tornetta. 'Just a camera and a pair of shoes, and the camera's been stolen.'

Part Three

LAT 21° 40′ N/LONG 120° 50′ E

To God let us pray:
Bless our voyage this day:
And through the Blessed Mother,
Our advocate on high,
Protect us from the waterspout
And send no tempest high.

—*Columbus*

How pleasant it is, when a gale of
wind is blowing, to stand on the shore
and watch the other fellow, out there,
in trouble.

—*Lucretius*

21

TOMAZOS, in the chartroom, was hidden from Yannopoulos the helmsman, and he took a quick swallow of whisky from the flask he had taken to carrying. He wasn't drunk, just depressed.

A radio fix told him that he was north of the desired course; he went on to the bridge and instructed Yannopoulos, 'Three degrees to starboard.'

It was evening and still light. Tomazos returned to the chartroom and examined the log. He accepted the entries made by Mollon, the previous officer of the watch: their course (true, gyro, standard and steering); the latitude and longitude; the steaming time from Hong Kong; their estimated time of arrival in Guam; the amounts of fuel used and remaining and those of water; the revolutions of the engines (port was 103·7 per minute, starboard was 104·7); standard compass error and gyro compass error (which latter was, as usual, nil). He noted Mollon's remark, in English: 'The Master attended a Fancy Dress Ball.' This was inaccurate, for the Ball was still in progress; in fact it had only just got going. It was what had triggered off depression and caused Tomazos to feel very lonely.

He did not like the sea or air temperatures, and he noted an increase in wind. He checked now and the anemometer told him what the force of the wind was. Since the ship herself created a wind the force of the true air of weather had to be worked out by a parallelogram of forces. Tomazos worked it out again and there was no doubt: the force of the wind was increasing.

He went on to the wing of the bridge. The surface of the sea reduced the wind by friction. The diurnal variation of sea surface temperature and that of the air at sea level was negligible normally, for solar radiation penetrated to a considerable depth and wave turbulence caused surface heat to be spread downwards. There was now a large variation. As well, Tomazos saw that the ocean swell was that of a different nature to the afternoon's sea. The waves were long – about 700 feet with a period of about twelve seconds. The height of each wave – from trough to crest – was not enough to disturb passengers; rather it caused the *Areopagus* to roll very slowly and, if anything, gave an impression of stability.

Before returning to the wheelhouse Tomazos stood facing the direction of the true wind. It had altered in an hour by nine points. He knew that the centre of low pressure would be 8 to 12 points now on his right hand, and he saw in mild alarm that this was the direction from which the big long waves were coming. The wind had veered, that is, moved clockwise from east to south or even south-south-west. The implications were that a big storm was from a hundred to five hundred miles away.

In the chartroom he examined the barometer. In the tropics the barometric pressure altered very little except for diurnal variation. Tomazos checked in the Pilot book as to what the barometric reading should be in the area for the time of year. He confirmed that the barometer itself was adjusted for height, latitude temperature and index error. But the reading was still five millibars below normal.

There were two other things, then, to do. While there was light he looked at the sky. Extensive cirrus clouds covered the southern half of the sky and on the horizon he fancied he saw altostratus.

It was not an ordinary storm moving about. Almost certainly it was a typhoon.

Tomazos phoned the engine room. 'Raise steam. There's a storm coming.'

He knew that the swell of the sea extended to a distance of a thousand miles from the storm centre and would make itself felt four hundred miles away.

Tomazos switched on a radar set. They were in the Bashi Strait, south of Formosa. The storm indicated by the swell was in the forward starboard direction, it seemed. It would be advisable to leave both radar sets on, one at a range of 48 nautical miles to watch the storm if it came that near, and the other at 12 nm to observe other ships and avoid them.

There was nothing on the 12 nm radar and no storm revealed on the 48 nm. That was a relief. It gave time for avoiding action, even a retreat to Hong Kong.

He went aft of the chartroom to the Turkish radio officer.

'Any recent weather signals?'

'Normal from Hong Kong.'

'How about Guam or Manila?'

'Nothing.'

'Radio other vessels and shore authorities that I suspect the presence of a tropical revolving storm south of our position.'

This was required under Article 35 of the International Convention for Safety of Life at Sea.

He ordered the stand-by: 'Go and inform the Captain that I would request his presence on the bridge.'

This, too, was an obligation upon the officer of the watch.

On the 48 nm radar was a small yellow pip at 34 miles. Another ship. While he waited for Captain Vafiadis, Tomazos recorded in the log the symptoms of the barometer and swell and, hesitating, for it was rather far off (but he wondered if the moment might come when, being nearer to the storm, she might need help) he recorded the echo of an unknown ship with a bearing of 2° to starboard of his present heading marker. At the moment he did not know if the vessel was approaching or steaming in more or less the same direction as the *Areopagus*.

Captain Vafiadis came on the bridge, caution and resentment on his face.

'Something wrong, Mr Tomazos?'

'I think there's a tropical revolving storm, south or south-east.'

Captain Vafiadis said, 'You *think* there is?'

Tomazos explained: 'There's been a change in the sea; the wind has veered nine points; it has increased to about force 6; and the barometer's gone down five millibars.'

'And what do your gadgets tell you?' the Master asked sourly.

'Nothing yet.'

'And the radio?'

'No signals yet.'

'What is the reading of the barometer now?'

'Down another two points.'

Captain Vafiadis thought about it. 'Thank you, Mr Tomazos, for informing me. You were right to do so. But my recollection is that the barometer will have to go down much more than that before we're in trouble: ten millibars in fifteen miles, perhaps, and as much as sixty in the storm centre.'

'Sir, the sea indicates an approach this way.'

'No, Mr Tomazos, I do not think so. The swell extends from the centre of the storm in a radius of a thousand miles. The thing itself is a mere thirty miles in diameter and should miss us by five hundred or a thousand miles. It will probably be moving west and will break itself on Hainan Island or turn north-east and dissipate on Hong Kong, which we have mercifully left at least five hundred miles behind.'

'Shall I keep you informed, sir?'

'Of course, Mr Tomazos. You see, if it is as I say, there is no point in turning back to Hong Kong; and if it is as you say, where can we run to? There is nowhere!'

'We could take avoiding action, sir.'

'We will, if it becomes necessary,' agreed the Master, and there was a touch of a sneer in his tone.

The Turkish radio officer, Barutcu, came on to the bridge. He informed them: 'Radio signal from the Philippines says that a typhoon passed over a few hours ago, putting them out of action. The storm was heading west-north-west.'

'Good,' argued Captain Vafiadis. 'It is as I say.'

Tomazos opened his mouth to dispute: 'But that was several hours ago, perhaps half a day. By now the storm could have turned in a clockwise direction, as the storms often do in the Northern Hemisphere.'

There was, he accepted, some truth in the Master's calm analysis. Even if the storm had turned round to WNW and even to a northern or NE heading, it might well miss them by hundreds of miles, and if it passed to the east of the *Areo-*

pagus, however close, the tendency of the storm centre – which revolved in an anti-clockwise direction (i.e. N, W, S, E) – would be to push the ship away from itself. There was good calm sense in the Captain's decision to go on, but there was commercial apprehension too. In theory, Captain Vafiadis *should* do something to protect his passengers, but in fact he was taking a risk to be sure of the Company's profits. The *Areopagus* was at last on schedule. The Company wouldn't be impressed by a timid Captain who returned in fair seas to Hong Kong. There would be fuel used, time wasted, immense harbour and pilot charges; the 550 passengers would expect their three or four heavy meals a day. Other possible cargoes in the next ports would be kept waiting and intending passengers would be irritated and some would make claims. Commercially, then, it was not easy for the Master to forgo his schedule.

Tomazos had almost forgotten the other ship seen on radar. It was still there, nearer, and he found with irritation that it was on a reciprocal course. A quarter of an hour later it had disappeared. There was a lot of clutter and when Tomazos had cleared some of that with the anti-clutter device he saw on the PPI (plan position indicator) at forty miles distance bright and distinct echoes of a storm. He knew that the radar meteorological echo was produced by moisture droplets scattering part of the incident radar energy back along a parallel path to the receiver. What disturbed him was the brightness: for the intensity of the echo depended upon the amount of water per unit volume, that is, upon the sheer bulk of the weather; and upon the size of individual water droplets.

Forty miles away and approaching with the sea and wind was a bad storm.

Tomazos altered course a few degrees to avoid the other ship and waited for the storm to define its quality on the little screen.

The storm began in the Doldrums, gathering volume and strength somewhere in the blank thousand miles between the Truk and Palau Islands, about 7½° above the Equator.

Very soon the wind within it reached Force 12 by the Beaufort Scale, that is, over 65 knots, which represented an air pressure of just under 17 lbs/square foot. The storm moved in the direction of 280°, that is, just north of west. The whole extensive disturbance progressed at 10 knots, increasing a little with latitude, but within a radius of 200 miles of its centre there were marked and very unpleasant differences. At two hundred miles the wind didn't exceed Force 7, and was less on the equatorial aside, and winds of Force 8 were the maximum at more than 100 miles from the centre. But hurricane-force winds blew within 75 miles of the centre and within 50 miles there were gusts of over 150 knots. The significance lay in that a 'standard wind' was about 16 knots and it exerted a pressure of about one pound per square foot. Under these sort of increased pressures the sea began to heave about in mountains – the more so as the winds of varying violence revolved. Further, as the storm moved along its track at 10 to 15 knots, the radius of these violently circling winds nearly doubled. Understandably, the swell of the sea extended a thousand miles from the storm centre. The currents of wind for hundreds of miles around were inevitably altered, too. The sky changed from the vast layers of cirrus cloud – some of which Tomazos had seen – to altostratus where the storm centre moved and as it passed there was much nimbostratus and 'scud'.

The typhoon passed north of Mindanao and crossed the Philippines just south of Manila. By now winds were reaching a velocity of 250 feet a second, that is, 156 mph. Boats were thrown from the harbours into streets. Trees were bent and broken. Automobiles were tossed around. Poles were snapped and power lines went down; fires began and soon roared. Broken pieces of tile were driven like shards of shrapnel into wooden boards and tree trunks.

In addition to the destruction by wind was the devastation by water. Such a storm approaching the coast of the Philippines caused serious flooding. The largest waves, originating in the rear right-hand quadrant of the storm, travelled through the cyclonic area and reached the shore where they caused a rise in the water in front of and 200 miles to the right of the line of advance of the storm. This rise began when the centre of the typhoon was 400 miles away and it continued until the typhoon had crossed the coast. The height of the flood level reached at the shore near the centre of the storm was 14 feet above the predicted tide level.

In a few hours the revolving tropical storm destroyed 341,271 houses, flooded or damanged 1,393,001 acres of crops and forests, and killed 154 people and 19,998 animals.

Scarcely fifty miles beyond this unhappy destruction and loss of life the track of the storm (ie, the direction taken by its centre) altered, and the whole revolving mass of wind and turbulence turned in the clockwise motion so that by latitude 15 North it was already moving north. The centre of the storm was two or three miles in diameter and fairly calm, but with confused and agitated water. Around the centre, revolving anti-clockwise, was the bulk of the storm, fifteen miles across, with winds of 100 mph and more, and massive waves fifty and even eighty feet high.

Captain Vafiadis was therefore wrong and had placed his ship in hazard. For the path of the storm was now north and it was likely to revolve even further, round to north-east. Whether it passed behind or in front of the *Areopagus* she would be in the dangerous semi-circle, with winds likely to thrust her further into the storm if the storm centre went behind her and liable to push her on to a lee shore in any case.

There were about 250 tropical revolving storms a year in this vast area of the Pacific and South China Sea, but by October the season was 'normally' over. There was often insufficient evidence available for an accurate warning to be given, and it was up to ships to be guided by their own observations. For frequently very little warning *could* be given of an intense storm because of its small diameter. A tropical storm was nothing like so extensive as the depression of higher latitudes. The winds had a spiral movement towards the centre.

Aboard the SS *Seattle Doll* they were aware that the storm was coming. They knew that it was vital to keep outside a radius of 200 miles of it, because at this distance the wind didn't exceed Force 7 and allowed freedom of manoeuvre. Often a tropical storm moved so slowly that a vessel ahead of it could easily outpace it; or if astern could overtake it. But to escape this storm a ship needed 20 knots at her disposal and this the *Seattle Doll* did not have.

The SS *Seattle Doll* was the vessel which Tomazos had seen as a yellow pip on the PPI on the radar. She was making 13½ knots and thus creating a wave system herself about a hundred feet from crest to crest. The speed of a wave depended on its size and those of the storm were overtaking the *Seattle Doll.* Soon three hundred feet waves moving at 23 knots overtook her and shook her. It was desirable to have the wave crest, not its hollow, under the stern, otherwise 'pooping' might occur, that is, the overtaking wave would break over the stern.

As the storm worsened visibility dropped to a maximum of a thousand yards and was at times zero. The *Seattle Doll* was not merely rolling but heeled over continually by the force of the wind, leaving her with very small margin for any further rolling to leeward. Despite closing down every inlet water was shipped in bulk through the ventilators, blower intakes and every small opening on the upper deck.

There was loss of steering control for ten whole minutes; the lights went out and the *Seattle Doll*'s one radar and radio cut out. The switchboard and some other electrical machinery short-circuited as they flooded and three fires began. Free water up to twelve inches flooded over her engine-room plate decks.

The wind carried away the forward mast which carried the radar reflector plates. This was one of the two reasons why the *Seattle Doll* had disappeared from Tomazos' radar. The other was that the beam of radar was narrow, like a searchlight probing. The *Seattle Doll* was dropping 'out of sight' into the immense troughs of water and by now the pencil beam of the *Areopagus*' radar was itself pitching up and down and thus missing the possible target.

The *Seattle Doll* was taking long rolls to leeward, as much as 45° and hanging in this appalling posture for whole seconds. Men could not secure gear and were themselves injured. At times men could not even stand upright.

The *Seattle Doll* was a merchant ship of 6,742 tons gross. She was twenty-seven years old and had a high metacentric height when she was without cargo. This was due to a combination of factors – a welded hull, lightweight machinery of low power, a broad beam and some permanent ballast worked into the hull. She was safe when fully laden, but excessive rolling was likely to set in when she was without cargo or temporary ballast. The ballast was needed for the unusual purpose of reducing her metacentric height. For this reason the ballast or cargo was carried as high in the vessel as possible, and at the moment 1,900 tons were stored in the 'tween decks. Extremely strong shifting boards should have been carried, but this essential for safety, while not neglected, was not good enough to withstand a typhoon. The shifting boards fitted had angle iron supports and these were already weakened in the storm so that some cargo had shifted to port and the *Seattle Doll*, if she had been in calm water, would have been seen to have a mean list of some 14°.

She was travelling from Vancouver to Hong Kong and Saigon with a cargo of oils, paint, explosives, mattresses, clothes and toe puff. Toe puff was made from layers of cotton or woollen material impregnated with cellulose nitrate, solvent rosin and dye. It was used to form the hard toe-caps of boots and shoes.

When smoke was smelt and found to be coming from the ventilator of Number 3 hold, which contained clothing and mattresses, the officers on the bridge were very worried, for the adjoining hold contained toe puff and the one beyond that explosives. Steam smothering lines were got ready – a man was at this point washed overboard but the storm allowed no mercy and they couldn't stop to find him. The steam saturated the mattresses and liquefied the explosives, which made them unstable.

No one worried about the toe puff.

Tomazos had seen the *Seattle Doll* twice on radar – once at 34 miles and again at 25 miles. Each time he looked at the tube he saw the sweep trace as it rotated in synchronization with the antenna; the range rings indicating distance; and a momentary heading-marker flash as the sweep trace passed the lubber line. The sweep trace was in fact a series of spots on the tube corresponding in speed to the emission of radio waves from the antenna. The spot moved from the tube's centre out to the azimuth scale, and being repeated at a pulse frequency of over 2,000 times a second, made it appear as a solid line. The brightness along its length had been interrupted when the reflected echoes had picked out the *Seattle Doll*, whereupon the reflected echoes increased the discharge of the electron gun to paint a bright spot on the scope. The micro-precision timing of transmitted and echoed waves – they travelled at about six millionths of a second per nautical mile – separated and indicated the distance. Each time the antenna directed the radio waves across the target – every two seconds as it rotated 30 revolutions a minute – the returned echo re-illuminated the pip of light in the tube. Tomazos had taken two readings, half an hour apart. Radar did not give the aspect of the other ship, but it gave range; and the *Seattle Doll*'s course and speed could be worked out from a combination of the times of the two sightings, the apparent bearing and the two ranges.

From these Tomazos had seen that the other ship, 25 miles away, was on a reciprocal course. He had turned a few degrees to starboard. She had then disappeared, and he could no longer plot her. It worried him only fractionally – on her behalf – and he deduced, correctly, that while the other ship was on the crest of a swell the antenna of the *Areopagus*' radar might be sweeping the other quadrants of the horizon, and as the radio waves passed over that location again in a beam only a few degrees in diameter the other ship might be down in the trough and thus not able to present her flat surface to the seeking signals. If so, it implied that the other vessel was in very heavy seas, and this was all too probable, since she was coming the way the storm was approaching.

He had left on the 48 nm radar set and soon it told him of his unpleasant position. He deduced it anyway with seaman's logic. The centre of the storm must be from 9 to 11 points to the right of the true wind, and this meant to starboard of the *Areopagus.* On the port side, twenty miles away, were the outlying rocks of the southernmost point of Taiwan. It was as if he was on a great clock, but did not know yet if the fingers were to place him at ten o'clock, noon or two o'clock. It was a clock that went the wrong way, so that at ten o'clock the fingers would sweep him out of the way. At noon he would be for a while in the calm of the centre where nothing rotated. But at two o'clock he would be carried with the fingers of the clock, for it was rising as well as revolving backwards.

The fury of water outside, the big drop in the barometer, and the rushing sky told him he was in trouble anyway. He had ordered all possible speed and the *Areopagus* was thrashing her way at 17·8 knots. The sea was large and Tomazos knew that by now passengers would be frightened.

Now he saw on the 48 nm radar the large solid circular shape of the storm and its vast whorls. It already occupied half the screen. From the curvature of the whirling cloud echoes he estimated that the centre was going to pass behind the liner. They were caught on the great dial at two o'clock and the revolving storm was likely to push the ship round into its own northerly path. The *Areopagus* was hurrying to get out of this dangerous quadrant. Captain Vafiadis had been warned but had taken the risk. But it was true, also, that no warning had been signalled. The Turkish radio officer rushed on to the bridge now – nearly falling as he did – with a warning of a tropical revolving storm, given high signal priority on an operational circuit. But this was hours too late.

It was totally dark now. The sea was enormous, confused and bad enough to worry even experienced sailors. It was at present on the starboard side and the *Areopagus* rolled very unpleasantly. As well, she remained heeled for long seconds. All over the ship, Tomazos knew, any loose objects would be sliding about – from glasses and ashtrays to saxophones and suitcases...

Captain Vafiadis had returned to the bridge, and he said

disagreeably now to Tomazos: 'I suppose you feel satisfied about this?'

Tomazos informed him: 'I have the wind four points on the starboard bow and we're making over 17 knots even now...'

'What do your gadgets tell you?'

'That the storm centre will pass five miles behind us.'

'I see,' the Captain said. 'We should get out of it soon then.'

His observation seemed offhand and a little callous in regard to the passengers' welfare. The Fancy Dress Ball had been abandoned of its own volition.

Now the old age of the *Areopagus* and her neglect began to be felt. The confused and enormous seas took hold of her and shook her. During each revolution in the water the propeller blades passed through regions of lower velocity in the wake field. This occurred when the blades were in the upper part of the stern frame aperture. Coming round to a position of about 60° away from this they encountered water of relatively high velocity and then again re-entered another lower velocity region in the lower part of the aperture. The level of the suction on the back of each blade increased until the peak negative pressure was lower than the local vapour pressure. The result was the separation of the air from the surrounding water and the formation of a cloud or sheet of 'cavitation'. Bubbles of air could not persist and imploded with violent mechanical hammering action on the blades.

This sometimes happened to the *Areopagus'* propellers, but now the port propeller had had enough. The surface of the blade was eroded and it began to weaken.

The heavy seas were confused and as well as rolling the *Areopagus* began to pitch and yaw. For whole seconds, then, the propellers were clean out of the water. They ran too quickly, added to general vibration, especially at the stern, and overheated the shafts and bearings. The port propeller couldn't take these variations and the blades began to buckle.

It was noticeable to Tomazos in the loss of performance, and (although not aware of the cause of failing power) he knew that the *Areopagus* wasn't going to escape the fury of the storm. It was unfortunate – but, surely, no more than that? – and he felt very sorry for the passengers who were in for a buffeting of several hours . . .

The strain on the propeller shafts with this violent alteration of torque – one second free to rotate too fast and the next having to cope with the effort as the propellers were plunged into tons of water – began to seek out other weaknesses in the structure, and the first gave way near the stern. The corner of the lift shaft opening in the strength (Metaxas) deck had been left almost square and not rounded off. The excessive stress of years and now of exceptional vibration started a local crack which spread right across the deck stringer plate and down the sheer strake until it stopped at a round porthole.

Tomazos heard about this via the telephone. Mollon had come on the bridge – so had Makris because of the storm – and it was he who answered the telephone. He said with sardonic Australian humour to Tomazos: 'If the ship doesn't split in half and we survive the storm I suppose the bleedin' tub'll catch fire.' He had scarcely said it when the alarm bell rang automatically. One of the telephones also rang. A breathless voice shouted into Tomazos' ear: 'The barber's shop's on fire, sir.'

'How bad?'

'Some spirit stuff's burning. A lot of smoke, sir.'

'Right,' said Tomazos briefly.

He estimated that flooding or damage due to objects falling had caused a short circuit. Passengers might be stumbling about, feeling sick, in a corridor now full of smoke, and he had no option but to drop the fireproof doors. The passengers might be cut off in an area heavily used. The fire-fighting squad would be tackling it, but with smoke and perhaps total darkness and a heaving sea it would be very alarming. And there were materials in the hairdressing saloons which could burn very fiercely.

He could limit the area because the main fire-resisting bulkheads – about 131 feet apart – with the fire-resisting boundary doors, divided the ship from the keel to the top of the superstructure into a number of fire-containing sections. The sprinkler system presumably wouldn't have put out a fire thriving on oils, but at least it had given early warnings.

Tomazos could also limit the flow of air feeding the fire by closing down the forced draught ventilation and the air conditioning. But it was very worrying, for the hairdressing saloons were in an area full of old-fashioned inflammable wood – the public rooms and cabins ... He was frustrated greatly by the central position of the saloons. They were in the bowels of the ship, but, worse, were amidships. A fire in the stern of the ship would be unable to spread forward because of the wind caused by the motion of the ship. If there had been a fire in the bows Tomazos would have reversed the *Areopagus* to cause her wind to drive the fire away from the ship. But a fire amidships and five decks down and in a giant storm which made experienced seamen clutch and crawl and fall ... It was something to be afraid of. He recalled the devastating fires at sea which were part of maritime history – the *Georges Philippar, Empire Windrush, Morro Castle, Lakonia* and *L'Atlantique* ... Later he learned that two of the crew had seen flames and had battered at the locked door to get at the fire – a mistaken heroism as it had allowed air to flow into the saloons.

Mollon lurched over to Tomazos and informed him – Tomazos was staring ahead through the small circle of glass which was swept clear of the rain and violent spray – 'The bleedin' goggle-box has gone.'

'Which one?'

'The twelve mile.'

The 12 nm radar set was a valve set, 1955 model, and therefore inherently less reliable than the subsequent transistorized sets.

Mollon persisted, 'I could use a drink. I feel terrible. Shall we start praying?'

'Change the scale of the 48-mile down to 12'.

'What for, mate?'

'There's another ship.'

It was almost totally dark on the bridge. There was just the bright red of the telegraph and a glow from the other radar set, still functioning. Tomazos could see that the other officers were unashamedly holding on to pieces of structure or leaning heavily. The *Areopagus* rose up like an elevator, sometimes already heeled, dropped as if a cable had been cut, then yawed ... She was handling rather badly, or else it was the worst storm he had ever been in.

He asked Yannopoulos: 'How is she?'

The seaman said, 'I think the port propeller has lost power. She is very heavy to hold on course.'

'The sea is pushing her to port.'

'That is true, sir.'

'Are you tired?'

'Not yet, sir.'

'It is quite a storm.'

Tomazos was very anxious about the other ship, that spot of light identified by an electric instrument ... He had carried out a manoeuvre dictated by the other vessel's relative heading. But she had 'disappeared' and he was now in no position to learn if she had also manoeuvred. There were no steering or sailing rules which provided that one vessel should manoeuvre and the other should not. She was still not visible on the alternative radar, which was functioning now on the 12 nm scale. It could be that she had about now passed the *Areopagus,* but Tomazos had a superstitious seaman's acknowledgement of luck, and luck was running badly. The fire was not extinguished, and the fracture would have been very disturbing in calm seas – or even in harbour – let alone in *this* ... In theory the two ships had met end-on (but at a very safe distance of 25 miles). Visually this was defined by Rule 18 of the Regulations as, in daylight, when each ship saw the masts of the other in a line with her own, and by night, as when each vessel was in a position as to see both the sidelights of the other. Tomazos had seen that this was the position at a distance of as much as 25 miles: he 'saw' that the other ship was end-on by use of an instrument. Rule 18 said *each* vessel meeting end-on should move to the right. Tomazos had done so, and had then gradually and naturally made a return to the original course. But suppose the massive sea was strong enough to push the other ship off course? It would be in *this* direction. And sometimes Rule 22 prompted an alteration to port to avoid cutting across ahead – although not, surely, at a distance as great as 25 miles: the tiniest alteration to starboard even by one ship should be more than adequate. Had the other ship 'seen' the *Areopagus* – at all? before her 3° turn to starboard? after returning to her original heading? Did her officers bother at all in this vast ocean to plot the relative movement of another ship – a tiresome exercise in these most uncomfortable conditions, and involving twenty minutes mathematics after two observations say half an hour apart?

He returned to his position by the small circle of glass, spattered with violent rain and sea spray as fast as it was cleared. He had just done so when the sea caused the *Areopagus* to rise seventy feet as she pitched, and to shudder. Tomazos clutched on to the nearest piece of metal, which happened to be the dial indicating the starboard engine revolutions. Behind him he heard someone fall and a cry from Makris: 'The Captain's fallen.' This was followed by the Master's angry retort as he struggled to his feet, 'I am in no need of assistance, Mister Third.'

Ahead, under a flash of lightning, Tomazos saw that the *Areopagus* was poised and that the scend of the wave was 70 feet. The propellers, out of the water at the stern, seemed to drill his teeth.

The spectacle in that flash was nerve-racking. But, worse, as the *Areopagus* rushed and dropped down a mountain of water Tomazos saw, beyond and rising as he fell, the lights of another ship. What was so alarming was that he saw *all* of them – in other words, the white light on a foremast, a similar white light on a mainmast fifteen feet higher, the red light on her port side and green on her starboard. All these indicated a vessel of over 150 feet in length. The light on the mainmast was required to be at least fifteen feet higher than the forward light. His eyes did the split-second mathematics and told him that this ship was only hundreds of yards away, at most a thousand.

His hand was already rising to the handle on the deckhead Mr Biggar had inquired about weeks before, and he shouted to Yannopoulos, 'Starboard, all you've got!' – a crude command, but Yannopoulos was already flicking the wheel.

Oh, God, Tomazos pleaded in his mind, the time available so inadequate that he did not, even in thought, enlarge the petition...

He had, in theory, a choice. No. There was no choice. The Rules said Starboard. But in the grim realities of the sea and seamanship he had a choice. He might order 'Stop!' to the engine room, followed at once by 'Full Astern!' to minimize a head-on collision. A collision, he knew, was almost inevitable. But an order to stop was only an engine order. The ship, even in this sea, would carry on forward, with her momentum driving her ahead and only slowing down gradually over a distance of miles even when the engines had been put 'Astern'. Under these 'Stop' conditions and without engine reversal a very large tanker might take an hour and cover nine miles before she was dead in the water. Abaft the bridge the ship – any ship – widened out to its maximum beam, where boilers and engine-rooms were situated. It was this two-thirds full-bosomed and -bottomed section which constituted most of the buoyancy of a ship. If the 'unsinkable' transatlantic *Titanic* had not turned away upon sighting an ice-berg that awful night in 1912 – if she had held her course – which would have required enormous strength of mind from the Captain – the fine bows would have folded like a concertina, but little buoyancy would have been lost. Turning, she had had her bottom and double-bottom ripped open... But it was inevitable, if the two ships were to collide end-on here and now, that neither would have slowed down much. To slow to a stop would have taken each from two to five miles. The reaction from the telegraph was too slow. The engineers had to receive the order Stop (that is, go into neutral like an automobile but with gears weighing tons), and then into Reverse... Otherwise the heavy gearing would smash to pieces.

The alternative choice, already made, was to turn to starboard, and if the other ship did the same there was a small chance of total escape, and a greater one of grazing.

If the other ship did *not* alter to starboard and the *Areopagus* did, there was a likelihood that the liner might be cut in two. Or, if the other ship altered to starboard, and was a big tanker one-fifth of a mile long, it was possible that the *Areopagus* would ram her port side near the stern ...

As well, in turning to starboard, even if carried out by both ships, there were dangers. The passage of a hull through the water was accompanied by a system of pressure and velocity changes that extended all round the ship – astern, ahead, underneath and on either beam. The velocity changed on the beam if it was close to a river bank or another ship : the water was restricted and therefore flowed faster. As the after body of most ships was fuller than the forebody, the effect was usually more pronounced towards the stern and the tendency was to turn the bow away from the solidity of the river bank or ship in close proximity. The two ships would be pushed together by the higher water pressures on their outboard side. Helm action could counter this if applied (as now) at a sufficiently early stage.

Nevertheless, the first effect of applying starboard rudder was to push the ship bodily to port, especially at the stern and the subsequent turn to starboard followed seconds later ...

Tomazos knew all this, knew that it was happening, was aware even that the storm, too, while confused, had its strength on the starboard side. Even so, his hand pulled the handle and the single long blast of the siren signalled to the other ship 'I am turning to starboard'. He had to give a chance to the other ship.

Aboard the *Seattle Doll* they had turned to starboard just prior to the signal of steam which they scarcely heard anyway.

On both ships men coiled, cowered, and flinched as they saw the other ship, in the violent odd postures dictated by the storm. Some men shouted, others froze to the spot, a few threw themselves flat ...

The two ships would have missed if they'd been granted half a minute more, or if the sea's agitation had been on their side ... As it was, they struck, port side to port side, ripping lumps out of each other, and passed, momentums greatly reduced, in a shower of sparks.

The *Seattle Doll* struck about midway between bulkheads 83 and 151 of the *Areopagus* so that only one main compartment (to begin with) was affected, and both boundaries were left intact. This was in fact the minimum damage to be expected in a collision and to be provided for ...

The deep fuel tanks on the port side were punctured by the impact. These were a quarter empty, so sea water rushed into the tanks and the asymmetrical flooding produced a heeling momentum of three thousand tons so that the *Areopagus* in seconds listed to 10°. Cabin accommodation was sliced, fractured or crushed down to the level of these tanks. The lights went out, although Tomazos didn't know this for long half-seconds.

Half a mile away the liquefied explosives crackled, burned through mattresses and reached the toe puff. The tons of toe puff, unknown to the crew of the *Seattle Doll,* was highly dangerous. The crew, already exhausted after hours of fighting fires and flood, now began in the energies of terror, to fight the fires in the explosives store. They were doing this when the toe puff exploded with enormous violence and split the ship in half. The buckled halves of the ship burned but did not sink at once. The storm tore at them. Lifeboats were burned or shattered. Men were brutally injured, killed or burned ...

On the bridge of the *Areopagus* there was some confusion, for the Captain, not quite on his feet, had been thrown by the collision and lay on the deck with a serious face injury. Tomazos had already signalled Dead Slow. The storm wouldn't allow him to stop, but he didn't want the propellers thrashing the sea in which men might be swimming. He must save them. God had, he believed, spared his old ship, but grim hours lay ahead.

He was filled, not with terror but emotion (but not, assuredly, in the stomach!). He recalled the simple message of trust and compassion which had been offered by the American child, Debbie, in the floating restaurant in Hong Kong. He was in charge of the ship. Captain Vafiadis was beyond responsibility now. Elaine passed briefly through his mind, but meaninglessly: she did not belong here. He did. He was tired but, in an odd way, exhilarated. *This* was his destiny. The misery caused by Elaine was trivial. He would see these passengers to safety. He would save some of those men thrown into the sea by the explosion. He would see this good old ship to harbour if it killed him. A small tender memory plucked at his mind: Kristina standing on the dock-side at Singapore, weeping, he had recognized, for *him*. He was glad that she was not here, subject to risk and injury and terror...

22

'I FEEL so ill,' Keith had confessed forty minutes before.

It was the first thing he had said in days which had any relationship to what had existed before – the friendship bordering on love, the days passed amicably.

His eyes had added in supplication, 'And I am frightened.'

Dimitrios had responded at once. It was true that he was the only person Keith could talk to in English down here, but that he should do so, even in sickness, warmed the Greek boy, who immediately was full of concession, near to tears.

'I have some pills,' he had told Keith. It hurt to do so, but he had admitted frankly, 'John gave them to me. You have to take six at a time...'

Keith had smiled ruefully. 'Six!' And then, equally open, he had claimed, 'It must be terrible out there.'

Dimitrios had told him with feeble humour, 'It's pretty awful down here,' and they had laughed, giggled together like schoolboys.

And now, forty minutes later, in total darkness and with water swishing about and men shouting and some groaning, Dimitrios pleaded aloud, unheard by these, 'My friend! Oh, God, save my friend.'

Dimitrios was lucky – very much a relative luck. He had

been up steel rungs ten feet above the deck when the *Areopagus* had collided. The jolt had thrown his feet from under him but his hands had held. His body had swung outwards, then returned; steel rungs clouted him across the chest and stomach, and winded him, but no worse.

All lights went out.

It was terrifying.

He heard water – or possibly oil – rushing about and shouts of fright, whole scores of yards away, another world.

The sensation was appalling – the ship's dreadful pitching and yawing didn't cease for a moment, but the multisonous cataclysmic tearing of steel was the noise of indifferent gods. And now the acoustic symptoms and indications were all unpleasant: steam hissing, water sloshing about in tons, metal groaning under stress.

He deduced that the lights had gone out as the result of flooding, and that every light on the ship would be off. Worse, every instrument operated by the generators would now be useless – radar, gyro-compass, cabin lights, lifts, telemotor steering, pumps, burners . . .

In this he was correct. The half-empty deep fuel tanks on the port side had been penetrated. There were tanks on port and starboard sides of a narrow central alleyway. At the forward end of it was a pump room containing the valves for controlling the flow from the tanks or flooding them with sea-water ballast. The aft end of the alleyway led into the generator room and as the alleyway was narrow and bounded on all sides by oil-tight and water-tight plating, no water-tight door had been fitted. The alleyway was now flooded with water and it was not possible to reach the flooding valves for the port tanks or equalize the heeling momentum, even if the tanks had been sound. Nor was it possible to stop the water in the alleyway from pouring into the generator room.

Failure in the electric power would mean failure of the forced draught and air preheaters. His shaken mind couldn't work it out. Violent cooling by water would be disastrous to the boilers and steam pressures. But so would a gross increase in heating.

He could smell burning paint and soot. Oh, God, he

thought in terror. A stack fire! The jolt of the collision has caused torching in the uptakes and the smoke pipe. He knew that sparks and even flames would be belching out of the stack, visible to the officers on the bridge . . . The whole ship could blow up. If oil vapour was billowing round the ship it only had to find somewhere with a temperature of about 750° Fahrenheit for autogenous ignition. It didn't even need a spark.

Steam hissed deafeningly in the darkness from ruptured piping and forty feet away molten metal cascaded into water with a hiss.

Dimitrios was shivering with fear in a huge boiler-room where steam or water or fire or suffocation might kill him. What could he *do*? Light. They all needed light. And shut off the main steam stop valve – and close the steam to the oil heater, close the atomizers and secure the oil lines and oil pump. Close the furnace tightly because a sudden rush of cool air (let alone water!) into the heated interior would damage the refractory surface lining and create chaos among tubes.

All these things were impossible. In theory he should go on and pump out the bilges as well! He was not sure whether during this dreadful day the bilges had been steamed out. If not, oil and oil vapour might be accumulated and ready to explode.

No lights, he cautioned himself, unless they have steam-tight globes . . .

He had a watertight torch somewhere. In his cabin!

What had happened?

Where was everybody?

Priorities. Shut off the oil supply by means of the quick-closing valves and stop the oil pump. Start the emergency generator. Shut off the main steam stop valve. But what if the distant control gear is under water? Then you'll have to climb up there and close it with the toggle-operated globe valve. In the dark? Do I have the physical strength?

He came down the steel rungs carefully and found that water was four feet deep. It meant – anything. All bad. Nothing good could happen . . . When water reached or penetrated the furnace walls . . . I'll have to shut down the high pressure boilers.

Chest deep in water he moved slowly, hot but shivering, breathing badly because ventilation had gone, gasping, 'My friend, oh, God, save my friend' – and bumped into Keith.

In the total darkness he identified Keith by a total awareness – a consciousness of height, the other's slimness, a scent of hair oil, a manner of breathing, love and terror emanating like radar emissions . . .

'Keith!'

'Dimitrios! We are lost!'

'No. Listen! If we can shut off the oil and the main steam valve and start the emergency generator—'

'Nothing can save us.'

'We shall save ourselves.'

'It is all so useless—' Keith submitted, meaning that everything was interdependent and now nothing functioned: neither the main steam equipment nor the host of auxiliaries operated by steam – the air cocks, drain valves, soot blowers, blow valves, steam flow indicators, the auxiliary steam stop valve . . .

'Yes, but we can save the ship. And the starboard engine will get us away . . . We *must*.'

'It is beyond my strength,' pleaded Keith, willing to die, get it over with.

'Please, my friend—'

'I cannot swim,' Keith admitted in terror.

Flames flickered in the darkness as drips of oil dropped on to hot exhaust pipes, little lumps of incandescence fell near them and floated, still burning.

Some lights came on unexpectedly – someone else had found the leads to the emergency generator. And with the familiar chaos of armoured wires, asbestos shielded pipes and steel around them it did not at first seem so bad.

There were two other men clinging to valve wheels. One was the Watch Engineer Officer. Three other men floated, injured or dead, burned faces and hair. Three were missing . . .

Dimitrios noticed that the water was pitching with the

ship, and that when the bows went down the water ran that way too, leaving the level here whole feet down.

The officer observed this, too, and stumbled towards the distant-control gear. The water returned, a foot higher, before he reached the position and knocked him sprawling yards past Dimitrios.

'My God!' whispered Dimitrios. 'Stay here, Keith.'

The water was up to the boy's neck. His eyes were wide in fear, but he shouted resolutely, 'I'll turn off the quick-closing valves.' His hands clung to the safety rail, but his feet moved.

Dimitrios allowed the water to carry him thirty yards to where he struggled against it. His hips smashed against protruding metal, his hands burned on something, the sounds frightened him, and all the time metal groaned and he could smell soot and paint and hear the roaring of the stack fire, the storm – he wasn't sure and didn't dare analyse.

He was climbing past the fire bricks and rear casing of the furnace and tubes towards the superheater. It was hot, foul, airless, and awesome. For this boiler was in trouble from all directions. Dimitrios knew that about a quarter of the volume of the entire boiler below the water line (including drum, tubes and water walls) was steam, and that only 15 per cent of the total volume was within the big tube. Each of the *Areopagus'* boilers evaporated a hundred thousand pounds of water each hour. There were vast volumes of steam at the temperature of fire seeking release . . . There might now, as a result of the impact, be extreme changes in the water level in the boiler – and whether it was 'swell' or 'shrinkage' the chances were high that the feed water regulator was out of order. The firing rate might have altered or even stopped . . .

He struggled, twenty feet up steel rungs, with the stop valve. It was old and resisted the power of his hands. Perhaps the thread was worn or it was the resistance of the boiler pressure. He struggled and cursed, ground his teeth. He was using both his hands and at the same time clinging because of the ship's extreme postures. He wept in frustration and called on God.

He had just finished when there was a flare-back. It was on the other side of the carbon steel casing by the burner openings. There was a violent concussion, like gunfire, a flash, and then hissing. Oil patches began to burn on the tide of water. The flare-back was, Dimitrios presumed, due to an explosion of oil vapour in the furnace or to the drop in the air pressure in the fire-room as the result of the failure (or deliberate stoppage) of the forced-draught blowers. Perhaps the fuel-oil pipeline joints or even the boiler walls had been disrupted by the collision . . . It was impossible to know if the furnace was closed up tightly in these conditions, and if it was not, and cool air or water got in, the refractory furnace lining would crack and tubes would become warped, to say the least of it.

He had done what he'd set out to do – perhaps saved the ship from exploding – and now he was panic-stricken. They must get out of here.

He had to swim or stumble to the proximity of the escape hatches through a flooded chaos of pipes and steps, bulbs, safety rails, gauges and dials with unbelievable readings, compressors . . . Patches of oil were burning, although the air was now so poor that the chances of an explosion had diminished.

He had done his duty. He could not be expected to know or care that the port propeller had buckled and the shaft had broken as the result of excessive pitching and rolling which had brought the propellers clean out of the water; and that the port turbine was only saved from overspeeding by an overspeed control valve . . . Nor was he to know that the bearing wear (caused by overheating) had in turn caused a change in the radial position of the port turbine rotor and resulted in decreased tip clearances, in fact resulted in the rubbing of blade tips against the casing, which at 5,000 revolutions a minute . . . Or that the collision had allowed air to get into the turbine casing because the shaft glands (which kept steam in and air out) had been jolted ... Or that the port double-reduction gears were now churning the oil at the bottom of the gear case into emulsion and causing the lubricating pumps to lose suction ... Or that some of the teeth of these giant gears were no longer meshing even adequately and some had broken . . .

The port engine was finished – from furnace to propeller – but he had saved the ship, prevented the massive power from being used against the *Areopagus.*

But there was a huge volume of steam still trapped and there might be ruptures through which it could escape. It was terribly dangerous and frightening. Hundreds of thousands of cubic feet of steam of a heat four or five times that of boiling water. Any failure – and there must be some – could annoy the steam, trap it, divert it in the wrong direction, or release it . . . As far as he knew he had bottled it up and it would cool to impotence. But he fled before its potential now, wanting steel between himself and this place.

The water was higher than his body and he had to swim. A line of oil burned as it floated. He had to swim under it, but a little clung to his clothes around his legs and buttocks . . . He screamed in pain.

He saw a face, two eyes shining in terror, Keith floating away to die.

Oh, God, save my friend, he petitioned inside his head. Not once did he alter his plea to God, save *me*—

He trod water and pulled the boy behind the neck, not certain of the exact technique of propelling another person.

It took like what seemed an hour to reach the bulkhead of steel, where vertical rungs could be climbed to the watertight escape hatches, and it tired him completely. He wanted to weep, he was so weak. He desired rest but had to be active to save Keith, who was thrashing about, albeit feebly, in panic.

There were two men there, but they were old, tired, and their oil-stained, scalded faces and burned eyes faced his way in hope. He would do something. They had not the strength to do anything further.

Dimitrios flinched as seventy-five feet away, red and vicious, a tongue of flame licked upwards. It vanished as quickly as it had appeared, and whole seconds later did its short travel again. His exhausted, terrified mind told him that this was the result of the collision now aggravated by the flare-back. There were removable panels in the casing of the boiler, built in for inspection, cleaning and repair. The joints between sections of the boiler were made air tight by means of asbestos gaskets between the flanges. But even these were not expected to survive thirty years of wear and a collision ... He understood the rhythm of the great belch of fire. It, like the water, went with the pitching of the ship . . . He wondered if the air-setting cement in the horizontal and vertical seams between insulating bricks would stand for all this violence of motion and temperature. Had anchor bolts been shaken loose? If there was an exit for the furnace flames to roar out of they were doomed. Flames would eat air. About 225 cubic feet of air per pound of oil were required for normal combustion in the furnaces.

The energy of panic urged him into action. Keith's fingers fought his as he released them, but after a while Keith, half-conscious and dazed and almost bereft of strength and will, realized that Dimitrios had curled his fingers round a steel rung. He had not the strength to climb to higher rungs, but knew that all Dimitrios asked was that he should hold on.

Dimitrios, meanwhile, climbed fifteen rungs, his own hurt body and saturated clothing a great burden. In a few moments, if they had the strength to climb the rungs, these other three would escape ...

He then saw in black despair that this was not so. The wheel spanners for removing the clips of the watertight escape hatches had been jolted free on impact and had dropped to the deck. They might be anywhere in a radius of ten feet, seven or eight feet under water.

He knew then that he was going to die.

It so weakened him that he nearly dropped. A flicker of rage passed through his body. The injustice of it, the malice of it! He had saved the boiler-room from explosion and earned the right to live with the passengers up there. It was cruel, it was Greek ...

Never again to delight in arrival, see the skyline of ships and harbour buildings and the mountains behind Piraeus, or feel the Greek sun burning on his back. Nor to stroll the seedy twisted streets and alleys of Plaka. Never to smell coffee roasting or drink rough wine. Never to stand outside his father's cottage and stare at stone valleys divided into tiny farms, nor to hear sheep bells. Old women in black siphoning water into jugs from a well. His mother, ageless but always old, wise, mellow, charitable, nothing of value in the world of Hong Kong and San Francisco, standing in a kitchen which had a wood-burning stove and nothing else, smiling her pride at her son who had gone to sea, achieved something . . .

Steam was escaping somewhere. It was inevitable.

He saw it gathering in hot clouds, filling the great volume of the boiler-room above him. It touched him, enveloped him, and he began to scream and retreat down the fifteen rungs to Keith and the two old men.

Oh, God, he petitioned, save *him*. He has done nothing to merit this . . .

23

THE BURSTONS lay taut on their bunks in cabin A 73, fully dressed and with the lights on. Marion couldn't misrepresent the situation to her children – there was a storm and it was nasty. The kids couldn't be expected to sleep if their parents weren't able to. There was some comfort in being able to see and to be dressed ready – for *what*? she wondered.

The cabin was L-shaped. Marion's lower bunk was at right-angles to the hull of the ship, right under the porthole, and Stella's was above her. Mike and Patricia were round the corner of the L by the door; and Bumble was in a cot in the middle space near to them. At Mike's feet, at the junction of the L, was the entrance to the tiny bathroom. Marion, then, could hear the ferocious slap of tumultuous spray on steel inches from her ears. All of them felt bodily the weight of the sea as it thumped against the *Areopagus*, shook her at will. The sensation was distinctly that the liner was nothing, a toy made of paper running in a mill stream during rain . . .

They were all rather silent, waiting for the storm to end; their fingers clung absurdly to the rims of their bunks and their arms stiffened to prevent themselves rolling off.

Patricia pleaded wretchedly, 'How long's it going to last? I'm scared, Mum.'

Marion reassured her, 'It's been on for two hours and we haven't sunk yet, kiddo, so I guess we'll survive.'

'It's gone cold,' countered Patricia.

Bumble was mercifully asleep.

Stella was still in party dress – they'd allowed her to go to *that*. 'Fancy paying money for this!' she contributed. 'We must be crazy.'

Marion sat up abruptly and cried, 'I forgot the washing' – like someone who'd left a gas tap on.

Mike sniggered. 'I'm not in need of a clean shirt right now!'

She disputed – to her it was important, a duty – 'I'm going to get it.'

Mike argued loudly, surprised, 'Don't be crazy, kid. You won't be able to walk that far. You'll fall down the steps.'

'They'll pinch it,' she declared.

'What, in *this*?'

'A woman had a line of nappies stolen. They're *mean*, some of them.'

'Forget it,' he insisted.

'Mike, we can't afford to lose clothes. Bumble's only got two changes of vests.'

He saw that she meant it, and was shocked. Didn't she feel frozen to the bunk with apprehension? 'I'll go,' he offered.

'You wouldn't know which is their stuff.'

He was really alarmed. 'Kid, this is rough. It's a typhoon or something.'

He had said it aloud, admitted what they all feared.

'It won't take a minute,' Marion ventured.

'Oh, let her go and break her leg,' said Stella cynically.

'Why don't *you* go?' he shouted, and this was the last Marion heard as she shut the door of the cabin.

She turned left and ran five paces to the main passageway

which ran fore and aft along this port side of A Deck. She clung to the rail and realized that Mike was right. Looking aft she saw the corridor rise to a terrifying angle – about 45° and then the dip attempted to drag her away. God! she thought, and the first notions of disaster touched her. But she had a streak of sullen obstinacy. Nobody was going to pinch her washing. As the *Areopagus* levelled and then began to rise up the next mountain of water she went aft, almost 'weightless', to the next turning, fifty feet away, and there turned left.

On the starboard aft side of this passage athwartships was a small opening where a spiral staircase descended to B deck. It had none of the grandeur of other stairways; it was strictly functional, with a descending diameter of perhaps ten feet.

B Deck itself was a little grubby. There were only a few cabins fore and aft, most of them single cabins without facilities. It had no carpeting, only linoleum, and there were the smells of oil and lavatories.

Nevertheless, the drying room was useful to Marion. Always very hot and dry, it aired saturated clothes in an hour or less.

Marion realized now as she took down the clean dry clothes that if she was to carry them she needed both hands and wouldn't have a hand free to grasp rails or prop herself on bulkheads. Still stubborn, she decided she could manage, and she did indeed have a good sense of balance.

She had just gathered a bulk of clothing, and was holding it in front of her chest, when the *Areopagus* and *Seattle Doll* collided. She heard the long blast of the *Areopagus'* siren, but it meant nothing to her.

She was thrown to the deck, but was fortunate. Her head missed steel by two inches and the soft dry washing cushioned her body.

All lights went out and she was in darkness so absolute she couldn't see her hands or the white of the towels she'd washed.

Being on the starboard side Marion didn't realize, despite the concussion of steel, that the *Areopagus* had hit something, and being on the lowest passenger deck she heard no cries or shouts or breakages . . . She was just badly startled and unable to see. She was sure that if she could get out of the drying room she'd find light. She gathered the clothes together by touch, fell over while on her knees searching, and was angry with the liner which was always blowing irons or failing in its public address system.

She struggled out of the drying room and found total darkness. Even then she only thought in terms of electricity failure. Typical! she condemned, and sought her way to the spiral staircase and ascended it. Once she had to cling with a hand, and lost some of the clothing.

At the top of the staircase she paused, not able to go further until there was some light.

She heard shouting distantly, and then an explosion, and at last realized with a shock that something very unpleasant had happened. In the same moment she could smell smoke and identified the position of anxious voices above her on Metaxas Deck.

Marion dropped the washing and loped over to where she thought the corridor along the port side would be. She was sure she'd found it, yes, because here was a hand rail. Her hands ran along the rail guiding her. The sensation of movement suggested that she was correct, going forward. And then the rail ended and her body collided with steel. They'd closed the water-tight doors and she couldn't get back to the cabin, to her kids and Mike. Fear crystallized into this one objective, with everything else of lesser relevance.

She shuffled back along the rail until she had returned to the junction. She went left and left again to the stairs which led up to Metaxas Deck, and went up, with the intention of going forward and then descending somewhere and finding the cabin.

Someone was shining a torch at the next junction.

Marion asked in the direction of the torch, 'What's happening?'

An agitated elderly voice said in complaint, 'There was a fire along there. It was terrible. I can't get back to my cabin . . . It's not good enough.'

The torch waved about in emphasis and Marion, breathing smoke, saw in the beam of light that here too, she was thwarted : a fire resistant screen had been dropped. She also saw a steward, who grinned and suggested optimistically, 'Open soon.'

There was nothing to stop her going up to Attica Deck. It was easy because of the guiding rail and steps.

She was still on the port side and groped forward along Attica Deck. It was a luxury deck and here and there small corridors ran athwartships with portholes at their endings. Incredibly, light shone faintly through the first one she encountered. Light was shining from *outside*.

Marion had to go and look, and in perplexity and horror she saw a ship burning. Half a ship? She wasn't sure. The vessel went out of sight at intervals, and when observed rose and fell unbelievable measures. Marion obtained some idea of the dimensions of the sea they were in the grip of.

It was now more than urgent to reach Mike and the kids. It was desperate.

She reached another junction of Attica Deck and descended to Metaxas, but encountered the metal of a second fire-resisting door. And here the area was flooded with water, and behind the screen of steel was fire. She *knew* because she could see its red outline at the bottom of the metal screen. Men were in there shouting and fighting the fire.

It meant that they had isolated the fire, but in doing so had isolated the central parts of Attica, 'A' and 'B' Decks. Mike and the kids were in that middle third of the ship below a fire. She was not.

There must be a way to get to them.

She decided to go higher and then further forward. It wasn't logical, but by now logic was being left behind, instinct was taking over.

Up one deck, at a similar junction, she ran into a crowd who had some torches. They were senseless with panic and she was absorbed, swept along. Voices were angry with fear and the curious logic of panic :

'They're abandoning ship—'

'The crew have gone.'

'There was an explosion—'

'We're on the wrong side; they'll never launch boats from this side—'

'That's my lifebelt—'

'Where's Arthur? We can't go without Arthur.'

'Go where, for Christ's sake?'

'They said to go to the Aegean Lounge.'

'Who said?'

'The man.'

'What man?'

'Come *on*! He wouldn't have said it if—'

'I don't want to.'

'You've got to.'

'In a little boat? I can't. I'd get pneumonia.'

'I've hurt my back,' a woman cried out with great fear and bitterness. 'Oh, my God, I've broken my back.'

She evidently expected someone to do something about her back, but no one did.

A child began to scream like a drill, and Marion felt the terrible communication of panic. It stopped the blood, emptied the head, yet the heart accelerated. She forgot absolutely where she was, lost all sense of orientation. Her mind fought hard against the crowd sensation which told her to flee senselessly. Panic poured into her stomach like hot soup. She resisted it with the mental instructions: Get back to Mike. Kids must have lifebelts on. Warm clothing. Orders. Wait for orders. From an officer or the public address system. If it works...

But the crowd wasn't interested. Terrified people carried Marion upwards, the crowd gathering others, and somewhere above a man was shouting in pure panic and bitterness: 'The boats! They've taken to the boats!'

Hands pushed her aside, to get past her, to hurry; they were more important, must be saved. 'Damn you!' she shouted into someone's face, and he or she made no objection. They'd reached the Parade Deck, and here was utter pandemonium, a great shouting, cold air roaring in from the sea, the crush of unseen elbows and shoulders, higher than hers. A terrible fear came to Marion. Had she missed some instruction? Had the rest of the family heard it and gone to the boats? Were they here in this mess? Had the kids got their lifebelts on? She could see through a window of the library (not that she identified her position) that boats were in fact being lowered. Fire somewhere gave sufficient illumination to see this. But Mike and the kids, surely, were trapped in that central third of the ship, contained by watertight and fire-proof doors and unaware of a fire one deck above them.

The motion of the ship knocked Marion over and in the same instant someone shouted 'The Greeks are deserting us!' and the crowd shouted, too, and stampeded. They trampled over her; shoes trod on her hands; someone fell violently and moaned, and Marion glowed with animal satisfaction. She fought with fury and loathing to get to her knees, bruised and breathless, afraid of suffocation.

Light came on suddenly, feeble and flickering, but enough to enable her to see the fantastic spectacle of scores of people – many still in fancy dress – carrying treasures – a camera or small case, a child – Many wore their lifejackets, incorrectly fastened.

They were unashamed, even under scrutiny in the light, fighting to get out on to the Parade Deck where a hurricane wind awaited them.

The ship, strangely enough, seemed less secure now that things could be seen. It had a list of about ten degrees, scarcely noticed in the tumultuous pitching, yawing and heaving.

Someone shouted, 'Get back! Where the hell are you going?' and she identified the voice as that of the Australian Second Officer, Mollon.

'They said the starboard side,' a man snarled.

'This is the port.'

'Out of the way,' roared the man. Marion had never seen him before. 'They're lowering the boats! We'll be drowned like rats.'

Mollon knocked this man cold with his fist. 'Now, listen!' he began, but the crowd swept past him.

Marion knew what he wanted to say – that if boats were

being lowered it was to save some of the crew of that other burning ship.

She was pushed out on to a wet deck, and instantly saturated, while a wind as solid as water knocked her over. A bell rang somewhere, and the public address system was operating, but out here it was a struggle to stay on the deck, not to let the terrible wind simply blow her away into the sea.

An oxygen cylinder rolled along the Parade Deck, knocking people over like ninepins, breaking limbs as it went. It ran into a pack of passengers who were fighting to get into a lifeboat. Greek stewards and sailors, in the boat, were pushing off these frenzied people and shouting about the other ship. A woman cried 'Save my baby! Take him with you! He's got no lifejacket!' And she dropped the baby into the arms of a sailor as the lifeboat descended. The man didn't know the baby was dropping. It bounced off him and fell into the sea. The woman gave an immense groan and ran wildly down the tilting Parade Deck.

Mollon was now standing near another lifeboat and punching passengers – men, Marion saw in shame – and shouting, 'They're not deserting you. For Christ's sake, there's a ship on fire. Can't you *see* it?'

But they couldn't, because both halves of the *Seattle Doll* had now sunk. And they didn't hear him anyway.

Marion was terrified, most of all of the wind. It hit her like a solid thing, roared across her mouth and into her eyes and inhibited her arms and legs. She was sure now that Mike and the kids wouldn't be here, and fought wind and gravity and berserk passengers to get back. A child's lifejacket, whipped away by the wind, slapped her cruelly across the face. People were hanging on to the rails, hysterical, afraid to let go. A man was endeavouring to pull a woman – presumably his wife – from the rails, but she clung to the metal with bitterness and insistence, and even blows wouldn't shift her. He was an old man weeping and with a rasping breath, and the next lurch of the *Areopagus* took him away, to be smashed against rails aft and lost overboard. The woman, who was howling like a dog, lost strength, and the wind took her, too, and sent her helplessly sliding down the deck, breaking limbs.

A child was sliding past Marion like wet rubbish, and Marion, clinging herself, caught it by the hair with one hand.

The crowd were threatening to throw Mollon overboard if he didn't allow them into the next lifeboat. Stewards battered with oars at hands, smashing the fingers that threatened this boat. It wouldn't function anyway – the davits were corroded – and so a senseless fight went on until another boat appeared, swung outwards as the *Areopagus* heeled, and forced the passengers by the rail to scatter. A few were knocked senseless. Mollon was shouting, 'Go into the lounge. You are in danger here.'

A few women collapsed on deck and wept hysterically.

Marion clung to the child, who howled. 'It's all right, kid,' she bellowed into its ear. 'I'll take you back to your cabin.'

She had forgotten about Mike. It was now a wrestling match between her and the elements and crazed passengers to get back into the lounge on the Parade Deck. She could see sparks and flames, which were coming from the aft funnel; and she breathed burning paint and smoke and was stung by hot ash. She had lost her sad perspective of the world – of Mike's tragedy and Stella's sullen dirty secrets. This was the limit of the earth – to crawl along a deck and fight the strength of a typhoon as it pressed on a door. The irony of travelling on a cruise, good money spent, was wasted on her for the moment. They could laugh later, if they survived.

The child, she saw now, was Phoebe, daughter of the woman from Darwin. Marion found this grimly funny, although she didn't understand why. She held the child in an iron grip : she was aware that it could be very satisfying to save *that* woman's child. Where was Mrs Smart-alec in this pandemonium?

Twenty persons were struggling to get out on to the open deck. The pressure of them at least held the door open into the interior of the Parade Deck. They were terrible to see, pitiful old men and women stampeding, and nothing waited for them out here except a greater terror of naked wind and water, injury, death, pneumonia at the very least, if shock didn't kill them anyway . . .

But she made no attempt to stop them, merely battered against the weight of them while the door was open (for her wrists hadn't the power to open it: she had a job doing it on a day when there was a mere breeze).

She fell inside, with the child, sprawling, and the first sensation, because of the absence of wind and sea, was of warmth.

She was at a junction where an elevator functioned (but not *now*) and the library met the Aegean Lounge. There was chaos. A hundred photographs and dozens of notices pinned to a notice board had been blown about like confetti at a spring wedding, and littered the deck. Broken glass, chairs, ashtrays, violins even, and a trolley had rolled or slid around, smashed themselves, and still careered about. Curtains had collapsed into floods of water and pools of seasickness.

She dragged the kid into the lounge, where several hundred people lay on the deck, or sat supporting themselves.

The Chief Purser, Demetropoulos, was one of the few people standing. Besieged by a bitter, frightened and anxious group of passengers, he was nevertheless aloof and immaculate. He was beautifully clean still in tropical white – just a rim of dirt along the collar where, perhaps, he ran a finger in exasperation; not even his shoes were splashed. His eyes were still directed just above his interlocutors, in fact beyond all this chaotic dreadful scene in the lounge – water and people vomiting and crying and arguing, and some motionless in injury or rigid in panic – and there was a slight expression of distaste on his face as if this sort of thing was all that could be expected from passengers. *Australians* indeed! He was saying to his interlocutors with repugnance, as if they had already demanded a refund, 'There is no question of abandoning the ship. What on earth *for*? We shall be in Guam in less than three days.'

They were frustrated by his calm, amounting, it seemed to them, to indifference. There was a terrible storm, a fire was raging, they'd heard a bang, some cabins were flooded, people had been hurt, there was rumour of another ship involved . . . They wanted qualified reassurance, not the deadpan phraseology of brochures.

Marion collapsed on to the lounge carpet and leaned against an armchair, holding on to the child. They were both soaking wet. Marion was out of breath and her heart wouldn't calm down . . . There was turmoil all around, the agitation of a crowd which didn't know what was going on. There was not a steward in sight. No one except Demetropoulos.

Someone began to sing.

Edgar sat at a piano while Ricky and one of the dancers clung on to the thing as it slid a little, held taut by thick rope, but with a few inches of slack. 'The bloody thing won't keep still,' shouted Edgar.

The Australian and New Zealand passengers took up the singing. Ricky chose the songs and Edgar played the piano. The dancer just smiled.

Ricky sang 'Show me the way to go home—' and there was laughter. Then, hesitantly, they all sang a Maori song called 'Now is the hour.'

It was an appalling chorus – old breathless quavering voices – but Marion (who did not sing) was touched, and she wept, understanding some rough quality specifically Antipodean.

The metallic voice interrupted with a rasp over the speakers (a few people cheered bitterly): 'May I have your attention, please?'

Edgar bellowed 'My God, are *they* still here?'

The passengers snickered, but were silent, desperately anxious for sense and order – and hope.

'This is the First Officer. The situation is serious, but has improved. We have had a minor collision with another vessel. The damage has been assessed and there is no cause for alarm, only for care. Some boats have been lowered, but these are to help the other ship. Before the collision there was a fire in the hair-dressing saloon on Metaxas Deck. There was also minor flooding as a result of the collision. A few people have been hurt. I am now re-opening the water-tight and fireproof doors on all decks so that passengers may return to their cabins if they wish and anyone needing medical attention should proceed to the surgery on A Deck forward on the starboard side. I am sorry you are having an unpleasant time and I ask for your calm. The storm may continue for some hours yet, but it will not get worse. Thank you.'

'Come on, kid,' urged Marion. 'Let's go find your Mum.'

A few other passengers struggled to their feet, but most remained where they were, too scared to move. They weren't quite convinced by the First Officer, and waited, anxious not to be trapped down below.

It took five whole minutes to do down the four decks. A Deck on the port side was flooded, and there was the smell of smoke. Stewards were struggling at the junction of an athwartships corridor and someone was screaming and evidently thrashing about. Marion saw the old man, in pyjamas soaked in blood, who was being helped, and her heart accelerated in the worst fear yet. A collision. 'A minor collision,' the First Officer's voice had told her. But it had caused enough structural damage to put the electricity out. She had been thrown. A ship burning. Somewhere metal had smashed into metal. Here, fifty feet from her own cabin, was a victim. Oh, my God, she thought, conscious now of the possibilities...

The stewards were, she realized, going from cabin to cabin now that the water-tight doors had been re-opened (temporarily? she wondered) looking for the injured. *This* was where they expected to find them. The blood-covered old man, groaning, had the forecast of reality for her.

There was shouting going on in the cabin she first sought. Marion knocked but went in anyway.

The woman from Darwin and her husband stared at Marion. The cabin was in a state of chaos. Two kids were weeping.

Marion said, shakily, 'Here's your kid. She was on deck.'

Silence. The woman had been weeping, Marion saw. She

was human after all. The woman from the Northern Territories said, and her voice was unsteady, too, 'I got to admit, Pom, that you're a useful woman to have aboard.'

'Thanks,' said Marion, as Phoebe ran to her mother, howling.

'What's it like up there?' the woman asked.

'A bit noisy. Something of a wind. Some people didn't like it and wanted to go ashore.'

'I can imagine,' acknowledged the woman.

It was the most satisfying moment in several years, but Marion was in a hurry, couldn't savour it. The buffalo hunter, as taciturn as ever, nodded his approval, and Marion withdrew.

She ran, as the ship dipped, her fingers touching the rail lightly, and she prayed aloud, 'Oh, my dear God, spare my family...'

Stewards were dragging out someone with red hair. The girl, Diane, smashed in the stomach, but screaming. And a small bundle on the linoleum of that cabin was the little old lady who knew the world was coming to an end soon. She had died without panic, knowing that God was justified in tearing the earth and sea apart...

Ambros and a steward officer were struggling with the door of the Burstons' cabin, but it wouldn't open more than an inch or two. They talked in Greek with terrible urgency to each other.

They sensed rather than heard Marion, and Ambros turned a sad peasant face to her. 'Ah, Missus!' he cried, in relief at her survival. But his eyes were full of sorrow for her, and what she must find beyond the door at which she now tore with her fingers.

Mike was lying there, fulminating, ready to get up and strike Stella, but allowing anger to ebb away, and feeling sorrow that it had come to this bitter relationship – when the two ships struck each other.

Thousands of tons of steel collided yards away from where he was lying in apprehension of the storm. The noise of impact was so total he was deafened, even fear was overcome.

He had no idea for whole seconds what it was. Rocks, we've hit rocks, his mind deduced, and the steel sides of the ships, scraping each other in no way modified this conclusion.

And then Patricia's bunk collapsed quite slowly on to him in total darkness, a burden of a couple of hundredweight, and the screaming began.

It was, he identified, Stella.

Patricia cried, too, in pure terror, just above him, and the child, Bumble, woke in her cot – which had been hurled five feet, although he was not to know that in darkness – but Stella's scream was special. It had the acoustic agony of the child under the station-waggon's wheels. He was the sonometer which could measure in exact degree that noise and the pain it represented.

There was, however, a difference.

He was not responsible this time.

Certainly it reduced him to jelly and fear, but seconds beyond that he was burning with the special love he had had for Stella until a few days ago—

'I'd give everything I have – my health, my money, my car, everything in the world...

But not my child.

You can't ask that.

He couldn't move.

For a moment he had the horror of serious injury, but in fact splintered wood lay on him and above him Patricia's legs tattooed as fast as her frenzied nerves could work them.

The baby howled in the fear of darkness and noise.

For the noise did not stop. A wind funnelled through metal somewhere – he didn't for a long time appreciate that it roared through a fractured hull – with a shriek that dulled the working of the senses. It had a force that was brutal, seemed solid, and which knocked the breath out of Mike. And it carried with it the fury of the sea – cold violent spray.

Patricia shouted, coherent in this immiscibility, 'Dad, I'm frightened. Oh, Dad, where are you?'

'Stay where you are,' he called out, an absurd instruction, but he didn't want her to fall or stumble into broken wood or metal. 'Cover yourself up.'

He fought to get the great burden off his ribs, and panic accumulated as he found that he couldn't.

Stella's screaming went on, terrible to hear, awesome, that she should know such words, plead so terribly, an appalling appeal to a crazy God she had betrayed.

He shouted, 'Stella! Stop that! Stop it! Save your breath. We're coming.'

I've got to get to her.

Where the hell is everybody?

They all let me down. Nobody'll come. They'll all fail . . . Ah!

He remembered that this had been his forecast and verdict a few weeks ago, his contempt for the second-rate passengers and vanities of the crew. Now he didn't want them to fail. They must not fail. I mustn't fail, he thought in anguish. Not this time.

Stella was groaning now, had already lost the strength to scream. Soon she'd be so cold from wind and water and loss of blood she'd die.

He levered with his knees and all the strength of his hands, and the bulk of wood above him shifted an inch or two.

If only there was light.

'Patricia!' he called.

'Dad, I'm frightened. Oh, Dad, are we going to die?'

'No,' he assured her. 'Listen. Get down.'

'I can't!'

'Of course you can.'

'I can't, I can't. There's no ladder. I can't see.'

'Climb down.'

'I can't.'

He waited a while and then said, 'Put your hand over the side of your bunk.'

His left hand sought hers. 'Where is it?' he asked.

'Here,' Patricia said uselessly. 'Where's Mummy? She'll die. Why doesn't she come back?'

Mike didn't know, didn't dare to analyse . . . He was glad that Marion had not been in her bunk underneath Stella's. She might have been screaming, too. But perhaps, where she was, it was worse. He had to get out and find her . . .

His hand found Patricia's arm, just by the elbow. With shock he found that there was a trickle of blood on it. He wanted to ask about this, to comfort her, but desisted, and instead told her, 'Your fingers must be only a few inches from the deck. Climb down, Patricia.'

'I can't. Why should I? I'm scared.'

'For Christ's sake!' he snarled, flaring into impatience.

But this made her howl in self-pity and terror; and he was abject: he knew that he had no right to expect a small girl to understand *this* . . .

'I'm sorry, kid. But I can't move out of here until you do.'

She slid past him, fingers clawing anxiously as though she was a hundred feet in the air.

'There's water,' she shrieked at him. 'We're sinking.'

'No. We're not.'

Mike was still unable to move the bulk above him. It was jammed in its hinges or something. Her weight had made little difference. He became desperate and kicked and pushed.

The light came on in the bathroom. The door which separated it from this cabin was closed, but there was now a rectangle of illumination around the door and it gave enough light in here to take away a little of the terror. Somewhere somebody was aware that the lights had failed, and had done something about it. Sooner or later, it followed, they'd come to find the Burstons.

'Patricia, listen. Go into the bathroom and tell me what it's like.'

'Dad, Stella, there's blood—'

'Never mind that. Go into the bathroom . . . Is it all right?' he shouted.

Patricia said into his ear, 'I don't know what you mean.'

'Is it flooded or broken or anything?'

'It's got water in.'

'A lot.'

'Just like here.'

He didn't know what that meant and didn't dare to ask.

'Take Bumble and go in there. Stay there.'

'I don't want to. I'm scared. How will you get out of there.'

'You just take Bumble. Be careful.'

'We can't get out of the cabin,' she told him. 'The door's gone funny—'

'All right. Go into the bathroom.'

He could see Patricia's legs stumbling about. 'Don't look at Stella,' he cautioned. 'Just go . . . I'll see to Stella.'

'I'm frightened. If we can't get out . . .'

'I know, I'm scared too. Just go.'

When she was in the bathroom with the baby he began to hack at the wood above him with a restricted arc for his feet, at the same time pushing upwards with his hands. It seemed beyond his strength and all the time Stella groaned and cried . . .

Something gave way after a while and the one end of the thing was free to lift higher. He kicked harder, hurting his feet brutally, and then struggled to get out. Splinters and torn metal tore his clothes and flesh as he did so, but he came out feet first and collapsed on to the deck where Bumble's cot was crushed and suitcases had slid about and there was perhaps half an inch of water.

He was instantly soaked by the howling moisture as it roared into the cabin through the fracture. He crawled towards Stella through a high pressure spray.

It wasn't possible to see exactly what had happened, but certainly the steel of the hull had crumbled like tinfoil and crushed the two bunks like matchwood, and in this mess his daughter was trapped. Oh, God, he thought, cold in fear, and sure that she must die.

She was groaning and shivering and mumbling. His hands, seeking her tenderly, encountered warm blood. She was lying in it.

'Oh, my little girl,' he cried.

'I'm hurt,' Stella said simply in a tiny voice, and stiffened and groaned.

'We'll get you out,' Mike said. 'You've broken a bone, kid, so keep as still as you can.'

He explored very delicately to see if she was smashed elsewhere, but her arms and legs seemed intact, as far as he could touch them, for blankets, wood and steel were all crunched together enfolding her.

Very carefully, but with the urgency of love and numbing apprehension, he wrenched off broken wood. The saturated air roared into his face from the sea and stunned and deafened him. The motion of the ship threw him about, but he tore at wood and metal, breathing heavily, nothing in the world but *this* . . .

He talked comfort and love to her, incoherently, and it seemed to reach her. She comprehended that his desperation was love. She thought he was sobbing.

Whole minutes later, consciousness coming and going, she felt his hands touch her hair and face, exploring tenderly for pain. She understood him perfectly now and was black with shame of the other thing.

It was important to tell him this. She might forget if she went to sleep now, and things might be different when she woke.

'Dad!' she whispered.

'Don't move, kid,' he requested. 'You're nearly free.'

'I'm sorry,' she sighed.

In the roar of air he heard it, understood it, and was overwhelmed with sorrow and love, and began to weep.

'So'm I,' he confessed.

'Why, Dad, you're crying,' Stella said in pleasurable shock amidst the agony.

He *cared*. It was like Mum said. It had warmth, in the end it was what mattered, who loved, who cared, not who wanted the cheaper stuff, necking and kisses, those hot shameful moments. She understood this and it warmed her and it was beautiful.

The stewards were battering at the cabin door. Mike heard Marion's voice and was relieved. She was all right and so was he. He hadn't failed.

24

THE Turkish radio officer, Barutcu, used the transceiver to send out the mayday signal of distress. He then adjusted an emergency transmitter so that it could, if necessary, be left behind should the liner be abandoned; it would continue to send signals after he had gone. Finally he prepared a battery transmitter which could float, and this he kept ready to carry to the lifeboats if necessary.

He did not believe that they would abandon ship, although he recognized that there might be wishful thinking here. But he had been through war, famine, revolution, earthquake and poverty and had no doubt that he would survive shipwreck too.

They were dragging the Captain off the bridge. This was interesting, for it left Tomazos in command. This was a good man, Barutcu considered, but embittered, and recently inclined to the bottle. It was worthy of perusal, for the experience of command, if survived, might eliminate the bitterness.

Barutcu understood the unhappiness. His own wife had been lost, but by death, not betrayal, and he had suffered . . . He stretched himself and was aware that his back was stiff. He poured out three-quarters of a glass of cider and drank it and waited . . .

Tomazos had many problems thrust instantly upon him in total darkness as he stood on an unstable bridge. His telegraph order to the engineroom was not answered. The ship's siren did not function now and Yannopoulos told him that the telemotor steering gear was dead in his hands. The public address system did not work. He was, however, able to close the 23 water-tight doors by hydraulic hand operation. The brochure lied when it talked of 'at the press of a button . . .'

The responsibility was entirely his and it was a heavy

burden at the end of a long chain: owners who ran this liner as part of an industry (oil and hotels), and whose responsibility was limited entirely on shore; governments, Greek and Panamanian in particular, but also every country, state and port had its particular rules about health, safety and facilities: the *Areopagus*, in reverse, had to be treated like a visiting Embassy; and, finally, at sea, the Master ...

These were the things he had to do – and there would be others as they occurred. Assess the damage (and adjust the trim accordingly); control any flooding; restore electricity, via emergency generators if that was necessary and possible. He must communicate to shore adequate reports of damage so that the authorities understood the gravity of the situation. He must assess the harm inflicted, or likely to be, upon passengers. They must be reassured, informed truthfully when he himself had information. Demetropoulos and his staff must check about children, lifejackets, the injured, people trapped in cabins or by the water-tight doors. He recalled the passengers' half-hearted cynical interest in life-jacket drill. Well, at any rate, they all had or had been issued with life-jackets. The ship was not crowded; there were plenty more if needed ... Crew and passengers not only wanted reassurance: they needed orders and instructions.

He said to Mollon, 'Get down there and take charge on the Parade Deck, Tom. You speak Australian! Tell me the situation.'

As he uttered these words the *Seattle Doll* exploded.

'Christ!' Mollon cried. 'Poor bastards.'

'If we can launch boats, do so,' Tomazos instructed. 'You'll have to do it as you find it, Tom.'

To Makris he said, 'The electricity's failed. I want a team of runners for orders. I want the whole ship assessed for flood, damage and fire ... If those automobiles have shifted, if ballast tanks have been punctured, or areas flooded, inform me so that I can employ pumps when we can use the damn things; and I can adjust trim ...'

Tomazos was aware that in this storm and collision passengers would be hurt. They'd be pounded by tables, chairs, lockers, heavy fitments wrenched from their fastenings ...

They were now, as he was, plunged into darkness, and some would be scalded by coffee, bruised by the instruments of the orchestra; crockery, glass and bottles would shatter; a flood of beer and spirit would ruin carpets. Spirits were inflammable: he recalled a serious fire due to burning spirits. Ashtrays would clang. Liquids would spill. In some cabins a colossal bang of metal would be followed by darkness and a sudden inrush of water, cold and shocking. They might be injured. Kids would be terrified ... Tomazos sent his first runner to the surgery to place the doctors on the alert. 'Tell them to organize an overflow. Tell them that I'll get extra blankets when I can ...'

He waited, frustrated, and helpless, to gather knowledge – what had been damaged, what had been flooded, and which of the thousands of usable instruments, engines and devices had been destroyed or simply waited for the restoration of electrical power. It was probable, he felt, that the main damage had been inflicted behind the collision bulkhead and as far as he could tell (for he had been frightened and had flinched, too) behind the bridge, on the port side. The frames like ribs were heavy angle bars spaced about three feet apart which extended vertically from the keel to the upper deck. Numbered from one near the bows to over 200 at the stern, they were divided every dozen or so by transverse bulkheads. This sub-division separated the *Areopagus* into water-tight compartments. But with a sea like this and steering gone, and perhaps steam power also lost, and possibly fuel pipes severed and high tension electric cables ready to spark off a fire as soon as electricity had been restored, and a fire raging still in the hairdressing saloon ... Anyway, there probably wasn't any whip damage – despite its bulk the liner was a flexible structure ...

The radar told him nothing for it, too, was out of action. But he knew that the *Areopagus* was beam on to a typhoon wind and that there was a lee shore a mere twenty miles away. Unless power could be restored they'd be smashed to pieces on rocks within two hours ... He understood which was the rotational direction of the revolving storm and was unable, until he had power, to bring the ship round. In the meantime, assuming his ship's survival, he had ordered boats to be lowered – if possible – to pick up possible survivors of the other ship, now burning and split in half ... Looking aft from the wing of the bridge – with the air howling around him and the spray saturating his clothes – he saw in horror that flames and sparks were coming out of the aft funnel of the *Areopagus*. An oxygen cylinder exploded as it rolled overboard. For a moment Tomazos had doubts about survival ...

Mollon ordered that the boats on the port side should be swung out. It would be impossible, because of the liner's heel, to get the starboard boats into a lowering position. The davits were designed for working with a list of up to 15°. The starboard boats could not be pushed uphill. This meant that the port boats with a total capacity of around 50 per cent of the passengers and crew were all that could be used. The excessive list now caused the lifeboats to swing far outboard from the hull at muster stations on the Parade Deck, and they could not be easily braced on to the ship's side.

Mollon and some sailors and stewards had to fight off panicking passengers to get away. One lifeboat wouldn't shift at all. Nor would the motor start on another. But Mollon's boat at last went round the stern of the *Areopagus* where its engine was swamped and cut out. Mollon stayed in the lee of the *Areopagus* and cursed and swore until the motor ran again. He then made towards the area where he believed the other ship had burned ...

Two boats got away from the *Seattle Doll*. About twenty men were in one and when it capsized another dozen also clung to it. As each huge wave broke over the boat one or two men were washed off.

A dozen men dropped or clambered into the second boat, which had been launched empty in haste and fear of an explosion. They let go the stern line. This in the darkness wrapped itself round the propeller of the *Seattle Doll* and became hopelessly jammed, together with the boat's rudder. The stern line was to tow rafts, but the boat could not get away from the *Seattle Doll*. The stern swung in to the metal ship and was holed just above the water line.

It was then that the *Seattle Doll* sank, taking the boat with her. The men were sucked into the sea.

A few survived and were in the water, treading oil, stunned and injured and, most of them, naked, when Mollon's boat came up. It was difficult in a towering sea to grasp and pull them aboard because they were covered with fuel oil and were slippery.

Other men from the *Seattle Doll* were on the life-raft, or clinging to it, or to a rope trailing from it – six men clung to the thick greasy rope – and these men were expecting to be towed by the boat which had now been holed and swamped. There was almost no visibility, breathing was difficult, and the sea was a cauldron. Huge waves flooded over the craft, whole feet over, and soon came water so powerful that it folded the raft like a sandwich, suffocating and drowning those men who had not fallen or been thrown clear. Some men swam away until they were seized with cramp, their muscles became constricted and they drowned. A few stayed where they had been thrown in the water, treading oil, until the liner's boats picked them up.

Not only were these unfortunate men slippery with oil, but some had broken limbs. Others had swallowed oil. Two were virtually rigid with shock and it was immensely difficult to get them aboard the boat and, later, the *Areopagus*.

Not having either electricity or the power of steam at least gave Tomazos the doubtful advantage of being able to consider what he would do when he did have one or both. And gradually information was brought to him by officers and sailors so that he had a good idea which parts of the ship were flooded and which cargo had shifted. Some of the twenty-two automobiles had snapped their steel cables and fallen over, but so long as they did not catch fire their weight was relatively trivial ... He was aware of which areas needed pumping. What he did not know was if any pumps were workable. An estimate of stability was made, using the cargo list corrected at Hong Kong, and in consultation with those blue and red markers which had amused Mrs Triffett, and which told of the positions and quantities of oil and water. Most of the cargo was still secured in a seaman-like manner to meet normal conditions ... The fore and aft trim was not too bad. She was down several feet by the bows, but this was not getting worse.

He did not drop the anchors, for he did not feel the *Areopagus* would come round readily to the sea even though her engines might be functioning; one, he knew for sure, was out of action. He needed more power to make even this manoeuvre, although he would certainly have to do something presently, power or not ... Soon he would have no sea room and any manoeuvres would be in the dangerous area of rocks ... The ship was already heeled 10° to port. No more water must be allowed to flood the port side or the *Areopagus* would roll and capsize. Pumping must begin on the port side ...

Electric power came on and the first thing Tomazos saw was that the surviving radar had failed – the picture had spun round. He smiled grimly. Captain Vafiadis would have approved of this failure!

His first telephone dialogue was with the Chief Engineer. He could scarcely hear Mr Bitsios, but at least this line hadn't failed as the voice whistle had.

'What's the situation?'

'Who is that?'

'Tomazos, First Officer.'

'Not the Captain?'

'He has been hurt.'

'Ah!' said Bitsios, in interest, possibly in satisfaction. 'So what are your demands?'

'Whatever you can give me, I can use,' Tomazos told him.

'I cannot give you much,' the Chief Engineer informed him. 'The port boiler and fire-room are finished. The port propeller shaft has broken. Even the turbine has steam leaks. No power, no power at all. Cavitation in the port screw undoubtedly even if we had power and a shaft ...'

'Is the port boiler dangerous?'

'Everything is dangerous. It is a madhouse down here. But some of my lads turned off the oil and main steam.'

'Any casualties, Mr Bitsios?'

'Ah, yes.'

'I am sorry.'

'We've got some of the boys out.'

'What about the starboard side?'

'We can give you power in a while. We'll see. Yes, now with light, we'll see. I will inform you, but as far as I know we have steam left and the starboard burners are functioning—'

'What about pumps?'

'Almost nothing. You could use the cruising and auxiliaries.'

These were duplicates for the small turbine pumps. They were motor driven and used in port. They had comparatively high efficiency, but their capacity was not great enough to meet the demands of the plant at high speeds.

'Any leakage of fuel?'

Bitsios told him the situation as far as he himself knew it – and it was as Tomazos thought: all flooding and damage was on the port side. Because of the list of 10° on that side he must not pump away the limited quantity of fuel available (on the starboard side) and usable for the surviving starboard burners to raise the steam for the long journey to Guam ... (They were nearer to Hong Kong, but had the storm between it and the *Areopagus*.) He would use fuel from the starboard side – 150 tons a day perhaps for three days – and the list should not be much aggravated, particularly if the flooded parts of the port side could be pumped ... There were hours more of typhoon winds yet to inflict alarm. He must never assume the probability of a calm sea ...

Nevertheless, his information was that it was safe to reopen the 23 water-tight doors, and he did this, albeit with misgiving – one heavy rush of water from an undiscovered fracture and the alleyways and lower decks could be flooded in instants. He now instructed Demetropoulos to order the stewards round the cabins.

The Australian surgeon rang him at this moment of decision.

Tomazos said, 'I was about to contact you. How are things?'

'Nikolaos, so bad I haven't time to talk about them. Can

you open the water-tight doors? If only for ten minutes. There must be people trapped and hurt. They'll die without urgent attention.'

'I'm doing that now,' agreed Tomazos. 'And I'm sending stewards to every cabin. I'll get them to bring blankets and towels afterwards. Maybe hot soup and sandwiches if we survive.'

'You think we will?'

'Yes, Daniel, there is a good chance ... Is there anything else?'

'We're a bit short on pain killers and other drugs. And maybe blood ...'

'I'm sorry, I can signal for drugs, but every ship will have fled before the storm. Perhaps an aircraft in a few hours. Send me a list and Barutcu will radio it ... What sort of blood do you need?'

'Any sort.'

'A lot?'

'I think so, Nikolaos.'

'I see ... It may alarm the passengers if I ask for it over the public address system ... Shall I wait half an hour?'

'If you think half an hour will make any difference,' conceded Dempsey. 'And Nikolaos. Get us out of here. Some of these people may die. Others have burns ... They need hospital.'

Despite many interruptions Tomazos was now able to give his attention to the main enemies – the sea and the weather. He took the helm from Yannopoulos, who had been on his feet on this spot for six or seven hours. Now that the *Areopagus* had some power he was able to obtain the feel of the wheel. The weight of the sea and weather was heavy on the starboard side, although the wheel lost resistance at times as the ship heaved in confused waters. In another storm he had once held the wheel against a beam sea for six hours, letting it spin free for ten minutes once an hour so that hydraulic power operation wasn't lost.

There was no question of leaving the *Areopagus* beam on to this sea and wind. The ship would be carried on to rocks if he did. In any case she was rolling very unpleasantly. She was not a safe ship with which to roll, and was likely to become the victim of synchronism. Even a large ship was like a pendulum and had a natural oscillation if set rocking, whether rolling from side to side or pitching bow to stern. It was possible for the waves to strike the ship at the same frequency as the roll – in synchronism – and unless a minor change of course or speed was carried out the vessel might roll wildly until its rail went under. Near this very area – relatively speaking – in 1944 three US destroyers had been steaming near the Philippines and had been caught in a typhoon. A fatal rolling had set in which had become more and more exaggerated until the leaning reached 70° when water had poured down the stacks and all three destroyers had sunk. The *Areopagus* already had a list of 10° and it was very dangerous for the sea to keep her rolling. She might begin to respond to component waves with frequencies that matched their rhythm, that is, to begin to roll just as each wave hit the side of the ship. Under such regular motion roll might build up until it became fatal.

But he could not bring her round, and this was very worrying. He *had* to bring her round. But the rudder had no effect even in the direct race of a screw at the present speed. And the port screw was out of action altogether. He saw that the starboard screw was doing 84 revolutions a minute instead of the normal cruising speed of about 130. This starboard propeller would have little effect in turning the ship's head as it had scarcely any leverage. If anything, the starboard screw would bring the *Areopagus* round to port, with sea and weather behind her, still driving her towards rocks. Reversing the starboard engine might help, but wouldn't be as strong as the high-pressure turbine which drove the ship forward. Further, the 'loose' water was forward and she would dip her bows very severely. With sternway on the ship the rudder, too, would be almost useless.

He wanted her to head into the sea and weather. Any motion forward, or even no motion at all, would then ride the storm, although there was almost as much danger in pitching as in rolling. Waves less than three-quarters as long as the ship would not produce extreme pitching, even if they synchronized with the *Areopagus'* own motion. Ships' hulls had been lengthened to defeat these critical waves, and successfully: such ships had defeated weather and maintained schedules. But here in this typhoon the waves were huge; they dwarfed the liner. Furthermore, to battle against them required exorbitant amounts of fuel and engine power. Tomazos had the fuel, but not much engine power.

Nevertheless, if he did not bring the ship's head round to face the sea she was doomed. And she wouldn't come round ... He knew the power of water and weather. A storm wave eighteen feet high could move ten-ton blocks of stone. Water could erode promontories, curved beaches and cliffs, sometimes overnight. He had read that if the temperature difference between a warm current and the adjacent ocean was 11° Centigrade, every cubic mile of the current would yield heat equal to that obtained by the burning of six million tons of high-quality coal ... Water held in the air was not merely potential precipitation. It was huge latent energy, amassed by evaporating molecules. The energy was released in storms – more than the energy of a 110-kiloton nuclear bomb. The updraught and downdraught inside a thunder head reached hurricane force. In such forces, even spread widely, the *Areopagus* was a speck of dust. Some of the waves she was submitting to were 110 feet high.

His only resource was to drop anchor. It was a terrible risk, for the sea could snap chain ... He decided to let go, not just one – for the *Areopagus* might still be dragged astern – but both. If this failed they could be lost and he would have to consider prompt emergency measures.

Port and starboard anchors were dropped. There was no sensation at all for a long time. And then he realized that the *Areopagus* had come round to the sea.

Tomazos asked Bitsios for all the power he could manage for the starboard engine.

The *Areopagus* rode her anchors. This one engine, with its overheated shaft and eroded propeller, exerted full power to ease the tremendous strain on the cable chains. In the lulls the liner surged forward a little and over-rode the anchors, only to be forced back again with the cables bar taut.

Tomazos attended to other problems, gave orders, spoke on the telephone, but all the time waited in fear for one or both cables to snap.

Once he had time to look at his watch and saw in surprise that six hours had passed, and he felt in faith that they were going to survive.

25

'I HATE you,' screeched Barbara, and it delighted Tornetta, proved fear but with spirit. She went on ranting: 'You're dirty and cruel and selfish.'

Tornetta tittered.

The accusation was, of course, true. It was necessary to diminish the personality of a woman by this mutual degradation. Otherwise she would gain a superior status and would be making demands. They quickly achieved arrogance and would have a man fetching and carrying in no time at all and, further, would sneer of it before others. Ah, yes, it was necessary to knock the superiority out of them; they had their other halves, were masochists, expected to be fouled and beaten. Anything for *love* . . .

He claimed, indifferently, 'You sound like a wife, not a mistress!'

The dancer flinched before this, for she could hardly deny the position of mistress: clothes lay scattered around the bunk, and she herself was nearly naked.

She struck at him and clawed across his nose with long nails before he could quite move his head back. She was tough; she wasn't going to cry. She felt unhappily that her position was far inferior to that of mistress. She had been just a tart. It hurt, inexplicably, because she was not guiltless enough to recognize that she felt dirtied. There had been a long procession of men, but none had made her feel like this. They had seduced her, true, but never despised her. This one held her in contempt even when he was satisfying himself grossly. It was why she had picked a quarrel deliberately.

He caught her wrist and bent it backwards. She had to go with the arm or scream uselessly in pain. She shared the cabin with another girl, Rowena, a tall dancer who was agreeable, tactful, and was now elsewhere, drinking. The soul of heavy-footed discretion. But dim, big and simple. Tornetta had eyed her with obvious approval: a lovely lay for someone...

'You're a ponce,' Barbara panted. 'And a thief. Do you think I don't know?'

Tornetta was not a man who acknowledged guilt, but shock blinked his eyes now. He would have to hurt this one...

He ignored her contempt. It meant nothing. Knowing these things she had still come begging for sex...

'But it was nice, wasn't it?' he mocked as he crushed her with an insolent hand. 'You wriggled. Why did you wriggle? And your belly – that didn't hate me. It rose up like a pudding in the oven.'

He could still smell the musty odour of her body's admission of enjoyment.

'I'll tell them,' she threatened. 'I'll tell them about the money you steal. They'll know what's missing. And I'll show them—'

'What?' he snarled, hurting her now so that sweat boiled out of her face and her breath steamed: she had never known she could be hurt like this. It was agony. Loathing filled her. She hadn't meant it – her evidence was vague anyway, although her instincts were correct: something about cabins and where he was at certain times. And the watch she had been given. It hadn't come from the ship's shop. So what was he doing with a woman's gold watch? One was missing. She'd heard a woman bellyaching. A pious middle-aged Australian. She'd hound Tornetta to the courts. She, Barbara, would give written evidence.

Tornetta read her thoughts.

'Where is it?'

'Ha!' she jeered.

He struck her with a fist, explored her wrists for tactile actualization. He released her and leaped off the bunk. He nearly fell over. God, the sea was bad. She couldn't run to the officers now – she was too naked. He knocked things furiously off the dressing-table. And then he rushed unsteadily into the small bathroom. He knew women's ways. She rose to follow, howling. He saw the watch behind jars of cream and rubbish.

And then there was the resounding crash of steel, tearing itself into slices, and instant darkness, and the tumult was so enormous, instantaneous and total that Tornetta was terrified. Not of the noise or of metal or because he was sent flying a couple of feet into the bathroom bulkhead by immense forces. But because for long moments he believed – he *knew* – that the God of his childhood was seeking vengeance on behalf of Mr Rossi.

That moment passed and he felt sick and emasculated, shivering with an ague. He couldn't think. Water was sloshing about somewhere, and the shower was on. He was standing in the shower? No. He identified the violent spray for what it was and presumed the ship was sinking.

Panic prompted him, the ruthless urge for self-preservation. The watch! It must have been sent flying. All the bottles had broken. He trod on broken glass and mess. Barbara was groaning, and asking for help. Pleading to *him*! Was there no end to the absurdity of women?

He lit a match, then another in haste. He had to find the watch and then get out. She'd never prove anything; she was so vulgar she wasn't even likely to be listened to.

A third match illuminated the gold watch, lying in the bath. Tornetta stuffed it in his pocket and tried to move. It was an effort. He was ill, very sick. He felt very sorry for himself. Life was burdensome. All these problems! The motion of the ship, he realized in darkness, was appalling. Why hadn't he noticed while enjoying the body of the dancer from Aberystwyth? It threw him about now so that just to try to stand was alarming. The liner was doomed. Nothing could survive. Pure panic flamed in him and he stumbled out of the bathroom. He could see nothing. She was groaning. The fool! If he did not see he was not responsible. To hell with her.

Using matches he found his own cabin. He heard people forward of A 145 – which was towards the stern – shouting and screaming. He ignored their distress. He had problems. He was sick. It was serious.

In the cabin Squibb was floundering about with a torch. The Joker had his life-jacket on.

He apologized shakily for what he felt was cowardice – to be dressed up ready to abandon ship.

'We've collided. There was a hell of a bang.'

But Tornetta wasn't interested in Squibb's examination of conscience.

'I am ill,' he said. It was important. 'Very sick.'

To feel ill was new to him, a novel experience. He expected Squibb to be interested, to offer sympathy and advice from long experience.

But Squibb whined sullenly, 'Serve you right. You deserve it.'

Tornetta was hurt. Anger accumulated rapidly. What a heartless little pig this was!

Squibb pressed his advantage. 'You laughed at me when I was so ill. You brought that dirty dancer here. You didn't fetch me a single cup of tea or ask how I was ...'

'That was trivial,' Tornetta justified himself.

He was very bitter. Squibb after all had been ill when other things were normal. That was nothing. It was not important. A man should need no commiseration at such a time. But this, this was different. They might have to abandon ship. He, Tornetta, should be helped, because otherwise he might be lost.

'Trivial, was it?' Squibb argued in resentment. 'You mean you don't give a damn. Let me tell you I was seriously ill.'

'You are a coward,' shouted Tornetta. 'You're dressed up ready to run. You are nothing, a man without testicles.'

He was hot with rage, frustration that such a fool should not see his own unimportance. Suddenly it became necessary and justifiable to hurt Squibb. The pious fool, he didn't know the beginnings of pain ...

'And you're a cheap vulgar barbarian,' stated Squibb.

Tornetta ran at the torch and hit Squibb in the stomach. The torch dropped but didn't go out. It shone on Squibb's shoes.

Squibb folded quickly. He was nothing. He knew little about violence. Tornetta smashed him up almost effortlessly. Only the motion of the ship prevented him from inflicting serious permanent injury. As it was, Squibb soon fell on to the deck and sobbed.

Tornetta took the torch. He opened cases in frantic haste. If the ship was going down he must be on a lifeboat at once, and there was no need to lose all the dollars he had acquired. He threw clothes around, and nearly wept in impatience, finding keys. He stuffed the dollars into one of Squibb's camera cases. All the time Squibb's voice snivelled petulantly: 'You'll be sorry ... I'll complain ... And that dancer ... You'll be punished ... Don't think you can assault people and get away with it ...' The snivelling reminded Tornetta of childhood. Someone – who was it? – who had whined because he couldn't defeat Tornetta, couldn't bear pain ... He, whoever it was, had expected Tornetta to forgo victory on the grounds that it was immoral for the big battalions to win ... Which had been nonsense. The big battalions inevitably won ...

He fastened his life-jacket with difficulty, and was worried that he might lose the camera case slung round his neck. He took it off and wound the strap round and round his wrist.

He left Squibb without a qualm, and fled, ignoring the pious claim that the torch was Squibb's. The big battalions had the *right* to win. It had always been survival of the fittest in Tornetta's world. If Squibb had beaten him into surrender and pleading he would not have expected any quarter – torches left for his comfort, minor qualms of conscience about whose camera case it was ...

He tottered aft to the nearest stairs, holding himself upright by the rail. He had no doubt that the *Areopagus* was doomed, although it would perhaps take time. He could hear screams and shouting and smell burning paint and smoke.

The torch shone on steel nuts. Tornetta was electric with fright. He had taken the wrong direction? No. He realized in dismay that the water-tight doors had been closed and he was trapped on 'A' Deck aft of amidships.

It was, by his own ethics, logical. He was small-fry; it was the ship's officers who were the big battalions here, and it was perfectly reasonable that they should drown him to prolong the life of the ship and others, including themselves ... He saw this instantly: it was what he would have done, and at any subsequent inquiry he would have had his interlocutors in tears of sympathy at his courage and foresight and regard for others. That was the way of the world. He normally accepted it, hypocrisy and fraud, but now he shouted 'Murderers! I shall drown! In the Name of the Perpetual Mother, open the doors ...' And he hammered on steel with his fist and, when that hurt, with the torch.

He was trying to get out. Seconds before Marion Burston had encountered the same steel door and failed to get *in* ...

His feeling of sickness had gone. It had been fear. He did not sit down and wail or expect help, as people like Squibb might do. He remembered something.

He had once opened a door along here, examining the area for possible theft. The door had the words Crew Only painted on it in new white paint. But just beyond in fading paint – perhaps from the original American ownership – was the label Emergency Exit.

Tornetta found this door now and beyond it was a tight spiral of cheap wooden steps, like the servants' backstairs of some mansion. There were no handrails, and the rolling of the *Areopagus* threw him down after he'd ascended three steps. He was hot with rage as well as panic.

The steps went up and up, exhausting him. Maybe they corkscrewed all the way up to the funnels ...

He came out by the ventilator intakes on the aft part of the Parade Deck, and at once saw the *Seattle Doll* split in two and burning, and, here, Greek sailors lowering lifeboats. His mind associated the two things incorrectly: a ship was burning, therefore *this* other ship was fatally wounded, too

... And fire and sparks were certainly pouring out of a funnel and there was the hot lash of smoke and bits of burning oil.

The sea and wind were terrifying, total, a life force, the God of the Old Testament in a rage. Tornetta fell over, knocked out of breath by the onslaught of air. He was immediately cold and wet through. His one hand held grimly on to the case of money. The other caught hold of metal, anything. Blood ran through his fingers where jagged brass cut him. Terror waited everywhere – even in a lifeboat there would be utter terror and cold and illness for hours. But the fear of death was greater and Tornetta ran into the crowd who were fighting to board a lifeboat.

Women were shouting, old men thrashing about with their fists. In the darkness Tornetta went through them easily, crippling three or four with his feet.

The lifeboat swayed outboard and people scattered with cries of terror unheard in the wind. The boat swung back and smashed old heads.

Tornetta had a grip on it now and a foot in the air. The Australian officer was shouting into his face, but frenzy possessed Tornetta. A sailor smashed something on to his hand and Tornetta doubled up and fell, all fingers of the hand broken. He fell over because there was no strength or balance in him. Other people trod on him without hesitation. He kicked at old women and men, rolled clear, was thrown by the motion and wind, but did not die as others did, because he had a rage to survive. He clung to a rail, screaming with fury as much as fear, and as the *Areopagus* dipped, scrambled half to his feet, his surviving hand clutching the rail by the deckhouse.

The pain was trivial in the need for survival. The big battalion had exercised its rights. The torch had gone and after a while he realized that he had let go of the satchel of money.

He wept in bitter frustration.

They had launched the lifeboat. He could see that it was empty. *See?* He could see! Lights had come on! What did it mean? It must mean that the Australian officer had been truthful, and that the purpose of launching the lifeboat was to save others, not the Greeks themselves . . .

Tornetta felt no shame about himself, although he was glad that identification was unlikely.

Light shone through from the lounge on to lifejackets, coats, a few shoes, a hat, and there surely to God, was the cloth satchel full of money?

It teased him as he groped towards it, sliding away from him. In a moment it would be exposed to the greater fury of crosswinds and go overboard.

He fell on it and rolled to the rails. Rolling over his hand caused agony. But he had recovered it, all that money. Squibb could do nothing. There'd be a re-shuffle of cabins. And a lot of shamed faces after all this. Officers weren't going to take much notice of anyone over trivialities like having girls sleeping in your cabin or a bit of a punch-up. They would have so much trouble getting the ship in order and dealing with larger complaints, injuries and compensation they'd be overworked for a fortnight.

He felt sure that the *Areopagus* was going to survive.

Beside him women had collapsed into hysteria. Men were waiting to attempt to crowd into the next boat swung on its davits. But Tornetta now wanted the 'safety' of shelter. He put the strap of the case round his neck and with his one free undamaged hand groped along the rail like a blind man until he came to the door and a confused mob struggling to get out and die.

He collapsed, saturated, on the carpet of the Aegean Lounge, among anxious mothers, weeping children, old men rigid in fright and anxious not to reveal the terrible fear which numbed them. A lot of the passengers were singing and the queer entertainments officer was, as usual, with his mate, Edgar, round the piano.

Tornetta watched them all without pity while he recovered from shock and exhaustion. Pious fools, singing hymns now, as though that would save them.

After a while he felt cold because of the soaking and the pain of his broken fingers, and very sad. A woman stared at him in horror and he saw that his one hand was covered with blood. It was nothing: social justice, as they would have called it in Sicily. Announcements came over the public address system, sometimes without breakdown... After a while Tornetta made his way to the surgery before anyone there would know that to have broken fingers on this night was an injury which proved panic and cowardice and indifference to others...

26

HEAVY chairs had been scattered round the edges of the Lounge for people like Miss Wearne to sit in and watch what they had not the physical strength to do and enjoy. But she was only able to obtain and occupy and sit very upright in a wooden chair, burping mulligatawny and chicken chow mein and taking a glass of beer now because she felt ill at ease. After an hour the diffused lights, the patterns and beams of varied bright colours, were too harsh for her. They flickered and diverged. It was like sitting in some strange diorama full of smoke and people shouting. People dressed in costumes which varied from the bizarre to the crudely vulgar.

Miss Wearne was still a little shocked even after weeks of cruising. Some of the girls pranced about with abandoned energy, itself coarse, in costumes to which they had clearly given much thought on how near naked they could be. They were, as usual, treated with gross equality and contempt by youths sweating heavily in garish shirts. Some of the older Australians and New Zealanders danced with old-fashioned carriage like people in an hotel ballroom, but others were crude with heat and drinking. That awful Mr Ballantyne, she noticed, had collected himself a brassy young woman of about thirty, and was battering at her senses with noisy vulgar flattery as well as alcohol. Miss Wearne liked the days better than the nights aboard the *Areopagus*...

There were three hundred people crushed into the lounge-ballroom. Coffee tables as well as the heavy chairs had been shoved out of the way. Stewards sweated through the mob with trays held high; they, too, were in fancy dress – red jackets with brass buttons, inside which they boiled.

'They're having a good time,' opined the old lady in a comfortable armchair next to Miss Wearne. She coughed in Miss Wearne's face. 'A great time.' Acoustics proved it – the band, shrieks, laughter, cries for the stewards. The woman's cracked parchment skin folded in puzzlement at Miss Wearne's feeble response of 'Yes'.

The vertigo was uncomfortable, but not yet unpleasant. It made Miss Wearne sweat in the face in anticipatory anxiety. Too many people for her tired body and mind to take along the retinae. The kaleidoscope of fierce lights would make anybody dizzy, was perhaps intended to... Was she going to be ill *here*? She had a fear now of being a spectacle, people staring in resentment, their fun interrupted. She had observed that the bulk of passengers weren't interested in those who became sick: they despised them...

Or was this vertiginous uneasiness due to the sea? There was an alteration in the motion quite hard to detect, but there, she was sure of it.

She stood up, in a posture of things recalled, important matters to attend to elsewhere. It didn't fool the other woman. 'Tired?' she inquired, sipping sherry through yellow teeth. 'Going already? I reckon they'll be at it until three this time.'

Miss Wearne ignored her.

On the way out she saw Debbie, chaste in some kind of Oriental flowing gown. The girl's face, heavily made up for once, black and fierce around the doe eyes, was anguished. She took her pleasures bitterly, Miss Wearne decided. She's been hurt again. Miss Wearne was aware that someone was causing the nice girl to be dejected. Debbie could not hide weariness of spirit.

She was dancing with the Deputy Purser, but broke off with apology as she saw Miss Wearne stumbling towards the exit close by. The faces of the orchestra stared coldly in failure.

'Are you all right?'

'Tired,' admitted Miss Wearne.

She was scared of death. It was here somewhere. But this was something she couldn't burden the girl with. She had to identify it and face it alone. It would be very upsetting to witness, she presumed.

'Are you going to rest?'

'Might as well,' acknowledged Miss Wearne. 'It's about time for an old bird like me.'

'I'll see you to the cabin. Excuse me,' Debbie said to Eleftheriadis, who nodded.

'You needn't have done that,' pointed out Miss Wearne, but greatly relieved. 'You must go straight back.'

'What for?' asked Debbie sourly. 'I might as well read a book.'

In the cabin Miss Wearne asked outright, 'What's the matter?'

'Oh, nothing, Miss Wearne.'

'I can't help, but I'd listen. Or perhaps I *can* help. Advice in cold blood, if you follow me ...'

The girl needed advice or consolation, Miss Wearne could see, but was too shy to unburden herself.

'You can say anything,' she prompted.

'I don't know what's the matter with me,' said Debbie. 'It's foolish. A kind of sea-sickness. He's a middle-aged man. But he did say – it's too tentative, Miss Wearne, for you to advise upon.'

'I understand. You suspect something?'

'Exactly. I'm suspicious. But it's absurd and I have no right—'

'You have every right. This man's a bachelor, isn't he?'

Debbie giggled in brief hysteria. 'Yes, but—'

'Then what do you suspect?'

'Oh, I don't know about *that*,' said Debbie, very embarrassed, scarlet in the cheeks.

'Then *what* did he say?'

'That's simple. That he'd take me to this ridiculous ball ...'

'But he's forgotten?'

'I suppose so.'

'He didn't turn up?'

'Worse.'

Miss Wearne probed carefully: 'You can't find him?'

'He's in his cabin.'

'You don't like to fetch him?'

'There's a woman with him.'

'A patient. She'll have gone now . . .'

'No. That woman, Mrs Triffett. She's very neurotic, impertinent, but beautiful, I'm afraid.'

'You *know* she's there? Ring him,' suggested Miss Wearne. 'Joke about it. Say you're suffering from acute melancholia . . . Shall I do it?'

'Oh, no, you mustn't,' Debbie disputed in shock. 'Still, that's a good idea . . .'

She lifted the telephone and asked for Dempsey's cabin. There was a long pause and then the telephone operator inquired, 'Is it urgent? I can use the public address system if you wish.'

'It doesn't matter,' said Debbie in haste, and she put down the phone.

Miss Wearne said gently, 'Not in his cabin?'

'No.'

'Nor the surgery?'

'I didn't bother—'

'Go on back to the ballroom, Debbie. He'll be there. If he comes here—'

'He won't be there.'

'Go and have a look.'

'All right,' said Debbie resignedly.

Miss Wearne cleaned her teeth, undressed and took a pill. They had said that if she was over-excited or dizzy through weariness, to take one and it would calm her, send her to sleep. She hadn't done so before because she'd been afraid. Now she wasn't. She was fatigued. The sea was beginning to toss about. If there was bad weather it would keep her awake in discomfort, and tomorrow would be a day of miserable exhaustion. She did not know the power of the pill, but had confidence in it: she would sleep for hours.

She fell asleep at once... Debbie's face stared at her in pleading. There was nothing she could do for the girl who had been so helpful. There was no one, you see. There never had been. Just my father and my older brother. They knelt at prayer in the sitting-room with mother. Albert read from the Book. Gas-light hissed. And a certain man. Jesus said. Her small hands touched the antimacassar. It was dark green. They'd sold it when Father died, but there it was. Time moved backwards. A dream of monuments and a ship entering a harbour – Salonika? – full of corpses, with its hull streaked with the excrement of the men from Gallipoli, dying of dysentery. A dream moving backwards. She saw Father reading about war, angry with someone, and then the columns of men, caustic, tough, sweating, and the guns lined up. She'd never seen artillery except beside monuments now despised. Five or six pieces of artillery and mules kicking and lines of tents on a hill—

The guns fired—

Miss Wearne gave a cry of shock, and awoke, refreshed by hours of sleep, but the dream was still there, a roaring of wind, and a sound of metal tearing.

She was dizzy, crazily dizzy, and cried out 'Debbie, I'm not well ... I'll have to have the doctor ... Your friend ...'

But she knew she was calling to no one, and the words were fumbled on her lips.

Amidst the noise which had no meaning was a silence which worried her. Debbie's.

'There's a terrible wind,' complained Miss Wearne, but uselessly. Or was it the roaring of illness in her ears?

Her fingers sought the lamp-switch. Illumination would be a comfort. Everything would be seen to be 'normal'. Debbie would be still at the ball.

The switch clicked but no light came on.

Miss Wearne heard shouting somewhere, and it had a note of urgency and demand. Something, she knew now, was terribly wrong. And she wasn't dizzy. It was the sea. They were in a storm of frightening proportions.

A brief pink incandescence illuminated the cabin and she

heard an explosion. The same two or three seconds revealed that there was something wrong with the cabin...

Above her head feet ran along the deck, which was Metaxas... The whole ship exuded alarm; it was possible to breathe panic, absorb it in the agitated belly.

Miss Wearne had a torch. She kept it so that she could go to the lavatory in the middle of the night without disturbing Debbie.

It was there, despite the motion of the ship, on the small shelf which folded right by her side, and which was for library books or ashtrays or cups of tea. She had no recollection of putting the torch there. Perhaps it had lain there for thirty hours or so.

Its narrow beam revealed that things had been thrown about. The cabin was a litter of cases and paper blew about.

Miss Wearne stepped out of her bunk. She was at once half soaked in spray, which was cold, and knocked out of breath by air pressure. Her bare feet trod into an inch of water, which was alarming, although Miss Wearne didn't think in terms of the *Areopagus* sinking, as A Deck was very high above the water.

Lying in the water was Debbie, strangely twisted, and blood floated on the water along with bits of tickets, the sheet which told of the Day's Events, and the Company's maps of Hong Kong, Singapore and Bali, given to each passenger.

Miss Wearne stooped in concern and horror, and her wig fell off and dropped into the water. It did not seem to matter.

Debbie was so tall she filled the cabin, even broken up – this was at once how Miss Wearne considered her. She turned the torch and saw that Debbie's bunk was tilted and the girl had been ejected violently. The bunk was liable to collapse on both of them. Miss Wearne found in surprise – she even had time to feel a pleasure in it – that she was not alarmed. She rang the bell for a steward, but she knew as she rang it that no steward was going to come. Stewards belonged to the normal times. Normality had ended. It mattered less to Miss Wearne, for she had the advantage that she was going to die anyway soon. Her mind was not interested in how *that* took place. It was the girl. She was one of a handful of persons in Miss Wearne's whole lifetime who had shown kindness and love. She had wondered how to ever repay this girl or reciprocate. Now she knew.

But her body's strength did not equal that of her mind. She tried to lift the girl, taking her under the arms, but Debbie groaned and thrashed about in misery.

The surgeon was a mere hundred feet away on the opposite side of the ship.

Miss Wearne lifted the telephone, but was not surprised to find that had failed, too . . .

There was a chair, a cheap thing of cane with a pattern of holes in its seat.

Debbie weighed only eight and a half stone. Miss Wearne sweated away at it. Her own pulse thundered, blood boomed in her head. But finally she accomplished what she intended. She sat the girl on the chair. She didn't know how dangerous this was in view of the bleeding, but was certain that if Debbie wasn't taken to the surgery she'd die. And Miss Wearne knew in grim realism that the surgeon wasn't likely to come *here* . . . He would be busy right now.

She tied the girl in the chair with stockings and a strap, tilted the chair and began to drag it. Debbie hissed with pain.

There was no light in the corridor, but Miss Wearne was undaunted. She could smell smoke and oil and hear shouting and the screams of children. She could do nothing about them. *This* was what she had to do with her frail sick body – drag a chair along a deck which tilted and jolted and heaved and dropped like a high-speed elevator.

Once the chair was dragged away from her by the force of the sea and the slope of the deck, and she would have lost it if she hadn't carried the torch. It meant dragging the thing over the same ground, and Miss Wearne was tiring. It was now her total and only desire – to get the girl to the surgery. She herself was cold and wet, without her wig and dressed only in nightdress, but her concern was so total that she hadn't even considered this indignity.

She had to hold the chair against sideways forces, and when she had gone about fifty feet these broke the chair, quite slowly, so that Debbie was hurt no worse.

Miss Wearne was now in pain herself – a malaise that had no centre, but caused her breathing to rasp, her heart to accelerate and her eyes to fail in their functions at intervals. But so far her body hadn't lost strength and she marvelled at its capacity as she perforce dragged Debbie, ignoring the pressures inflicted by the sea and gravity.

She then found that the water-tight steel door had been closed. It was so frustrating that tears of rage trickled out of her eyes. She collapsed to her knees and then, unable to stop it, sagged on to her ribs, twitching and gasping, lancinating agonies flickering like electrical shocks in her chest and head. All in vain, a pointless love, she thought bitterly. A failure, as usual.

Some lights came on and after a few moments the water-tight door opened. She saw that the girl was in a terrible mess. She stood up and again dragged her, heavier now that she had gone slack into unconsciousness.

Round the corner and sixty feet athwartships she arrived in hell. Many injured people, most of the men almost naked, lay about, groaning, stinking of oil and blood. She could not get into the surgery because of this overflow. No one would take any notice. They rushed about frantically, nurses and some women Miss Wearne recognized as passengers.

Behind Miss Wearne other injured arrived, having crawled or been dragged or carried.

She heard a man's voice say with irritation, 'This one is dead.'

Miss Wearne became callous: she dragged Debbie over the legs of these smashed seamen, and collapsed by the surgery entrance. A cat miaowed and the same man's voice ordered brusquely, 'Get that damn cat out of here.' And Debbie said, slowly but quite coherently, 'Not a cat, Daniel.' The man's locution became discomposed. 'My God! *You!*' he cried, and Miss Wearne knew that she had succeeded. This man was a doctor, the friend whom Debbie loved.

No one took any notice of *her*, wigless and absurd and in

pain. And as soon as the tenacity of purpose was no longer needed Miss Wearne's body succumbed. Pain ripped her to pieces very briefly and in a few seconds she was dead.

But it was as she had wished; better in fact.

She had desired a small obituary, to be known as a tiny news item. Now, instead, she was part of a headline, a thousand times wilder than she could have anticipated. Countries which she, as a geography teacher, retired, had never heard of, through agencies and syndicates, would print and announce the words about a liner in a storm and collision far away ... All around the world in places – some in darkness and some at noon – people would tell of the irony of a woman (now dead) who had won a ticket for a cruise ...

27

'THIS one is dead,' Dempsey said brusquely.

He was frustrated already, and sick with shame, inexplicable self-disgust. There was great relief in the return of light, feeble and flickering though it was. It had been a nightmare attending to Captain Vafiadis. The nurses – Anna and Sophia – had run straight on duty, untidy, no doubt, their hair in disorder (he'd felt Sophia's hair tickling his nostrils as she'd held the torch for him to get at the Master). Sister Eleni and Dr Zafiropoulos turned up soon after. It was ironic. His first casualty, the Master, who had fractured face bones. His pulse was up and his blood pressure down – it was something to worry about, the Captain should be on shore, and all Dempsey could do was treat him for shock. Ridiculous! And ominous. Dempsey presumed that others would be coming ...

The light revealed the dreadful mess – sailors lying there covered with oil, naked or half naked, groaning, brutally gashed, bloody. And passengers beginning to crawl in or be dragged. An old woman in nightdress, wig lost, straining; she'd be blasted by shock presently, get pneumonia ...

A cat miaowed.

'Get that blasted cat out of here,' Dempsey demanded.

A faint child's voice said, quite humorously, but tired, fading, coming through pain : 'Not a cat, Daniel.'

'My God! *You!*' he acknowledged desperately, the shame like a physical weariness weakening him. If. That awful word. If he had considered her, attended to her at this ludicrous fancy dress nonsense instead of – doing what he had done – she wouldn't be here . . .

'How do you know?' he asked automatically, but saw the prone steward, saturated and bloody, grinning, and understood.

'They have oil in their stomachs. Make them vomit,' he ordered Pauline. 'Fingers down the throat. I'll buy you a new pair of shoes,' he promised frivolously. There was at present enough energy and perspective in him for surplus breath. Soon there would be nothing . . .

He was already swamped. He had proposed to Zafiropoulos that the seriously injured should be brought into the surgery and waiting-room and the walking injured should go to his cabin and an ironing-room, both of which were warm. But already he was overcrowded and these men lay at the junction of a corridor which ran athwartships. He had to leave organization to others.

Volunteers were coming. Miss Reidy, who was trained, and a doctor from Adelaide, had already arrived. Of the other two doctors, one had disembarked at Singapore and the other at Hong Kong.

He said to Zafiropoulos, 'Let me deal with this one, Pan . . . A lot of these men have swallowed or inhaled fuel oil. We'll just have to wait until the effects have worn off, and then we can see if they really do have intra-abdominal or intra-thoracic injuries. They might not.'

'I'll sedate them,' said Zafiropoulos, 'when your friend has made them vomit.'

Some of the men were restless in pain. Others were so exhausted they were already asleep.

He phoned the bridge and explained his position to Tomazos.

The operating table was small and narrow, with the general appearance of an enlarged ironing-board. It was a fixture, which was good in a situation in which everything movable or loose could be thrown about. But it spared the patient none of the motions inflicted by the storm. Three times patients fell off. The operating table was at right-angles to the fore-and-aft structure of the hull. When the ship pitched, then, it was bad, but Dempsey could hold his posture with braced and stiffened legs, and opposite, whoever was helping him could do likewise and, in addition, could brace her buttocks against a cupboard. However, the massive sea was on the starboard side, but unfortunately not with consistency. It did unexpected things. Rolling was far worse than pitching, and it lifted Dempsey whole feet above his patient, or caused the liner to hover where he was tensed to expect a dropping sensation. Or the ship shook herself like a wet dog, so that his hand, doing delicate things, was liable to be thrust aside by a great force. To counter all these powerful centrifugal and gravitational forces with his brain and muscles was terribly exhausting, and he had already tired his body in making love to Pauline this night ... In addition he was human enough to be frightened, although working overcame this to a large extent.

One patient slid forward and fell off the table like a sack of coal before either Dempsey or Anna could save him. Indeed, they were themselves sent sprawling. Another fell off sideways but was prevented from falling heavily by Dempsey. Nevertheless, for a patient with *his* injuries to fall at all was fatal, and the only excuse Dempsey had for his conscience was the certainty that this patient would have died anyway.

After that, where the injuries permitted, he strapped the patient to the table.

Others were administering the anaesthetics without the time even to consult Dempsey. This meant that if the others' diagnoses were different appalling errors might be made. But the symptoms and injuries made it all too clear what was the matter with each patient.

Debbie had a ruptured spleen. Her pulse was up, but thin

and weak, too rapid. She was groaning quietly and he pleaded, 'Not long now, Debbie. Nothing too serious. I'll operate on you myself.' He was very anxious about her, conscience stricken, and administered the anaesthetic himself.

'Help me get her on to the table,' he instructed the two Greek nurses.

He cut into her left side under the ribs. It was very difficult to hold himself steady. She could do without the spleen. It only stored blood. He was hopeful for her. It was bloody heroic of that old woman to drag the girl here. He'd go in a while and see—

He saw that the girl's right hand was stained green. It was not important, but caution made him look. And her fingers were clutching tenaciously to the small green jade 'three-legged' ship he'd bought. It was, he recognized bitterly, like himself, a phoney. Dyed.

They were brought in to him fast now, already anaesthetized and slack. Men and women with broken ribs sticking out, or jabbing into their own lungs and causing haemorrhages and suffocation. If blood had got into the lungs he reduced the pressure by draining with a needle. A few ribs had punctured the patients' hearts and these were dead.

Another had a ruptured liver and he could not do much. A plasma drip and leave it alone ... If Guam was more than 1,500 miles away, what did it mean in terms of time? Four days at normal speed. How long in an injured ship? Too long and too far. She wouldn't survive. A helicopter? No. They didn't have that kind of range. Oh, God. How useless I am. Do your best, man. Get on with it and stop snivelling.

Sometimes Eleni was opposite him, sometimes Pauline, or Anna, or Zafiropoulos took his place and he did other things. Once Pauline came, white in the face. 'Oh, Daniel, it's awful.'

He was so concentrated that he was ready to strike her if she became hysterical; he'd believed that she had guts.

'No,' she cried, identifying his mind's content. 'I mean I can smell burning paint.'

Dempsey knew instantly to what she referred – the fortune

teller in Hong Kong. 'Then we'll survive,' he said harshly, 'because she had other things in store for you.'

'Of course,' agreed Pauline simply. 'Sorry, Daniel ... I'm glad to be here to help.'

He understood this, too, and had time to smile grimly at her : here was an end to trivialities, and to phoney despair and to foolishness : here was something real ...

Some faces he recognized and naturally he wanted these to live ... Here was one now, pale as a lily, a sad, beautiful, tired Greek face. It was the mother whose little daughter he and Eleni had fought for. Now he must fight for the child in the womb and for the mother herself. She had been hurt by a blow in the abdomen and the general shaking of the *Areopagus* and was weary because of sea-sickness. He gave her ergotmetrine to shrink the womb, and packed the bleeding vagina with yards of gauze. He did not know where to put her, for he did not wish her to die of shock at what she saw ...

Here was a red-haired girl he'd noticed before, when she'd been cheeky and strutted about wiggling her buttocks and pleased to be stared at ... Now she had broken hip and right arm and was screaming and terrified of pain and the quantities of blood. He was already running short of splints, but there remained a few inflatable ones. He treated her with pain killer, plasma and for shock ...

He stretched himself, stiff after crouching and cutting at flesh, and straining his muscles to keep reasonably still while the *Areopagus* slopped about, dropped sixty feet, went on surviving ... He went to see how Debbie was and to search for the old lady who had dragged her in. The old woman was dead ...

Mr Ballantyne staggered into the surgery, carrying across his shoulders the immense burden of Pybus, who was by no means slack. Pybus must have weighed sixteen stone and Ballantyne had carried him – how far?

'Hi, doc,' greeted Ballantyne breathlessly, indifferent to the blood and chaos. 'He fell down two lots of stairs. Sober at that.'

'Put him down ... Easy does it.'

'He looks a bloody mess,' said Ballantyne frankly – and it was true : Pybus' clothes were stained with blood.

'A broken bone or two,' deduced Dempsey. 'Pretty frightening for the patient though.'

'It's nothing,' whispered Pybus, white-faced but full of interest in his own situation. 'Hey, doc. Remember that bet? Do you reckon you stand a chance of winning it now?'

'Yes, I'm going to win it,' claimed Dempsey. 'Now shut up while I jab you and do nasty things.'

He was too busy to thank Ballantyne. He could hear him talking to Sister Eleni. 'Hey, Sister. You want muscle? Someone to fetch them? Someone to shift these poor bastards?'

Sister Eleni acknowledged with grim humour: 'Yes. Thank you. Would you move those corpses out of the way?'

Now came the men from the engine room, carried by others, or by the entertainers, or young men who had appeared and were anxious to help.

These were grim because they were scalded and burned by oil. He needed blood and telephoned Tomazos again: 'I've got to have it now' – 'Any particular sort?' – 'Group identification is not vitally necessary. I just want to bung it in. Blood Group O universal donors, if you want it to sound good. And I need it in a hurry, Nikolaos.'

He could hear the announcement over the public address system in the distance at once.

The severity of blistering depended on the loss of plasma in the total skin area. It was usually referred to in percentage terms. And these poor devils had been scalded by steam and burnt by flaming oil, and their percentages were often high. He had to leave the burns open and powder with antibiotic, in this case he was fortunate enough to have a fair amount of cicatrin. He couldn't suspend them, which would have been ideal. They could not be protected from shock with blankets. Some of them couldn't even be turned over ... He gave them half a grain of morphine intravenously to start with, and plasma ... None had the mild red skin of first degree burns. They had blistering, which was second degree, and two of them were raw, which was third degree.

Here was a face he recognized, one of these two. He

identified a scar he had stitched a mere ten days ago. The boy who'd gone crazy with jealousy and belted that steward. Had he merited *this*? The boy died as Dempsey's hands approached sympathetically. It was perhaps a mercy for him, but Dempsey wanted, suddenly, to weep ...

He was conscious of eyes staring at him, eyes in a dark face, full of terror and appeal.

'You'll be all right,' he reassured the other boy. 'It'll hurt though, like hell ...'

The boy's eyes followed him about.

'My friend?' he breathed.

'Sorry,' said Dempsey.

He couldn't hide it at such a moment.

Tears watered the dark boy's eyes. He made no noises of protest or pain as Dempsey removed bits of clothing which were sticking, burnt, to his body.

There were many minor injuries to attend to while Dempsey waited for major cases or Zafiropoulos did surgery. People with smashed fingers, scalded arms or legs, shocked people.

Sister Eleni said, 'The old man has died.'

'Which old man?'

'The whisky man with the bad heart.'

Pybus. 'Ah!' was all Dempsey's acknowledgement. What was there to say? He now owed somebody $100. An unknown daughter.

Things were getting a little better inasmuch as they were organized. Towels, blankets, blood, sandwiches ... People to carry stretchers, although these, thank God, were no longer needed. He presumably had all the badly injured now. They'd gone round the cabins – youths and dancers, stewards and volunteers – with stretchers, but had wasted time by first going round the starboard half of the ship ... Dempsey heard announcements, meant to be encouraging, but grimly funny, and sometimes broken off because of the failure of the public address system.

And then the girl began to scream.

Dempsey was attending to someone and he knew which girl it was and he deduced *why*. He hesitated. Sister Eleni rushed up and beseeched earnestly, 'Daniel, I know you're busy . . . I can do that . . . She's disturbing people . . . I can't comfort her.'

'I understand.'

The girl was lying on blankets on the deck, screaming. She had been unconscious when brought here. It was his fault, inexcusable. He knew what she had woken to . . . She stopped howling now, but the sound of terror still came shuddering through her teeth as if she was shivering and her teeth, even clenched, chattered. Dempsey thought that he had never seen anyone so frightened, and he pitied her because it was nearly as bad as she thought it was . . .

'Stop it, girlie,' he ordered.

The wild eyes looked into his and there was faint recognition, and even a respect for medicine, doctors, authority.

She swallowed and gulped and said shakily with effort, 'I've lost my legs. There's nothing there.'

She was so frightened it even lashed him a little and he wasn't certain what to do. But he stroked her face gently with a hand spotted with blood.

'You poor girl. But it's not that bad. Your legs are still there. Touch them, girlie.'

She believed him without doing this.

'But they won't work.'

Dempsey looked into the attractive eyes above the hawked nose. 'It's tough, girlie. Your nerves are crushed, I think,' he lied. She couldn't at present take what he had to tell her. 'If it'd been higher up your lungs wouldn't have worked and we don't have an iron lung here so you'd have been a gonner. What's your name?'

Very reluctantly – because she was now ashamed – she told him: 'Stella.'

'You're going to be all right, Stella. More or less.'

'God hates me,' she whispered with simple finality.

He marvelled at the way the human animal could stand anything if the spirit was intact, but went to pieces otherwise. He knew this was enormously important to the girl, might even decide the physical result. Mumbo jumbo? Ridiculous? Or incredible, beautiful, a proof of something?

He was stirred for all that. If there was a God He was too subtle for Daniel Dempsey, and too apparently callous. But he had days when he knew he had failed, not God ...

'Why should God hate you?' he asked outright. 'And not me?'

'I'm ashamed. I know He does.'

'Nonsense!' barked Dempsey, forthright, almost frivolous. 'On this ship lots of people have been hurt, burned, smashed up and even killed. Because they're guilty of human sins? One is an unborn baby, who may not survive. You think this opera was laid on to punish *you*? The vanity of you! Does it hurt?'

She stared at him.

'Not too much.'

'Well, then. Don't be ashamed any more, Stella. I shouldn't think you've been any more wicked than I have since we left Australia! You can start again, can't you? I'm going to ...'

She asked, oddly, 'Can I listen to the radio?'

'When we can find one.'

'I want my Mum and Dad,' she pleaded.

'As soon as we can,' he promised.

Someone said, 'There's a cup of tea ready, doctor.'

'I could use it,' he agreed.

He leaned against a cupboard, now emptied completely of instruments except for one drill. Good God! he thought, for there had been thirty pieces in there. Have we done that much? What's the time?'

Seven hours had passed since the collision. The *Areopagus* still pitched and heaved. He presumed that she would survive. That was something.

Pauline came and stood by his side.

'Tired?' he asked.

'Yes.'

'So'm I. But we're winning, Pauline. It's nearly over for us.'

She said shakily, weeping, 'Daniel, my dear—'

Dempsey went hot in shock, identifying her terror.

'What's the matter?'

'I'm not joking,' she insisted very earnestly. 'I'm not clowning this time ... But I can't seem to do anything with my left arm or leg ... And I've got a cold,' she concluded.

He saw the spinal fluid running out of her nose, and knew in fear that he would have to use that drill.

'Oh, Christ,' he protested in the anxiety he couldn't hide. 'Can you *see?*'

'I'm so tired I can't see properly ... It's peculiar. Double, I think.'

'Look at me.'

'That's a pleasure.'

He saw that her pupils were unequal in size.

'You love to frighten me, don't you, Mrs Triffett?'

'Am I a phoney?'

'Did you fall?'

'You bet I did! When we'd – finished – I got dressed, remember? And I was thrown when the big bang ... I cried but I didn't tell you ...'

'What did you hurt?'

'My head. But it wasn't bleeding or anything and the pain went.'

'Pauline, you've hurt yourself.'

'But how?'

'Intercranially.'

'Big nasty word.'

'Inside your silly lovely head. You hurt yourself on the right-hand side, yes?'

'How did you know?'

'I'm going to have to operate. There's pressure inside your head due to bleeding.'

'Is it serious? You look worried.'

'If it isn't done it would soon be serious.'

'This is a funny cruise, Daniel Dempsey.'

'I'm satisfied with it.'

'Will it make me ugly?'

'Not a hope!' he told her. 'I'll look after you.'

She said, 'I'll agree to that ... What will you do to me?'

He told her, evasively, 'I'll give you an anaesthetic and you'll be out for a few hours. That's all you'll ever know.'

'You mean that's all you're prepared to tell me?'

'I shall operate myself.'

'You look tired, Daniel, but I wouldn't have anyone else.'

Presently he watched her slip into unconsciousness, and it was as if he'd never seen such a thing before.

They were running short of antibiotics. He hoped that they had something else as well as penicillin, which did not get across the blood stream into the spinal fluid. There was great danger of infection, although she had not broken her ear-drum, which often happened in this type of accident and made the area susceptible to meningitis.

He worked with Sister Eleni, cursing unashamedly aloud as the liner still did its best to cope with the sea.

An hour went by like ten minutes. When he had finished he was wrung dry, but Pauline was safe. It was incredible that the white unconscious face should be the same one which, not many hours ago, had stared into his, shameless, loving what he did...

Sister Eleni went to answer the telephone. Why the hell, he wondered, doesn't someone else do that?

She returned and looked round the surgery strangely – at the chaos of cardboard boxes, emptied hurriedly, cylinders lying about, wedged with books, at blood...

Dempsey said brusquely, 'For Christ's sake, Eleni, stop fidgeting.'

'There was a telephone call.'

'I don't give a damn. To hell with telephone calls.'

'From Nikolaos.'

'Oh,' he qualified.

'He says that the barometer is going up rapidly.'

Dempsey looked at the head under his care. What would his patients and staff say in Sydney when this cheeky ridiculous thing became his wife? He smiled at the sad witty face of the Greek Sister. She still didn't approve of Pauline, and he acknowledged humbly, 'Thanks be to God.'

'Not bad,' suggested Sister Eleni, staring round again, and red in the eyes, 'for a Panamanian ship run by a lot of phoney dirty Greeks?'

'Not bad at all,' he conceded.

He went to see who was alive and dead.

Debbie still eyed him, he noticed, in that absurd manner.

'Thank you,' she said, 'for saving me.'

'Don't thank me,' he told her. 'Thank the old lady in your cabin. I didn't fetch you. I'd forgotten you, Debbie, for which I'm very sorry.'

The confession interested her. 'You can't think of everything,' she suggested.

The girl Stella's parents were coming away solemnly. They looked like people who'd been kicked in the stomach. Dempsey was tired. They'd have to sort it out themselves ... The girl was unconscious.

Her father asked, 'It's very serious, isn't it?'

Dempsey said, 'Yes.'

'What did she break?'

'Her lower spine. I'm sorry,' Dempsey said, 'that I can't put it better or give you more pleasant news.'

'What does that mean?' the mother inquired, but she knew, Dempsey could see. It had some bitter attraction to hear it aloud.

'It means she's lost the use of both legs.'

'You mean,' probed the father, 'that she's become a paraplegic?'

'Yes.'

The mother began to shake and tremble. The tears seemed to come from somewhere very deep, some other anxiety which had been subdued for a long time. Oddly, she clung to her husband in desperate apology and pleaded, 'I'm sorry, Mike. Forgive me. I love you.'

The girl's father touched his wife's head with great tenderness.

'Please,' Dempsey requested, prodding them with the flat of his hand in tough sympathy. 'Go somewhere else. I've had a bellyful.'

The woman didn't even see Dempsey. 'You know what I could do with, Mike? I could do with a drink.'

Her husband gave a brief bitter laugh. 'I could use one myself.'

They didn't seem hysterical, so Dempsey, attracted by the

idea, said, 'I shouldn't think the bars are open! It's six in the morning! Have some brandy. I'll join you...'

He poured it out, half a tumblerful each.

'The sea's calming down,' the man said.

'Stella asked for you,' Dempsey said. 'Sorry. I should have told you. She wanted to listen to the radio and she wanted her Mum and Dad.'

They stared at him.

'She doesn't know what's happened,' suggested the mother.

'Oh, yes, I'm quite sure she knows what's happened,' Dempsey opined.

'She's a wonderful kid,' the father said.

'You know what I want, Mike?' the woman asked.

The man shook his head.

'I want to go back,' the woman told him.

'I'll drink to that,' the man agreed. 'But not by bloody ship, kid...'

28

TOMAZOS shaved for the first time in thirty-six hours, and put on a fresh shirt. It was just possible that soon he might be able to have a few hours' sleep.

The sky was blue and the sea scarcely more than choppy. The *Areopagus* limped along at a steady ten knots with a list reduced to 5°.

He went down to the Parade Deck and into the Aegean Lounge, where many of the passengers had gathered, as requested. Demetropoulos, as immaculate as ever, joined him with Eleftheriadis at the entrance.

There was a buzz of excitement and curiosity and even laughter as the three of them made their way to the dais and the piano which leaned now because of a broken leg. The smashed chairs, glasses, torn curtains, blood and vomit had long since been cleared; only the atmosphere of recent events hovered...

As Tomazos turned to address them the passengers began to cheer him. It went on for a long time and they meant it and he was moved.

Tomazos then said, 'That was kind of you . . . But let us truly give thanks to God. All sailors do this . . .'

They were willing and eager to do so. He viewed them with affection and cynicism. He had heard of the way they had behaved. They lived from one year's end to the other without God, most of them. But goodness, how hard they'd prayed during the hours of peril! And many had panicked and done shameful things, or done nothing. Now, shaken, almost killed by nature and bad luck, they were grateful, penitent, wished to expiate. But in a few days or weeks, back in the environment of money and words, where anything could be proved, the feeling of gratitude would pass and they – with others urging them on – would consider how to make a profit. They'd remember their views about the lifeboats corroded in the davits; the oxygen cylinders rolling about; they'd think of many things which they did not think of now. Complaints and justifications would pour into the Company's office along with their claims for compensation.

Meanwhile, here and now, they were in the comparatively safe and final half of a drama. American destroyers steamed alongside. Aircraft occasionally flew overhead. One had dropped drugs. The galleys and bars were functioning again. They were garrulous in relief. Ahead lay the excitement of talking to journalists, relations and friends, a lifetime of conversational material – nothing would ever better their dialogue fillip: 'When we were on the *Areopagus* . . .' Gradually their own confused parts in the storm and collision would become magnified . . . A few, more shaken than they knew, would in the weeks and months ahead, have strange illnesses – dreams and claustrophobia which would send them running into the garden, sweating and weeping, in the middle of the afternoon, or wake them in the night and send them downstairs searching for drugs.

Here, however, they responded to the situation with good humour.

Tomazos, too, felt that mild humour would please them.

'Once again,' he acknowledged, 'the *Areopagus* has fallen behind schedule—'

They roared with laughter and applauded.

'We'll be in Guam,' Tomazos told them, 'the day after tomorrow. All being well.'

They thought this qualification funny, too.

Tomazos informed them : 'We're on one engine room, but it is in perfect condition . . . Captain Vafiadis, as you know, was injured in the collision, but sends his blessings and apologies to you all . . . I know,' Tomazos continued after some applause, 'that you all wish to go on with this cruise—'

Subdued laughter.

'—but the *Areopagus* is bound to be under repair for some time in Guam. The Company is therefore making arrangements for you to fly to San Francisco and join another ship – of this line, I'm glad to say. Alternatively, we will fly you to wherever your ticket says, and perhaps elsewhere if this unfortunate situation has caused you or your relations inconvenience or anxiety . . . The Chief Purser and his assistant will be here throughout the day to note your intentions . . . If anyone wishes to ask questions about this ship I am here for another hour . . .'

They were a little shy of him, but their own situation fascinated them, and twenty or thirty – anxious, it seemed, to acquire information to authenticate gossip – questioned him for the whole hour, and listened in absorbed interest to his perspective of what had happened.

One of them brought him a drink of whisky.

'Here's to you,' the man insisted cheerfully.

But Tomazos refused, pleading, 'Sorry, but I'm on duty, and have a mountain of things to attend to.'

He had not felt sorry for himself for the same thirty-six hours and did not suppose he ever would again.

There was an oil fire burning on Guam, and long before they saw land the passengers could see the thick black column of smoke rising into the hot blue sky. The sea was that of the Company's brochures : calm and as blue as paint.

Gradually the island came into view, low green hills, dusty

in the heat, palm trees limp in still air, a concrete harbour entrance.

'Port 20,' Tomazos ordered and the *Areopagus* swept round in a perfect approach. It was most undesirable to be seen approaching a harbour entrance leaving a cautious zig-zag wake behind the ship. Despite its present weaknesses the liner came round leaving an unhesitating arc. Someone, Tomazos saw, was by a lighthouse filming the arrival.

He took two tugs just outside the harbour. It would have been possible to enter Guam without tugs at all, but he did so in consideration of his passengers, and because he was not certain of the strength of the bows. Each tug – one to port and one to starboard – secured its towing hawser abaft the most obvious area of damage.

They entered the large harbour and proceeded slowly past five nuclear submarines, packed alongside each other like tinned herrings. There were at least a dozen American destroyers and cruisers in the harbour, and a space tracking ship, with its enormous white dish, and all of these which had steam up blew a welcome with sirens.

It was always an exciting moment putting one of the Company's liners alongside a mole or jetty. The *Areopagus* was, after all, a big ship. It seemed easy and tedious to the passengers, but to the captain or officer of the watch it was a challenge. Conditions, even in an 'easy' harbour such as Guam, were never the same as last time. The wind would be blowing from a different quarter, or half a gale, or, as now, not at all. Any current might be setting a different way. Even the depth of water in different harbours of the world made a difference, for the screws could not exert their full propulsive effort in shallow water. And as speed dropped off the effectiveness of the rudder diminished until the point was reached when the ship lost steerage way and no longer answered the helm.

The passengers lined the rail in silence, impressed perhaps, or aware of what might have been their destiny. Ahead by water storage tanks and buildings was a crowd. And a band was playing. The sound of music concussed the morning air and it was impossible not to be stirred. People were waving and cheering, standing on automobiles to do so. TV cameras were at work.

Tomazos took a third tug at the stern for the actual going alongside and berthed with infinite caution starboard side to the harbour. 'Finished with engines' he telegraphed as the head and stern lines, breasts and springs were run out to the bollards. He wondered if the *Areopagus* would ever sail again.

The military band, he was able to notice now, was playing 'There's Nothing Like a Dame'. Because the American Army liked girls? No. They were attributing fine female characteristics to the *Areopagus*. He was touched...

The gangways went down and at once people swarmed aboard. It was impossible to stop them or turn away this American expression of emotion. Among them were stretcher bearers, US Navy surgeons, sailors, newsmen, local people, and, of course, insurance assessors, local officials and two men from the Company. A TV team set itself up on deck and without authority began questioning passengers. They even questioned officers if they could. Tomazos, taking a party round to view damage and to talk to Captain Vafiadis, heard a TV man ask Mollon, 'Can you tell me, in depth, of your emotive reactions in the stress?' Mollon laughed and said, 'Sure. I was bloody scared.' A pressman inquired cynically, 'Is this thing insured?'

It went on for hours. Tomazos had to take the Company's representatives and the insurance men to lunch and go on talking about the log, documents, when was the radio last tested? The lifeboats? Boiler tests? Then *why* in his opinion did this or that happen? When had he first heard of a possible storm? Who decided to continue on that course? These were difficult questions to answer for one who wished to remain loyal to Captain Vafiadis. They invited the Chief Engineer up to the bridge in the afternoon and attempted to take him apart. But Bitsios was cynical and bitter and asked searching counter-questions which made their faces red and angered them.

Halfway through the hot tiresome afternoon a steward whispered in Tomazos' ear: 'There's a lady to see you, sir.'

Tomazos was startled.

'Where?'

'On the Parade Deck, starboard side forward.'

He thought it must be Elaine, and he hurried to see her, his mind in minor tumult. And it was her, standing by the rail. Typically she was looking the other way, not bothered as some relations obviously were. Elaine never forgot to be poised. Only once . . .

She turned as he was very near, as if she had some special instinct reserved for beautiful women. Other women might turn too soon and have time to lose their expression, to allow it to freeze or sag. Not Elaine. She was perfectly dressed, as if Guam had been a place she'd been about to visit anyway.

'Nikolaos!' she greeted.

She allowed herself to be kissed somewhere below the chin but above the throat.

'I didn't expect to see you, Elaine,' Tomazos admitted frankly.

'I was very frightened for you. It was on the TV news and the radio—'

'Did you fly here?'

'Of course. They said the *Areopagus* was making for Guam. The kids were fascinated. They never had any doubt at all, of course.'

'How are they?'

'Oh, they're all right.'

'And you, Elaine?'

'I'm fine; just the same as ever.'

But this, of course, was not so.

'I'm glad,' he said.

'Will they promote you?'

He laughed. 'I hardly think so! There will be Inquiries for *years*!'

'But you brought her safely back—'

'I was not looking for reward. It could have been done by any officer. We all contributed.'

'I can see where the fire burned the funnel and superstructure.'

'Yes, that was alarming, although the fire in the hair-dressing saloon was perhaps more dangerous.'

'What will you do now?'

'I don't know. Eat and catch up with sleep, I hope!'

'I'm staying at the Palm Leaves,' Elaine told him.

She was perplexed when he did not respond. She felt she had conceded more than enough. She refused to be abject because she'd never been abject. Nor apologetic. The gesture of flying thousands of miles was in itself, surely, sufficient apology?

She had no subtlety at all. She had come and that was enough. There was no penitence or remorse. Only a very beautiful woman could expect to get away with such arrogance.

It was touching and it might have been enough, but he had been close enough to death to know that it wasn't. Charm, he knew, soon deteriorated to hypocrisy. He had suffered the misery of her unfaithfulness and had recovered. She had been lost in the storm. He wished her no harm, but she was now a stranger, albeit attractive.

His eyes looked over the rail and he saw something which startled him.

'Excuse me,' he said.

Elaine blinked in unexpectation, stiffened in shock and coloured with anger. But he had gone before she could manifest her resentment, and she could see him pushing past people and going down the gangway in urgency. She had come on impulse, in pride, and now regretted it.

She saw that he was on the dockside, talking to somebody else. Christ, how *rude*! She'd come all that way and he considered the ridiculous ship more important than—

Then she saw that it was a young woman, a Greek in some absurd uniform . . .

Tomazos greeted her with pleasure, 'Hello, Kristina. Nice of you to come. I am glad to see you,' he acknowledged outright.

Kristina blushed, which was absurd, and said in haste, 'That pleases me.' She moved her feet about and her hands fidgeted with an airline bag in agitation. 'How are you?' she asked.

'Sober,' he told her, smiling. 'I've given up drinking. The posture did not suit me . . . How's the airline?'

'Very understanding,' Kristina told him. She paused and then asked 'Will the *Areopagus* ever sail again?'

'I'm not sure,' Tomazos said. 'The Company is thinking of acquiring a South African liner which has come on the market. It has stabilizers and bow-thrusts, everything.'

'Do you think,' Kristina began to inquire, 'that there's any chance—?'

'Oh, yes,' Tomazos said with certainty. 'I'm sure there is . . .'

29

TORNETTA looked cautiously out of the porthole. He was in a luxurious cabin on Delphi Deck. The Brother had insisted. There had been some talk of whether Squibb should come, too, but Tornetta had conveyed it, very delicately, that Squibb was not only a boor. He was not a gentleman. Alas, he was a coward. He, Tornetta, hinted at disgraceful cowardice and an ugly scene in the cabin, and the Brother, who had heard rumours of such things, nodded sagely. He was a do-gooder, but inevitably full of curiosity. He had to have facts in order to do good. Tornetta did not like supplying facts. However, Mr Brook – which was the man's name – spent much of the three days on do-good committees with others. They sat at tables in the Lounge and tirelessly noted passengers' complaints and financial losses. He consulted with Demetropoulos, but got little satisfaction out of the Chief Purser, whose English had suddenly deteriorated.

Mr Brook retired to bed at about ten, with a ritual as irritating as Squibb's. He talked in the darkness, and Tornetta was bored into fury which he could not express. But

Mr Brook was 'safe', and Tornetta accommodated him with pleasantries, lies and care.

He was away now, talking to the Company's representatives, staking his claim of importance and authority on behalf of the passengers, very polite but quite ruthless and insistent.

Other passengers had fled from the *Areopagus* as fast as they could, and with their customary selfishness had fought for first position on the buses to the hotel or Boeing or whatever it might be. But an irritating number of people hung about. Tornetta had kept well out of the way of journalists and TV cameras. He wanted to vanish without giving his name to anyone.

It irritated him enormously. What did they all *do*, these people standing in the sun? What was there to talk about so endlessly?

These two, for instance. An American in shirt sleeves and one of the engine-room crew. They stood by a water tower and gossiped idly. An hour went by. Tornetta seethed with anxious fear. Soon Brook would be back and he'd be committed to some damn nonsense. It had been very difficult not to become involved in the man's do-good work, become a committee member. Tornetta did not want to lose goodwill or the status of gentleman into which the fool had put him on account of his 'friendship' with Mr Rossi. He had had to claim agony in his hand and utter exhaustion.

Tornetta had not seen Barbara, but he had observed Squibb an hour ago, loaded with his cameras and cases, staggering with others to a bus. Some girls had been waiting at the foot of the gangway to hand to each passenger who descended a plaited palm hat, green and fresh from local trees. Squibb had thrown his cap away to put on the green hat with a dull joke. He was indestructible . . .

A large American sedan stopped a hundred yards away and Tornetta saw two men stroll towards the ship. A girl ran after them and strode with them. The trio hesitated and talked to someone at the foot of the gangway. This man shook his head vaguely.

The three began to walk up and down slowly, chattering.

le 13. Socioracial Distribution of the Population of Cochabamba Province, by Partido, 1788

	Total		*Socioracial Category*					
tido	*Number*	*Percent*	*Spanish*	*Mestizo*	*Cholo*[a]	*Indian*	*Mulatto*	*Black*
:habamba (Cercado)[b]	22,305	17.8	6,368	12,980	0	1,182	1,600	175
aba	7,614	6.1	1,249	2,290	0	3,805	269	1
acarí	26,937	21.5	3,277	6,280	1,597	14,770	996	17
za	37,615	30.0	6,682	12,192	0	16,355	2,366	20
ue	22,137	17.7	1,238	3,936	1,286	15,158	496	23
paya	8,637	6.9	1,275	1,493	0	5,620	247	2
'otal								
umber	125,245		20,089	39,171	2,883	56,890	5,974	238
ercentage								
total		100.0	16.0	31.3	2.3	45.4	4.8	0.2

rce: Viedma, "Descripción geográfica," AGN, Sala 9, Intendencia, 5.8.5, Aug. 10, 1793. This is the original manu-
ɔt on which the subsequent Bolivian publication was based. As Sánchez-Albornoz has pointed out (personal com-
ıication and *Indios y tributos*, 167), several of the population figures given in the manuscript were printed incor-
y in the published Bolivian version.
ficially defined as persons of one-quarter "white ancestry."
e Cercado was the district of the provincial capital—i.e., the city of Cochabamba and its environs.

acculturative pressures in this region. Cochabamba had a larger proportion of real or alleged mestizos—nearly one-third of the population—than most other provinces of Peru. Less than half of the province's inhabitants were classified as Indians, even by Viedma, who, as intendant was intent upon increasing tribute revenue. By way of comparison, about 21 percent of the population of the entire viceroyalty was mestizo and about 60 percent, Indian.[7] Acculturative influences were most marked in the Cercado district of Cochabamba proper, where mestizos outnumbered Indians by more than ten to one, and in the valley of Cliza, where there were about three-quarters as many mestizos as there were Indians. Some 25,000 mestizos (nearly two-thirds of all the mestizos in the province) lived in these two partidos, and so did about two-thirds of the province's 20,000 Spaniards. Large numbers of Indians, on the other hand, were found in the western river valley of Arque and the partido of Tapacarí. Of those Indians who lived on Spanish rural properties or in towns outside the jurisdiction of the five pueblo reales, about 60 percent lived in the Spanish parishes of the three central valleys.

The Cercado

The town of Cochabamba, with its surroundings, was still the province's center of power and commerce in the late eighteenth cen-

7 Ibid.

tury, even though it was not the largest district in population. It was the provincial capital, nesting in the rich alluvial plain that received the waters from the two higher valleys of Sacaba and Cliza and from the northern and western quebradas of the Valle Bajo. Situated at an altitude of 8,200 feet, the city of Cochabamba and its hinterlands were surrounded in the west and north by the Cordillera Oriental and the towering peaks of Tunari, whose snows fed the volcanic lakes and streams that irrigated the bottomlands and cooled them during the summer months of November through January. To the east of the city rose the small mountain chain of San Pedro, separating the Valle Bajo from the valley of Sacaba. Low-lying hills to the south also cut Cochabamba off from the higher valley of Cliza. The city was strategically situated at the axis of the three central valleys connected by two narrow corridors—one leading to Sacaba and the frontiers beyond, the other leading to the vast, open valley of Cliza and points southeast.

The climate and the drainage by mountain streams helped make the Valle Bajo one of the richest arable areas in Alto Perú. Sandy, rocky soil, poor in organic materials, was found in higher parts of the valley, especially at the base of the northern cordillera, but in the central parts of the valley, alluvial deposits and ravines left by torrents and flooding after the rainy season were high in organic nutrients. The alluvial soil, with low levels of salinity, gave the highest crop yields in the valley. Agrarian studies of the Valle Bajo in the twentieth century show that in this valley, 70 percent of flat cultivable land were irrigated (though only 20 percent of all valley land had an abundant supply of water).[8] The evidence of agricultural conditions in the eighteenth century is, of course, less clear-cut. Both Paula Sanz and Viedma alluded to the lands of the Cercado as the richest in the province. "Extensive irrigation allows [cultivators] to plant vegetables, strawberries and fruit trees, and fodder in great abundance," Viedma observed in 1788.[9] Maize and wheat were also cultivated on irrigated land in the district, though many farmers allocated drier, less fertile lands to their wheat and potato crops. Yet despite relatively high yields, agrarian enterprises in the Cercado district provided a small portion of the region's grain production. The Cercado had 18 percent of the province's total population and yet

8 Carlos Camacho Saa, *Minifundia, Productivity, and Land Reform* (Madison, Wis.: Land Tenure Center, 1966), 16.

9 Viedma, *Descripción geográfica*, 46.

produced only about 8 percent of all its tithed grain.[10] Perhaps many cultivators devoted themselves to horticultural and other crops that were not tithed, or perhaps the Cercado's urban concentration left relatively little room for agrarian activities.

Viedma reported that the Cercado boasted fourteen large haciendas, "which resemble small villages inhabited by Indians and mestizos who till the soil of their rancherías as tenants of the landowners who possess them."[11] He was probably referring to the largest haciendas in the city's immediate environs—haciendas such as Calacala, with 34 adult Indian males; Queruqueru, with 34; Sivingani, with 21; Caracoto, with 39 tributary families; and the enormous Santa Vela Cruz y Tamborada estate, with 112 tributaries in 1786. These were surrounded by smaller holdings, listed as *pertenencias*, which supported only two or three Indian families and perhaps a few other peasants who were not registered in the tribute system.[12]

Not all the Indians resided on haciendas, however. According to the 1802 padrón, about a thousand of them lived in poor urban barrios, such as Colpapampa, Caracota, and the hillside of San Sebastián, or outside of town, on the Pampa de las Carreras, for example.[13] Many Indians leased plots of land from the monasteries in order to grow their own food. Others worked as domestic servants, craftsmen, or traders. Many Indian and mestizo men and women were self-employed or did piecework, spinning and weaving rustic cotton textiles. Viedma wrote that "in the city [of Cochabamba] and many towns throughout the province, [people] manufacture the ordinary cotton cloth that they call *tocuyos* for local consumption and for

10 Average tithes collected during the five-year period from 1806 to 1810 provide a rough guidepost to the relative magnitudes of grain production among the different partidos (excluding the pueblos reales, which did not pay full tithes). In the Spanish valley zone, for example, there was a considerable difference between the amounts of cereal produced in the Cercado district and the Cliza valley. While Cliza was drier in parts than the eastern end of the Valle Bajo, the district produced significantly more grain than did the smaller, more densely populated Cercado area.

11 Viedma, *Descripción geográfica*, 45.

12 AGN, Sala 13, Padrones, 18.2.1, Leg. 46 (1786-1787), ff. 104v.-106v., and 18.3.3, Leg. 53 (1802). Whereas Viedma focused his attention on the more opulent estates, tribute collectors inventoried large and small properties alike, in search of tributaries. The 1802 padrón, for example, listed thirty-one rural properties in the Cercado where tributaries lived and worked.

13 AGN, Sala 13, Padrones, 18.3.3, Leg. 53 (1802), f. 212.

export to the highlands, Tucumán, and even Buenos Aires.[14] The 1801 census listed one cloth factory in Cochabamba where twenty-four adult men and thirty-five adult married women operated the treadle looms and spinning wheels.[15]

Though these Indians were assimilated into urban life, engaging in all kinds of commercial pursuits and sometimes seeking opportunities to shed their ethnic identity and free themselves of tribute dues, many members of the urban plebe never learned to speak Spanish. Viedma observed that the urban poor of Cochabamba spoke no other language than Quechua, and he expressed concern that Quechua was seeping into the speech of "respectable women."[16] This was to be expected, since these women dealt directly with servants and with the market women every day of their lives. The large influx of urban or semiurban Indians and mestizos would inevitably affect European culture, to the consternation of this erudite and proud Spaniard. Yet the poor urban dwellers of Cochabamba did not constitute a homogeneous acculturated group that had adopted and diluted the norms and customs of the dominant class. Many natives clung to fragments of their own culture in the midst of urban life. In the very heart of the Cercado district, for example, parcels of land called *yncacollos* still belonged to the "comunidad de yndios de Tapacarí y Capinota," according to the 1802 census.[17]

The concentration of town dwellers in the Cercado made it the largest commercial center in the region. According to Paula Sanz, "there are many prosperous vecinos, food is abundant, and all kinds of cloth are traded here."[18] Viedma concurred in his report: "You can find all the necessities of life in the plaza every day of the week; food is very moderately priced, including meat and bread and all kinds of vegetables, fruits, and fowl. . . . From distant provinces, they bring in salt, dried fish, wines, aguardientes, and sugar."[19] But the intendant pointed out that the merchants imported very little wine (in contrast, it might be added, to Potosí's enormous import trade in spirits) because of the peculiar passion for the chicha which local women distilled from maize. Viedma seemed scandalized by the volume of

14 Viedma, *Descripción geográfica*, 47.

15 AGN, Sala 13, Padrones, 18.3.3, Leg. 53 (1802), f. 212.

16 Viedma, *Descripción geográfica*, 46.

17 AGN, Sala Padrones, 18.3.3, Leg. 53 (1802), f. 212.

18 "Descripción de Cochabamba," f. 2.

19 Viedma, *Descripción geográfica*, 46.

consumption of this alcoholic drink. He estimated that, each year, 200,000 fanegas of maize were turned into chicha and drunk by the "vulgar" and even by the "decent" people in the region.[20]

The Partido of Tapacarí

Not far west of the city of Cochabamba lay the much smaller Spanish parish of Quillacollo. It was bordered on the north by the pueblos reales of El Paso and Sipesipe and on the south by serranía. The parish of Quillacollo was in the partido of Tapacarí; it occupied most of the Valle Bajo, except for the Cercado and the western ravine and highlands of the pueblo real of Tapacarí. It was the main parish of haciendas and the westernmost extension of legal Spanish land occupation. As such, it may be contrasted with the town of San Augustín de Tapacarí, where few Spaniards lived. In his study of the partido of Tapacarí, Sánchez-Albornoz describes San Augustín and Quillacollo as two poles, one Indian and the other Spanish, competing for land and labor.[21] In geographic and commercial terms, however, Quillacollo was more oriented to the eastern end of the valley than to the western. It lay along the royal highway that connected the river valleys of Arque and the altiplano to the capital city and points east. Although Quillacollo had its own market on Sundays, the parish sent some of its grain surpluses to Cochabamba, Arque, and Oruro.[22] Textiles and agriculture occupied most of its laborers. Viedma mentioned that "no other town [in the province] dedicated itself as much to cloth weaving." He estimated that five hundred cholos and mestizos were engaged in this craft as artisans or wage workers in the factory owned by Pedro del Cerro, which made bayeta and ordinary cloth.[23]

20 Ibid., 47. The consumption of chicha gave much of the stimulus to the cultivation of maize. Viedma may have exaggerated the volume of chicha consumption, but his emphasis on its importance to maize production was well founded. The most highly valued irrigated lands in the central valleys were usually earmarked for maize, and the best fields yielded two harvests in good years. By contrast, wheat was usually grown on tracts of unirrigated land in the cooler highlands. The first known figures on maize and wheat production in the region were published in the Dalence census of 1846, which showed that the department of Cochabamba produced 189,136 fanegas of wheat and 476,794 fanegas of maize in a "normal" year. See José María Dalence, *Bosquejo estadístico de Bolivia* (La Paz: Editorial Universidad Mayor de San Andrés, 1975), 238.

21 Sánchez-Albornoz, *Indios y tributos*, 172-173.

22 "Descripción de Cochabamba," f. 3.

23 Viedma, *Descripción geográfica*, 67.

Sacaba

While the parish of Quillacollo was noted for its textile workshops, the valley of Sacaba—which lay on the other side of San Sebastian hill from Cochabamba—was famous for its wheat crop, an "abundant and superior wheat crop" said Paula Sanz, "that feeds the capital city."[24] In parts of the Sacaba valley, settlers had introduced a system of mixed farming, whereby animal husbandry and pastoralism in the highlands and cereal cultivation in the valleys were mutually dependent, striking a delicate ecological balance similar to that in many grain regions of preindustrial Europe.[25] Landlords carved out large tracts of land in the valley for the cultivation of wheat, maize, and fodder crops. Since the Sacaba River was dry most of the year, the vecinos had their workers construct reservoirs in the northern highlands above the Sacaba valley, which caught rainwater during the summer. Canals and ravines channeled water from these reservoirs and from small streams to the valley estates during the dry season. As in many regions in the Andes, creole landlords adopted the native custom of distributing scarce water in turns according to a strict time schedule. The elaborate irrigation system in Sacaba mitigated the otherwise wide variation in crop yields, "so that in general, the harvests are good."[26] Viedma reported that rural Indian, mestizo, and mulatto tenants cultivated superior qualities of wheat, maize, and alfalfa on Sacaba's largest haciendas. These peasants often had access to their landlords' pastures at higher elevations: "in the cordillera, the tenants keep their sheep and cattle in estancias."[27] Each year, the shepherds drove their animals down to the valley, where the animals would graze on and fertilize the recently harvested fields. Some landlords took advantage of the annual journey by requiring the pastoralists to work in the fields, cutting the last of the ripened wheat. For example, the herders of Ucuchi, an estancia tucked away in the remote cordillera to the north of Sacaba, were expected to work for a month on the valley lands of their lord to fulfill a labor obligation demanded of them as part of their rent. In

24 "Descripción de Cochabamba," f. 2.

25 B. H. Slicher Van Bath, *The Agrarian History of Western Europe, 800-1850* (London: Edward Arnold, 1963); Joan Thirsk, ed., *The Agrarian History of England and Wales (1500-1640)* (Cambridge: Cambridge University Press, 1967), vol. 4, chaps. 2 and 3.

26 Viedma, *Descripción geográfica*, 53.

27 Ibid.

addition, they paid rent in kind and money to their landlord each year.[28]

Cliza

A small mountain chain separated the Sacaba valley from the Cliza, the largest of the three central valleys. Stretching some thirty miles long and an average of seven miles wide, the Valle Alto of Cliza lay at an altitude of 8,700 feet. Because of its altitude, Cliza suffered from a chronic shortage of water. Its shallow rivers virtually disappeared during the dry season, though they frequently flooded during the rainy season. (It is telling that even after the agrarian reform of the 1952 revolution, many peasants of Cliza were unable to reorient the traditional maize and potato cultivation to intensive horticulture because of a lack of irrigation.)[29] The deficiency of water, together with a scarcity of alluvial deposits, meant consistently lower yields than in the Sacaba and Cerado parishes, greater fluctuations in yields from one year to the next, and diminishing returns from the soil after fewer years of cultivation. In the early nineteenth century, the market value of unirrigated maize and wheat land was only between 10 and 20 percent of the market value of the permanently irrigated soil in the most desirable valley zones. An inventory of the hacienda Chullpas in the Cliza valley, made shortly after independence, showed that its most valuable land was assessed at a rate nine times higher than its least valuable cultivated land (table 14).

Several factors may have compensated for the limited supply of water in the Valle Alto. First, its sheer territorial size, a total 150,000 acres, allowed landlords and peasants to increase production expanding the area of arable land. The narrow belt of land skirting the mountains was traditionally planted with wheat, while maize and potatoes were usually cultivated in the more fertile, partially irrigated central and eastern valley zones. Second, the proximity of higher elevations allowed peasants to cultivate tuber crops; oca, for example, should be planted in small patches of dry land and in soil

28 "Arriendos y tasaciones (con sus obligaciones, tareas, yuntas, urcas y leña) de los arrenderos de la estancia Ucuchi," AHMC, Leg. 1096 (1801-1808).

29 Camacho Saa, *Minifundia*; Leonard E. Olen, *Cantón Chullpas: A Socio-Economic Study of the Cochabamba Valley of Bolivia* (Washington, D.C.: Foreign Agricultural Reports, 1948); Richard W. Patch, "Social Implications of the Bolivian Agrarian Reform" (Ph.D. diss., University of Michigan, 1956).

Table 14. Assessed Value of the Hacienda Chullpas, in Cliza, 1828

Type of Property	*Number of Fanegas*	*Price per Fanega (pesos)*	*Value*
Permanently irrigated maize land	26	450	11,700
Partially irrigated maize land	30	250	7,500
Cultivable land outside hacienda	12	240	2,880
Unirrigated maize land	84	100	8,400
Unirrigated wheat land	154	50	7,700
Uncultivated rocky soil	30	30	900
Saltpeter	41	20	820
All land			39,900
Buildings, tools, and house			3,200
Total			43,100

Source: "La venta y remate pública de la hacienda Chullpas," AHMC, Leg. 1083 (1827).

with a high salt content.[30] Potatoes were also cultivated; they required less acreage than maize and far less than wheat (though labor requirements were heavy), and their growing cycle was somewhat different from that of maize and wheat. Potatoes could be planted starting in late September and harvested in late March or April, whereas maize and wheat were usually sowed and harvested a little later in the valleys (see figure 10). Even the limited cultivation in the serranía surrounding the Cliza valley afforded some insurance against the caprices of nature and the fluctuations of the yields of unirrigated valley acreage.[31] Finally, Cliza had rich grazing lands, especially in the central zone, which supported abundant herds of cattle and oxen, sheep, mules, and horses.[32] Livestock provided manure and draft power for plowing the extensive grain fields and for hauling freight. The supply of meat, wool, and tallow was secondary to those functions.

In the late eighteenth century, the Cliza valley was the most populous and productive zone in the province. Some 37,600 people, 30 percent of the province's inhabitants, lived in the valley's parishes of Tarata, Punata, Paredón, and Arani (see table 13). In 1786, the partido of Cliza had the largest concentration of Indians in the province, having experienced probably the greatest increase in that segment of

30 Guillermo Urquidi, *Monografía del departamento de Cochabamba* (Cochabamba: Tunari, 1954).

31 Olen, *Cantón Chullpas*, 35-36.

32 Viedma, *Descripción geográfica*, 76.

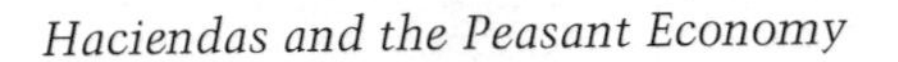

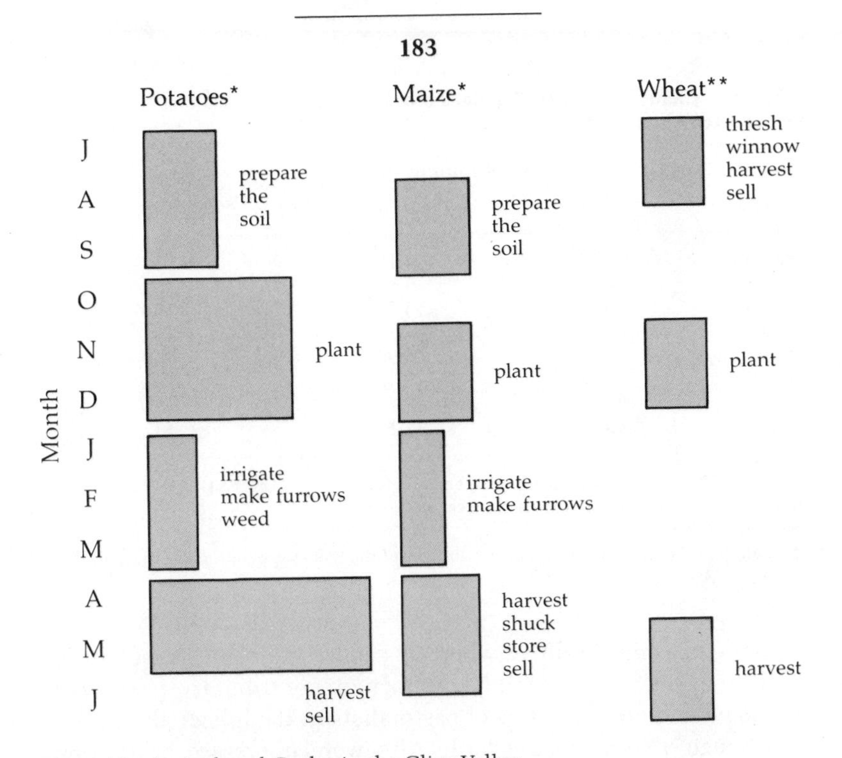

Figure 10 Agricultural Cycles in the Cliza Valley
Source: Bryan Anderson, unpublished. (I am grateful to the late Bryan Anderson for making this chart available.)
Note: Width of bar indicates relative intensity of labor input.

the population among all of Cochabamba's partidos during the preceding century (table 15). The size of its population and territory made Cliza the largest agricultural producer, to judge by the average tithe revenues: In the first decade of the nineteenth century, the partido of Cliza (which was under the ecclesiastical jurisdiction of the bishopric of Santa Cruz) generated 39 percent of the tithe income from the five partidos of Cochabamba province.[33] Viedma reported that most of the 17,000 Indians (as well as a substantial number of mestizos) lived on "an infinite number of haciendas, which appear to be small hamlets."[34] Although Viedma had despaired of enumerating all these rural properties, royal tax collectors in 1802-1808 listed 153 haciendas and 24 estancias and small holdings (*sitios*) throughout the Cliza valley. Some were indeed hamlets, like the ha-

33 Derived from data in ANB, MI, tomo 2, 6-VI (1825).

34 Viedma, *Descripción geográfica*, 77.

Table 15. Change in Indian Population of Partidos of Cochabamba between 1683 and 1786

Partido	*Number of Indians*		*Percentage Change*
	1683	*1786*	
Cercado	1,170	4,182	+ 257
Sacaba	866	3,805	+ 339
Tapacarí	5,693	14,766	+ 159
Cliza	3,581	16,227	+ 353
Arque	2,922[a]	14,906	+ 410[b]
Ayopaya	9,759	5,420	− 44
Total	23,991	58,122	+ 142

Sources: AGN, Sala 13, Padrones, 18.1.1, Leg. 41 (1683); 18.1.3, Leg. 43 (1683); 18.2.1, Leg. 46 (1786); 18.2.2, Leg. 47 (1786); 18.2.3, Leg. 48 (1786).

[a] No data for Caraza.

[b] This increase is inflated because of the absence of the Indian population of Caraza in the data for 1683.

ciendas Cliza and Chullpas, where 954 and 200 Indians, respectively, lived alongside a comparable number of nontributary peasants.[35] Others were merely clusters of pastoralists in the higher altitudes.

Although visitors to the Valle Alto were impressed by its opulence, all but the most perfunctory or optimistic of them expressed concern about population growth, poverty, and unemployment. Viedma observed that because of overpopulation, there was not enough industry "to occupy so many idle hands."[36] Colonial authorities during this period were acutely aware of the growing pressure on valley resources, and they proposed various schemes to alleviate it (see chapter 7).

But if Cliza was a zone of a proliferating peasantry of Indians and mestizos, and of extremes of wealth and poverty, it was also an area of intense commercial and artisan activity. As we shall see, in years of abundant harvest, many peasants who leased or sharecropped parcels of land sold their own small surpluses in local ferias in the valley. The Cliza feria, in particular, became a bustling livestock and grain market every Sunday morning. Cliza was also noted for its domestic chicha industry. Other industries flourished in the valley, including glass blowing and the manufacture of soap, gunpowder, and textiles.[37]

35 AGN, Sala 13, Padrones, 18.3.4, Leg. 54 (1802-1808).

36 Viedma, *Descripción geográfica*, 77.

37 Ibid., and "Descripción de Cochabamba," f. 2.

Arque

In the western reaches of the province, the land gathered into folds that formed rugged, arid mountains in western Tapacarí, Arque, and Ayopaya. This jumble of mountains cut off the region's broad, fertile valleys and principal towns from the altiplano and the main arteries of trade along that high plateau. The bulk of Cochabamba's population was isolated by the eastern sierras that formed the most rugged and inaccessible extension of the cordillera. Traversing the province from west to east, travelers would begin their journey on the high plateau surrounding the city of Oruro and gradually work their way down precipitous switchback trails until they eventually encountered shallow streams that joined at lower elevations to form the Tapacarí and Arque rivers, which cut and twisted their way through the mountains and eventually flowed into the Río Grande. There were two main passageways through the cordillera to the central valleys: one went through the pueblo real of Tapacarí; the other and more traveled one went through the valleys of Capinota and Arque.

The western partido of Arque was a district of sharp ecological contrasts wrought by the numerous tributaries and rivers that had gorged out moist, fertile, warm valleys. Peasants planted some of the province's best maize and fruit crops in the valleys of Caraza, Capinota, and Arque. But the partido also had the highest number of estancias. Thousands of Indians inhabited the hills and remote high valleys of Arque, where their sheep and cattle could graze and they could plant traditional highland crops undisturbed by the river-valley traffic or the competition for access to superior quality soil.[38] In the fertile quebradas, at elevations ranging between 7,900 and 9,200 feet, some fifty-odd hacendados took advantage of their favorable location and the abundant river water to cultivate grains for export to Oruro and other provinces. Hacendados who owned lands near the banks of the Arque and Colcha rivers built canals and dams to chan-

38 The partido of Arque apparently had the greatest number of property units inhabited by tribute-paying Indians of any of Cochabamba's districts. Consequently, although the growth of its Indian population between 1683 and 1786 probably paralleled that of the Cliza valley, Arque's Indian population was distributed more widely: an average of only nine tributary families inhabited each rural property. On the other hand, Arque's mixed-race population was relatively small compared to the number of mestizos in Cliza and the Cercado. Thus, the overall demographic profile of Arque was one of a predominantly Indian population, distributed between a few large grain estates and milling operations located in the river valley, on the one hand, and a multitude of smaller properties, including many estancias, scattered across the mountainous interior of the partido, on the other. (For a discussion of Arque's only pueblo real, Capinota, see chap. 4.)

nel the water to irrigate their fields and to harness the power of the rivers, which ran swiftly after the rainy season, to drive their grain mills. Almost one-third of the grain mills in the province of Cochabamba were located along the banks of Arque's waterways. In the parish of Arque proper, thirteen hacendados were registered in a 1799 survey as owners of sixty-two mills, each of which represented considerable capital investment. In the poorer parish of Colcha, upriver from Arque, nine hacendados operated thirty-one mills.[39] The lands and mills of Arque, located along the trade corridor connecting the central valleys to the altiplano and blessed with water power, gave some landowners of the parish a critical advantage in the marketing and processing of maize and wheat destined for the colder lands of the altiplano provinces (see chapter 6). Furthermore, landowners in the parishes of Arque and Colcha exercised control over most of the water power and the arable and pasture land in those parishes, even if they didn't monopolize grain marketing or pack driving. Curiously, though, Viedma reported in 1788 the existence of mitmaq lands still controlled by the Indians of Challacollo, whose principal ayllus were located in the province of Paria.[40] Most of the Indian land in the Arque parish was high pasture, but Viedma also mentioned the existence of twelve *fanegadas* of irrigated maize lands, which yielded a rich and abundant crop after a good growing season.[41] But even though vestiges of precolonial land patterns remained, Arque nevertheless had become an important Spanish trade route that connected grain haciendas, mills, and highland markets.

Ayopaya

In the northeast corner of the province of Cochabamba lay Ayopaya, the most isolated and varied of the partidos. The western part of the district was bordered by the cordillera, and most lands in Ayopaya were situated well above 10,500 feet. Ayopaya's landscape of snow-covered peaks, cold, wind-swept puna, and pastureland resembled that of Sicasica and other highland provinces to the west. But in deep crevices and in the northern escarpment, where steep moun-

39 "Real visita a las molinas de grano," AHMC, Leg. 1213 (1799).

40 Viedma, *Descripción geográfica*, 70.

41 Ibid. Viedma added that the land was "administered by the cacique of that pueblo [Challacollo], whose products . . . must be worth more than 1,000 pesos . . . [as much] as if he owned [the land] through rights of primogeniture." In later years, the Indians leased some of their lands and mills to a creole: "Exp. seguido a nuevo remate . . . de la hacienda y molinos de Arque," ANB, EC no. 7 (1816).

tains sloped down to the tropical yungas, the land was extremely fertile. Some of Ayopaya's eighty-six haciendas were located in these pockets, and they produced cash crops such as sugar cane, cotton, ají, maize, peanuts, and tropical fruit. In the dry land at high elevations, most hacendados raised stock and cultivated wheat and potatoes. Life seemed bleak on these estates, even to the seasoned traveler of the Andes. After touring the district, Viedma observed that "the human condition is even worse in Ayopaya than in the other districts. The Indians shoulder the burden of agricultural work and are at the mercy of tyrants whose only title of authority is that of 'employer.' "[42] And if living conditions were not sufficiently depressed, the recent Indian rebellions had left visible scars all over the countryside; Viedma saw the charred ruins of many haciendas and chapels.

Against this grim contemporary description, the partido's Indian population loss is thrown into bold relief. In 1683, Ayopaya's native population of 9,759 was the largest in the province. However, over the next century, the number of Indians declined by 44 percent, to 5,420 in 1786 (see table 15). Much of this loss was probably due to emigration, especially adult Indian men.[43] The reasons for Ayopaya's loss of native population are not hard to discover. Viedma's description of the exceptionally harsh conditions of life on Ayopaya's highland estates would support the proposition that most emigrants in the late eighteenth century were refugees from poverty and landlessness. An alcalde of Yani in 1773, decried the intolerable burdens that a rapacious corregidor had placed upon the local population and also alluded to deepening impoverishment in the backlands of Ayopaya.[44] Indirect evidence suggests that many peasants of Ayopaya sought better lives on the thriving coca plantations (*cocales*) of Chulumani, northeast of the city of La Paz. Thus far, there is no demographic study of Ayopaya's population movement that can be compared to Klein's monograph on seasonal labor migration between the alti-

42 Viedma, *Descripción geográfica*, 57-58.

43 In comparison to the Indian population in other partidos (outside the pueblos reales), Ayopaya's native population had the most imbalanced sex ratio (66.6 adult and adolescent males per 100 adult females), the highest proportion of widows (24 percent), and a relatively high proportion of absent tributaries (13 percent). AGN, Sala 13, Padrones, 18.2.1, Leg. 46 (1786); 18.2.2, Leg. 47 (1786); 18.2.3, Leg. 48 (1786).

44 "Testimonio del expediente de teniente de Ayopaya contra el corregidor de Cochabamba," ANB, EC no. 139 (1773).

plano province of Pacajes and the yungas, but that study does not show the powerful attraction the cocales exerted on the highland Indians and the intensive labor requirements of those enterprises.[45] There is reason to believe that the yungas also drained the native population from the highland estates of Ayopaya in the second half of the eighteenth century. The two principal European informants, Viedma and Paula Sanz, commented on the strong trade currents between Ayopaya's highland haciendas and the flourishing coca enterprises in the tropical lowlands. In 1781, Paula Sanz mentioned that the maize and wheat farms of Ayopaya's four parishes fed "the pueblos of the yungas and the city of La Paz"; and later Viedma reported that llamas, alpacas, goats, sheep, horses, and cattle grazed on "excellent pastures in the estancias of Ayopaya, and the export of cattle to the yungas is very profitable," and he described the mestizo mule drivers (*arrieros*) who brought grains, flour, and dried meat from Ayopaya to La Paz.[46] It is not unreasonable to conjecture that, while "sheep ate men" on the bleak steppes of Ayopaya over the course of the eighteenth century, those native peasants who sought relief from the grinding poverty of the partido followed the new trade route and cattle trail to the tropical lowlands, where they settled and worked for a spell on the coca plantations before moving on—or dying.

Peasant Smallholding

The complexity and variety of tenure arrangements on eighteenth-century estates in Cochabamba defy any attempt to construct a typology of agrarian enterprises along classic European lines. Some historians have identified Latin American analogues of feudalism: e.g., the wheat and cattle estates that Chevalier described for a region of seventeenth-century Mexico.[47] Some haciendas undoubtedly resembled the *Gutsherrschaft* type of manorial organization that devel-

45 Klein, "Hacienda and Free Community."

46 "Descripción de Cochabamba," f. 3, and Viedma, *Descripción geográfica*, 57-58.

47 Although Chevalier was not the first historian to conceptualize the Mexican hacienda in terms of the European manorial economy, it was he who, as Van Young has pointed out, "brought the great estate down from the level of abstraction to that of historical reality," and in the process described seigneurial relations that bound peasants to their lord and cloistered them on autarchic estates: Van Young, "Mexican Rural History," 9ff. For a more theoretical treatment of feudal enterprises in Poland, see Witold Kula, *An Economic Theory of the Feudal System* (London: New Left Books, 1976).

oped in certain regions east of the Elbe River in the seventeenth century, under the stimulus of the cereal export trade. In this model, landlords cultivated large territorial units by drawing on the labor of a servile peasantry.[48] One hacienda in the Cochabamba province that fit this model was that of El Convento, in the Caraza valley. It was owned by Augustinian monks, and its labor force consisted of seventy-eight yanacona families, whose status was permanent and inherited, along with a number of tenants, who at least theoretically had more leeway to negotiate tenure arrangements.[49] However, El

48 There is some disagreement about the nature of land tenure in an enterprise of the *Gutsherrschaft* type, but most historians agree that it was organized around the direct cultivation of the demesne by service tenants, who engaged in corvée labor and also had tiny cottage holdings. The estate was a micropolitical unit: power was held primarily by the landlord, and tenants were subject only indirectly to a territorial prince. Perhaps the first systematic attempt to make explicit comparisons between this form and Latin American haciendas was Cristobal Kay, "Comparative Development of the European Manorial System and the Latin American Hacienda System: An Approach to a Theory of Agrarian Change for Chile" (D. Phil, diss., University of Sussex, 1971); see also Cristobal Kay, "Comparative Development of the European Manorial System and the Latin American Hacienda System," *Journal of Peasant Studies* 2 (1974): 69-98. Other discussions of the *Gutsherrschaft* enterprise are Slicher van Bath, *Agrarian History of Western Europe*, 156-157 and passim; and Perry Anderson, *Passages from Antiquity to Feudalism* (London: New Left Books, 1974), part 2, esp. 246-265. The comparison between certain "hacienda regions" in Latin America during periods of expanding agricultural export trade and the seigneurial system on eastern European estates during the wheat export boom has been a theme of interest to several other historians as well; see, for example, Mario Góngora, *Encomenderos y estancieros: Estudios acerca de la constitución social aristocrática de Chile después de la Conquista, 1580-1660* (Santiago: Editorial Universitaria, 1970), 121-122; and Mörner, "Spanish American Hacienda," 211-212.

Just as Europeanists have interpreted the "second serfdom" as a response to the stimulus of the export market in grains, Latin Americanists have seen the intensification of coerced labor on rural estates in the context of market stimuli and the inadequate or insecure supply of cheap labor. See, for example, Macera, "Feudalismo colonial americano"; Eric Hobsbawm, "A Case of Neo-Feudalism: La Convención, Peru," *Journal of Latin American Studies* 1 (1969): 31-50; Carmagnani, "Producción agropecuaria chilena"; and Mario Góngora, *Origen de los inquilinos de Chile central* (Santiago: Editorial Universitaria, 1960). However, there is no consensus about the extent to which landlords restricted the mobility of their rural laborers through debt or other mechanisms. On this subject, see Gibson, *Aztecs*, 252-255, and Arnold J. Bauer, "Chilean Rural Labor in the Nineteenth Century," *American Historical Review* 76 (1971): 1059-1082, and "Rural Workers in Spanish America: Problems of Peonage and Oppression," *Hispanic American Historical Review* (1979): 34-63.

49 "Real provisión sobre no ser yanaconas los indios de la hacienda de Carasa,"

Convento's relatively heavy reliance on yanacona labor distinguished it from most other haciendas of the time.

On most haciendas where the owner continued to administer the demesne, seigneurial relations covered a broad spectrum of tenure arrangements. Labor prestations were important components of rent, and tenants usually also paid cash and delivered shares of their harvests, however meager. Extra services, such as domestic labor, might also be woven into this web of obligations. But the amount and mechanics of labor rent varied significantly. One hacienda might require the seasonal migration of highland herders and cultivators down to the hacienda's valley lands, where they would work for a month in the maize or wheat fields.[50] On another, a dozen Indian households had fixed labor obligations, and the mayordomo hired seasonal wageworkers during harvest time to help cut and gather the wheat and cart it to the mill and then to the city of Cochabamba.[51] On still others, each tenant household was responsible for recruiting extra workers during the planting and harvest seasons if the household was unable to meet its obligations unaided.[52] In many cases, this responsibility forced tenants to sublet parcels of their leaseholds

ANB, EC no. 6396 (1747). On the hacienda of La Leguna, in Punata, a landlord tried to rent out his tenants to his landowning neighbors. In 1772, the tenants filed suit against him, charging that he was trying to force them into "yanaconazgo." The tenants complained that the landlord even bestowed new surnames on them, so that their very identity would be lost. "Bernardo y Pablo Sola, indios de Cochabamba, sobre pretender sujetarlos de servidumbre de yanaconazgo . . .," ANB, EC no. 216 (1772).

50 "Arriendos y tasaciones . . . de los arrenderos de la estancia Ucuchi," AHMC, Leg. 1096 (1801-1808).

51 "Exp. por doña Francisca de Valencia y Cabrera contra Ygnacio Beltrán sobre la administración de la hacienda Parotani," AHMC, Leg. 1090 (1807).

52 "Exp. por el indígena Estaban Pablo contra su patrón Manuel Almarás en la hacienda Caporaya," AHMC, Leg. 1273 (1795). This strategy of shifting the burden of mobilizing and paying labor to tenant households was a common practice in other parts of Latin America as well; see, for example, the discussion of rent obligations on estates in the León region of the Bajío in David Brading "Estructura de la producción agrícola en el Bajío, 1700 a 1850," in E. Florescano, ed., *Haciendas, Latifundios, y plantaciones en América latina* (Mexico City: Siglo XXI, 1975), 128, and David Brading, *Haciendas and Ranchos in the Mexican Bajío: León, 1700-1860* (Cambridge: Cambridge University Press, 1978), 113-114. For a more general discussion of the variety and combinations of forms of rent payment, see Magnus Mörner, "A Comparative Study of Tenant Labor in Parts of Europe, Africa, and Latin America, 1700-1900," *Latin American Research Review* 5 (1970): 3-15.

to members of a marginal labor force (*arrimantes*) who would reciprocate by working for them during the busy seasons. In that way, a tenant family might break the limits imposed by the household size (and number of productive laborers) to carry a heavier burden of rent labor. From the landlord's viewpoint, this method shifted the burden of labor recruitment from the manager and owner to the peasant household. Thus, even on estates where labor obligations bore down hard on peasant households, there was usually an intricate network of obligations binding peasants to the landlord, as well as to other peasant families with differential rights and access to hacienda resources.

In contrast to the *Gutsherrschaft* form of organization was the *Grundherrschaft* form, in which the landlord leased his entire estate to a large number of small-scale cultivators, who paid him rent in cash or shares of the crop. This, too, had its parallels in the Cochabamba valley. In part because of the custom of dividing inheritance, property units rarely survived intact during their transmission across generations; rather, the drift was toward fragmentation of ownership. Under such circumstances, labor services were less useful than cash tenancies and sharecropping. However, this diffusion of production among peasant households was still a long way from peasant proprietorship and from the creation of a kulak class.

Most haciendas were probably operated with some combination of demesne agriculture on a limited scale and peasant smallholding on the bulk of their land. Landlords often reserved parcels of the most fertile wheat and maize lands, whose harvest went directly into the hacienda storehouses for future consumption, tithes, or sale. The rest of the land would be distributed among the resident tenants, thus using hacienda resources as payments to a permanent labor force.[53] A detailed inventory of Aramasi, a middle-sized hacienda lo-

53 A previous study has emphasized "hacienda resource payment" as a strategy of landlords to avoid having to make cash payments to permanent or seasonal laborers. Landlords allowed peasants to graze their animals on the estate's pastures, cultivate parcels of arable land, collect firewood or ichu grasses, etc. Over the long term, this strategy may have increased the relative power of tenants, who had "cheap access to hacienda resources and at the same time could not be prevented from leaving the estate." Juan Martínez Alier, "Relations of production on Andean haciendas," in Kenneth Duncan and Ian Rutledge, eds., *Land and Labor in Latin America: Essays on the Development of Agrarian Capitalism in the Nineteenth and Twentieth Centuries* (Cambridge: Cambridge University Press, 1977), 146. A pioneering work on the internal relations between rival peasant and landlord economies within a rural property unit is Rafael Baraona, "Una tipología de haciendas en la sierra ecuatoriana," in O. Delgado, ed.,

cated in the Spanish parish of Calliri, provides an anatomy of that estate's internal land divisions.[54] In 1784, its assessed market value was 9,653 pesos. Like most haciendas, it had a large expanse of pasture and scattered pieces of arable land at varying altitudes across the highlands. It also included moist valley land, where maize was cultivated, though it had much less of such land than many other haciendas situated in the central valleys. Aramasi combined the raising of livestock with cereal and potato cultivation. The landlords owned no grain mills, but they had considerable assets in draft animals (40 plow oxen) and freight animals (12 burros), as well as 100 sheep. Aramasi's wheat yield in 1784 amounted to 268 fanegas—a poor return, no doubt, in that year of severe drought. Among the tenant population were about eighty or ninety Indians,[55] together with an unknown number of mestizo tenants. Together, the tenants occupied, or had access to, more than half of the hacienda's arable land, in addition to the open pasture in the highlands (see table 16). The largest single category of land was the area leased to arrenderos, which constituted 45 percent of the hacienda's territory. The "owner's land" represented only 7 percent of the estate's area, although almost 30

Table 16. Land Use on the Hacienda Aramasi in Calliri, 1784

Land Use	*Area*	
	Fanegadas	*Percentage*
Total hacienda	409[a]	100.0
Demesne land	150	36.7
Owner's land	30	7.3
Hacienda land	120	29.3
Under lease	212	51.8
Indian administrator's land	12	2.9
Indian maize land	15	3.7
Land cultivated by arrenderos	185	45.2
Unclaimed or waste land	47	11.5

Source: "Hacienda Aramasi," AHMC, Leg. 1066 (1784).
[a] Excluding open range land.

Reformas agrarias en América latina (México City: Fondo de Cultura Económica, 1965), 688-694.

54 "Tasación de la hacienda Aramasi, en el valle de Calliri," AHMC, Leg. 1066 (1784). The estate, owned by Mónica Berbete Corilla y Paniagua, was located in the lower reaches of the Tapacarí River valley. Its lands bordered the hacienda Milloma, owned by Tapacarí's cacique family, the Liro de Córdovas (see chap. 4).

55 AGN, Sala 13, Padrones, 18.3.4, Leg. 54 (1808), f. 181.

percent was categorized as "hacienda land," whose yields probably were used to cover operating costs (including liens and debts). Thus, it is clear that most of the hacienda's resources were under peasant control. On paper, the hacienda appeared to be a cohesive property unit under central administration, but the fragmentation of land tenure meant, in effect, decentralized agricultural production.

The details of Aramasi's tenure pattern suggest a high degree of internal differentiation among the rural tenants (see table 17). The individual leaseholds ranged in area from five fanegadas to seventy, and in total assessed value from 36 pesos to 525. Moreover, some lands were cultivated collectively by the arrenderos; these were most likely irrigated maize fields, whose yields were the source of chicha for ceremonial festivities. Finally, some lands were leased to the two Indian authorities, alcalde and the hilacata, who performed such functions as mediating rent relations and coordinating cultivation of the collective maize lands, as well as carrying out certain religious duties. This political/religious hierarchy probably overlapped with the hierarchy based on differential access to land. The hacienda peasants thus managed to combine household production with communal production along traditional lines.

Table 17. Area and Value of Leased Lands on the Hacienda Aramasi, 1784

Arriendo	*Area (fanegadas)*	*Assessed Value (pesos)*	
		Per Fanegada	*Total Value*
Calanchulpa	35	15	525
Ocororuni	10	10	100
Luiuluiuni	6	6	36
Guañagagua	20	8	160
Tacocolpa	15	10	150
Torrini	20	10	200
Taconi	15	10	150
Ychocollo	20	8	160
Ajuri	15	15	225
Tacocuchi	8	12	96
Copafina	10	15	150
Vilca	6	12	72
Santa Rojas	5	10	50
Chapiloma	25	8	200
Quesera	70	8	560
Lands of the hilacata	8	10	80
Lands of the alcalde	4	10	40
Communal maize land	15	24	360

Source: "Hacienda Aramasi," AHMC, Leg. 1066 (1784).

It would be overly simplistic, therefore, to see land tenure and labor arrangements on the haciendas exclusively in the European mold of *Gutsherrschaft* or *Grundherrschaft*. Hacienda organization in eighteenth-century Cochabamba was variegated and fluid, and different patterns could be found simultaneously on a given estate. Tenants usually paid rent in some combination of cash, kind, and labor prestations. In return, they often received payment in hacienda resources, "gifts" of food and drink, and sometimes cash wages. If there was any single most common pattern, it was sharecropping. On both large and small haciendas, tenants often worked certain lands "in company" with the landowner. In many cases, the sharecropped lands were subsidiary parcels, apart from the main *arriendo* for which the tenant paid rent. The landowner usually furnished seeds, draft animals, and tools in exchange for half or more of the harvest, though there were also many other arrangements.[56] Sharecropping thrust agricultural production almost entirely into the hands of peasant cultivators, marginalizing the economic role of the property owner. At the same time, it provided a measure of subsistence security to the smallholder, by sharing the risk of crop failure between the cultivator and the landlord. This was particularly important on temporal lands, where yields fluctuated widely. Thus,

56 Sharecropping arrangements were generally made in verbal contracts, but court suits, wills, and estate inventories give us some information about their terms. Some of the arrangements were fairly formal and relatively equitable. For example, a widow who inherited part of the hacienda Mamanaca, in the parish of Tarata, entered into a *sociedad* (association) with her sharecropping "partner." She agreed to supply the land, seeds, oxen, and plow; her partner provided his "work, industry, and assistance," paid half of the fixed costs of production, and was liable for part of the estate's debts. The harvests were to be divided evenly, but a part of the tenant's share went to cover his half of the fixed costs. "Doña Juana de Dios Urquidi en sociedad con d. Manuel Balencia," AHMC, Leg. 1423 (1790).

On the hacienda Liquina, in the Cliza valley, the owner—also a widow—supplied only the land, while her tenant partner had to provide the seeds, tools, and animals. This widow complained that, despite her impoverishment and lack of liquid capital, she was unable to sell her "mulattoes," since her tenants were "really more cholos than mulattoes" and were therefore considered free men and women. "Exp. por doña Juana Ysabel Garrido Morales contra doña Marañón," AHMC, Leg. 1175 (1761).

On still another hacienda, Chacarilla, sharecroppers worked with day laborers. The tenants sharecropped some of the estate's lands, providing seeds as well as their labor. But during the harvest, the landlord also brought in five day laborers (*peones jornaleros*), who provided only their labor in return for a small fraction of the crop. "Tasación de la hacienda Chacarilla," AHMC, Leg. 1144 (1803).

tenants who owed fixed rents, which could easily take two-thirds of their harvest in a bad season, could look to their sharecropped lands for some relief. The landlord, on the other hand, had to reduce the amount of product he could claim in a year of calamity. In many cases, though, even sharecropped lands provided slim protection against a subsistence crisis when weather conditions were especially bad.

The multiplicity of sharecropping arrangements on the Cochabamba haciendas brings to mind the process of increasingly intricate tenure patterns that Geertz has described for parts of Indonesia during its colonial period.[57] Borrowing the concept "involution" from its original aesthetic context, Geertz used it to characterize tenure systems that grew more encrusted and complicated, like a spider web that neither grows nor shrinks, but becomes ever more intricate in detail. There was an internal dynamic to land-tenure arrangements, although the changes did not fundamentally alter agrarian class relations, either in the Indonesian context that Geertz studied or in eighteenth-century Cochabamba. Instead, the arrangements developed, as Geertz put it, "through technical hairsplitting and unending virtuosity," giving them a kind of gothic texture.[58] From within the formal agrarian structures of property ownership in Cochabamba was emerging an active peasantry seeking subsistence niches and negotiating for as much economic autonomy and security as it could wrench from the landowners. The elaboration of tenure patterns reflected the increasing presence of small-scale cultivators in the province and the diffusion of agricultural resources among them.

One force behind the dispersion of production units was the fragmentation of property ownership. Evidence of this phenomenon, one that plagued hacienda agriculture in many parts of Spanish America, is found in wills, notarized records of land transactions, padrones listing property units and their owners that can be traced through several decades, and estate inventories.[59] Records of *hijuelación*, the

57 Clifford Geertz, *Agricultural Involution: The Processes of Ecological Change in Indonesia* (Berkeley and Los Angeles: University of California Press, 1963).

58 Ibid., 81-82.

59 Although uncatalogued and unorganized, the notarial books and the records of judicial proceedings housed in Cochabamba's municipal archive provide rich documentation of land-tenure arrangements, land transactions, inheritance patterns, and encumbrances on landed property. The documents are full of examples of people buying, selling, bequeathing, inheriting, and encumbering small,

bequest and subdivision of property, in the late eighteenth century offer examples of the dismemberment of rural properties as they were willed to a widow, several offspring, and members of the regular and secular clergy who were expected, in return, to remember their benefactor in their prayers. Real-estate transactions also show the movement of land titles, not only and not primarily to whole estates, but to bits and pieces of them.[60] A survey of property boundaries and deeds made in 1748 revealed that fragmentation of ownership had proceeded quite far even by then. Landowners frequently claimed several scattered plots of land, while lands registered as a single property unit often listed multiple owners. The hacienda Mamata in the Cliza valley, for example, was owned by five individuals, each of whom paid the tax on a part of the estate. A neighboring hacienda, Liquina, also had several owners.[61] Records of formal ownership often provide only ambiguous evidence of real economic power and landlord-tenant relations, but this diffusion of property suggests that the landowning class was losing its grip on the institutional foundations of its power. Increasingly, it was engaged in internal competition for control over property units that were crumbling under the weight of the Spanish partible-inheritance laws, accumulated indebtedness, and uncertain returns on agricultural investment.

Yet, in eighteenth-century Cochabamba as in colonial Indonesia, the trend toward small-scale agricultural production had less to do with land-ownership patterns than with the way land was worked. Geertz's emphasis on the elaboration of labor relations on estates

---

scattered pieces of property. The notarial books, in particular, contain numerous accounts of land transactions involving fragments of haciendas.

60 The records of rural real-estate transactions in Cochabamba in 1781 show that only three out of eighteen transfers involved the sale of an entire hacienda; the other fifteen sales involved small plots of ground. In 1785, the real-estate market was brisker, but of the thirty-eight recorded land sales, only ten were whole haciendas. AGN, Sala 13, Contaduría, 27.1.1 (1781) and 27.1.5 (1785).

61 The survey listed 121 hacendados, who paid a total of 5,486 pesos in taxes and fees, ranging from 10 pesos, for several fanegadas of poor land, to 400 pesos, for several haciendas in Cliza that belonged to one individual. But almost three-quarters of the property owners paid less than 50 pesos in settlement fees for various small, dispersed properties. "Composiciones y amparos de haciendas, tierras, y estancias de Cochabamba por D. José Antonio de Zabala," ANB, EC no. 100 (1748). Tribute collectors also sometimes noted the internal fragmentation of ownership. In the 1803 padron of Punata, for instance, the hacienda-estancia complex known as Tambillo y Chirusicollo was listed as being owned by several families. AGN, Sala 13, Padrones, 8.3.3, Leg. 53 (1803), f. 56.

applies equally well to the maize valleys of Cochabamba. It was economic involution "from below": the gradual dispersion of hacienda resources among a dense peasant population that engaged in intensive cultivation of maize on parcels of land that often yielded two harvests a year. These small-scale cultivators rarely appear in contemporary sources, but their proliferation signaled a divisibility of agricultural inputs and outputs that continued to characterize agrarian patterns in Cochabamba into the twentieth century.[62]

Peasants Confront a Landlord

Yanaconaje was the bedrock of the rural labor force on Cochabamba's early haciendas. Reluctantly recognizing the need of hacendados to have an assured supply of labor, the Toledan state institutionalized subservient labor relations on the grain haciendas in the eastern valleys of Alto Perú. Although nominally free, the yanaconas were reduced to the status of dependent, immobile workers whose inferior position was passed down through the generations, sentencing their progeny to similar lives of hardship and stigmatization. But Andean migrants from the highlands moved into the Cochabamba valleys over the course of the seventeenth and eighteenth centuries, and as their numbers grew, yanaconaje receded into the background. By the end of the colonial era, yanaconas constituted only about 3 percent of the Indians in the region, and nearly all of them lived on large haciendas in the Cliza valley. Of the 1,393 yanaconas counted in 1805, the Augustinian hacienda of Achamoco alone was home to 78.[63]A few equally formidable enterprises, most of them also under control of a monastic order, had managed to preserve their property

62 Studies of land tenure in the Cliza valley on the eve of the 1952 revolution have shown the region polarized between large neofeudal estates, such as the monastic hacienda Cliza, and estates in an advanced degree of fragmentation, such as the neighboring hacienda Chullpas. Although the hacienda Cliza is better known, it was probably more the anomaly. See Patch, "Social Implications," and Olen, *Cantón Chullpas*. A major research project on the peasant economy and regional differentiation in the valleys and highlands of Cochabamba has recently been undertaken by a group of sociologists and anthropologists under the direction of Jorge Dandler. A description of the research design and a discussion of preliminary findings can be found in Centro de Estudios de la Realidad Económica y Social, *Programa de investigación sobre la economía y desarrollo regional de Cochabamba* (La Paz: CERES, 1981, mimeograph).

63 AGN, Sala 13, Padrones, 18.3.3, Leg. 53 (1802-1808); and 18.3.4, Leg. 54 (1802-1808), f. 64; AGN, Sala 9, Intendencia, 5.8.7, Leg. 6 (1805).

and to shield the vestiges of their servile labor force from the disintegrating forces of change.

Meanwhile, on the 680 or so rural properties scattered across the province's five partidos, most of the workers were arrenderos—tenants, as distinguished from the bonded yanaconas. Their relationship to the owner was, at least theoretically, mediated through the market. They were supposed to be free to negotiate the terms of rent in accord with certain regulations, and their rent was supposed to bear some relationship to their access to hacienda resources and land-use rights, although in the late eighteenth century the colonial state tried to standardize rents by pegging them to the size and assessed value of leaseholds.[64] But in fact, neither the market nor the state determined the relations between landlords and tenants. It was, rather, the force of custom which determined peasant expectations of landlord behavior and the (unequal) exchanges between them.[65] Although norms varied from hacienda to hacienda, and over time, it was widely expected that landlords would afford tenants some access to hacienda resources in addition to their individual arriendos: perhaps the right to collect firewood, to graze sheep on the estancia, or to call upon the landowner for cash advances or credit. Assistance in the event of famine or personal misfortune, and gestures of generosity and of ritual kinship at particular moments in the life course of a faithful tenant, were unwritten forms of patronage and protection that peasants had come to expect of their landowners. Although acutely aware of class cleavages, rural tenant laborers counted on their lords to provide a small cushion against subsistence crisis, a symbolic measure of security that legitimated the tradition and terms of tenancy. When the terms of exchange shifted sharply

64 In Mexico at about the same time, the standard ground rent was ten pesos per fanega of cultivated land: Brading, *Haciendas and Ranchos*, 75 and 198.

65 Scott, *Moral Economy of the Peasant*, 179ff. In the last years of the eighteenth century, tenants sometimes resorted to judicial tactics in an effort to bring about a degree of landlord compliance with royal regulations, when they believed that custom no longer served their interests. Yanaconas, however, were considered to be subordinated and bound to the person of the landowner and to the property. Custom forbade them to negotiate over the terms of their status; even their subsistence came directly from their overlords, in the form of stipulated rations of food and clothing. RAH, ML, 9/1962, tomo 37 (Nov. 19, 1794), f. 289v. On the maintenance and breakdown of patron-client relations on some haciendas around the turn of the twentieth century, see Erick Langer, "Labor Strikes and Reciprocity on Chuquisaca Haciendas," *Hispanic American Historical Review* 65 (1985): 255-278.

against them and a landlord abused his power, it was not uncommon for peasants to resist, through flight or direct political confrontation.

One of the more visible conflicts in the region erupted in 1795 on the grain hacienda of Caporaya, located in the valley of Caraza. Judging by the padron of 1786, Caporaya was a middle-sized estate, inhabited by some two dozen Indian families and probably a considerable number of nontributary tenant households. By custom, the smallholding tenants of Caporaya had provided various labor services to the landlord, and they also worked some parcels of land "in company." In 1781, the property had been sold, and the new owner, Manuel Almarás, had tried to impose harsher terms. In the eyes of the tenants, he thus violated the norms that had governed rent relations on the hacienda up until then. Speaking in Quechua, one Ygnacio Condori (who bore no relation to the cacique of Tapacarí) described the labor prestations demanded of him and other arrenderos. A translator dictated his testimony to the court notary, who recorded it in the third person.

> This year they [the arrenderos] planted [on the demesne] some 40 fanegas of wheat, two fanegas of maize, and twelve of barley. This work is a heavy burden to bear, but they must also weed, harvest, thresh, winnow, shuck the corn and move the grain to the storage huts. For his labor, he [Condori] is paid one-half a *real* [per day], along with usufruct rights to three *viches* of maize land and three fanegadas of wheat land.[66]

These terms were much worse than the previous ones. Another tenant added:

> Under the old labor arrangement, each Indian contributed only two yoke of oxen, along with the plowmen [*gañanes*], and he who had no yoke to lend could satisfy his obligation with his own labor in the wheat, maize, and quinoa fields. But in the last four or five years that Almarás has owned this property . . . each Indian must contribute eight yoke of oxen and the plowmen, even if he has none.[67]

Another arrendero also complained of the demand for "eight yoke of oxen accompanied by peones," in addition to the extra eight days

66 "Exp. por el yndígena Esteban Pablo contra su patrón Manual Almarás en la hacienda Caporaya," AHMC, Leg. 1273 (1795), f. 7v. A *viche* was an area of land equivalent, in the Cochabamba region, to about one-sixth of a fanegada.

67 Ibid., ff. 9v.-10.

of field work they did "without wage or any compensation." Furthermore, Almarás required each tenant to gather firewood for the hacienda and for the townhouse in Cochabamba.[68]

These heavier labor obligations placed additional burdens on other members of the household as well, since they had to make up for the labor thus lost on their subsistence plots. Yet at the same time, Almarás also forced arrendero women and children to work for less than the customary compensation for their labor. Women were put to work "spinning and weaving and fermenting maize flour, for making chicha."[69] They also performed various subsidiary tasks on the estate, such as preparing for the customary festivities at threshing time (*la trilla*). Unlike the seasonal field work of men, women's rent labor was continuous. And, according to the aggrieved tenants, the women were subject to harsh discipline by the hacendado's wife, who managed the obraje and, they said,

> keeps Condori's wife almost a perpetual slave, spinning cotton and wool. She hardly finishes spinning one bag of wool, when she is handed another. She receives only one real, instead of the customary day's pay of two reales . . . The wife of Almarás forces all the women on the hacienda to weave . . . but they get no payment except a little salt or wheat.[70]

The children's task was to tend the landlord's livestock. The tenant households had to take turns in supplying a child to serve as shepherd for a month in the distant estancia lands. One tenant complained that the children had to sleep for a month outdoors on the cold puna, keeping vigil over the master's flocks. If a tenant had no child to spare, he had to hire a neighbor's son to serve. Although this type of labor obligation was not uncommon, it was usually paid for at the rate of one peso a month, but Almarás paid only four reales.[71]

Behind the expressions of moral indignation, the broad outlines of the labor regime of this hacienda, can be discerned. Peasant testimony about work obligations before the new regime suggests how heavily the entire tenant household was burdened. Aside from the obligations accruing to arrendero households that corresponded loosely to the size and quality of their leaseholds, there was an im-

68 Ibid., f. 1v.

69 Ibid., f. 1.

70 Ibid., ff. 7v and 10.

71 Ibid., f. 10.

plicit division of labor by age and sex. The witnesses made frequent references to the "old ways," before Almarás purchased the property, when the men tilled hacienda land while their women spun and worked the treadle looms in the hacienda's workshop. There seemed to be a consensus that this arrangement was not unjust, nor was it regarded as objectionable that the arrenderos lent yoked oxen and plowmen on certain days of the year.

But Almarás failed to honor an implicit code of reciprocity. He demanded more labor and gave less in return than had been the case in the past, and in the process he jeopardized his own legitimacy and status. In effect, he violated the tenants' rights by demanding servicio personal and thereby reducing the status of free arrenderos to one of intolerable servitude. Until the moment these tenants challenged the authority of the landowner, peasant defiance was met with lashings and other physical abuse. In protest, Condori, at one point in the testimony, proudly declared himself to be a free person, not a "miserable yanacona."

The confrontation that broke out on this hacienda was provoked by the transfer of ownership. A new master, driven by greed or perhaps simply unschooled in the nuances of patron-client relations, aroused the moral outrage of his tenants and unwittingly sabotaged his own enterprise. But tenant agitation was not unusual in Cochabamba in the late colonial period. Growing population pressure on irrigated valley lands, heavier alcabalas and tribute, meager and fluctuating harvests, and growing landlord reliance on income from their tenantry combined to sharpen tensions between peasants and landlords. The form and content of such conflicts probably varied considerably from one hacienda to the next, and most of them never reached the colonial courts. But the strong presence of the state, following the great Indian rebellions, and its renewed effort to intervene in the private domain, probably encouraged some peasants to engage in "judicial politics" against their immediate overlords, even at great risk to their own future. Just as Andean peoples once protested the excesses of corregidores who violated the royal regulations on repartos, so rural tenants pressed their cases against extortionary landlords by measuring their obligations against royal regulations. The arancel introduced in the court proceedings against Almarás specified that a tenant was required to pay ten pesos and to work for two days for the landlord for each fanegada of irrigated maize land that he cultivated; a fanegada of wheat land was worth two pesos and two-fifths of a day's work; a fanegada of barley land, one peso and one-fifth of a day's work; and the site of the tenant's hut, one day of work.[72] Thus, a standard was provided by which peasants could protest the claims of a landlord or bargain for more favorable rent terms.

Furthermore, it was in the interest of the Bourbon state to pay attention to peasant grievances in order to prevent them from taking flight. Intent upon taxing forasteros residing on haciendas in the region, the Bourbons wanted to curtail the movement of Indian peasants in the valleys. The tenants knew how to exploit that fear. The peasants of Caporaya warned colonial authorities that their tyrannical lord "was driving all the miserable Indians to distant places in Vallegrande and the yungas, which is hurting the royal treasury."[73] Another witness threatened to flee the hacienda and follow the tracks of other refugees to unknown places in Ayopaya.[74] They realized that the colonial state had a stake in stabilizing agrarian class relations, even in the confines of the hacienda, and their bargaining position in the late eighteenth century was thereby improved (see chapter 8).

Peasants As Traders and Artisans

In contrast to the stark antagonisms of peasant-landlord relations that were exposed in the courtroom, class tensions in the marketplace seem diffuse and opaque. Yet it was probably in the realm of distribution, and specifically in the growing participation of rural smallholders in the product market, that peasants (in the aggregate) most affected the balance of class forces in the region. In the ordinary pursuit of a livelihood, peasants of the central valleys came out from under the weight of their rent obligations to participate in local markets. At weekly ferias, they congregated before dawn and haggled until well past midday over prices of wheat and maize, potatoes, coca, tocuyo and bayeta cloth, raw cotton and wool, salt, tallow, ají, fruits, sugar, cows, sheep, goats, mules, and oxen. Some of these transactions took the form of barter.

The central marketplace in the region was found on the outskirts of Cochabamba on Saturday mornings. Satellite markets flourished on Sundays in the towns of Quillacollo and Cliza; Tarata's feria took place on Tuesdays. Contemporary Europeans commented on the abundance of staples in the marketplace of Cochabamba: "Every day

72 AHMC, Leg. 1273 (1795), f. 23. Sharecropping Indians were exempt from these obligations.

73 Ibid., f. 1.

74 Ibid., f. 7v.

you can find . . . foodstuffs in the plaza selling at very moderate prices; the bread is as cheap as the meat, and there is every kind of vegetable, fruit, and fowl."[75] Indian traders (*manazos*) provisioned the towns with meat, after slaughtering the cattle they had driven from pastures in Mizque and Vallegrande. Most of the traders were women: *bayeteras* and *algodoneras*, who sold cloth, yarn, and cotton, and *capacheras*, who peddled vegetables, fruits, breads, and other items from their baskets and mantas.[76]

The rhythm and volume of commerce in staples were subject to the vagaries of agricultural conditions, of course. It was therefore still a shallow and periodic product market in which the smallholders participated, and a bad season could virtually eliminate them from the scene. In fact, as we shall see, the landowning class counted heavily on occasional harvest failures to make their much larger profits. But the advent of regular peasant markets in the central valleys signaled the emergence of a channel outside the channels controlled by landlords and large merchants, through which peasants could trade among themselves on their own terms and in accord with their own marketplace etiquette.[77] Peasant smallholders also diffused the

75 Viedma, *Descripción geográfica*, 46.

76 "Encabecimiento de mercaderes y comerciantes," AGN, Sala 9, Intendencia, 27.3.4 (1793-1794).

77 The development, internal dynamics, and social significance of retail or subsistence marketplaces in regional economies in Spanish America is a topic that has not yet attracted the attention of many historians. Assadourian's structural analysis of the internal market that revolved around the export economy of Potosí points to the importance of such studies, but analyses of regional marketing networks are still the domain of anthropologists. However, the historical and ethnographic work of Sidney Mintz has opened new perspectives on the topic; see, for example, his "Caribbean Marketplaces and Caribbean History," *Radical History Review*, no. 27 (1983): 110-120. This study, concerning the development of an internal market system in Jamaica during the eighteenth and nineteenth centuries, complements Mintz's earlier, conceptual work on "horizontal" class linkages that are reinforced by exchange relations in periodic peasant markets: "Internal Market Systems As Mechanisms of Social Articulation," in V. F. Ray, ed., *Proceedings of the 1959 Annual Spring Meeting of the American Ethnological Society* (Madison: University of Wisconsin Press, 1959), 20-30. On the notion of commodity exchanges governed by an egalitarian market etiquette, see Karl Polanyi, *The Great Transformation: The Political and Economic Origins of Our Time* (Boston: Beacon, 1944), 46-47. For contemporary analyses of peasant markets in the Cuzco region and the role of monetary transactions and reciprocal exchange, see Antoinette Fiorvanti-Molinié, "Multi-Levelled Andean Society and Market Exchange: The Case of Yucay (Peru)," in Lehmann, ed., *Ecology and Exchange*, 211-230. On ferias in contemporary Cochabamba, see Wolfgang Schoop, "Los ciclos rotatorios de los comerciantes ambulantes en las ferias se-

sources of supply for local towns in the region. The multiplicity of smallholders and the economic involution of tenure relations also fragmented into many small pieces the units of agricultural distribution, rendering small traders more vulnerable to harvest fluctuations. The imagery of an antlike economy, so often used to describe the regional economy of Cochabamba today, captures part of the picture of the petty commodity production and trade that was beginning to flourish at the time. Periodic market participation reinforced the economic viability of the peasant family economy by diversifying its subsistence activities. Yet from the perspective of agrarian class relations—the insertion of peasants as traders and artisans into the regional economy cut deeply into the economic power of landlords. Not only were landowners losing their grip on the distribution of hacienda resources inside their estates, but they were also witnessing a multitude of small-scale producers entering the commercial circuits and eroding their commercial monopoly.

This competition from peasant producers stimulated considerable commentary and complaint by landowners and municipal authorities. They grumbled about the overabundance of food crops, the depressed cereal prices, and the sluggish grain market (see chapter 6). The unregulated bread market was the greatest source of dissatisfaction. "There is no control over price, weight, or quality in the sale of meat and bread; people sell wherever they like in this city, and however they can," wrote Viedma in 1788. [78] Thirty years later, cabildo members were still complaining about the "anarchic" bread market.[79] They worried about all the bread sellers who did not belong to the bakers' guild. After harvesting their wheat and maize and turning it into flour, many peasants then procured the necessary firewood and aniseed, baked the dough in their own earthen ovens, and sold the bread from baskets on the streets of Cochabamba and other towns. According to council members, Cochabamba and other valley towns were ringed with earthen ovens. In 1824, Intendant Martín Ruíz de Somocurcio lamented the situation:

> Nowhere else in the world are the essentials of life sold without being properly weighed. Only in Cochabamba are the people disposed to accept whatever an old, usurious haggler is willing to

manales de los valles de Cochabamba," *Arbeitspapiere* (Universität Bielefeld), no. 13 (1978).

78 Viedma, *Descripción geográfica*, 46.

79 "Informe . . . sobre la contribución de harinas . . .," Dec. 1, 1817, in *Digesto de ordenanzas, reglamentos, acuerdos, decretos, de la municipalidad de Cochabamba* (Cochabamba: Heraldo, 1900), 3:242-247.

give them for their money. The infinite expansion of the guild [of breadmakers] and the fact that most are mestizos and of the most miserable station in life are insuperable obstacles to regulating the sale of this vital necessity.[80]

The intendant probably expressed the feeling of many government officials, after some forty years of attempts to establish an effective municipal grain market. At least since the arrival of Viedma in 1784, intendants had tried to assert government control over retail grain sales and to levy a tax on the flour purchased by members of the bakers' guild. "From the beginning of my term," Viedma wrote in exasperation, "I wanted to regulate [the meat and bread] trade . . . but I failed in spite of all my efforts."[81] In 1817, the cabildo compiled a list of 450 bakers, who annually purchased 20,000 fanegas of corn flour and between 40,000 and 50,000 fanegas of wheat flour. By issuing licenses to the bakers, the municipal government once more tried to restrict the number of people selling bread and to regulate the prices and quality of flour and bread.[82] In 1824, during the last years of colonial rule, Intendant Ruíz de Somocurcio proposed yet another scheme to control the sale of grain, a plan that was clearly in the interests of Cochabamba's largest landowners, some of whom served on the town council.

Ruíz de Somocurcio called for the formation of a joint stock company, the Sociedad de la Panadería Pública, (Public Bakery Association), which would exercise a monopoly over the sale of bread in the city. The intendant argued that this course of action would allow the state to raise needed revenue through levies on the wholesale purchase of flour, while granting a monopoly on the retailing sale of bread to a few of the city's wealthiest vecinos—those who purchased company shares at five hundred pesos each.[83] Although the plan was never implemented, the proposal itself is interesting. The intendant, seeking to raise 50,000 pesos annually from the local population to supply funds for the royal army, realized that one of the greatest favors he could do for the wealthier hacendados of Cochabamba was to give them a monopoly over the local grain trade, wiping out the competition they faced from the petty merchants and producers by

80 "Don Martín Ruíz de Somocurcio al cabildo," Mar. 8, 1824, in *Digesto de ordenanzas*, 3:272.

81 Viedma, *Descripción geográfica*, 46.

82 "Informe . . . sobre la contribución de harinas . . . ," 3:242-247.

83 "Don Martín Ruíz de Somocurcio al cabildo," 3:272-280.

dismantling the numerous ovens that ringed the city.[84] The small-scale producers who sold bread directly to the consumer would be forced out of the market. The municipal procurator, who represented the community before the cabildo, criticized the intendant's proposal, arguing that it would hurt the region's poor farmers, who were already destitute from more than a decade of intermittent warfare. The procurator advocated "absolute, free trade" in the region.[85] The minutes of the last council meetings of the colonial era show that the procurator had some sympathizers among the more antiroyalist members of the cabildo, though others perceived the existing grain market as almost barbaric, serving no one's interest—no one's, that is, except that of the "poor farmer."

Open-air markets at dawn, swarming with haggling peasants; caravans of llamas and traders trekking down from the western highlands during harvest season to barter in the valley ferias; mule trains loaded with sacks of flour en route to Oruro after a good harvest; the fluid movement of perishable commodities across the open valleys: these were the signs of a regional marketing system that local authorities failed to harness or stamp out. For some peasant producers, participation in the rural marketplace made possible individual accumulation, and the very existence of the markets must have created opportunities for some to manipulate the terms of exchange to their own advantage. Thus, while the emergence of peasant markets eroded the economic power of the landholding class, it advanced the process of social differentiation within the peasantry. A thin layer of petty commodity producers and traders in the valleys probably prospered and accumulated small patrimonies, which they bequeathed to their children. Their legacies are rarely documented, but the occasional will that surfaced during a legal dispute among the heirs or that found its way into a notarial book does reveal something about the sources and limits of peasant prosperity in Cochabamba of the late eighteenth century.

The most detailed testament of a peasant located among the trial records in the municipal archive of Cochabamba was written by a mestizo arrendero, Ramusa Almendras, who lived on the hacienda Chimboata in the Cliza valley.[86] Her daughter identified her as an

84 Ibid., 272.

85 "Sr. gobernador intendente al rey," May 7, 1824, in *Digesto de ordenanzas* 3: 282-284.

86 "Testamento de Ramusa Almendras de la hacienda Chimboata," AHMC, Leg. 1055 (1810).

elderly tenant of the estate, who, with the help of her children, had tended sheep and cattle and "worked hard to increase her possessions." After her husband abandoned the family, fleeing as a "fugitive from the law," Ramusa hired her son-in-law and others to help in the field work on her rented lands. Though there is no mention of commercial activities, the peasant woman must have engaged in them to some degree, for she had managed to accumulate a modest amount of wealth. Her net worth was estimated at 260 pesos at the time of her death, and her small legacy consisted of stored wheat, maize, potatoes, and quinoa and sheep, goats, oxen, mules, and horses. She had done well, by contemporary standards, but she had never acquired title to even a small piece of arable land in her own name.

The few wills, hacienda inventories, and notarial records available indicate that some peasants did acquire, through purchase or inheritance, a "small area" of maize land or a parcel of temporal land in the highlands. It was not unknown for a landlord to bequeath small plots of land and a few animals to his faithful yanaconas.[87] But even among the more prosperous peasants, land acquisition was no easy proposition, if only because land was so expensive. One fanegada of partially irrigated maize land, for example, was assessed at 250 pesos in the late eighteenth century—the approximate monetary worth of all of Ramusa Almendras's worldly possessions. Land purchase thus required either substantial amounts of cash or access to credit, and these were largely restricted to the local landholding elite (see chapter 6).[88]

87 For example, Don Vicente Caero of the hacienda Muela bequeathed "good land, not stony waste land" and some animals to his two yanaconas and their children: "Testamento de don Vicente Caero," AHMC, Leg. 1213 (1756).

88 Colonial sources rarely give the occupation of parties engaged in land transactions. The main clue as to whether title to property was being acquired by a peasant is a reference (or lack of reference) to the socioracial status of the purchaser. Usually, records of property transfers mentioned the "race" of the buyer if he was mestizo, ladino, cholo, or Indian. In the late colonial era, few titles passed into the hands of Indians or mestizos, according to the notarial records. In contrast, notarial records of the 1830s and 1840s routinely registered the occupation of both the buyer and the seller of land, and it was not unusual for peasants, laborers, and artisans to acquire or rent small properties in those years. A typical case was the purchase in 1840 of five and a half viches of land in the hacienda Oronata, with rights to the mita de agua for two hours every fifteen days, by a weaver and his wife, a seamstress: "Venta de tierras de sra. Bartolina Nava," AHMC, Leg. 1410 (1840). In 1833, a peasant (*labrador*) and his wife, a spinner (*hilandera*), signed a five-year lease for two estancias in the mountains

Perhaps the most important obstacle to peasant accumulation was simply the fact that most peasants lived at the mercy of seasonal and cyclical fluctuations of crop yields. Subsistence insecurity, the universal bane of peasant existence, made the equilibrium of the peasant family economy persistently precarious. Growing population pressure on the unirrigated lands, which suffered first and most severly from a shortage of rainfall, exacerbated the situation. Viedma's concern about "idle hands" and the "growing mixed-blood population" in the late eighteenth century reflected these problems. For many peasant households, even "normal" harvest fluctuations could bring hardship. During the fifteen years between 1786 and 1800, a period of relatively moderate fluctuations, the price of a fanega of maize went up as high as twenty-eight reales and down as low as sixteen reales per fanega (see figure 11 below). Even for those smallholders who endured (or capitalized on) chronic economic insecurity, a severe drought or other calamity could spell ruin. In the late eighteenth and early nineteenth centuries, the region experienced three subsistence crises: one associated with the 1781 rebellions; a second during the drought of 1784; and a third which was the result of a prolonged drought around 1804. These disasters transformed many peasants into beggars and paupers and destroyed the wealth of even those peasants who had had the makings of petty rural proprietors.[89]

The insecurity attendant upon small-scale agriculture, together with the growing opportunities for petty commerce in the towns and

---

bordering the pueblo real of El Paso: "Contrato de arrendamiento de tierras," AHMC, Leg. 1376 (1833), f. 223. Future research may find that peasant proprietorship was more common after independence. It may also be true, however, that the acquisition of land titles by peasants and artisans was more frequent in the late colonial period than the notarial records indicate. It seems likely that the intensified tax pressures on peasant households, together with the economic disruptions caused by war and agricultural crises, impeded the process of land acquisition by smallholders in the last decade of colonial rule.

89 A more detailed discussion of agricultural fluctuations and of their differential impact on the peasant and landowning classes is found in chap. 6. See also Larson, "Rural Rhythms of Class Conflict." On agricultural cycles and the secular stagnation and decline of staple prices in eighteenth-century Alto Perú, see Tandeter and Wachtel, *Precios y producción agraria*. The most systematic, long-term analysis of agricultural price and production trends pertains to eighteenth century Mexico; see the pioneering work of Enrique Florescano, *Precios del maíz y crisis agrícola en México, 1708-1810* (Mexico City: Colegio de México, 1969); Brading, *Haciendas and Ranchos*, chap. 8; and Richard L. Gardner, "Price Trends in Eighteenth-Century Mexico," *Hispanic American Historical Review* 65 (1985): 279-326.

ferias of the central valleys, motivated many peasants to diversify their economic activities. Though short of capital and land, and lacking the economic autonomy that land ownership might have bestowed, many rural people applied their "idle hands" to primitive manufacturing. When peasants could no longer assemble a variety of lands in different ecological niches or call upon their community for aid in times of stress, they found new forms of social insurance: selective engagement with commodity production and exchange, and a combination of agriculture, pastoralism, trade, and manufacturing. Thus, in the Cliza valley and on the outskirts of Cochabamba, a family of maize cultivators might also manufacture chicha and sell it to other peasants at the ferias. Wheat growers in the Sacaba valley crafted rustic furniture for sale in the nearby towns. Rural laborers in the Quillacollo parish made tocuyo (see chapter 7).

When, in 1774 and again in 1780, colonial authorities sought to increase alcabalas and regulate overland trade in the viceroyalties of La Plata and Peru, they encountered strong opposition from the popular classes of Cochabamba. It was the cholo peasant-artisans of the central valleys, particularly of Cliza, who launched the most visible protest. The "guilds of tocuyo weavers, tailors and shoemakers, ironmongers, and soapmakers" were part of the "popular commotion," and local officials worried about their power to "disturb the peace." Indeed, the procurador advised against the tax increases, because of the "poverty, indigence, and scarcity in which most inhabitants of this province find themselves living."[90] Like their forebears who revolted against the threat of tribute levies in the 1730s, the smallholder-artisans in the 1770s and 1780s constituted a powerful political force against tax reforms.

As petty commodity producers, the valley peasants were remolding the contours of the regional economy, diversifying production and evolving a network of peasant markets. They were giving shape to an emerging peasant economy, one that was outside the domain of the traditional Andean community and that has made a deep imprint on the region down to the present day. Most important, they were forging a rival economy that increasingly encroached on the economic power of the landowning class.

90 "Exp. seguido con motivo del amago de revolución en Cochabamba, con datos de los impuestos que de cobran de los frutos de la tierra," ANB, EC no. 57 (1781); and "Informe del corregidor sobre los pasquines y la comoción popular en Cochabamba," AGI, Charcas, Leg. 505 (1774).

CHAPTER SIX

The Landowning Class: Hard Times and Windfall Profits

In the early colonial period, grain haciendas sprang up like mushrooms around the cities and towns and some mining camps—wherever town dwellers concentrated in large numbers and preexisting Andean settlements posed little obstacle to the overseas colonizers. Two hundred years later, in the late eighteenth century, most hacendados were still supplying food to nearby urban areas. Given the growing population, some landowners could count on rising property values to secure more loans or to press for more rent.

But in general, times were hard for the owners of the grain and livestock estates of Andean America, or so at least they complained. The secular stagnation and decline of agricultural prices in Alto Perú during the second half of the eighteenth century narrowed the margin of return on grain sales. Many hacendados, including those in Cochabamba, found themselves confronting competition from a class of smallholders (mostly tenants and sharecroppers) who periodically brought small quantities of staples to the market, depressing the prices of those crops. The centrifugal effect of Spanish partible-inheritance laws compounded the problem. By the late eighteenth century, the transmission of land ownership through inheritance had fragmented many property units into parcels and pieces and had reduced haciendas to mere paper units of reckoning. But the effects of these internal corrosive forces on the landlord class depended ultimately upon the profitability of agriculture and upon the strength of regional and extraregional markets.

Grain Haciendas in Decay

Almost everywhere in eighteenth-century Spanish America, landlords complained of low returns on capital investment in grain agriculture. In his survey of agrarian studies, Mörner found that the average return on capital invested in agriculture (including specialized crops) did not exceed 6 percent at that time.[1] Most agricultural enterprises, particularly grain haciendas, were burdened with multiple liens—mortgages and various "annuities" (annual payments on charitable bequests and other "pious works")—that siphoned off large portions of income. Haciendas in the Mexican province of Oaxaca, for example, carried accumulated debts that absorbed as much as two-thirds of the capital value of those estates.[2] Brading postulated that "the [Mexican] fortunes created in mining and commerce were invested in land, there to be slowly dissipated or to be gradually transferred into the coffers of the Church."[3] Of course, the fact that most landlords were deep in debt to the church cannot be ascribed simply to competition from small-scale cultivators, mismanagement of the enterprise, or conspicuous consumption by a "prestige-oriented" class. Many landowners complained that the high costs of production absorbed most of the returns they got from the sale of their staple crops. One Martín de Garmendía, a hacendado of Cuzco province, said that "for every peso paid for a unit of grain, five percent is paid for annuities and rent, ten percent covers tithes, 20 percent pays salaries and wages, and 40 or 50 percent covers transport costs."[4] Although his cost accounting is perhaps incomplete, unrepresentative, and even inaccurate, Garmendía's estimate of freight costs is striking. It emphasizes the formidable logistical obstacles faced by the owners of grain estates who tried to reach beyond the markets in their immediate vicinity. Similarly, Florescano found that most grain enterprises in central Mexico during the eighteenth century were handicapped by poor roads, high transport costs, and extremely narrow markets.[5] The hacendados of the Bajío who built irrigation works and turned maize patches into wheat fields were among the fortunate few who could take advantage of the expanding

1 Mörner, "Spanish American Hacienda," 204; see also Magnus Mörner, "Economic Factors and Social Stratification in Colonial Spanish America, with Special Regard to Elites," *Hispanic American Historical Review* 63 (1983): 335-370.

2 William Taylor, *Landlord and Peasant in Colonial Oaxaca* (Stanford, Calif.: Stanford University Press, 1972), 140-142; see also Arnold J. Bauer, "The Church and Spanish American Agrarian Structure, 1765-1865," *Americas* 28 (1971): 78-98.

3 Brading, *Miners and Merchants*, 219.

4 Quoted in Magnus Mörner, "En torno a las haciendas de la región del Cuzco desde el siglo XVIII," in Enrique Florescano, ed., *Haciendas, latifundios, y plantaciones* (Mexico City: Siglo XXI, 1975), 363.

5 Florescano, *Precios del maíz*, 88ff.

market in staple crops. Like the early chacareros of Cochabamba who supplied cereal to Potosí during the sixteenth-century silver boom, the landlords of the Bajío set out to conquer the staple markets of Guanajuato, America's eighteenth-century silver capital in Mexico. The thriving grain estates in the province of León in the Bajío apparently were among the exceptions that proved the rule.[6]

If most hacendados found their agrarian operations limited by geographical barriers and capital scarcity, landlords throughout the Andes saw their situation deteriorate sharply after 1780. The crown's decision to create the viceroyalty of La Plata in 1776 and then to open Buenos Aires to direct trade with all Spanish ports in 1778 increased foreign competition manyfold and diverted the flow of silver toward Buenos Aires. Merchants in southern Atlantic ports channeled European goods to Alto Perú and beyond to Cuzco, Arequipa, and even Lima. Although Cuzco and the coastal sugar and cotton plantations and vineyards continued to send products to Alto Perú after 1780, those commodities were often traded for European textiles rather than for unminted or coined silver, as had been customary in earlier times.[7] To make matters worse, the flood of European textiles undermined the interregional trade in rustic cloth that was produced in Andean obrajes and workshops. The Cuzco region, among others, suffered a sharp decline in the export of textiles.[8]

Meanwhile, as the traffic across the pampas grew heavier, the merchants of Buenos Aires competed with hacendados throughout the Andes for cargo animals, especially mules. During the six years between 1776 and 1781, the estancias of Salta and Córdoba exported 70,000 mules (at eight to nine pesos per animal) to Peru, and between 1790 and 1800, another 30,000 (at thirteen to sixteen pesos per mule).[9] Mules became scarce and expensive in many parts of Peru,

6 Brading, *Haciendas and Ranchos.*

7 J. Fisher, *Government and Society in Colonial Peru,* 133; Céspedes del Castillo, "Lima y Buenos Aires"; and Febres Villarroel, "Crisis agrícola en el Perú."

8 Mörner, "En torno a las haciendas," 357; and Mörner, *Perfil de la sociedad rural.* For a comprehensive and fascinating study of rural society in the Cuzco area, see Luís Miguel Glave and María Isabel Remy, *Estructura agraria y vida rural en una región andina: Ollantaytambo entre los siglos XVI y XIX* (Cuzco: Centro de Estudios Rurales Andinos "Bartolomé de la Casas," 1983).

9 John Lynch, *Spanish Colonial Administration, 1782-1810: The Intendant System in the Viceroyalty of the Río de la Plata* (London: Athlone, 1958); Nicolás Sánchez-Albornoz, "La saca de mulas de Salta al Perú, 1778-1808," *Anuario del Instituto de Investigaciones Históricas,* no. 8 (1965): 261-312.

and freight costs rose accordingly. Moreover, the crown's determination to raise state revenue in the colonies prompted it to increase the sales (alcabala) and transit taxes on most colonial items of trade, and muleteers had a difficult time evading these taxes after the state built customs houses at strategic points along the most heavily traveled routes.

Agrarian interests in the southern Andes were also dealt serious blows by native insurgents in 1780 and 1781. In Cochabamba and other regions, rebels destroyed haciendas and mills, burned crops, and slaughtered landlords' herds. The royal armies sometimes struck back by burning the crops and stealing the livestock of Indians.[10] Rebellions also often broke out along main commercial arteries; the insurgents blocked trade routes between the central valleys of Cochabamba and the altiplano, for example, and cut off food supplies to Oruro and other highland markets.[11] Viedma reported that, several years later, many landowners of Cochabamba had still not recovered from the losses they suffered during the rebellion.[12]

Imbued with the doctrines of the physiocrats and vested with enhanced authority by the crown, Viedma and other intendants who arrived in the Andes in 1784 turned their attention to the ailing regional economies of their districts. As instructed in the Ordinance of Intendants (1782), they set about the tasks of inspecting their intendancies and gathering information on population, roads, commerce, industry, and Indian villages. In their reports, they described sluggish markets, underproductive estates, and depressed agricultural prices in a rich land of abundant and varied vegetation.[13] Some authorities traced the root cause of Peru's agricultural decline to the disposition of labor. Macera has argued that the frequent complaints of labor scarcity in eighteenth-century Peru were not related to the Indian population curve, which after all was on the upswing again.[14]

10 Campbell, "Recent Research on Andean Peasant Revolts," 27.

11 Ibid., 28; and Mörner, *Perfil de la sociedad rural*, 119ff.

12 He mentioned, for example, that in 1787, newborn calves had still not replenished the herds of cattle lost during the Indian uprisings. AGN, Sala 9, Intendencia, 5.8.4, Leg. 3, May 1, 1787.

13 Viedma's report is analyzed in chap. 5. A brief summary of it may also be found in Tibor Wittman, "Sociedad y economía de Cochabamba: La 'Valencia del Perú' en 1793," *Revista de Indias*, no. 31 (1971): 367-376. On the intendancies in Lower Peru, see J. Fisher, *Government and Society in Colonial Peru*; for Alto Perú, see Lynch, *Spanish Colonial Administration*.

14 Macera, "Feudalismo colonial americano," 168ff.

Contemporary observers said that the problem lay in the work habits of native peoples. In 1751, the crown echoed this opinion: "The indolence, sloth, and laziness of those natives towards all kinds of work is notorious."[15] Along with the colonial authorities, the crown feared that, with the abolition of the repartimiento de mercancías, the Indians would slip back into their idle ways. The intendant of Arequipa, in his report, confirmed that Indians had become more inactive since 1781, and he declared that the crown must prod them to work if Peru's economy was to flourish again.[16]

Viedma was one of the intendants who expressed alarm about the decay of Alto Perú's economy and specifically of its granary, Cochabamba. He made many comments about the contrast between nature's bounty and the human misery he saw around him. His reports were filled with descriptions of vagrants, abandoned highland towns, decaying haciendas, and an impoverished population that consumed chicha in excess. But unlike many of his colleagues, Viedma ascribed the decline to narrow markets and a "crisis of overproduction." In his view, peasant laziness was not necessarily congenital, but was rather a social malaise that crept over the land as monetary incentives weakened and markets became glutted. In his 1788 report, Viedma wrote:

> Agriculture is one of the most important sectors of the economy; but it is necessary to search for outlets so the cultivator's labor will always be justly remunerated. There is little use in cultivating more wheat and maize [in Cochabamba] when experience has shown us that the lack of demand in the outlying provinces has depreciated the price of these products, such that the price of a fanega of wheat or maize does not reach even one peso. . . . We must be aware of this overabundance [of grain] in order to be able to find a solution to the problem; for this is the fundamental cause of people's sloth and laziness. As people attain the means of subsistence so as not to be forced to gaze at the ancient face of hunger, they are content with [the traditional crops like] maize, potatoes, and ají . . . as they pass through a

15 Edict of June 15, 1751, quoted in Golte, *Repartos y rebeliones*, 84.

16 Victor M. Barriga, *Memorias para la historia de Arequipa*, 4 vols., (1786-1791) (Arequipa: La Colmena, 1941-1952), 1: 107-108; also cited and summarized in Zavala, *Servicio personal*, 3: 91-92. On similar views, recast in liberal ideological terms, among nineteenth-century Chilean landowners, see Arnold J. Bauer, *Chilean Rural Society from the Spanish Conquest to 1930* (Cambridge: Cambridge University Press, 1975), 148.

languid and licentious life. It would not be so were these fruits scarce.[17]

Viedma was here expressing his view of the causes of economic backwardness, revealing how influenced he was by neomercantilist currents of thought. Yet he himself had observed at first hand that peasants in the crowded valley of Cliza had turned to handicrafts to supplement their meager income from farming; and the "hamlets of arrenderos" who lived in the Cercado district were among the legions of petty traders who converged upon the ferias of Cochabamba, Quillacollo, and other towns. Thus, Viedma's empirical observations of economic activity in the central valleys (see chapter 5) did not seem to support his precepts about peasant lassitude and depressed grain prices. Certainly the landless laborer who received the statutory daily wage of two reales hardly considered food prices to be "deflated"; nor from a regional perspective could grain prices in Cochabamba be considered exceptionally low.[18] When Viedma addressed the problem of idle and redundant laborers, he was articulating the viewpoint of his class—one that interpreted economic decline in terms of overproduction and lack of market demand and price incentive. Yet even while they tried to plumb the causes of "peasant lethargy," Viedma and his fellow landowners paradoxically found themselves challenged by increasing competition from a profusion of small-scale cultivators.

Perhaps it is not surprising, then, that the intendant rarely reported to the Consulado, the royal trade guild in Buenos Aires, the problems of scarcity or high food prices in the region. In 1784 and 1804, when all of Alto Perú was beset by severe, prolonged drought and by famine and bands of wandering beggars, Viedma did write of human misery and hardship. In a series of reports about agricultural conditions between 1785 and 1800, however, he stressed the region's abundant grain supplies and reserves and the moderate prices of food. In September 1796, for example, he reported that the harvest of that year, together with grain stored from the previous year, had inundated the local market. Peasants in the neighboring highland provinces also enjoyed favorable planting conditions in those years, and the intendant noted that Cochabamba's farmers therefore shipped

17 Viedma, *Descripción geográfica*, 159-160.

18 The average price of grain in Cochabamba was about eighteen reales in an ordinary year, while in the Bajío it hovered around fourteen reales. Brading, *Haciendas and Ranchos*, 184.

little grain to the highlands. He reported that "even Cochabamba's inflated and numerous population would be incapable of consuming all local [food crops] over the next two years."[19] Even when the weather was bad, as in the early months of 1787, the intendant predicted no serious food shortage in the region, for he declared that sufficient grain had been stored from previous harvests to feed the local population adequately. He continued to remain confident during the poor harvest of 1787. On September 1, he reported that much of the crop had died for lack of rainfall, but he considered current grain prices (twenty-two reales per fanega of maize) to be relatively low nevertheless, again because of the existence of grain reserves that people could draw on.[20] (For additional details, see table A-5.)

This pattern of one or two successive years of ordinary to abundant harvests followed by a year of poor harvest, due to extensive flooding, as in 1788 and 1797, or to drought, as in 1792 and 1807, recurred with almost uncanny consistency between 1785 and 1800. Yet despite this variation, Viedma never reported serious shortages of wheat or maize. When frost and drought ruined the crops (especially in the highlands) in 1792, Viedma assured the Consulado that maize was still readily available, at the price of twenty-four reales a fanega. So it was also in 1797, 1799, and 1800. Yet prices in those years were fluctuating widely (see figure 11). Perhaps Viedma was assessing the significance of the fluctuations not from the peasant's and wage laborer's point of view but from the perspective of landlords finally able to dispose of some of their surpluses.

One of the best informants about the profitability of haciendas in Cochabamba was Juan Felipe Negrón, who had come into possession of the hacienda Chullpas in the Cliza valley, an estate that Viedma had purchased earlier (in 1805) in the hope of founding an orphanage on the grounds. After Viedma's death in 1809, his widow sold most of the property. Following the Wars of Independence, the estate was assessed at 50,084 pesos, most of it in the form of some four hundred fanegadas of land, especially its irrigated maize fields (see table 15 above). Chullpas was unquestionably one of the wealthiest and largest estates in the region, yet when it was auctioned off in 1828 (bringing 55,125 pesos), it seemed to be in a sorry state. Its buildings and mills were crumbling, and the property carried various ecclesiastical benefices and liens amounting to 30,000 pesos—more than half of its assessed value. Furthermore, the estate had not weathered

19 AGN, Sala 9, Intendencia, 5.8.3, Leg. 2, Sept. 6, 1786.

20 Ibid., 5.8.4, Leg. 3, Sept. 1, 1787, and Dec. 31, 1787.

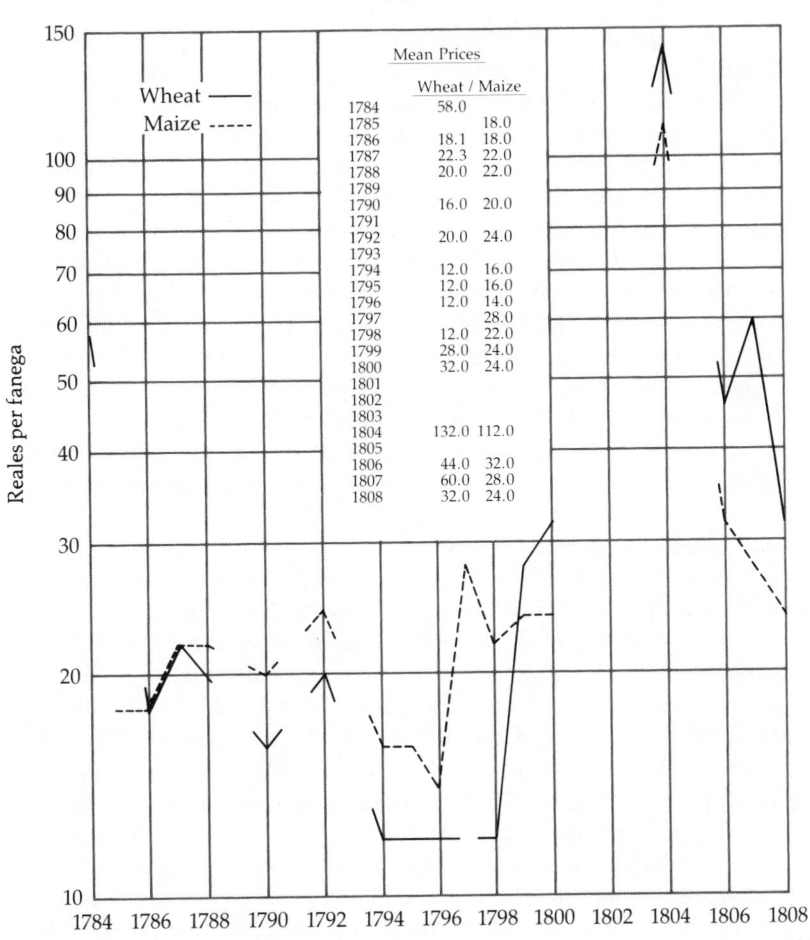

Figure 11 Wheat and Maize Prices in Cochabamba, 1784-1808
Sources: AGN, Sala 9, Intendencia, 5.8.3, Leg. 2; 5.8.4, Leg. 3; 5.8.5, Leg. 4; 5.8.6, Leg. 5; 5.8.7, Leg. 6; 5.9.1, Leg. 7; and 5.9.2, Leg. 8.

the transition to republican rule very well. Between the last colonial census in 1804 and the time Negrón registered a complaint about property taxes in 1828, the resident Indian population had declined from 207 to 70.[21]

Negrón spoke of a serious problem that faced many landowners in

21 AGN, Sala 13, Padrones, 18.3.3, Leg. 53 (1804); "Don Juan Felipe Negrón, vz. de Potosí, se remató . . . la hacienda Chullpas (cantón de Toco)," AHMC, Leg. 1360 (1828); "Venta y remate público de la hacienda Chullpas," AHMC, Leg. 1083 (1827).

the late colonial period. Access to water made the difference for him between the possibility of prospering or the near-certain prospect of falling deeper into debt. Negrón captured what water he could from the Toco and Quaiculi rivers to irrigate his maize fields, but neither he nor his predecessors had invested in the construction of irrigation ditches, reservoirs, or sluices to ensure a more reliable supply of water. He complained that the system of rotational irrigation (the mita de agua) did not provide sufficient water to allow him to harvest two crops a year. Thus, unlike some of his more fortunate neighbors, Negrón had to cope with the uncertainties of rainfall. According to his own accounts, a spectacular harvest of 3,000 or 4,000 fanegas of wheat and maize might be followed the next year by a "normal" yield of 2,000 fanegas, with prices in a good year at about ten to twelve reales per fanega and in the normal years at sixteen to eighteen reales. Gross income in a good year would therefore be between 4,000 and 5,000 pesos; in the normal years, between 4,000 and 4,500 pesos. Negrón estimated that his production costs in a good year would be 3,000 pesos, but only 1,500 pesos in an ordinary year. Consequently, net income in a good year represented between 2 and 4 percent of the value of the land, while in an ordinary year it represented from 5 to 6 percent—although all those figures are somewhat higher than was actually the case, since Negrón failed to include in his production costs the amounts required for annuities, interest on his debts, and seed for the following year.[22] However crude Negrón's accounts may have been, they revealed the inner logic of demesne agriculture: landlords reaped their highest returns when the weather was unfavorable and prices were thereby higher.

Deprived of distant markets and of any incentive to increase agricultural production, the landlords of Cochabamba turned inward and developed a system of storage and distribution that was adapted to the conditions of harvest fluctuations. When drought, frost, or flood reduced competition from the smallholding cultivators, the large landowners (individual and corporate) who had stored grain from previous years had a chance to profit considerably. From this perspective, it is understandable why Viedma reported that, even after moderately poor harvests, there was no serious shortage of food in the region. The large landowners were able to turn the vicissitudes of nature to their own advantage.[23] It was commonplace, in times of

22 AHMC, Legs. 1083 and 1360, f. 231.

23 Florescano, *Precios del maíz*, has shown how landlords in central Mexico were able not merely to take advantage of high prices but even to create them.

food shortage, for them to release their stores of grain onto the market in small quantities, or else to increase their exports to the western highland markets, in order to keep the price up. That is what the cabildo of Cochabamba, for example, discovered during an inspection of the granaries of haciendas in the Cliza and Cochabamba valleys that had been prompted by the drought of 1784.[24]

The landowners who benefited most from crop failures were those who controlled extensive irrigation works that continued to water their maize fields even after several weeks of little rainfall or who at least had the political leverage and authority to command access to periodic distribution of scarce water. As Negrón acknowledged, "It doesn't matter whether maize sells for five or six pesos if it withers on the stalk for lack of irrigation; in that case, an hacendado is apt to lose everything."[25]

During an inspection of flour mills in several parishes in 1799, royal authorities had occasion to interview many hacendados who operated water-driven mills on their estates. The owners expressed their dissatisfaction with the prospect of paying a tax of one real per fanega on the grain they milled. The owners were also worried about their access to water. Especially for those who had invested substantial amounts of capital in their milling enterprises—a typical mill was assessed at between 3,000 and 4,000 pesos in the late eighteenth century—the supply of water was critical. How landowners fared in the struggle over water depended partly on the location of their mill in relation to the quebrada, where streams had carved out mountain ravines and spilled down into the valley bottomlands. One miller, José de Severicha y Foronda, complained that the landowners who had higher land frequently siphoned off the river water upon which he depended to power his grain mills. Consequently, he was able to operate the enterprise only five months out of the year for lack of water, and under these conditions, he told the inspector, he rarely made a profit. In fact, Severicha presented detailed accounts to prove that only the earnings from properties he owned in the Cliza valley made it possible for him to operate his mills in Quillacollo. If he were not so fortunate as to own haciendas in Cliza, he said, he could never pay his debts or prevent the foreclosure of his property. "For the truth is that the earnings of a poor asendado [*sic*] are hardly sufficient to cover costs and to allow him to retain the title of 'asen-

24 "El procurador general al cabildo," Feb. 10, 1784, in *Digesto de ordenanzas*, 3: 128.

25 "Venta y remate público de la hacienda Chullpas," AHMC, Leg. 1083 (1827).

dado' when asendados spend more than they earn."[26] It is very likely that Severicha exaggerated his case and professed poverty in order to dissuade the inspector from levying the tax. Yet the inspector who toured the mills compiled a catalogue of complaints concerning the risks and costs of the milling enterprises. Even under optimal conditions of abundant harvests and plentiful water supplies, mills operated only three to six months a year. Returns fluctuated sharply from one year to the next, and millowners feared floods even more than drought. In the words of one millowner in the river valley of Tapacarí, "Milling depends upon rainfall, and drought can silence all the wheat mills in the region; but when torrential rains swell the rivers and spill over the banks, all traffic and trade with highland Indians ceases and many mills are destroyed."[27]

These millowners and hacendados were expressing the discontent that landowners felt in most regions of narrow, circumscribed markets. Like peasants whose very subsistence and petty mercantile accumulation were jeopardized by the fluctuation of harvest yields, landlords themselves could not break loose from the cycle: their profits from agriculture were derived from scarcity, high prices, and the subsistence needs of the peasant class. If hacendados diversified their operations and invested in several mills, they might partially make up for the low returns on the sale of maize and wheat after plentiful harvests by the fees they charged for turning peasants' grain into flour. But returns on their capital investment were always vulnerable to the weather.

In addition to their concerns about water, weather, and competition from small-scale cultivators, many landowners also perceived a deeper threat from the commercial opening of Buenos Aires in 1776 and especially from its opening to direct trade with Spanish ports after 1778. Of course, the hacendados had little fear of direct competition from Spanish agrarian enterprises. The problem, rather, was that the traffic in silver and in European goods in the port of Buenos Aires drew heavily upon the freight animals, particularly the mules and horses raised on the grasslands of Salta and Córdoba. Muleteers drove fewer pack animals northward into the Andes to sell to hacendados and local merchants. Wholesale merchants of the southern port city began to assume control of the means of overland transport in the viceroyalty, leaving many regions with acute shortages of mules and horses.

26 "Real visita a las molinas de grano," AHMC, Leg. 1213 (1799).

27 Ibid. (interview with Mariano Vergara).

In Cochabamba, landowners had not been able to replenish all the horses and mules lost during the Indian uprisings, when the city had dispatched a large band of militia to La Paz to break the rebels' stranglehold on that city. In the 1780s and 1790s, hacendados saw the price of mules rise from between fifteen and twenty-five pesos to more than thirty-five pesos. The shortage of freight animals alarmed Viedma and other provincial authorities, and they protested the situation in reports and letters to the consulado in 1800 and 1801.[28] Only the wealthiest landowners owned enough pack animals to transport their own harvest to distant markets. Most property owners and small-scale producers were unable to transport their grain, even when periodic shortages forced up staple prices considerably, except by the use of professional pack drivers or other intermediaries who owned mule trains. This scarcity of pack animals conferred an additional advantage on the region's large landowners and merchants.

In Viedma's view, the new trans-Atlantic trade arrangements posed another, perhaps more serious, threat to the local landowners. In 1788, he wrote: "Spanish goods are regularly imported to this city [Cochabamba]. Luxury is fashionable now, and many consume [Spanish] articles of trade, occasioning the flight of money, which the province can ill afford."[29] In the same report, he estimated that the local population spent 200,000 pesos on European merchandise, about 35 percent of the total value of all (colonial and European) imports in 1788.[30] When checked against yearly alcabalas on imports, Viedma's estimate appears to be much too high.[31] Furthermore, the amount of European goods that traders brought into the province varied considerably from year to year. But Viedma's criticism of hacendados who lived beyond their means, frittering away their income on such items as Spanish silks, was not surprising under the circumstances.

Indeed, insolvency of landowners was a matter of some concern in the 1780s. In 1783, the cabildo of Cochabamba took note of the encumbrances and debts that burdened most estates in the region and expressed alarm that, two years after the Indian uprisings, many ha-

28 AGN, Sala 9, Consulado, 4.6.4, tomo 14 (1800 and 1801), especially ff. 56-56v.

29 Viedma, *Descripción geográfica*, 47.

30 Ibid., 144.

31 For details, see Larson, "Economic Decline and Social Change," 230-240.

cendados had still not resumed payment of their obligations to creditors.[32] Some forty years later, at the time of independence, an angry landowner who decried government plans to tax property owners remarked that "Those who call themselves landowners in this province actually own a ridiculously small part of their property; in most cases, landlords whose estates are worth ten, fifteen, or twenty thousand pesos own less than a third of the property."[33]

Wills and inventories (*tasaciones*) of family properties in the late eighteenth and early nineteenth centuries show that, in most cases, between one-third and one-half of the total assessment was encumbered by loans and various forms of obligations to the church (*obras pías* and *capellanías*). As historians have shown for other regions, encumbrances on rural properties tended to accelerate the turnover of property, for by assuming the payment of obligations, purchasers could buy the real estate for a smaller cash outlay.[34] In transfers of property ownership in Cochabamba in the 1780s, the average purchaser paid cash for only about 50 percent of the assessed value of the property.[35] Property sales usually included the transfer of all or most debt obligations to the new proprietor. Sometimes loan contracts forbade the subdivision of property, but most of them stipulated only that the hacienda be kept up and the assessed property value maintained. When several heirs inherited an encumbered hacienda, they frequently assumed a portion of the debt obligations, in accordance with the value of their share of the inheritance.[36]

The largest moneylenders in Cochabamba province were its seven monasteries. At the time of independence in 1825, the sum of their outstanding loans was more than 600,000 pesos (table 18). Church liens on property that year were worth a little more than the estimated value of the province's exports in 1788.[37] The monasteries extended credit (*censos*), with the property as collateral, at a fixed interest rate of 5 percent annually. Sometimes credit was extended in perpetuity (*censos en compra*) in exchange for an annual fee paid to

32 AGN, Sala 9, Intendencia, 5.8.2, Leg. 1 (1783).

33 ANB, Ministerio del Interior, Prefectura de Cochabamba, vol. 2 (1825).

34 Mörner, "Spanish American Hacienda," 198.

35 AGN, Sala 13, Contaduría, 21.1.1 (1781) and 27.1.5 (1785).

36 See, for example, the division of the hacienda Muela among several heirs, in "Hijuelación de la hacienda Muela, en Arani," AHMC, Leg. 1067 (1817-1833).

37 The total value of the province's exports in 1788 was estimated to be 620,906 pesos. Viedma, *Descripción geográfica*, 156.

Table 18. Principal and Interest of Loans Held by Cochabamba's Monasteries, 1825

	Principal		*Annual Interest*	
Monastery	*Amount (pesos)*	*Percentage of Total*	*Amount (pesos)*	*Percentage of Principal*
Santa Clara	222,480	34.9	7,662	3.4
San Augustín	117,919	18.5	4,066	3.4
Santa Theresa	114,625	18.0	3,779	3.3
Santo Domingo	79,912	12.5	3,296	4.1
San Francisco	54,199	8.5	1,672	3.1
La Merced	38,653	6.1	1,223	3.2
La Recolección	9,720	1.5	406	4.2
Total	637,508	100.0	22,104	

Source: ANB, Ministerio del Interior, tomo 2, no. 236 (1825).

the monastery; in other cases, the loans were made for a seven-year term.

The richest ecclesiastical institution in Cochabamba, and the largest lender, was the Franciscan convent of Santa Clara, located in the city of Cochabamba. In 1825, it held 222,480 pesos in mortgage loans, more than one-third of the value of all ecclesiastical loans in the province that year. Santa Clara was a large nunnery, with a resident population of sixty-three nuns and their personal servants.[38] The "sisters of the black veil" who graced the courtyards of Santa Clara were mostly the daughters of wealthy hacendados, who paid the convent a "dowry" (in effect, an entrance fee) of between 1,000 and 3,000 pesos and sometimes in addition pledged an "endowment" of annual payments. Such, for example, was the arrangement under which Tomasa Liro de Córdova, daughter of the cacique of Tapacarí, Guillermo Liro de Córdova, entered the convent on the eve of the Túpac Amarú uprisings.[39]

Santa Clara built its financial empire, however, not so much on the proceeds from its dowries or benefices as on the reinvested profits of its agrarian enterprises. The convent was probably the largest landowner in the Cochabamba province during the eighteenth century. In 1648, Francisco de Varga bequeathed to it twenty fanegadas of rich, irrigated maize land in the Cliza valley. The assessed value

38 Viedma, *Descripción geográfica*, 38; Gabriel René Moreno, *Ultimos días coloniales en el Perú* (La Paz: Juventud, 1970), 172.

39 AHMC, Leg. 1444 (1780), f. 718.

of the hacienda Cliza in that year was 40,000 pesos.[40] Over the next century, the convent's financial managers invested in neighboring land and properties. By the early nineteenth century, the nunnery's hacienda Cliza extended across 860 fanegadas of bottomland. In 1825, the minister of the interior in the newly established republic registered 565,400 pesos as the total assessed property value of Santa Clara. The estate's wheat and maize fields alone were estimated to be worth more than 300,000 pesos, and sale of the harvested crop brought in 17,000 pesos in that year alone.[41] Nothing was said at that time about the size of its labor force, but in the last colonial tribute census in 1803, the resident Indian population numbered almost one thousand.[42] In terms of its wealth, size, and income, this latifundium dwarfed other estates in the region.

There was no central registry of ecclesiastical real estate, but occasional references make it clear that other orders had substantial investments in land as well, if to a lesser degree than the Franciscans. The Augustinians held lands in the village of Tapacarí, and they owned the wealthy hacienda El Convento in the valley of Caraza, where sixty-three yanaconas served the mendicants in 1747,[43] and the hacienda Achamoco in the parish of Tarata in the Cliza valley, where seventy-eight yanaconas lived and worked in the early nineteenth century.[44] The Dominicans owned lands and mills on the large hacienda Vinto on the outskirts of Quillacollo.[45] A Carmelite convent owned high-altitude pasture and crop lands and tropical lowlands in the parish of Yani (partido of Ayopaya), and in the early nineteenth century it leased out the hacienda Yani to someone who planted potatoes in its puna land, maize in warm, sheltered niches, and sugar cane in the tropical, low-altitude acreage.[46] The Jesuits,

40 Damian Rejas, *Tercer centenario de la fundación del Monasterio de Santa Clara (1648-1948)* (Cochabamba: Universal, 1948), 5-6.

41 ANB, Ministerio del Interior, tomo 2, no. 236 (1825).

42 AGN, Sala 13, Padrones, 18.3.4, Leg. 54 (1803).

43 "Real provisión sobre no ser yanaconas los indios de la hacienda de Carasa," ANB, EC no. 6396 (1749).

44 "Exp. por el Convento de San Augustín . . . sobre la devolución de las haciendas de Hachamoco en arrendamiento," AHMC, Leg. 1175 (1806).

45 AHMC, Leg. 1457 (1765), f. 510.

46 "Exp. por Ciprián Cartagena contra la administración del Monasterio del Carmen sobre . . . la hacienda de Yani," AHMC, Leg. 1062 (1782); AGI, Charcas, Leg. 236, Nov. 8, 1724 (on the foundation of the Santa Teresa convent and the

too, had made inroads into the Cochabamba valleys before 1767.[47] In some parishes, like Caraza and Cliza, monasteries owned some of the best lands and probably ran the most efficient and profitable agrarian enterprises. The Augustinian friars, for example, rarely parceled out their land to arrenderos, but instead maintained tight control over a servile yanacona population.

Notwithstanding these investments in land and the shrewd management of estates, however, it is probable that most ecclesiastical capital, including the assets of Santa Clara, was in the form of loans. At least from the perspective of the cash-hungry individual landowner, at once heir to a splintered estate and beset by rising freight costs and fierce competition over irrigation water, it would seem that the friars and the women of the black veil collectively monopolized the supply of loan capital and rural credit in the late eighteenth century. No wonder, then, that at the time of independence, many landowners expressed hostility toward their pious creditors and often renounced their obligation to redeem their debts to them.[48]

Pressed from below by peasant producers during years of good harvests and from above by the claims of ecclesiastical creditors, many landowners gave up management of their agrarian enterprises and lived off the rent from their tenants. When Viedma and cabildo members bemoaned the decay of agriculture, they spoke for landowners who were witnessing the erosion of their economic position in local society. Some hacendados did improve their estates by building irrigation ditches and small reservoirs to increase productivity and enhance their ability to profit during seasons of scanty rainfall.[49] Others, like Almarás of the hacienda Caporaya, tried to extend the area of arable land and to press their tenants for more labor time to sow the new acreage (see chapter 5). But many other landowners, perhaps the majority, considered only two options to be economi-

hacienda Yani; Adolfo de Morales kindly allowed me to consult his notes on the contents of this document).

47 Several large estates that had been owned by the Jesuits, such as the haciendas Calliri, Paucarpata, Marquina, and Quirquiavi, were later mortgaged or leased as *obras pías* by the *Junta de Temporalidades*, and the income from the properties was used to support orphanages and other charities. AGN, Intendencia, 5.8.2 (1802).

48 ANB, Ministerio del Interior, Prefectura de Cochabamba, vol. 2 (1825).

49 For example, in the 1770s and 1780s, the owners of the hacienda Muela, in the Cliza valley, invested in irrigation works for "many fanegadas of land": "Exp. por don Juan de Díos Mariscal contra Pedro Pablo Lara," AHMC, Leg. 1099 (1772-1787).

cally viable. As a wealthy cleric said in his will, his heirs could either parcel out his land (*usufructar*) among small-scale tenants, who would work the land as sharecroppers or pay rent in labor or cash, or else lease the entire estate (*arrendar*) to another landowner, a prosperous peasant, or the former overseer.[50] For a landowner burdened with debt and with little access to cash or further credit, the latter was often the more attractive alternative.

In some cases, a landowner had to lease his estate to avoid foreclosure. In a contract drawn up in 1780, the owners of the hacienda Ayguaico in Cliza explained that they were forced to lease "the hacienda, its houses and gardens, and all its lands," including "13 fanegadas of fertile maize land cultivated by Indian sharecroppers," in order to pay debts amounting to more than 4,000 pesos to the convent of Santa Clara. The owners, three brothers, were to supply the first year's seeds, and the leaseholder (*arrendatario*) would make an immediate payment of 250 pesos "in order to free the hacienda from seizure by creditors [*censualistas*]" and would also pay an annual rent of 400 pesos, as well as covering the costs of maintaining and improving the hacienda.[51]

Where a landowner was unable to raise funds for investment, a short-term lease might serve as an alternative way to make improvements on his land. The owner of the large hacienda La Banda in the Arque, for example, stipulated in a lease contract that the arrendatario was to "improve the hacienda, mills, and garden" of the estate; if that requirement were not met, the rent would be raised by fifty pesos (to two hundred pesos) at the end of the two-year lease.[52]

The other means by which a landowner could generate income from land was through a *censo enfiteútico* (or *venta enfiteútica*). Like

50 "Testamento de Blas Mendez de Rueda," AHMC, Leg. 1450 (1781).

51 "Contrata de arrendamiento de la hacienda Ayguaico," AHMC, Leg. 1444 (1780). In contemporary parlance, *arrendamiento* referred to a formal lease arrangement, whereby a written contract stipulated the terms of exchange. Most such contracts ran for two to nine years, although the arrendatario usually had the right to terminate the contract at midpoint. Leaseholders usually had to post bond for the rent, which generally ranged between 5 and 8 percent of the property's assessed value. In addition, they also assumed the burden of the property's fixed costs. Thus, an arrendatario was usually a person of some economic means and social standing. In contrast, a tenant or renter (arrendero) was a peasant who merely paid a customary rent in labor, cash, and/or kind for the right to use one or several parcels of arable land and pasture for one year.

52 "Contrata de arrendamiento de la hacienda La Banda," AHMC, Leg. 1450 (1793).

the arrendamiento, the censo enfiteútico gave the buyer access to land and its product in return for an annual cash payment, but in this case the arrangement was to endure for the lifetime of the buyer (and sometimes would be continued by his heirs as well).[53] Such contracts were most frequent in the last years of the colonial period, when the increasing difficulty in securing loans and the indebtedness of many of Cochabamba's landowners probably made the prospect of a steady income over a long period of time seem quite attractive.

Tithes As a Mode of Accumulation

Despite the pressures on landowners in the late eighteenth century, a few individual hacendados still managed to accumulate wealth. Negrón, the Cliza hacendado who has been mentioned before, alluded to the existence of an elite that controlled large tracts of rich, permanently irrigated lands and that prospered while other landowners and peasants saw their crops wither if the rains were late or light. Many of these propertied men also exploited the opportunities afforded by tithe collection. A shrewd "tithe farmer" would gather together grain reserves from many peasants and hacendados in a particular parish and then dispose of them at times when prices were highest, especially in the arid highlands, where drought often etched deep scars in the landscape.

Every year, about twenty tithe farmers (*diezmeros*) bid for the right to collect roughly one-tenth of a parish's grain harvest (except in the parishes of the Indian communities, where they collected somewhat less than a tenth). The amount of tithe revenue which the church received depended on the final auction price of the tithe. The revenue from Cochabamba's parishes that were in the archbishopric of Charcas ranged between 25,000 and 40,000 pesos during the last decades of the eighteenth century and the first decade of the nineteenth; the parishes in the Cliza valley, which were part of the bishopric of Santa Cruz, usually produced between 10,000 and 25,000 pesos more.[54] The amount a prospective tithe farmer was willing to bid depended on his expectations of financial gain, and those expectations were influenced to some degree by the outlook for the coming

53 "Censo enfiteútico de la hacienda Coñacoña," AHMC, Leg. 1270 (1774); "Censo enfiteútico de la hacienda Marcavi," AHMC, Leg. 1360 (1840), f. 162v.

54 Larson, *Explotación agraria*, 132-137.

harvest. A comparison between tithe revenues and Viedma's reports on planting conditions will show the relationship.

In 1785-1786, Viedma said planting conditions were favorable (table A-5); as may be seen in figure 12, tithe revenue for 1786 amounted to about 23,000 pesos—a relatively low sum, with the parishes in the Cliza valley especially contributing little. In 1786-1787, planting was late because of drought, and Viedma predicted a poor harvest in two trimester reports in late 1786 and early 1787; tithes rose to 42,000 pesos. The next year, 1787-1788, cultivators enjoyed good rainfall, and an abundant harvest was expected. In 1788, tithe income dipped slightly. Thus, there seemed to be an inverse correlation between the anticipated volume of grain production and the amount of tithe revenue. Between 1774 and 1809, tithe revenue peaked sharply twice: in 1783-1784 and in 1803-1804. Tithe farmers paid the church 114,000 pesos in 1784 and 122,735 pesos in 1804, which were both years of extreme food scarcity. At the end of 1804, Viedma wrote that thousands of peasants had been forced off their lands in search of food to eat. The other side of the picture was that considerable profits accrued to a few speculators, who were able to sell the maize they had stored or collected in tithes for as much as 112 reales per fanega that year. Florescano's conclusion that, in Mexico, landlords gained at the expense of peasants during times of crop failure is applicable to Cochabamba as well.[55]

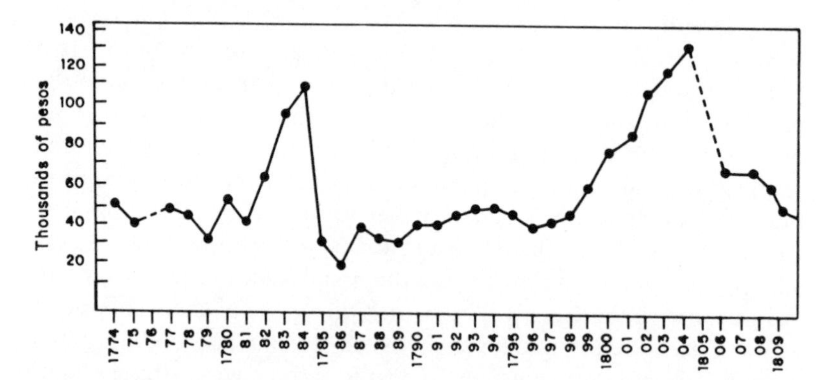

Figure 12 Tithe Revenue from Cochabamba's Parishes, 1774-1810
Source: Derived from data in Larson, "Economic Decline," 437-440.
(Parishes in the districts of the Cercado of Cochabamba, and in Sacaba, Tapacarí, Arque, Ayopaya, and Cliza only.)

55 The auction price of tithes reflected anticipations of the market value of grain, not its actual volume or value after harvest, and it is therefore but a crude

It is difficult to realize that, even in the midst of famine, tithe farmers still managed to expropriate one-tenth of the harvest of peasant households. Some peasants must have found ways to resist the tithe collector's demands. Many of the beggars who flocked to the soup kitchens opened by Cochabamba's two nunneries in 1804 were undoubtedly peasants who had abandoned their fields to avoid tithe, rent, and tribute exactions, as well as to feed themselves. One may imagine that tithe collectors were not a little nervous about their own safety as they made their rounds, forcing peasants to open their near-empty storage huts and surrender part of the crop, sometimes including even the seeds saved for next year's planting. But the evidence is that tithe collectors suffered no financial loss during famine periods. They were known to seize anything of value, preferring livestock if they could not find sufficient grain.

There is not yet sufficient information with which to calculate precisely the rate of return that tithe farmers received, but there is one important clue. In 1774, a royal treasury official argued that many tithe farmers managed to avoid paying the alcabala of 4 percent (later raised to 6 percent) on the value of the tithe. Furthermore, this official proposed that tithe farmers be taxed on the value of the grain sold, rather than on the auction price. In the course of his argument, he pointed out the considerable difference between the two amounts:

> If the tax were levied on the sale of tithed grain, royal revenue would increase; for the tithe farmer who bids 10,000 pesos for the right to collect the tithe in a parish will often sell the grain he collects for 15,000 or 16,000 pesos.[56]

This suggests a 50 or 60 percent rate of return. The significance of that rate is the more striking in view of the facts that the rate of return on most loans was fixed at 5 percent and that the rate of return on the capital value of agricultural enterprises in Cochabamba was rarely more than 4 or 5 percent. In fact, the profit on tithe farming was more than an investor could reasonably hope to realize in any other activity in the region. Under these circumstances, tithe

---

and indirect indicator of the relationship between grain production and prices. For other studies of tithe revenue and agricultural price fluctuations, see Carmagnani, "Producción agropecuaria chilena"; Bauer, "Church and Spanish American Agrarian Structure"; Brading, *Haciendas and Ranchos*; and Tandeter and Wachtel, *Precios y producción agraria*.

56 "Autos . . . contra el alferéz real . . . sobre los diezmos," AHMC, Leg. 1213 (1774).

speculation was the most "rational" form of economic behavior on the part of the landed elite.

The mechanics of tithe farming also stimulated realignments within the landowning class. Members of the propertied class who wanted to participate in the tithe venture had to close ranks. Each year they bid, the tithe farmers were required to post a bond. Since a considerable portion of their own property was often already burdened by encumbrances, prospective speculators usually turned to other landowners for help in posting this bond, and usually this meant those among their kinfolk, fictive (or ritual) kin, and in-laws who possessed unencumbered land. A study of the surnames and kin ties of frequent tithe speculators in the late eighteenth and early nineteenth centuries strongly suggests that members of the wealthiest landed families tended to trade places from year to year as speculators and bondsmen. In 1790, for example, everyone who successfully bid to collect tithes named at least one bondsman, and at least one-third of these bondsmen were a spouse, an in-law, a sibling, a cousin, or a parent.[57]

The forty or so individuals who were involved in tithe farming each year belonged to a fairly exclusive club. The entry requirements were the usual ones: property assets and good connections. Thus, the effect of this enterprise on the social hierarchy was to sharpen the differences within the landowning class between the small, interlocking elite of tithe speculators and the larger number of insolvent landowners who lived primarily off the proceeds of rents from their tenantry. Tithe farming also gave the upper tier of the landholding class economic leverage over peasant smallholders, since it allowed speculators to manipulate the terms of exchange to their own advantage when scarcity gave them a monopoly over the grain market. For tithe farmers, the cycles of natural calamity compensated, in some measure, for the secular stagnation of agricultural prices and the competition of smallholders in "normal" years.

For speculators and landowners, then, "rentier strategies" of accumulation tended to alter the significance of private property in perhaps subtle but important ways. Where once the valley chacareros and hacendados had been on the moral and political defensive against a colonial state that sought to subordinate private agrarian

57 Kinship links were reconstructed by matching the surnames on tithe records against those in the records of notarized economic transactions of other kinds. Many of these surnames appeared as diezmeros and bondsmen on tithe lists in the postindependence period as well.

enterprise to an extractive model of exploitation, the landowners of the late eighteenth century no longer needed to buttress their case with titles, fees, and court cases legitimating land ownership and occupation. Where the structure of land ownership had once led to large-scale grain production destined for export to Potosí, hacienda ownership in the eighteenth century did not necessarily imply demesne agriculture or guarantee profits on grain exports. As we saw in chapter 5, the structure of land ownership was only an imprecise guide to the pattern of agrarian production and class relations. The accumulative strategies of landowner-speculators suggest that landed property was valued not as a factor of production but as an indirect means of securing cash and credit. Above all, unencumbered land was valued as collateral: the qualification for entry into tithe farming and other forms of investment requiring insurance. Within the small circle of landowners able to take heavy risks on speculative ventures, the "circulation of collateral" allowed a degree of flexibility. Landowners who could not post bond on a risky investment at one moment might call upon kinsmen to put up collateral for them, and the favor would be reciprocated at some later date. Under these circumstances, of tight credit and cash and an ever-shrinking pool of unencumbered land to serve as collateral, kinship and reciprocal relations within the landowning elite served as important instruments of economic defense, which could be brought into play to serve the interests of landowners who had abandoned large-scale grain production as the principal source of accumulation.

Elusive Markets of the Altiplano

Francisco de Viedma may have been aware of the competition between small-scale farmers and large landowners in the Cochabamba valley, but the intendant was more concerned about the declining demand for the valley's produce in the "outlying provinces." Yet his own evidence seems to contradict his conclusion that Cochabamba had no market outlet for its staples. In the same report of 1788 in which he lamented the withering of demand in the outside provinces, he estimated that the region had "exported" in that year 200,000 fanegas of wheat and maize, worth some 450,000 pesos (at the relatively high unit price of two pesos two reales). This represented 75 percent of all commodities shipped out of the province along the western trade routes to the altiplano. In addition, pack drivers carried an estimated 160,000 fanegas of flour, worth 40,000 pesos, from the mills of Arque and Tapacarí to the western districts and points beyond. On the other hand, according to Viedma's figures, the region's wide variety of handicrafts accounted for less than 20 percent of the total value of commodities going to extraregional markets; the value of tocuyo exports, for example, was 75,000 pesos, or 12 percent of the region's out-going trade. Despite its economic diversification in the eighteenth century, Cochabamba still provided inhabitants of the altiplano and the highland towns primarily with maize and wheat.[58]

The overproduction that disturbed Viedma thus had not meant a return to a "natural economy" or to subsistence production. Viedma's views simply reflected the landlords' feelings about their weakening mercantile position as provisioners of the mining town. Viedma expressed the frustration of many large landowners, who felt that, in most years, the mining markets were beyond their commercial reach. Entrusted with the task of stimulating agriculture in their intendancies, Viedma, Paula Sanz, and other Bourbon administrators acted on the premise that success in this task depended upon the export of crops and handicrafts to the mining towns. Paula Sanz, in his report of 1794 on the importance of mining and the mita at Potosí, declared that hacendados in the most fertile regions of the viceroyalty had fallen on hard times. Wheat grew abundantly in the provinces of Cochabamba and Chayanta, he said, and yet landlords did not prosper, because of the declining price of wheat at Potosí. He complained that the price did not go above thirty-two reales per fanega and sometimes went as low as twenty reales.[59]

Although Viedma opposed Paula Sanz's proposal to extend the mita, he shared his colleague's belief that without the stimulus of cash derived from trade with the mining towns, the colony would inevitably decline. Viedma's hope for his region's economic recovery

58 Viedma, *Descripción geográfica*, 137. It may be that the prominence of cloth in Cochabamba's export trade was even greater than Viedma's figures indicate. Only a few years later (1794), Paula Sanz estimated the value of Cochabamba tocuyos shipped to Potosí at 40,000 pesos (see table 19), and since Potosí was probably the major market for Cochabamba textiles, it is unlikely that the region exported almost the same value of cloth to other extraregional markets.

59 Paula Sanz, "Contestación al discurso [sobre la mita]," cited and discussed in Zavala, *Servicio personal*, 3: 104. On the secular stagnation and decline of prices in Alto Perú during the second half of the eighteenth century, see Tandeter and Wachtel, *Precios y producción agraria*, and chap. 3 above. On trade and commerce at Potosí, based on the Paula Sanz census, see Marie Helmer, "Commerce et industrie au Pérou à la fin du XVIIIe siècle," *Revista de Indias*, no. 10 (1950): 519-526.

was shaped by his perception of Cochabamba's earlier prosperity. "There is no doubt," he wrote in 1788, that "no other province is so rich in fruits" as Cochabamba.

> The region is a natural provider for the puna provinces, where nature has been so miserly with her blessings on the infertile and arid earth. Yet it is a land of bald hills and cold winds which hides glittering riches in its veins. If those riches could but be discovered and pulled from the depths of that deep earth, we would see the renaissance of an era of prosperity. Cochabamba would need no branch of industry other than the cultivation and export of wheat and maize.[60]

However, legend as much as entrepreneurial spirit shaped contemporary consciousness about the possibilities of the mining economy. The tales of Potosí's wealth during the second silver boom two centuries earlier led the Bourbon reformers to picture an age of unlimited opportunity that blessed the most fortunate adventurers and the shrewdest entrepreneurs. Yet, even as German technical advisors converged on the mineral-rich mountain in the 1780s to introduce the latest technology, the mountain itself stood as testimony to decadence. Much production had been abandoned to gangs of weekend scavengers, and whole sections of the city, which once teemed with 150,000 people, were now pockmarked with deserted huts. Despite the fact that Potosí still imported large quantities of goods from other parts of the viceroyalty, the town had not recovered its earlier commercial power. In comparison to the volume, intensity, and profitability of trade in the late sixteenth century, Potosí's market in staple goods had withered considerably. Paula Sanz estimated that the city had imported, from both elsewhere in the colony and Europe, less than four million pesos worth of goods in 1794—less than two-thirds the value of imports in 1603.[61]

60 Viedma, *Descripción geográfica*, 164-165.

61 "Descripción de la villa," 380; AGI, Charcas 697, Socasa, Nov. 19, 1794. (A printed copy of the census of trade of 1794 made by Paula Sanz may also be found in AGN, Biblioteca, *Telégrafo mercantil* 1 [1801].) Paula Sanz noted that his estimate excluded one million pesos worth of chicha and between 100,000 and 200,000 pesos worth of livestock; elsewhere in the report, however, he said that the value of chicha sold in the city amounted to only 203,515 pesos. See also Zavala, *Servicio personal*, 3:106, and Helmer, "Commerce et industrie au Pérou." In a recent study by Tandeter and his colleagues, comparing the figures of the 1794 census of trade to alcabala records on goods imported to Potosí in 1793, it was found that the census greatly overestimated the value of wines and

As intendant of Potosí, Paula Sanz was convinced not only that recovery was possible for the mining town but also that it would lead to economic renewal for all of Alto Peru.[62] Even in 1794, Potosí still attracted 2,806,700 pesos worth of goods. Most of these commodities (80 percent) were produced within the colony, even though in smaller proportion than had been the case in 1603 (90 percent). The largest suppliers of goods to Potosí were the vineyards of Moquegua (see table 19). Muleteers and merchants, probably conducting most

Table 19. Origin and Value of Imports to Potosí, 1794

	Value	
Place of Origin	*Pesos*	*Percentage*
Moquegua	1,111,000	39.6
Europe	600,000	21.4
Environs of Potosí	405,000	14.4
Cuzco	280,900	10.0
La Paz	103,000	3.7
Atacama, Lipez	59,000	2.1
Cochabamba[a]	54,000	1.9
Chuquisaca[b]	31,000	1.1
Chichas	30,000	1.1
Lima	27,800	1.0
Paraguay	25,000	0.9
Oruro	17,000	0.6
Other areas	63,000	2.2
Total	2,806,700	100.0

Source: AGI, Charcas 697, Socasa, Nov. 19, 1794.

[a] Goods imported from Cochabamba consisted of tocuyo cloth (40,000 pesos), coca (10,000), wooden furniture (2,000), hides (1,000), and soap (1,000).

[b] Most of the goods imported from Chuquisaca consisted of semitropical commodities that had actually been produced in the missions of Mojos and Chiquitos and then shipped to Chuquisaca, taxed there, and reexported to Potosí.

---

aguardiente and underestimated the value of coca, thus inflating the importance of large-scale imports of high-priced commodities and deflating the importance of the fragmented trade in coca, which was partially controlled by Indians and mestizos. (Enrique Tandeter et al., "El mercado de Potosí a fines del siglo XVIII," in Harris, Larson, and Tandeter, *Participación indígena*, 379-424.) Nevertheless, this study confirms the decline of Potosí's mercantile power between the late sixteenth and the late eighteenth centuries. Moreover, the recovery of the mining industry in Potosí did not bring about a corresponding increase in trade. As Tandeter's earlier research had shown, the increase in the output of silver was accomplished by "squeezing" the mitayos, whose wages were insufficient to support any large volume of trade (see chap. 3).

62 Paula Sanz, "Contestación al discurso," in Zavala, *Servicio personal*, 3: 104-107.

of their business from Arequipa, moved aguardiente and wine across the cordillera to the mining town. The "environs of Potosí" provided the town with low-priced commodities like salt, quinoa, resin and pitch, wood, and explosive powder. Most long-distance trade involved either specialized cash crops (coca, sugar, and cacao) or textiles (bayetas de obraje and tocuyo).

In Cochabamba, it was the artisans, not the cultivators or landowners, who capitalized most on Potosí's market. Weavers sent 40,000 pesos worth of cloth, and carpenters and soap-makers also sold their products there. Except for a small supply of inferior quality coca, no crops were recorded as being sent from Cochabamba to the mines. However, that may only be because the crown levied no alcabala on the sale of wheat and maize and thus no tax record was kept on their movement. It seems likely that there was a considerable, though "invisible," trade in grain, as Viedma's 1788 report suggested.

Patterns of interregional trade in cereal became vividly clear during periods of food shortage. In 1781, for example, colonial authorities declared an emergency in Potosí and requisitioned food crops from surrounding provinces. Supplies of flour began to dwindle dangerously in August of that year. By late September, wheat reserves in the city's storehouses had diminished to one thousand fanegas, enough to supply the city for only eight days. Indian rebels had managed to close down the royal highway across the altiplano, cutting off all traffic and trade to Oruro and Potosí. Peasant armies were swarming over the countryside, stealing grain from hacienda granaries to provision themselves and their comrades. In Potosí, it was reported that eight hundred Indians had converged on the town of Chunguri (located in the temperate lowlands near Ayquile, in Mizque) to seize grain. "They proceeded to provision themselves without paying for it, [which is not surprising,] considering that these people are known for their lawlessness and sedition; perhaps they seized the grain to aid their other Indian comrades, who want to throw off the yoke and end the subjugation of which they have been victims."[63] Other insurgents stole or seized food and animals in Pitantora and other valleys in the province of Chayanta.

Members of the municipal government invoked a 1582 ordinance that required cultivators and landowners within a twelve-league radius of Potosí to transport and sell their harvest to the municipal

63 Exp. 550, AGN, Sala 9, Hacienda, 33.2.2, Leg. 23 (1781), f. 13v.

council in years of severe food shortages.[64] (The ordinance had been enacted to undermine the monopoly that wholesale merchants had tried to establish over the grain trade.) The council also mandated that all landowners in the four provinces of Porco, Chayanta, Tomina, and Yamparaes transport and sell one-half of their harvest to Potosí.[65] These measures failed to overcome the food shortage, and the audiencia of La Plata in 1782 extended them to the provinces of Cochabamba, Tarija, and Chichas.[66]

The harvests of Porco, Chayanta, Tomina, and Yamparaes were the hope of Potosí authorities not only in times of scarcity, but also, apparently, in normal years. The landlords of Cochabamba found plenty of competition during most years from wheat cultivators in the provinces of Chayanta and Pitantora. A contemporary wrote that "the best wheat is cultivated in Pitantora, and the grain trade is the most opulent branch of commerce. . . . Pitantora regularly provisions Potosí with flour, though many neighbors from Carangas, Paria, and Porco travel to Chayanta to negotiate big grain deals during the harvest season."[67] This report probably underestimated the importance of the Chayanta ayllus as suppliers of grain to the market of Potosí. These ayllus marketed large quantities of wheat at the mines well into the nineteenth century, before the advent of free-trade policy and of Chilean wheat imports weakened their competitive position. Platt's study of Chayanta has underscored the crucial role that the ayllus played as suppliers of wheat and other food crops.[68] Part of their success derived from the fact that they still had access to lands in multiple ecological tiers: lands in the puna and valleys, often separated by several days' walk. During the entire colonial period, they preserved a high degree of collective self-sufficiency.

The ayllus historically had been closely integrated into the mining town's economy through multiple mercantile links, but they had retained control over the distribution of the communal resources, risks, and surpluses related to their commercial activities. In fact,

64 BNB, AP, tomo 5 (1585-1590), f. 309v.

65 Exp. 550, AGN, Sala 9, Hacienda, 33.2.2, Leg. 23 (1781), f. 17.

66 "Sobre la escasez de granos en Potosí," ANB, Sublevación de indios, vol. 5 (1782).

67 Pedro Vicente Cañete y Domínguez, *Guía histórica, geográfica . . . del gobierno e intendencia de la provincia de Potosí* (1789) (Potosí: Colección de la Cultura Boliviana, 1952), 246.

68 Platt, *Estado boliviano y ayllu andino*, chaps. 1 and 2.

the kurakas commercialized wheat production on communal lands in order to pay tribute to the colonial (and later, the early republican) state. Thus, mercantile activities were traditionally subordinated to collective needs and responsibilities. They did not intensify the processes of internal differentiation within ayllu society. The "kuraka model of mercantilism" that Platt describes had a logic quite distinct from the processes of mercantilization that were at work within Tapacarí society (see chapter 4).

From the perspective of Cochabamba's hacendados, already pressed by the smallholders and petty traders in the valleys, the commercial activities of the Chayanta ayllus were yet another source of commercial competition in a time of shrinking and unstable market demand. In addition, the haciendas of Pitantora and of other valleys in Chuquisaca, Tomina, and Yamparaes enjoyed closer proximity to Potosí's market. Increasingly, the profits from trade in Cochabamba grains were contingent upon the conditions of supply, and particularly on the fluctuation of harvest yields.[69] Crop failure in the highlands and valleys favored Cochabamba's landowners in two ways. First, it reduced or eliminated the competition from the small-scale producers and traders who normally participated in local retail markets. Second, it forced more highland Indians to trade directly with the landowners and tithe speculators who, for the time being, monopolized the supply of grain.

Intendant Viedma was quite aware of the oscillation of market demand in the "outside provinces." In the late months of 1786, as officials began to forecast a poor growing season, the optimistic Viedma commented that profit would compensate for the hardship wrought by prolonged drought in the highlands.[70] A while later, he wrote that "the scarcity of water usually drives many people down from the nearby provinces and impels them to purchase the provisions necessary for their own subsistence."[71] In 1792, he again reported drought, and he noted that it always took its toll first in the altiplano. In the valleys and quebradas, landowners could draw water from reservoirs and mountain streams during the early phase of a

69 For a discussion of the significance of harvest fluctuations and the dynamics of internal markets in precapitalist societies, see Pierre Vilar, "Réflexions sur la 'crise de l'ancien type': 'Inegalité des recoltes' et 'sous-développement'," in *Conjoncture économique, structures sociales: Hommage à Ernest Labrousse* (Paris: Mouton, 1974), 37-58.

70 AGN, Sala 9, Intendencia, 5.8.3, Leg. 2, Jan. 3, 1787.

71 Ibid.

drought. Thus, landlords whose crops survived the dry spell and who stored their reserves could expect Indians to come down from the parched cold lands of Paria and Sicasica in search of food.[72]

We still know little about the nature or magnitude of commercial transactions during the food crises that struck every few years in the late eighteenth century. Viedma's observations suggest that the puna Indians were forced into the market to obtain small quantities of grain that their own cracked soils could not yield. However, it is probable that many highland Indians trekked down into the valleys of Cochabamba to obtain food even in bountiful years. One glimpse of this trade is given by a creole miller who lived in the town of San Augustín de Tapacarí. In 1799, he told the royal mill inspector about his enterprise.

> The Indians who wander through this quebrada come from the intendancies of La Paz and Puno. They purchase grain and grind it into flour during the three months of harvest [June, July, and August]. Most do not return for at least another year . . . and in the month of September and thereafter, few Indians bring their grain to be milled. This is the usual rhythm of the mill industry in the parishes of Tapacarí and Paria. The mills depend upon rainfall, and drought halts most wheat mills. On other occasions, it rains so heavily that the river floods, and the puna Indians cannot travel down through the ravines and gorges to purchase grain and grind it in our mills.[73]

If the highland Indians regularly came down into the valleys to obtain maize, wheat, ají, or other crops, why did Cochabamba's landlords and tithe speculators depend so heavily upon shortages to reap large returns? It is probably because in years of normal or abundant harvest, the highland Indians had the option of bypassing the large grain dealers and dealing directly with small-scale peasant producers and traders in the ferias. By doing so, highland Indians retained some control over the terms of exchange. It is quite likely, for example, that many highland Indians bartered salt, quinoa, and potato seeds with the small-scale maize cultivators of the central valleys. But even when they were closed out of this trade, enterprising landlords,

72 AGN, Sala 9, Intendencia, 5.8.5, Leg. 4, Apr. 30, 1792.

73 "Real visita a las molinas de grano," AHMC, Leg. 1213 (1799).

speculators, and merchants were able to resort to other advantages they had—for example, the proximity of grain mills, or their freedom from municipal price regulations.[74]

The towns of Arque and Tapacarí offered several such advantages, which turned them into marketplaces dominated by wholesale grain dealers. First, the towns were located to the west of the central valleys—out of the commercial orbit of most small-scale grain cultivators, who could not afford to pay the costs (four or five reales per fanega) of shipping maize there from the Cliza valley.[75] Second, municipal authorities gave up trying to regulate prices in those towns. Viedma complained in 1787 that it was "impossible to regulate prices in Arque, as it is a port town to the western provinces, where prices fluctuate according to the volume of export."[76] Third, the towns were situated along river gorges and surrounded by grain mills. Seed and flour could be purchased in one marketplace, often from one grain merchant, without the need of traveling another two or three days eastward into the central valleys of Cochabamba. Not surprisingly, grain traders could fetch considerably more for their product in Arque and Tapacarí than in Cochabamba.[77]

In the eighteenth century, then, the so-called export trade in Cochabamba grains had its terminal point in the "port towns" of Arque and Tapacarí. Except perhaps when grain prices were unusually high, merchants and speculators were rarely willing to pay the cost of freight to market their grain in the cities of the altiplano. Instead, they sent some grain to the western river valleys, stored the rest in granaries on the outskirts of town, and then waited for chang-

74 It was not uncommon for hacendados and millowners in the valley of Arque to try to "capture" trade and commerce with the transient Indians en route through the valley. In 1715, the corregidor of Cochabamba accused the creole hacendado Luís Paniagua and other landowners and millers of forcing highland Indians to purchase maize from them. Ironically, the official also accused the Indians of Sicaya, who owned a hacienda and mills in the pueblo real of Capinota, of forcing other Indians to grind their wheat and maize in their mills. "Exp. de la audiencia de Charcas sobre los perjuicios que los hacendados infieren a los indios forzándoles a moler sus granos . . . ," ANB, Minas, tomo 147 (1715).

75 "Apelación interpuesta por López Roque, indio tributario de Arque," ANB, EC no. 24 (1759).

76 AGN, Sala 9, Intendencia, 5.8.4. Leg. 3, Sept. 1, 1787, f. 4.

77 For example, in 1792 a fanega of wheat cost twenty reales in the city of Cochabamba and twenty-four reales in Arque. AGN, Sala 9, Intendencia, 5.8.5, Leg. 4, Apr. 30, 1792, f. 3.

ing conditions to improve their market position. During the months after harvest, especially in years of drought, the large landlords of Cliza and other parts of the central valleys stationed their Indian and mestizo agents, porters, and watchmen in Arque and Tapacarí to oversee the storage and marketing of their crops.[78] In those years when the highland Indians were forced to deal with the large grain merchants, the market towns of Tapacarí and, particularly, Arque flourished with activity. They became the nexus between the worlds of the highland Aymara Indian and the valley creole landlord-speculator.

The Cochabamba landowners in the late colonial period faced the same logistical barriers that existed for grain hacendados in other parts of the Andes. In spite of the economic recovery of Potosí and Oruro, those markets did not generate the demand that had once stimulated large-scale grain production and exports from the Cochabamba valleys. Conditions had changed since Vázquez de Espinosa's time, when Cochabamba was said to have sent a million pesos worth of grain to Potosí each year. The age of long llama caravans and mule trains carrying food crops up the Arque River gorge through alpine passes to Potosí was no more.

Although he may not have realized it, Viedma's diagnosis of Cochabamba's "crisis of overproduction" reflected the long-term structural transformation of the regional economy and of its position in the internal market of the southern Andes. On the one hand, the diffusion of supply among a growing population of small-scale producers eroded the position of landowners and merchants, creating an alternative basis of commercial exchange among valley peasants as well as between them and the Indians migrating from distant highland villages. On the other hand, the large grain farmers and merchants were more and more moved to the margin of the long-distance grain trade with Potosí. The nature of Potosí's economic recovery, based primarily upon more intensive exploitation of the mine laborers, and the rise of Chayanta ayllus and grain estates in the southern valleys of Chuquisaca and Porco as provisioners of the mining market undercut the position of Cochabamba's grain export-

78 A description of marketing arrangements comes from a priest who accused his Indian agent in 1758 of stealing grain (the defendant stated that the loss was due to rodents in the granaries). In the course of the trial, both the priest and the agent referred to the existence of Indian middlemen in Arque who served as agents for hacendados of the Cliza valley. "Apelación interpuesta por López Roque, indio tributario de Arque," ANB, EC no. 24 (1759).

ers, particularly in the last years of the eighteenth century, when pack animals were becoming scarce in the region.[79]

Thrown on the defensive, landlords and merchants resorted to commercial and speculative strategies designed to exploit the precariousness of peasant agriculture, especially among highland Indians. Valley landowners who owned permanently irrigated maize fields were in a particularly advantageous position for capitalizing on the trade with Arque and Tapacarí. A poor harvest would not only drive more Indians down from the highlands; it would also wipe out the small surplus that otherwise allowed many valley arrenderos to participate in the ferias as petty traders. The profits of the wealthy landowners and tithe speculators therefore rode on the periodic subsistence crises of the peasantry.

But while landowners never gazed at the ancient face of hunger, the uncertainties of and dependence upon periodic agrarian crises irritated them. Some of them proposed reformist schemes; the influence of the Bourbons and the growing interest in rejuvenating the regional economy stirred hopes and sparked new initiatives. For a while, there seemed to be pragmatic remedies for the region's economic malaise.

79 It may well be that the city of Oruro was a more important market for Cochabamba's grain in the late eighteenth century than was Potosí, but so far there has been little research into this trade. There was almost no reference to the Oruro market in the documents consulted for this study.

CHAPTER SEVEN

The Spirit and Limits of Enterprise

When Don José Gómez Merino made his rounds as administrator of the royal tobacco monopoly in the 1790s, he would gaze out of the carriage window at the seasonal forests of cornstalks that were neatly framed by narrow ribbons of sunlit water. He must have felt some frustration as he pondered the potential of cultivating specialized crops that would burst the rigid constraints on the local market. Instead of maize sucking the rich nutrients from the soil simply to nourish the local plebe, Cochabamba's fertile lands could turn the province into a local Andalucía, with a thriving viticulture or orchards of olive trees yielding crops for export to lucrative distant markets. Such marketable commodities as wine, olive oil, hemp, or flax would break the region's economic stalemate and integrate it into a dynamic colonial market economy, to the benefit of the region's innovative landowners and merchants.[1]

Gómez Merino's ideas were skeptically received, but they were part of a new spirit of enterprise that emerged among a small circle of colonial administrators and landowners late in the eighteenth century. After the creation of the intendancy in 1784, and before the onset of the famine crisis of 1804, visions of economic reform and growth beguiled a few would-be entrepreneurs and administrators,

1 Gómez Merino did draw up detailed proposals for regional economic reform, calling for state promotion of viticulture, olive-tree cultivation, and the production of hemp and flax. See "Plan de administración de la provincia de Cochabamba presentado por D. José Gómez Merino al Virrey D. Pedro Melo de Portugal, en el que trata del comercio, industria, y agricultura de la provincia," RAH, ML 9/1667, tomo 12 (n.d., early 1790s), ff. 81-89; and "Plan de desarrollo agrícola, industrial, y comercial para la provincia de Cochabamba presentado por D. José Gómez Merino," RAH, ML, 9/1667, tomo 12, July 17, 1794, ff. 223-226. Viedma vigorously objected to these proposals: see "Sobre el plan de desarrollo presentado por Gómez Merino," AGN, Sala 9, Intendencia, 5.8.5 (1796).

who thought they saw a way out of the region's economic stagnation, endemic poverty, and involuted land-tenure pattern. It seemed to point eastward, toward the largely unsettled, uncharted tropical lowlands that had been conjoined with the corregimiento of Cochabamba to form the intendancy of Santa Cruz de la Sierra. The heartland of Cochabamba was now enveloped by an administrative territory that not only embraced the tropical lowlands around Santa Cruz but also extended northward into the Amazonic basin lands of the Mojos Indians. The perceived potential of lowland agriculture drew the attention of reformers away from the tiresome problems of grain agriculture and peasant "idleness" in the central valleys. There would be no need to rationalize agricultural production on valley haciendas (with the inevitable resistance that it would provoke), when a verdant frontier beckoned. If tapped, tropical resources might offer a mercantile solution to the decline of the landowning class.

But the promise of prosperity did not only lie beyond the remote eastern precipice that dropped off into the jungle. For a few years, a small number of merchants realized high returns on an unlikely commodity produced in the very interior of the peasant economy. Fortuitous circumstances in the late 1790s suddenly turned the rustic cotton textile called tocuyo into a commodity that was in demand all over the viceroyalty of La Plata. This "poor man's cloth," woven on the looms of Cochabamba, had a commercial appeal that was the envy of all wholesale dealers. Even beyond the immediate material returns, the commercialization of tocuyos sparked the imagination of reformers who saw in textile manufacturing the potential for sustained regional economic growth—it was no further away than the weaver's workshop on the edge of town. The problems and possibilities of economic reform in Cochabamba were determined as much by the region's natural and human resources and its agrarian class structure as by imperial political and economic forces.

All across the Andes in the late 1780s, a new breed of professional bureaucrat communicated a spirit of reform and interpreted the royal will to improve social conditions in the colonies and weave them more tightly into the web of Bourbon absolutism. Some royal officials emphasized political integration and royal control, with little regard for economic reform. Others sought to rationalize and centralize administration in their districts only within a context of economic change and regional growth. Inevitably, these latter administrators confronted the contradictions of economic and political reforms that were influenced by Spanish mercantilism and dictated by the imperatives of an imperial state. But the arrival of practical reformers, ostensibly to rejuvenate regional economies, was bound to inspire dreams and kindle hopes. Cochabamba's intendant, Francisco de Viedma, was such an individual. His humanism, ambitions, and energy inspired the imagination of what might be—if only his economic plans were implemented. His dreams of economic recovery, and his attempt to reconcile regional interests with those of the Bourbon state, would eventually dissolve in disillusionment. But for a while, Viedma carried the ideals of the Spanish Enlightenment and mercantilism to the backwaters of the empire, where they caught the fancy of a small regional elite.[2]

Viedma was very much a man of his times, influenced by the European doctrines of mature mercantilism, with its stress on production and trade.[3] Like the well-known reformist ministers of Philip V and Charles III, Viedma appreciated the fact that Spain's economic and political strength depended upon the injection of specie into manufacturing and agriculture. Yet he was fully aware that a nation's wealth could no longer be measured simply in terms of the quantity of specie, as the sixteenth-century bullionists had contended. Contemporary economic thinking prescribed a large dose of state intervention to stimulate agricultural production, manufacturing, and commerce. Mercantilists were in agreement that the state had to promote production in order to establish a favorable balance of trade, while also maintaining terms of trade that were advantageous to producers in the mother country. In Viedma's homeland, a campaign was underway to promote wool and cotton manufacturing and to tear down the internal and overseas barriers that stifled commerce. The opening of Buenos Aires to direct trade with Spain and the creation of the viceroyalty of La Plata were but two reforms that marked Spain's new determination to knit the colonies more closely into the fabric of Spanish metropolitan economy—theoretically, for the benefit of both parties.[4]

2 There is not yet a biography of this exemplary administrator, but see the prologue written by Hector Cossío Salinas to Viedma, *Descripción geográfica*, 11-26. On intendants and the reform era, see J. Fisher, *Government and Society in Colonial Peru*, and Lynch, *Spanish Colonial Administration*. On reforms affecting the audiencia, see Mark A. Burkholder, "From Creole to *Peninsular:* The Transformation of the Audiencia of Lima", *Hispanic American Historical Review* 52 (1972): 395-415.

3 The keystone study of mercantilism is Eli Heckscher, *Mercantilism*, 2 vols. (New York: Macmillan, 1955). An important historiographical critique of the concept is D. C. Coleman, ed., *Revisions in Mercantilism* (London: Methuen, 1969).

4 For economic policies in Spain, see Earl J. Hamilton, *War and Prices in Spain, 1651-1800* (Cambridge: Harvard University Press, 1947). On economic and intel-

Far from the salons and academies of Spain, Viedma hoped to apply his wisdom and his knowledge of political economy to the rejuvenation of the fields and workshops of Cochabamba, a region he was convinced offered as much potential for development as any region of Spain. As we saw in the last chapter, he attributed many of Cochabamba's economic problems to the withering of the mining-town markets for its maize and wheat. He hoped, almost wistfully, for a silver boom that would transform the internal commodity market of Alto Perú. But Viedma was a pragmatist as well as a dreamer, and he developed an integrated plan to diversify Cochabamba's economy. He wanted to steer the regional economy away from its dependence on grain farming by developing a local mining industry, expanding the textile industry, and introducing specialized crops that could overcome the logistical obstacles to long-distance, overland trade. If mineral operations were successful, he believed, Cochabamba would be free of its dependence on distant markets for cash accumulation. But even if they failed, the intendant was convinced that the production or procurement of tropical agricultural products (cacao, coca, sugar) would revive the region's export capacity and channel specie into the pockets of local entrepreneurs. The challenges were to persuade members of the local elite to put up the necessary risk capital and to replace the old sources of cash.[5]

Tropical Horizons

Viedma looked beyond the eastern frontier of European settlement to the tropical and subtropical lowlands for solutions to the economic malaise that afflicted the hacendados of the central valleys. If

lectual trends in eighteenth-century Spain and America, see Robert J. Shafer, *The Economic Societies in the Spanish World, 1763-1821* (Syracuse: Syracuse University Press, 1958); Richard Herr, *The Eighteenth-Century Revolution in Spain* (Princeton: Princeton University Press, 1958); J. Muñoz Pérez, "Los proyectos sobre España e Indias en el siglo XVIII: El proyectismo como género," *Revista de estudios políticos*, no. 81 (1955): 169-185; Stanley Stein, "Reality in Microcosm: The Debate over Trade in America, 1785-1789," *Historia ibérica*, no. 1 (1976): 111-119; David Brading, "El mercantilismo ibérico y el crecimiento económico en la América latina del siglo XVIII," in Florescano, ed., *Ensayos sobre el desarrollo económico*, 293-314; J. Muñoz Pérez, "La publicación del reglamento de comercio libre de Indias de 1778," *Anuario de estudios americanos* 4 (1947): 615-664; and Henry Kamen, "El establecimiento de los intendentes en la administración española," *Hispania* 24 (1964): 368-395.

5 For a critical assessment of Viedma's report on the regional economy, see chap. 5. Among other such reports, those of Gómez Merino (see n. 1) and Tadeo Haenke stand out. The latter's proposals for the promotion of textile manufacturing are discussed below.

landowners were to diversify agriculture and invest in specialized crops, they would inevitably have to colonize those lands, on the far side of the treacherous divide, to the east and north of their safe, familiar valleys. This was not an empty terra incognita; rather, the lowlands were sparsely populated by numerous tribes of hunters, gatherers, and fishermen, many of whom had been "reduced" (see chapter 2) and grouped into "nations," as the Spaniards called them. Four of these nations—the Mojos, Chiquitos, Chiriguanos, and Yuracarees—lived in nucleated settlements in several different ecological zones of the lowlands.[6]

Viedma had a two-pronged plan for bringing commerce and civilization to the tropical frontier. First, colonial authorities would have to incorporate the lowland tribes into the mercantile economy. Second, the tropical regions would be colonized by agrarian entrepreneurs and by Indians and mestizos relocated from the densely populated valley of Cliza and the Valle Bajo to the new lowland plantations.

Viedma's tracts on the history and potential prosperity of the lowlands demonstrate the scope of his vision and ambitions.[7] Although he did not know the jungle missionary settlements at first hand, he carefully studied the reports, censuses, and maps that charted the location and size of the lowland communities and the exportable resources (see figure 13). There were the Mojos villages, strung like beads along the remote northern rivers and tributaries that drained into the Amazon basin. A map drawn in 1769 showed seventeen reducciones of Mojos;[8] however, in a report made in 1788 by Lázaro de Ribera,

6 There is a substantial literature on the lowland tribes in the eighteenth century, particularly the Mojos and Chiquitos peoples. See, for example, Josep Barnadas, "Las reducciones jesuitas de Mojos," *Historia boliviana* 4 (1984): 135-166; David Block, "Links to the Frontier: Jesuit Supply of Its Moxos Missions, 1683-1767," *Americas* 37 (1980): 161-178; Georges Desdevises du Dezert, "Les missions des Mojos et des Chiquitos de 1767 à 1808," *Revue hispanique* 43 (1918): 365-430; and Gabriel René Moreno, *Catálogo del archivo de Mojos y Chiquitos* (1888) (La Paz: Instituto Boliviano de Cultura, 1976).

7 Although his report on Cochabamba is far better known, Viedma devoted at least as much effort to writing about the pueblos and reducciones of the tropical frontier. Many of his reports and letters on the Indians and the Spanish colonizers of the lowlands are included in the Bolivian edition of his *Descripción geográfica*. However, the confusing organization of the book makes it difficult to distinguish one document from another and to identify their archival origins. Where a cited document does not appear to be part of *Descripción geográfica*, its title or subtitle will be given.

8 "Mapa que comprende las misiones de Moxos y Chiquitos," AGI, sección 5,

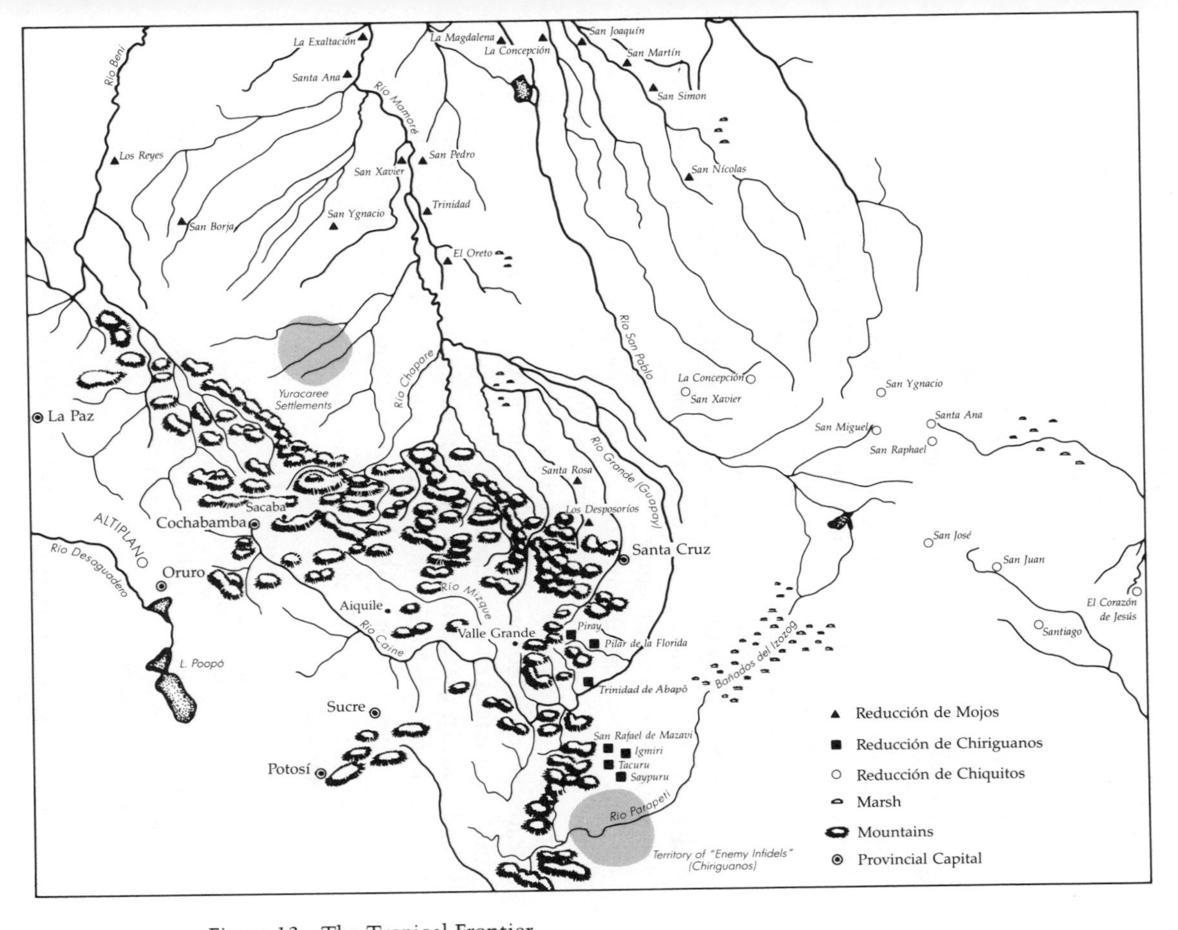

Figure 13 The Tropical Frontier
Source: Adapted from the map in "Mapa que comprende las misiones de Moxos y Chiquitos," AGI, Sección 5, Charcas 502, no. 78 (1769).

governor of the Mojos province, only eleven such villages were recorded.[9] Not more than 22,000 people lived in these settlements.[10] Located deep in the tropical forest, they were believed by Viedma to be potentially the most prosperous villages. The rich soil and humid climate would be favorable for crops of sugar, maize, rice, yucca, and fruits, which could be transported by river raft during certain seasons of the year.[11]

To the southeast of the tropical forest lay scattered settlements of Chiquitos, who were maize cultivators and herders inhabiting hot savannahs that extended as far north as the eighteenth parallel, where grasslands gradually gave way to dense, tropical undergrowth. The Chiquitos' villages were reached only by long overland treks nearly to the outer edge of Spanish territory. The 18,840 people who inhabited ten Chiquitos pueblos in 1788 attracted the attention of colonial authorities more for their strategic proximity to the Portuguese settlements of Mato Grosso than for the resources they controlled. As long as the Chiquitos were properly administered and remained loyal vassals, they served as a first defense against Portuguese encroachments.[12]

The Yuracarees inhabited the tropical lowlands of the present-day province of Chaparé, to the northeast of Cochabamba. Two priests from the Cliza valley managed to "reduce" and convert many Yuracarees in the 1760s and 1770s, but neither Viedma nor Ribera offered any estimate of their numbers. Viedma foresaw lucrative plantations and trade in the territory of the Yuracarees, so close to the central valleys of Cochabamba, if new trails were blazed and their villages opened up to trade with the higher, temperate maize valleys.[13]

Charcas 503, no. 78 (1769). The locations of mission settlements on this map are shown in figure 13.

9 On the report and administration of Lázaro de Ribera, see Alcides Parejas, "Don Lázaro de Ribera, gobernador de la provincia de Moxos (1784-1792)," *Anuario de estudios americanos* 33 (1976): 949-962.

10 Viedma, "Ventajas que resultan a los mismos indios . . . dándoles en libertad como los demás del Perú . . .," in his *Descripción geográfica*, 209 (cited hereafter as Viedma, "Ventajas").

11 Ibid., 211.

12 Viedma, "Males que padecen estos indios, privándoles de la libertad y perjuicios que se infieren a los vecinos de Santa Cruz," in his *Descripción geográfica*, 200 (cited hereafter as Viedma, "Males"), and Viedma, "Ventajas," 209.

13 Viedma, "Nueva reducción de San Carlos, de indios de la nación de Yuracarees," in his *Descripción geográfica*, 127.

The most famous inhabitants of the tropical slopes of the cordillera were the Chiriguanos. In the sixteenth century, even in the zeal to extend commercial coca cultivation deeper into the tropics, there was anxiety about provoking the wrath of the fierce Chiriguano warriors. Indeed, the Incas themselves had fortified the eastern borders of their empire specifically to guard against the Chiriguanos.[14] Over three centuries, Spanish missionaries had managed to pacify many Chiriguano tribes, and the founding and survival of the city of Santa Cruz was testimony to their partial success at "domesticating" the Chiriguanos. Yet even in the 1780s and 1790s, the Spaniards feared for their lives in the territory around the Parapetí River. Tacuarembo, Sauce, Piriti, Ubau, Iquacti, Timboy, and Parapetí were indicated as lands of "enemy infidels," where neither Christianity nor civilization had penetrated. Repelled yet fascinated, Viedma described these fearsome heathens, with their painted bodies, leather skins, and bows and arrows, in vivid detail. He was most disdainful of their idleness, "their habits of consuming chicha and lying about in hammocks,"[15] and he was determined to advance the cutting edge of Christendom into this bastion of barbarism.

Yet, even if the persistence of heathenism among the Chiriquanos irked this moralistic Christian, he took comfort in the success of several missionary settlements situated to the south of Santa Cruz. The town of Trinidad de Abapó, in particular, was a model missionary community of industry and self-sufficiency, and Viedma made it a showcase for his proposed reforms of the other lowland villages. The people of Abapó tended livestock and cultivated small amounts of cotton to supply their own textile workshops. Priests had established "spinning schools," where spinsters and young girls kept themselves occupied in "useful tasks." Young boys attended a separate school, where they studied the Scriptures and learned to read and write or were trained as weavers or carpenters. The town had a healthy economy, in Viedma's view, because it exported some of its goods to Santa Cruz and Chuquisaca. But more than its economic success, Viedma praised Abapó for the moral foundations upon which it rested—for its "spiritual, temporal, and economic govern-

14 "Visita a Pocona," and *Repartimiento de tierras,* 14 and passim. On the Chiriguano frontier in the sixteenth century, see Thierry Saignes, "Une frontière fossile: La cordillère chiriguano au XVIe siècle," 2 vols. (3rd cycle doctorate, University of Paris, 1974).

15 Viedma, "Descripción y estado de las reducciones de los indios chiriguanos," in his *Descripción geográfica,* 239.

ment." He saw the mission town as a beacon of light in a sea of darkness where moral turpitude, sloth, and sensuality seemed to flourish as luxuriantly as the tropic vegetation.[16]

For Viedma, the question of frontier development had a historical dimension which made it all the more urgent. Industry and the social fabric of life in the mission communities had deteriorated sharply since the expulsion of the Jesuits from Spanish America in 1767. Viedma had only praise for the Christian education, government, and economic enterprise that the Jesuits had given to their Indian wards. In the villages of the Mojos and Chiquitos, the order had patiently chaperoned their trustees along the path from barbarism to civilization and, in the process, raised their material standard of living. With the loss of these dedicated missionaries, the villages had been deprived of their moorings and had cast about on the seas of corruption and indolence. The secular priests assigned to administer the villages after 1767 were responsible for the "desolation, inactivity, vice, and perversity" that reigned thereafter.[17] When civil administrators finally took note of the situation in the early 1780s, a "new plan of government" for the mission Indians was formulated by Ribera. But while Intendant Viedma lauded the aim of this plan—to turn over the administration of the villages to civil authorities—he nevertheless opposed it, on the ground that merely to "transfer the economic government from ecclesiastical to secular hands" left untouched the main problem, which was the colonial authorities' control over the distribution of crops and goods produced by the Indians.

> They deposit all their precious manufactures in the hands of their administrators, who keep the closest accounting to prevent the Indians from hiding their wares; in return, the Indians receive most wretched clothing of skins and food to eat; for while the Indians are permitted to keep maize, bananas, yuccas, and fruits, they must surrender their other crops, such as cacao, coffee, sugar, and . . . beeswax.[18]

Furthermore, the civil administrators required the Mojos people to carry their tribute in canoes, paddling many days against the current,

16 Viedma, "Gobierno espiritual, temporal, y económico de las antiguas reducciones,"in his *Descripción geográfica*, 242-244.

17 Viedma, "Males," 194.

18 Ibid., 202, 203. On Ribera's plan, see also Parejas, "Don Lázaro de Ribera," and Barnadas, "Reducciones jesuitas," 160-162.

to Port Jones or Port Paila and from there to trek overland to the royal receiver in Santa Cruz.[19]

Against popular opinion on the matter, Viedma proposed that the lowland Indians be granted a degree of economic autonomy. The issue at hand was the Indians' capability for self-government and communal self-regulation. Where there was no cultural tradition of community; where warrior tribes had managed to fend off the Incas, restricting the eastern edge of Tawantinsuyu to the high valleys of Cochabamba, Pocona, and Tarija; and where the jungle and the arid plains made sedentary agriculture a futile endeavor, there was ample room for skepticism. Indeed, Viedma himself did not challenge the judgment of the early ecclesiastics who, in the sixteenth century, had said that the lowland Indians were "incapable of governing themselves, unlike the rest of the Indians in the kingdom of Peru."[20] It was for that reason that the Jesuits had been given the task of domesticating them. But times had changed, and Viedma argued against the perpetuation of their wardship under civil administrators. To support his case, he invoked philosophical and juridical arguments, from the preachings of Bartolomé de las Casas to the legal code of Juan de Solórzano, which sanctioned the freedom of America's native sons and daughters.[21] With painstaking detail, he described the legal status of tributaries and yanaconas, to demonstrate that, unlike them, the lowland Indians continued to live in a state of unfreedom that was unjust and without cause.[22]

However, even if they had a moral claim to freedom, it might still be questioned whether, "after so much time in the reducciones, . . . they were civilized and capable of trading their own fruits and goods and of paying tribute."[23] Lacking first-hand evidence with which to make his case, Viedma drew on the empirical observations of Ribera concerning the moral character of the Mojos and Chiquitos. For Ribera himself had praised the Mojos as "the most able, industrious, and loyal vassals that the king had in all his kingdoms."[24] But whereas Ribera concluded that the Indians deserved protection from

19 Viedma, "Males" 203.

20 Ibid., 195.

21 See Juan de Solórzano Pereira, *Política indiana*, 5 vols. 1647 (Madrid: Iberoamericana, 1930).

22 Viedma, "Males," 191-203.

23 Ibid., 195.

24 Ibid., 201.

unscrupulous traders and the corrupt influences of commerce, Viedma argued that the Mojos were skilled artisans and traders who were capable of defending their own interests. Indeed, Viedma projected a utilitarian and acquisitive image of *homo economicus* onto the lowland native. Despite centuries of subservience, the lowland Indians were capable of "rational action." All that was necessary, in the intendant's view, was to tear down the barriers of protection, unlock the missions' resources, and release the Indians from wardship. The returns from trade would encourage the lowland natives to work harder in agriculture and industry. Eventually, their economy would flourish and the lowland villages would become models of economic progress.

To Viedma, then, the mission towns of the jungle offered an opportunity for the development of industrious villages, from which tropical commodities and the products of native handicrafts could be produced for export to urban centers throughout the viceroyalty. The crops to be grown might replace imports from distant lands. The Indians in these villages were "disposed" toward commerce and industry, and they were uncontaminated by the sloth and corruption of Cochabamba's mestizos and cholos, "who are not motivated by noble causes, the glory of a prize, the fear of punishment, or even the hardships of neediness."[25] Whatever the mixture of Rousseauian innocence and yeoman industriousness with which Viedma characterized the lowland native, his proposal was rather unorthodox. At a time when the crown was designing ways to shield highland villages from extortionist traders, in the aftermath of the 1781 rebellions and the abolition of the repartimiento de mercancías, Viedma was pressing for "free trade" with the mission Indians. While the intendants were expected to resurrect some features of the Toledan model of village society throughout Alto Perú, Viedma went further and advocated assimilationist policies that would integrate the jungle Indians into the market economy.

Perhaps it was a radical plan.[26] But in Viedma's mind, it held much hope for the stimulation of the sluggish economies along the eastern frontier. Once the lowlands entered the "modern age" of trade, industry, and cash-crop agriculture, the merchants and entrepreneurs

25 Viedma, "En que se hacen demostrables las muchas proporciones que presenta la naturaleza a la mayor prosperidad de la provincia," in his *Descripción geográfica*, 168.

26 However, Viedma's opposition to Ribera's plans was supported by the Council of the Indies in 1805. Barnadas, "Reducciones jesuitas," 160.

of Cochabamba and other nearby areas would take advantage of the new situation. Their geographical proximity to the tropical frontier would allow them to serve as middlemen in the traffic between jungle and highland. Eventually, new trade routes would penetrate the unexplored riverways and cross the eastern savannahs that bordered Portuguese territory. Viedma even envisaged a major lowland highway stretching from the Parapetí River (after the last barbarous Chiriguanos had been conquered) to the town of Jujuy. This new road would throw open a hitherto inhospitable land to progress, prosperity, and Christianity.

But trade was not enough to propel Cochabamba out of its economic lethargy. Viedma wanted the lowland regions to be colonized by rich landowners willing to risk investment in plantation agriculture. He thought the possibilities for commercial agriculture were endless: cacao plantations would displace imports from Caracas and Guayaquil; coca fields would rival the established cocales of the yungas east of La Paz; rice paddies, cotton fields, and sugar plantations would substitute jungle crops for coastal imports. Alto Perú's tropical frontier would be turned into the central source for all the specialized agricultural commodities traditionally imported from distant lands. It was an ambitious plan, but Viedma was convinced that the penetration of tropical lands would allow a few enterprising planters to reap high returns on their investment and would provide a way for the upper tier of Cochabamba's landowning elite to leave grain cultivation to their peasant tenants and initiate new agricultural enterprises where they would presumably have more control over the terms of exchange.[27]

Viedma focused his plan of jungle colonization on two areas: the hinterlands of the city of Santa Cruz and the newly opened territory of the Yuracarees. In the region around Santa Cruz, colonization had already taken root. Many of the huge ranches in the vicinity of the

27 Viedma, "Gobierno espiritual, temporal, y económico de las antiguas reducciones," in his *Descripción geográfica*, 262, and "Ventajas," 219. Viedma also proposed the administrative breakup of the intendancy into two parts, one centered around the old corregimiento of Cochabamba and the other around the city and frontier hinterlands of Santa Cruz. (p. 213.) Much documentation on the lowland tribes in the late Bourbon period is lodged in the Real Academia de Historia, in Madrid. See, for example, "Documentos referentes al gobierno de las misiones de Mojos y Chiquitos después de la expulsión de los jesuitas," RAH, ML, 9/1733, tomo 76 (1777-1780), ff. 37-48, "Informe del obispo de Tucumán . . . sobre las reducciones de los Yuracarees, cerca de Mojos y Cochabamba," June 10, 1804, RAH, ML, 9/1731, tomo 76, ff. 27-36.

town had cane fields, and the region exported small quantities of a sugar of inferior quality sugar to the western highlands. Viedma had learned of a recent discovery that sugar flourished in the rich top soils of the tropical forest. Thirteen years after deforestation and the beginning of cultivation, the cane still thrived there. (On the drier plains, in contrast, the soil was exhausted after only three or four harvests of sugar cane.)[28] However, the sugar mills in the region were among the most primitive in America. These mills (*trapiches*), driven by mules, lost a large part of the cane juice. The problem of technological backwardness was compounded by land-tenure customs that, Viedma believed, discouraged sugar planters from investing capital in more modern machinery. No landholder in Santa Cruz had a title of ownership, since the lands had never been divided and distributed among the earliest settlers. Instead, the landholders were in the position of "homesteading" [*dominio precario*], and this lasted only "as long as they have livestock and cultivate their lands [*chacos*]."[29] The absence of private property and the inability to transmit property rights by inheritance were the principal factors responsible for the region's economic stagnation, in the intendant's view. Viedma believed that with a new set of property laws, the landholders would be more inclined to improve their mills and cut back the forests to extend their cane fields.

But Viedma harbored even greater hope in a plan to develop the Yuracaree territory near the Chaparé River. Located to the north and northeast of Cochabamba, the Yuracaree lands already had attracted the interest of many hacendados of Cliza. The two priests from Cliza who had reduced and converted the Yuracarees had also cleared patches of forest to plant coca. By Viedma's time, fifty-two cocales had been established in one area of the Chaparé River basin. Most coca enterprises failed after several years, however; the intendant explained these failures in terms of poor cultivation and storage methods.[30] In his opinion, progress and development mainly depended upon the education of the farmers, the diffusion of technical skills, and the acquisition of modern equipment.

Curiously, the labor question did not figure prominently in Viedma's grand scheme. Yet intensive labor, both permanent and seasonal, would be needed to clear the land, plant the cane and coca,

28 Viedma, *Descripción geográfica*, 112.

29 Ibid., 113 and 163-164; AGN, Sala 9, Intendencia, 5.8.6, Leg. 5, Oct. 12, 1798.

30 Viedma, *Descripción geográfica*, 135-136 and 162.

and harvest the crop. Given the past difficulties in exploiting the Indians, Viedma can hardly have assumed that these labor needs would be satisfied by the Indians. (In fact, his only apparent concern in this regard was to end the bondage of captured Chiriguano Indians, who were bought and sold publicly in an unregulated slave trade that still thrived in Santa Cruz.)[31] His proposed solution to the labor problem was the massive migration and resettlement of peasants from the crowded central valleys of Cochabamba. Viedma saw this as an opportunity for them, too:

> For the Indians who till the soil on the pitiful parcels of land the owner gives them, there will be an alternative to the misery that burdens people in their lowly station in life; the mixed bloods who compose the majority of Cochabamba's population will be employed as laborers, and they will be forced to forget their idle ways.[32]

Thus, the colonization of the lowlands would alleviate the social and demographic pressures in the heartland of Cochabamba. With remarkable foresight, Viedma's scheme anticipated, by almost two centuries, the opening of the Chaparé jungle to small-scale colonizers who cultivated coca and other crops for the markets of Cochabamba. Like Viedma's plan, state-directed colonization in the middle of the twentieth century was designed to shift peasant population from Cliza and the Valle Bajo to the sparsely populated tropics. The intendant had the imagination to realize that colonization was not only a commercial opportunity but also a safety valve for restless peasants beset by the uncertainties of subsistence agriculture. Harnessing the jungle to commercial enterprise was a solution to widespread poverty, vagrancy, and threats to the public order.

If Viedma's plan seemed extravagant, he nevertheless recognized that practical measures had to be taken before people would risk their capital in it. The most serious and immediate need was for transportation. The direct route to the Yuracarees was hazardous, exposing travelers to the perils of cold and treacherous mountain passes. "The trail is one of the most torturous ones in the kingdom

31 "Auto del gobernador intendente de Cochabamba . . . prohibiendo el servicio personal de indios llamados 'piezas sueltas' de Santa Cruz," Aug. 17, 1787, RAH, ML, 9/1733, tomo 78, ff. 95-98; and "Informe del yntendente de Cochabamba [sobre] encomiendas de Santa Cruz, sus yndios, y su tributo," RAH, ML, 9/1733, tomo 78, May 13, 1792, ff. 139-153.

32 Viedma, *Descripción geográfica*, 162.

of Peru," Viedma admitted. The icy winds and avalanches endangered "particularly those poor people who migrate down to the jungle to work on the coca haciendas"; the mountainous route offered no pasture for pack animals, and water was extremely scarce.[33] The alternative route—across the high valleys of Cliza and Mizque, descending into Santa Cruz, and then downstream by river raft—could take as long as four or five months to traverse. Ever since the 1760s, local officials had been petitioning the audiencia of La Plata for permission to build a road from the city of Cochabamba to the region of the Chaparé and the Yuracarees, and Viedma added his weight to this plea. He argued that direct access to the Yuracaree missions would vitalize trade between the high maize valleys and the new coca plantations and would bring traders into contact with the Yuracaree and Mojos communities. Merchants would exchange maize for coca and other tropical commodities, which Cochabamba middlemen would then ship to the mining towns and cities.[34] The royal treasury, the traders, and the packdrivers of Cochabamba would all reap profits from this trade. Furthermore, Cochabamba "would avoid the annual loss of 98,000 pesos exchanged for some 14,000 baskets of coca imported from La Paz." Viedma realized that the coca dealers of La Paz, by the same token, would seek to prevent the construction of a road to the Yuracarée forests and the development of a major coca-producing region there. But he tried to convince the crown that such competition would be healthy for the economy of Alto Perú: first, because it would lower the price of coca and therefore the cost of sustaining mineworkers at Potosí; and second, because the population of La Paz would then not depend so heavily upon the proceeds from coca and would turn to other economic pursuits, such as mining.[35]

The political and merchant elites of Chuquisaca objected even more strongly than those of La Paz to Viedma's proposal to build a road down into the jungle. As long as Santa Cruz was the only point of passage to the northern jungle missions, Chuquisaca—the seat of the audiencia of La Plata—benefited the most from the jungle traffic. Chuquisaca was also a central transit point between Santa Cruz and Potosí, and the flow of tropical commodities from the lowlands to Potosí generated a considerable amount of tax revenue for the local

33 Ibid., 134-135.

34 Ibid., 160-165, and Viedma, "Ventajas," 210-211 and passim.

35 Viedma, *Descripción geográfica*, 162.

treasury. The new road would divert much of this traffic away from Chuquisaca and to Cochabamba. The elites of Chuquisaca had no wish to cede the city's privileged position to a rival.[36] Monopoly and privilege were considered the principles of economic advantage, no matter how many proposals set forth the ideals of unregulated trade and technological innovation. The precepts of mercantilist thought posited a static economy, in which one port's gain was another's loss. The hot, wet forests of the Chaparé River basin may have adjoined Cochabamba, but Chuquisaca's trade monopoly over the Santa Cruz route to the lowlands blocked any direct linkage between the two regions. This conflict illustrates how, even apart from imperial policy, the politics of regionalism could stifle the economic initiative of reformists. Viedma encountered an intransigent group in Chuquisaca that thwarted his efforts to advance the frontier of colonial settlement into the untapped forests.

Another impediment was that investors would be reluctant to sink scarce capital into enterprises that offered no guarantee of success. Viedma's plans met with considerable skepticism among the local creole elite, accustomed to speculative ventures in tithes, usurious investments, and rent income.[37] While they may not have analyzed their notions of economic life, most merchants and landowners probably held fast to the mercantilist preconceptions of a "prevailingly inelastic demand . . . changeable not so much by economic forces as by the dictates of authority."[38]

In a world where most people still lived at the margins of subsistence, where roads were few and treacherous, and where even Potosí's apparent recovery was attenuated by a sustained population decline that weakened market demand in that town, most people perceived the feebleness of market demand even for exotic tropical commodities. The entry of commercial capital into the eastern frontier, either through trade with mission Indians or through plantation agriculture, would not take place without state intervention on behalf of such enterprise. Even embedded in Viedma's plans, stressing individual initiative as they did, was the implicit assumption of state support. Obviously, if exchange relations between the mission Indians

36 "Yncidente importante sobre la apertura de un camino desde Cochabamba a los yndios Yuracarees, y comunicación con las misiones de Moxos," RAH, ML, 9/1723, Tomo 68 (1807), ff. 91-94.

37 See chap. 6, and Lynch, *Spanish Colonial Administration*, 79.

38 D. C. Coleman, "Eli Heckscher and the Idea of Mercantilism," *Scandinavian Economic History Review* 5 (1957): 19.

and itinerant traders, were to be established on the basis of free trade, the state would have to dismantle the protective barriers that stood in its way. If plantations were to sprout in the jungle, the state would have to sanction private property, open up access to the lowlands, and help provide cheap labor.

The problem of labor supply was also serious. Colonization and the cultivation of sugar, cotton, and coca, were all labor-intensive activities, requiring large amounts of cheap labor long before they realized a return. Viedma offered no plan for labor recruitment, but he expected the plantations to draw their workers from the underemployed laboring poor of the central valleys. Implicit in his scheme is the principle of extra-economic coercion. How else but through corvée labor would the "redundant" mestizo and cholo population "be forced to forget their idle ways" through hard work on the plantations? Would it require a new rotative system of forced labor, an imposed relocation of people to the lowlands, or perhaps merely the enactment of vagrancy laws that would legitimate the removal of "idle" Indians and mestizos to the plantations? Viedma never cared to follow his proposals through to their logical conclusions. But he anticipated the structural limits on new enterprise in the jungle, and he implicitly accepted the need for state action to provide cheap labor to the fledgling plantations. Political force, more than market incentive, would determine the feasibility of his plans.

Thus, when Viedma found that the state was fundamentally indifferent to his proposals, he was unable to attract creole interest in them. The crown's inertia only deepened the skepticism of his own constituency. The landowning elite, even those who enjoyed some degree of liquidity, were content to invest in a variety of local enterprises and leave the commercial conquest of the tropics to the fertile imaginations of "progressive" reformers. It would take another two hundred years for Viedma's plan to be realized. In the meantime, however, events far from the valleys created overnight a bonanza for the local textile industry. In 1796, entrepreneurial attention was suddenly drawn to the tocuyos.

War and the Textile Boom

During his tour of the province in the 1780s, Viedma noticed with keen interest the considerable number of workshops where spinning wheels and looms hummed with activity. Cochabamba had a primitive industry that supplied rustic cotton cloth to local consumers. That this regional industry had eluded most European observers in the past is not surprising: it was primarily a cottage industry, dispersed among the huts and workshops of peasant families. Like so many other primitive textile industries in early modern Europe, the manufacture of tocuyos in Cochabamba got its start in the effort of peasants to diversify the basis of their livelihood. Sometimes textile production was carried out as part of the rent that tenants owed to a hacendado, but probably in most cases, peasant families independently engaged in making tocuyos for their own use and for exchange in the ferias and towns in the central valleys. Bayetas were also sold in the ferias, but most of them were imported from the provinces near La Paz, Chucuito, and Cuzco.[39] In contrast, tocuyos were a local product that clothed and bandaged the laboring poor.[40] Their manufacture was a by-product, during the late colonial era, of the subsistence pressures on smallholding peasants, on the one hand, and the growing opportunity for retail commerce in the markets of the central valleys, on the other. In pursuit of subsistence security, peasants had turned to part-time trade and artisanry.[41]

Contemporary sources give no precise estimates of the number of people engaged in cloth production and marketing in Cochabamba.

39 A sample of entries in the royal alcabala records of Cochabamba showed a wide variety of goods being imported into the region. (The sample consisted of every fifth entry during seven two-year spans—1777-1778, 1782-1783, 1787-1788, 1792-1793, 1797-1798, 1802-1803, and 1807-1808—for a total of 1,313 entries.) However, such common items of consumption as bayetas, rough clothing, and coca predominated. Bayetas alone constituted about 30 percent of the value of all imported taxed goods. Their main origins were the regions of La Paz, Oruro, and Cuzco. Highland textiles might have been one major item of trade between highland and valley peasants (who exchanged it for maize and other valley products). For a more detailed discussion of the alcabala sample and the import trade into the region, see Larson, "Economic Decline and Social Change," 234-240. There were, of course, obrajes on many haciendas (see chap. 5), but the commercial production of woolen textiles on rural estates seems to have been relatively minor in scale. It is notable that Viedma's only mention of such an enterprise concerned the decline and abandonment of the region's most famous obraje, Hulincate, in the Sacaba valley (*Descripción geográfica*, 53).

40 "Memoria de don Juan Carrillo de Albornoz," Apr. 15, 1804, AGN, Sala 9, Intendencia, 30.7.5, Leg. 56, Exp. 6 (hereafter cited as "Memoria de d. Juan Carrillo de Albornoz"); and Barriga, *Memorias para la historia de Arequipa*, 1: 53. Barriga's report is summarized in Zavala, *Servicio personal*, 3: 86-89.

41 For a brief discussion of peasant economic diversification into craft production in Europe, in response to the forces of population pressure and capital shortage, on the one hand, and the growth of retail marketing networks, on the other, see Slicher van Bath, *Agrarian History of Western Europe*, 217ff.

In 1788, Viedma mentioned that five hundred cholos and mestizos occupied themselves in cloth manufacturing in the parish of Quillacollo.[42] Tocuyo weavers were also found in the partidos of the Cercado and Tarata, in the Cliza valley. In 1804, two years after the end of the textile boom, Juan Carrillo de Albornoz mentioned the figure of three thousand weavers.[43] However, the British envoy, John Barclay Pentland, stated in 1827 that some twenty thousand people were involved in textile production at its height (presumably in the late 1790s).[44] That may well be a gross overestimate, or perhaps Pentland was including spinners as well as weavers.

In any event, it appears that the scale of tocuyo production in Cochabamba was greater than that of any other region in the Andean world in the last years of the eighteenth century. Arequipa was the nearest rival, but in the late 1780s, for example, Arequipa's intendant reported that its weavers generally produced about 124,000 varas of cloth each year, while Viedma estimated Cochabamba's cloth exports at the time to be 300,000 varas annually—and that presumably does not include the cloth sold or bartered in local marketplaces.[45] The observations of Tadeo Haenke, a German naturalist who resided in Cochabamba for many years, confirms the impression of the strength of the textile industry in Cochabamba: "The province . . . consumes [as much cotton] in its looms as all the other [provinces] combined."[46]

Despite the importance of the industry, curiously little information has been left to us about the forces and relations of production in it. Most contemporary observers focused attention on the primi-

42 Viedma, *Descripción geográfica*, 67.

43 "Memoria de d. Juan Carrillo de Albornoz."

44 United Kingdom, Foreign Office, 61/12, General Consulate, John B. Pentland, *Report on the Bolivian Republic* 1827, f. 176 (hereafter cited as Pentland, *Report on the Bolivian Republic*).

45 Barriga, *Memorias para la historia de Arequipa*, 1:53; Viedma, *Descripción geográfica*, 137, 139-141.

46 Tadeo Haenke, "Memoria sobre el cultivo de algodón . . .," in *Telégrafo mercantil*, AGN, tomo 2, no. 36 (1801), f. 291. Haenke estimated the annual importation of cotton into Cochabamba at between 30,000 and 40,000 *arrobas* in about 1799. In 1788, Viedma had put the figure at 11,000 arrobas (*Descripción geográfica*, p. 145). However, in 1798, at the height of the boom, Viedma also estimated that some 30,000 arrobas of raw cotton were entering the province each year (AGI, Charcas, Leg. 436, Apr. 3, 1798). An arroba was equivalent to about twenty-five pounds.

tive conditions under which people worked. In Haenke's words, equipment was "poorly constructed," and the laborers lacked "the use of those [English] machines that facilitate and abbreviate different tasks."[47] The machinery that was turning the cities of Manchester and Belfast into the textile workshops of the world and launching England's industrial revolution was not to be found in the Cochabamba valleys.

As is typical in a cottage industry, different members of the family participated in distinct phases of production. Women and children worked in the preparatory phase: cleaning, plying, and spinning the cotton into yarn.[48] A peasant woman would purchase or otherwise obtain raw cotton from a cotton merchant (*algodonero*) and fashion it into yarn in the spare moments of her agricultural work day. The central task of weaving was man's work, and it required some skill, investment in a treadle loom, and considerable blocks of time. Women and children then completed the job, stretching and sometimes dying the finished cloth. Unless production was on consignment, women also took on the responsibility of marketing the cloth. Symbolically, perhaps, weaving enjoyed primacy in the hierarchy of tasks. But the auxiliary tasks—preparing, spinning, and stretching the cotton—required more labor time. As a result, female spinners generally outnumbered male weavers by more than three to one. Together, they constituted an army of invisible textile laborers who blended silently into the rural landscape.

Cochabamba's tocuyos readily competed in the urban markets of Alto Perú against the cotton cloth from Arequipa and the dyed cottons of Quito, but most trade remained local and in the hands of small-scale peddlers. Merchant capital did not capture a significant portion of the tocuyo trade until the last decade of the eighteenth century. Several factors inhibited the development of the large-scale production and distribution of tocuyos before that. The administrative and commercial reorientation of Alto Perú, away from Lima and the Pacific coast and toward Buenos Aires and the Atlantic coast, increased the flow of Spanish goods to the new viceroyalty of La Plata. Following the division of the Peruvian viceroyalty and the abolition of the repartimiento de mercancías, the docks of Buenos Aires were increasingly laden with bolts of Catalan cloth destined for markets in the interior. The Bourbon "free-trade" reforms of 1778, along with generous state subsidies, led to a rapid growth of

47 Haenke, "Memoria sobre el cultivo de algodón," f. 293.

48 Ibid., f. 293; Pentland, *Report on the Bolivian Republic*, f. 176.

the textile industry in Spain; in only a decade, between 1775 and 1784, the production of cotton textiles increased threefold.[49] Moreover, the cotton cloth that came off the looms of Barcelona were superior in quality to the rough homespuns of Cochabamba and Arequipa. Finally, English merchants were selling cotton cloth and the rustic calicoes of India throughout the viceroyalty. These contraband textiles leaked through southern Atlantic ports and were smuggled across the Brazilian frontier. They were ubiquitous and invariably undersold domestic cotton textiles. No wonder, then, that Francisco de Viedma complained in 1788 that the importation of European cloth was "draining the province of scarce money."[50] The result was that the price of tocuyos in Alto Perú began a drop in about 1771 that continued for the next two decades.[51] Local merchants saw no promise of return in trying to sell tocuyos in distant markets. Its production was left in the hands of petty producers and traders who were trying to eke out a livelihood.

But every so often during the eighteenth century, imperial rivalries and trade wars caused a sudden turn of fate. In 1796, Great Britain declared war on Spain and sent its navy into the mouth of the La Plata River, sealing off the port of Buenos Aires. This economic isolation, in the midst of Spain's imperial crisis, created a market for tocuyos that had never existed before. Across the pampas, in Chile, and in Alto Perú, urban consumers were forced to seek local supplies of cotton, woolen, and linen textiles.[52] Tocuyos broke through the previous constraints, supplying markets as distant as Buenos Aires.

49 James C. La Force, Jr., *The Development of the Spanish Textile Industry, 1750-1800* (Berkeley and Los Angeles: University of California Press, 1965), 15.

50 Viedma, *Descripción geográfica*, 47.

51 Tandeter and Wachtel, *Precios y producción agraria*, 27 and 29-30.

52 See Pedro Santos Martínez, *Las industrias durante el virreinato, 1776-1810* (Buenos Aires: Editorial Universitaria de Buenos Aires, 1969), esp. chap. 2; and Jose María Mariluz Urquijo, "Noticias sobre las industrias del virreinato del Río de la Plata en la época del Marquéz de Aviles (1799-1810)," *Revista de historia americana y argentina* 1 (1956-1957): 85-118; Ricardo Caillet-Bois, "Un ejemplo de la industria textil colonial," *Boletín del Instituto de Investigaciones Históricas* 14:20, nos. 67-68 (1936): 19-24; and Assadourian, *Sistema de la economía colonial*, 191-208. For comparisons with the impact of the trade wars on colonial textile production, particularly cotton cloth, in Mexico, see Brading, "Mercantilismo ibérico," 312, and esp. G. P. C. Thomson, "The Cotton Textile Industry in Puebla during the 18th and 19th centuries," in Nils Jacobsen and Hans-Jürgen Puhle, eds., *The Economies of Mexico and Peru during the Late Colonial Period, 1760-1810* (Berlin: Colloquium, 1986), 169-202.

Even the upper classes now had to be content with the itchy tocuyo cloth for their undergarments.[53]

Under this stimulus, the volume of production of tocuyos began to climb. In 1788, Viedma had estimated that cloth worth 60,000 pesos left Cochabamba for "outside provinces" (excluding Mizque). In 1798, Pedro Canals, the provincial treasurer, stated that registered tocuyo exports in the previous year were valued at 88,085 pesos (at the unit price of two reales per vara, the unit price Viedma reported in 1788).[54] This represented a 47 percent increase in less than ten years. The treasurer further estimated that in the first three months of 1798, tocuyo exports amounted to 46,156 pesos—more than three times the value of tocuyos exported in the same three-month period in 1788. Although both Viedma and Canals reported the unit price of tocuyos to be two reales per vara, the price rose during the war years to two and a half reales and more.[55]

But while demand was great, the factor market was still a bottleneck for Cochabamba textile producers and merchants. Raw cotton came from the Peruvian coast, around Moquegua and Arequipa. Supply was erratic, and during the war, the price climbed steeply. An arroba of cotton that cost about two pesos four reales in 1788 cost as much as six pesos ten years later.[56] Cotton imports caused a heavy cash outflow, estimated to amount to 180,000 pesos in 1798.[57] It was the cotton planters and algodoneros who were capitalizing most on the tocuyo bonanza.

The reformers, who had always had their sights set on the tropical frontier, saw a solution to the problem: cultivate cotton in the low-

53 Haenke, "Memoria sobre el cultivo de algodón," f. 293, and AGN, Alcaldía, 1799 (according to a personal communication from Susan Socolow).

54 Viedma, *Descripción geográfica*, 137; "Correspondencia con los gobernadores e intendentes de Cochabamba y La Paz," Apr. 16, 1793, AGI, Charcas, Leg. 436.

55 In the 1780s, a vara of tocuyo rarely sold for more than one and one-half reales; by 1799, it normally fetched two and one-half reales. In Buenos Aires, the price stabilized at around three and one-half reales during the shortage. Tandeter and Wachtel point out, however (*Precios y producción agraria*, 30) that this price increase was a modest one in historical terms. It merely returned the price to the levels before 1770, when European competition began to depress them.

56 Viedma, *Descripción geográfica*, 145; "Correspondencia con los gobernadores e intendentes de Cochabamba y La Paz," Apr. 3, 1798, AGI, Charcas, Leg. 436.

57 Viedma, *Descripcíon geográfica*, 145. In 1827, Pentland (*Report on the Bolivian Republic*, f. 180v.) noted that most raw cotton imported from the Peruvian coast for Cochabamba's looms was sold in the marketplaces of Paria and Tapacarí.

lands of Santa Cruz and vertically integrate the tocuyo industry. This would not only make textile manufacturing more profitable but would also promote the colonization of the jungle. The backward linkages of the cloth industry would at last open up the frontier to commercial agriculture. Viedma was enthusiastic about this idea, and he petitioned the viceroy and the king for permission to cultivate cotton in the region of Santa Cruz. But it was Tadeo Haenke who most ardently championed the cause of cotton cultivation in the region. In 1799, he wrote an essay (published in the *Telégrafo mercantil* of Buenos Aires in 1801) presenting the case to the royal authorities. He deplored the region's dependence on coastal cotton imports and reminded the crown of the importance of the tocuyo industry for the entire colony during the blockade.

> During the present war, tocuyos have been the only resource of these interior provinces. With the end of communication with Europe . . . many people would have gone about naked had it not been for Cochabamba's tocuyos. In consideration of all the circumstances . . . it is necessary to stimulate the cultivation of cotton in every way possible and to develop the textile industry that is now in its infancy.[58]

But how could Haenke expect the crown to sanction the expansion of manufacturing in Cochabamba when it favored Spanish textiles and promoted their export to the colonies? Haenke confronted this issue head on, arguing that the tocuyos posed no competition to Spanish cloth. Spanish and colonial textiles appealed to two different markets: the imports to the creole elites who could afford their higher cost, and the tocuyos to the poor. Thus, metropolitan and colonial textile industries were complementary, not competitive. If any imperial power competed with local textile manufactures, it was England, which was beginning to distribute India's crude cottons. But in any event, Haenke argued that the demand for all kinds of textiles in the viceroyalty was beginning to outpace the supply, even under normal trade conditions.[59]

If Haenke thought there was little reason to prohibit local cotton cultivation and manufacture, he saw one compelling reason why the industry had to survive and grow. Like Viedma, Haenke was concerned about poverty and social unrest in the central valleys. In the burgeoning textile industry, the growing mass of marginal small-

58 Haenke, "Memoria sobre el cultivo de algodón," f. 293.

59 Ibid., ff. 291-292.

holders and landless laborers could find subsistence security. In 1799, textiles constituted the one sector of the local economy that could absorb greater numbers of impoverished peasants seeking subsidiary work outside of agriculture.[60] If the industry survived the end of the European blockade, it might offer a solution to the region's anemic economy.

The day of reckoning came only a year after Haenke's report was published. With the signing of the Peace of Amiens in 1802, the British lifted their blockade. The sharp increase in alcabala revenues from imports in 1804 and 1805 signaled the renewed influx of European cloth, as well as other goods, into Cochabamba.[61] In 1806, the British invaded La Plata and reopened the continent to contraband trade. In the meantime, all of Alto Perú had suffered acutely from harvest failures and famine. As early as 1804, the optimistic and ambitious proposals of Haenke were already unrealistic. The authorities in Cochabamba tried to adjust their thinking to cope with the unfolding crisis.[62]

An 1804 report on the state of the tocuyo industry, and its prospects, reflected the newly conservative thinking on regional economic reform. Written by Juan Carrillo de Albornoz, a wealthy creole merchant and member of the cabildo of Cochabamba, the report stated almost matter-of-factly that many of the region's 3,000 looms had fallen silent and the industry was virtually dormant.[63] At issue, therefore, was not cotton cultivation or the vertical integration of the industry, but simply its survival under the impact of European

60 Ibid., ff. 293-294.

61 Revenue from alcabalas on Spanish goods rose from 2,852 pesos in 1802 to 8,887 pesos in 1805. However, it dropped off sharply in 1806, to 2,443 pesos, presumably because of the British invasion of Buenos Aires and the collapse of overseas Spanish trade. AGN, Sala 13, Cajas Reales, Leg. 23 to 34 (1801-1806). (For complete figures on alcabala revenues on imported and colonial goods carried into Cochabamba, see Larson, "Economic Decline and Social Change," 447.) The problem of European competition with colonial textile producers was compounded by increased Catalan demand for Peruvian cotton. It became more difficult and more costly to procure the raw materials needed to produce tocuyos in the region. Thus, Cochabamba faced "double competition" from the privileged and stronger metropolitan cotton industry of Barcelona after the Peace of Amiens.

62 On the condition of the tocuyo industry, see AGN, Sala 9, Consulado, 4.6.4, tomo 14, Apr. 15, 1804, ff. 80-80v. For a discussion of regional economic decline during the first decade of the nineteenth century, see chap. 8.

63 "Memoria de d. Juan Carrillo de Albornoz."

competition. Carrillo de Albornoz proposed tighter regulations on tocuyo weavers to improve and standardize the quality of the cloth. He wanted to restrict manufacture to guild members who operated looms that had a stipulated number and size of combs. Given sufficient quality control, the tocuyos might appeal to the upper classes and break through the class barrier that had limited their market. Reminiscent of the English Statute of Artificers of 1563, which tightened guild regulations over the woolen-cloth industry in reaction to the collapse of the export boom,[64] this proposal was a medieval remedy. It did not threaten metropolitan interests or challenge royal policy; it simply tried to restrict cloth production to "professional" weavers so that tocuyos might compete against the finer cottons of Europe. The class bias implicit in the proposal is obvious: the industry would neither employ nor clothe the laboring poor, but rather would serve the interests of the wholesale merchants and a small guild of *tocuyeros* who complied with municipal regulations. Control over production would pass entirely into the hands of the mercantile elite and municipal authorities.[65]

To a certain degree, that had begun to happen spontaneously under the impact of the textile boom. During the war years, merchants discovered that tocuyos were yielding high returns, and they injected capital into the marketing of both raw cotton and finished cloth. In Buenos Aires, tocuyos fetched prices high enough to more than offset the costs of the overland transport that was necessary during the blockade.[66] Those who stood to profit most were the merchants who monopolized the carriage trade. The shortage of pack animals in the region, which had existed ever since the 1780s, threw much of the long-distance trade in tocuyos into the hands of a privileged few.[67] In fact, the situation was serious enough to have led local authorities to register complaints with the consulado of Buenos Aires in 1801.

64 See F. J. Fisher, "Commercial Trends and Policy in Sixteenth-Century England," *Economic History Review*, 1st ser., 10 (1940): p. 113.

65 Carrillo's proposal was supported by Viedma and, in 1806, it won the endorsement of the consulado. "Memoria de d. Juan Carrillo de Albornoz," and Santos Martínez, *Industrias durante el virreinato*, 43.

66 That had been one of Carrillo de Albornoz's arguments: "Memoria de d. Juan Carrillo de Albornoz," f.86.

67 Tandeter and his collaborators estimate that approximately 50 percent of the trade in tocuyos to Potosí in the year 1793 was conducted by a few large merchants. Enrique Tandeter et al., "El mercado de Potosí a fines del siglo XVIII," in Harris, Larson, and Tandeter, *Participación indígena*, 409.

They declared that, even when the merchants agreed to carry cargo for other traders and artisans, they charged fees far in excess of the stipulated rates, and they demanded cash advances.[68] Such practices excluded many small-scale producers or traders from the long-distance tocuyo trade.

If large-scale merchants monopolized the channels of supply to distant markets, they probably also had some impact on relations of production during the textile boom. Rather than rely on the fluctuating supply and uneven quality of cloth that came off the looms of the many rural artisans, some merchants distributed raw cotton to selected artisans and then marketed their finished cloth. For the best of these artisan-clients, the merchants probably even provided financing. An occasional legal dispute brings such credit and debt relations to light. One of the most acrimonious disputes involved Carrillo de Albornoz himself, who sought to collect 295 pesos of a loan of 1,200 pesos he had made to a tocuyo *maestro*.[69] One can only speculate about the extent to which artisans lost their economic autonomy to merchant creditors or gradually abandoned agriculture to make their living (and meet their debt obligations) through more or less full-time craft production. Haenke alluded to the growth of an urban artisanate in a passing observation that "inferior classes of people are able to earn the better part of their subsistence from [the textile] industry."[70] Thus, the injection of merchant capital into the tocuyo trade probably accelerated social differentiation among the craft producers, widening the gulf between the rural cottage weavers and an urban group of artisans.

But the emergence of an urban artisanate was doubled edged. For while the urban, professional weavers, who constituted an informal guild, benefited more from the textile boom than their rural counterparts, they were probably also increasingly subordinated to merchant capital. There is little evidence that the profits in the industry "trickled down" to the producers. Indeed, more than ever, urban artisans were now vulnerable to the shifting winds of the colonial market.

68 Pedro Ariscain to consulado, Dec. 10, 1800, AGN, Sala 9, Consulado, 4.6.4, tomo 14; Ariscain to consulado, Feb. 15, 1801, ibid.; and Juan Carrillo de Albornoz to consulado, Apr. 15, 1804, ibid.

69 "Autos por el regidor de . . . D. Juan Carrillo de Albornoz contra María Vargas (madre del maestro de tocuyo) en cuanto a un préstamo de 295 pesos," AHMC, Leg. 1213 (1804).

70 Haenke, "Memoria sobre el cultivo del algodón," f. 291.

Merchant involvement in the manufacture and distribution of tocuyos during the war years suggests that a rudimentary "putting out" system was beginning to develop, in response to increased market demand. However, while some merchants may have created a clientele of producers, merchant capital did not alter production in any significant way. Merchants did not concentrate production in factories, hire wage workers, or acquire machinery with which to rationalize the productive process. In other words, the shift toward urban-based artisan production in the late 1790s did not contain the germ of capitalist relations. The accumulative strategy of the merchants was to monopolize the supply of pack animals rather than to invest in production. Furthermore, the merchants diversified their investments and holdings, always hedging their bets against sudden misfortune or a downturn in the market. Notarial records show that wealthy wholesale merchants like Juan José Eras y Gandarillas, Francisco García Claros, Francisco Ventura Valiente, and Juan Carrillo de Albornoz owned large parcels of land, speculated in tithes and bonded one another, and engaged in moneylending. They also held prestigious political posts or occupied high ranks in the local militia. Despite their financial capacity and the climate of reform, merchants remained locked in their old ways, unwilling to plow their wealth into manufacturing.

Beneficiaries of the de facto barriers of protection, the merchants knew that their profit on tocuyo exports was at the mercy of international events, which could once again flood the viceroyalty's marketplaces with European cloth. An additional deterrent to investment was the firm royal resistance to proposals to grow cotton in Santa Cruz and Mizque. Clearly, then, there was little alternative but to confine investment in tocuyos to the distributive realm, so that capital could be quickly withdrawn or diverted when the collapse came and Spanish America's market was delivered, once more, to the European cloth manufacturers. That way, when peace was followed by the flood of Spanish textiles, Cochabamba's merchants could shift from exporting tocuyos to importing Catalan's fine linens and cottons.[71] The local merchants could make such adjustments; the artisans would be left to fend for themselves.

71 Thomson's research on the cotton textile industry of Puebla provides an illuminating comparison with Cochabamba's crafts. Although significantly more developed, the Mexican cotton industry suffered similar political and market constraints in the eighteenth century. Even when the cotton textile industry thrived in Mexico, also during the imperial trade wars that cut off European imports, the local merchant class assiduously avoided capital investment in pro-

During the 1780s and 1790s, economic reformers and pragmatic entrepreneurs discovered the limits of enterprise in the colonial context. As they sought ways to alter agrarian class relations and break the "class stalemate" between peasants and hacendados in the central valleys, they came up against economic, political, and ideological obstacles to regional economic growth. Those obstacles were not peculiar to Cochabamba, but they stood out starkly to contemporary observers because the potential for economic growth in the region seemed so great. The proximity of tropical resources and the textile boom inspired proposals for economic reforms and briefly raised hope. The economic thinking of the time, combined with events on the world scene, suggested that sustained growth was possible even within the constraints of imperial rule and a shallow, unstable colonial market. But nowhere in the Andes was there greater disparity between economic plans and action, between ambitions and reality. What was to be a colonial showcase of industry and agriculture had collapsed, by 1804, into a morass of drought, famine, and misery.

So far as Alto Perú was concerned, the Bourbon decades were a period of frustrated economic reform. Behind the promise of reform there lurked a stronger colonial state bent upon extracting more surplus in the form of higher tribute and taxes on economic activity. While innovative individuals may have looked to new enterprises to stimulate the regional economy, the Bourbon state sought ways to harness the Indian communities, once more, to the mining industry of Potosí. More than ever, Spain needed fresh revenue with which to finance the empire and beat back the British.

---

duction. Like the Cochabamba workshops, the industry of Puebla did not undergo internal reorganization or modernization during the brief boom periods before independence. It, too, was dealt a serious setback by the Peace of Amiens and the re-emergence of Barcelona as the major European supplier of cotton cloth. However, Thomson also shows how Puebla's textile manufacturing did grow and begin to transform its internal productive organization in the middle of the nineteenth century, thus taking a divergent path from Cochabamba's craft industry. See Thomson, "Cotton Textile Industry in Puebla," and his "Puebla between Mine and Metropolis: Three Cycles of Growth and Decline, 1532-1850" (paper presented at the Seminar on Economic Imperialism and Latin America, University of London, Nov. 5, 1979).

CHAPTER EIGHT

The Ebb Tide of Colonial Rule

The shift in the global balance of imperial forces in favor of British hegemony posed a grave threat to Spain's overseas territories and lent a sense of urgency to the Bourbons' reformist ideals. In the third quarter of the eighteenth century, the Bourbons hastened to export those reforms to Spanish America, where an "enlightened Spanish absolutism" might fortify the colonies against British encroachment. The introduction of reforms signaled the end of a long period of neglect and the reconstitution of a centralized, interventionist colonial state that primarily served the interests of the empire and the metropolitan elites. But the reforms also touched the everyday lives of most people in the colonies. The face of empire showed itself in myriad ways: in newly formed militias, in toll houses and an army of tax collectors, in ubiquitous tribute officials, and in a growing number of officious *peninsulares* who occupied many of the highest posts.

Principal among the latter were the intendants appointed to replace the corregidores and to administer the new, enlarged administrative units. The intendants were the linchpin of imperial reform, as they were vested with broad responsibilities in matters of justice, finance, war, and general administration. Where the viceroy once enjoyed supreme power over fiscal affairs, the intendant now assumed responsibility for the management of royal tax collection in his own territory. Where once the audiencia tended to all important judicial matters, the intendant might adjudicate disputes or dispense justice in certain situations. The concentration of power in the hands of (for the most part) Spanish intendants was one mechanism of tightened royal control over the colonial hinterlands.[1]

1 J. Fisher, *Government and Society in Colonial Peru*; Lynch, *Spanish Colonial Administration*; Burkholder, "From Creole to *Peninsular*"; Leon G. Campbell,

The obverse of these changes was, of course, a reduction in the power and jurisdiction of other colonial authorities. Viceroys lost some jurisdiction over fiscal matters, and colonial magistrates found their juridical authority impinged upon by vigorous intendants who did not hesitate to mix their executive and judicial functions. Within the colonial political elite, the reforms provoked or exacerbated conflicts on all levels: individual, institutional, cultural, and ideological. For most creole authorities, therefore, the reforms were a mixed political blessing: they threatened to undermine traditional authority and prestige, even though they also promised to strengthen the bureaucracy as a whole and grant it broader powers. A strong colonial state was going to be resurrected on a weak foundation of elite factionalism, jurisdictional disputes, and petty rivalries.[2]

All of this was manifested in Alto Perú. Four intendancies were carved out of the western altiplano provinces and the eastern grain valleys and tropical lowlands, and the new intendants undercut the authority of the viceroy—whose power had in any case never effectively penetrated the interior mountain provinces—and undermined the semiautonomy of the audiencia of La Plata as well. Not only did the four intendants serve as a countervailing force to the magistrates, since they were directly subordinate to the superintendant of Buenos Aires; they also took over some of the judicial functions of the oidores. Furthermore, the new audiencia of Buenos Aires absorbed some of the powers of the older, inland court.

In this new situation, the factionalism and tensions endemic to late colonial rule in Alto Perú turned some of the proposed economic reforms into highly charged political and moral issues. When the Bourbons forced colonial authorities to come to grips once again with the labor problem at Potosí, for example, they were plunged into a bitter debate over the attributes of a functioning mita. At base, it was a political struggle, cloaked in ideological garb, but it recalled the ideals of Toledo's era some two centuries earlier, and it diverted the attention of authorities from the brutal social effects of increased

---

The Military and Society in Colonial Peru, 1750-1810 (Philadelphia: American Philosophical Society, 1978).

2 Góngora, *Studies in the Colonial History of Spanish America*, chap. 5, esp. 174-175. For a prime example of the endemic jurisdictional disputes among colonial authorities in the Bourbon years—the rivalry between Victorián de Villava, president of the audiencia of La Plata, and Intendant Francisco de Viedma over the power of the latter—see Lynch, *Spanish Colonial Administration*, 253.

colonial taxation until, by the end of the first decade of the nineteenth century, it was too late.

The Poverty of Reform

Compared with the spectacular growth of Mexico's silver mines in the late eighteenth century, Potosí's slow recovery was unimpressive to the Bourbons, all the more so as world silver prices were pegged to production costs in the most productive mines of Mexico. Silver mining at Potosí was not particularly profitable in the late eighteenth century, and it no longer attracted entrepreneurs in possession of capital or courage. Some administrators pinned their hopes for increased production on the technical assistance offered by the German Nordenflicht expedition (1788-1789) to Potosí.[3] For others, labor was the critical factor.

As discussed in chapter 3, the proliferation of small-scale, independent miners had weakened the bargaining position of the azogueros, who had reluctantly come to accept kajcheo as a necessary evil if the free mingas were to work at all. Increasingly, mine owners and renters fell back on the piecework system (see chapter 3) to squeeze more labor time out of the dwindling number of mitayos at Potosí. But the intensification of exploitation in the mines had intrinsic limits, if the labor force was to reconstitute itself from day to day and week to week. Azogueros complained that the heaps of discarded ore and earth bore no more nuggets of silver that could be plucked from the rubble. If production was to increase, ore had to be cut from deeper lodes in the mountain. Mineowners needed more ore pickers and carriers if production was to be sustained, and the arrendatarios who leased mines were desperate for more workers.[4] Thus, if the Bourbons were serious about stimulating mineral production and royal revenues, they would, according to many reformers in Alto Perú, have to increase the number of mitayos who could be subjected to the regimen of piecework. Once again, the mines needed forced subsidization by Andean peasant economies.

The intendant of Potosí, Juan del Pino Manrique, was one who

3 Rose Marie Buechler, "Technical Aid to Upper Peru: The Nordenflicht Expedition," *Journal of Latin American Studies* 5 (1973): 37-77; Marie Helmer, "Mineurs allemands à Potosí: L'expédition Nordenflycht (1788-1789)," *La minería hispana e iberoamericana* 1 (1978): 513-528.

4 Cañete y Domínguez, *Guía histórica*; Tandeter, "Rente comme rapport de production," chapts. 3 and 4.

argued for an amplified mita. Pino Manrique opposed royal instructions to model Potosí's renovation after the successful Mexican mines that functioned without forced labor. He believed that, given Potosí's inferior quality of ore and its uncompetitive position, its survival demanded a revitalized mita. He rejected the alternative of abandoning the Cerro Rico to the kajchas, who already infested the mines and chipped away at their interior works. Mining would succumb to an underground world of anarchy if some measure of power were not restored to the mining elite. Control over a compulsory labor force, subject to tareas, would widen the margin of gain and dislodge the mingas from their semiautonomous place in the industry.[5]

The argument, of course, was not new. But times had changed since the debate over the logistics and morality of the mita in the early seventeenth century. Perhaps out of fear of provoking Indian unrest only fifteen years after the great rebellion, or perhaps inspired by the fashionable ideals of the Enlightenment, some colonial authorities expressed reservations about the proposals of Pino Manrique. After all, Mexico's success had proven that colonial mining could prosper without a system of forced labor. There might be a less onerous way of inducing peasants to take their turn in the silver mines. A climate of ambivalence clouded the issues, and political resentments and rivalries that had not existed during the earlier debate added fuel to the fire.

The main protagonists in the renewed debate, which took place between 1793 and 1797, were Francisco de Paula Sanz, successor to Pino Manrique as intendant of Potosí, and Victorián de Villava, president of the audiencia of La Plata. Presiding over a weakened court, Villava turned against the azogueros and, in his "Discourse on the Mita of Potosí," challenged Potosí's intendant to justify the mita in terms of the common good of the colony.[6] Following the precepts of mercantilism, Villava asserted that agriculture and industry were the foundation of the economy. He contended that a monoculture, revolving around the production of the "universal commodity,

5 "Representaciones del gobernador de Potosí, Pino Manrique, sobre la ordenanza de minería," June 16, 1786, cited and summarized in Zavala, *Servicio personal*, 3: pp. 71-74; Tandeter, "Rente comme rapport de production," 279-304.

6 Victorián de Villava, "Discurso sobre la mita de Potosía" (1793) in Ricardo Levene, *Vida y escritos de Victorián de Villava* (Buenos Aires: Peuser, 1946), xxx-xxxiv.

money," was unhealthy when agriculture and industry stagnated. And why should the mining elite receive a special subsidy while industrious subjects engaged in agriculture and industry were left to their own devices? Other mines survived without benefit of a mita; so should Potosí.

Villava's assumption that Andean mining enterprises could thrive without mitayos challenged conventional thinking about the nature of the Indian. It was because of this basic issue of the "moral character" of the native, as Zavala has remarked, that Villava introduced Enlightenment ideals into his discourse:

> Look with shame upon those historians who, lacking philosophy and politics, have been so weak as to doubt the rationality of those miserable people [the Indians]. To this day, most look upon Indians as children or machines. Yet education makes of a man the person he wishes to be. An Indian transplanted to London could become a loyal and eloquent member of the opposition party, or [in Rome], a wise counselor to the pope.[7]

Villava's compassion and idealism set him apart from his peers and made him the leading spokesman against such institutions as the mita. He denied the prevailing belief that "racial inferiority" explained why Andeans shunned mine work or appeared passive and sullen before their colonial masters. In his view, the greed and despotism of the colonizers had forced the Indians to acquire "unattractive" character traits.

Villava's views were rather unorthodox even compared to the thinking of open-minded men like Viedma. The two men shared similar outlooks on many subjects, including an admiration for the Jesuit management of mission Indians in times past. Curiously, however, Viedma hedged on the issue of the mita. "I leave this sensitive issue to a pen other than mine," he wrote in 1788.[8] Although he apparently had no intention of advocating abolition, he did raise his voice against certain "excesses" related to the institution. Viedma was troubled, for example, by the plight of mitayos who re-

7 This paraphrase of Villava's argument is found in Zavala, *Servicio personal*, 3: 101. The content of the entire debate is discussed in great detail in ibid., 3: 100-128.

8 Viedma, *Descripción geográfica*, 178. See Viedma's descriptions of the tarea system and other hardships faced by mitayos in ibid., 178-180. See also ANB, Minas, tomo 129, no. 1177, Dec. 12, 1794, and "Exp. de los mitayos de Capinota sobre los tributos," ANB, Minas, tomo 129, no. 1170 (1792).

turned to an uncertain fate in their village, and he protested the suffering of valley Indians who had to live and work in the harsh climate of the puna. But Viedma's comments were pragmatic in tone; they lacked the philosophical depth or moral conviction of Villava's writings. Moreover, Viedma and Villava were political rivals, even more than they were intellectual companions.[9]

In the 1790s, however, Villava confronted the entrenched interests of Potosí's economic and political elites. Among their leaders was the intendant, Paula Sanz, surely a worthy opponent. Paula Sanz had traveled extensively throughout Alto Perú and had compiled statistics and notes on many aspects of the area.[10] He knew how to capitalize on his worldliness. He cast himself as a pragmatist, cut from a different cloth than the armchair philosopher Villava, who rarely left the stuffy chambers of the Chuquisaca court.

His proposed strategy was to expand the mita (or the "new mita," as it was called) and to impose tighter regulation on compulsory labor. Together with Pedro Vicente Cañete y Domínguez, Paula Sanz issued the so-called Caroline Code, based upon Toledan ordinances and other legislation and intended to correct the worst abuses suffered by the mitayos. The mita would be "cleaned up" and expanded to incorporate more Indians. Furthermore, the tarea system would not be left to the dictates of individual greed and violence; it would be regulated and rationalized. Much as the crown had tried to do in the 1750s with the repartimiento de mercancías, the intendant now proposed to regulate the tarea regime while granting it legal sanction.[11]

In 1794, Paula Sanz, invoking his authority as intendant, ordered the dispatch of 184 Indians from the pueblos of Pocoata and Aymaya, in the province of Chayanta, to serve as mitayos to two miners, Luís de Orueta and Juan Jaúregui, who had invested in new mining equip-

9 See Zavala, *Servicio personal*, 3: 155.

10 Ibid., 3: 102-103. One of Paula Sanz's reports is discussed in chap. 5. His chief ally, Cañete y Domínguez, wrote the definitive report on Potosí, *Guía histórica*. See also René Arce, "Un documento inédito de Pedro Vicente Cañete en torno a la controversia de la nueva mita de Potosí," in Martha Urioste de Aguirre, ed., *Estudios bolivianos en homenaje a Gunnar Mendoza* (La Paz, 1978, mimeograph), 119-124.

11 Rose Marie Buechler, "Mining Society of Potosí, 1776-1810" (Ph.D. diss., University of London, 1974), chap. 3; Tandeter, "Rente comme rapport de production," chap. 5; Zavala, *Servicio personal*, 3: 102-107; Buechler, "El intendente Sanz y la 'mita nueva' de Potosí," *Historia y cultura* (La Paz), no. 3 (1977): 59-95.

ment under the guidance of a member of the Nordenflicht expedition. At the same time, he assailed the secular priests of the Indian communities of Alto Perú for their "hypocrisy" in opposing the mita, and obstructing the recruitment of mitayos. Paula Sanz scorned the prelates, who, he said, preached against the injustices of the mita while subjecting their native parishioners to tyrannical rule, compulsory labor, and extortion.[12] It was an assault that recalled the earlier attacks against the corregidores during the heyday of the repartimiento de mercancías (see chapter 3). But the corregidors had long since been banished, and it was now the local religious authorities who were responsible for the mita's decline, even while the Indian population was growing. Not surprisingly, Paula Sanz pushed the clerics squarely into the political camp of Victorián de Villava. What had begun as a polemic and a rivalry between Villava and Paula Sanz became a political and ideological battle that implicated the church.[13]

The intendant's order to dispatch new mita companies aroused the priests and missionaries in Chayanta. The irate prelates hastened to La Plata, where they found the sympathetic ear of Villava. The court suspended the intendant's order in March 1795, and this decision was affirmed by the viceroy a month later. In addition, several rebellious caciques in Chayanta who had been deposed during the struggle over the mita were ordered reinstated. Subsequent orders from Madrid and Buenos Aires sought to restrain the power of Paula Sanz to expand the mita in his intendancy.[14] These actions were probably motivated, in part, by fear of worsening the situation in an already volatile province. There was little moral impulse behind them; the crown was basically indifferent to the Caroline Code and did not seriously entertain abolitionist options. It simply wanted to navigate a less treacherous course in the economic revitalization of Potosí.

Instead of applying naked coercion to increase the flow of migrant peasants to Potosí, the intendants of Alto Perú were to pursue basic agrarian reforms aimed at reconstituting the Indian villages around Toledan principles. In the aftermath of the 1781 rebellion and the dismantling of the corregimientos, the time was ripe for community reform and renovation. Village society had degenerated to its nadir

12 Buechler, 'Intendente Sanz," 61 and 63; Zavala, *Servicio personal,* 3: 11 and 116.

13 Buechler, "Mining Society of Potosí," chap. 4.

14 Zavala, *Servicio personal,* 3: 100 and 126; Lynch, *Spanish Colonial Administration,* 182-183.

during the last years of the repartimiento and the Indian wars. Now that the corregidores had been banished and the native rebels exterminated, the Bourbons believed that social reform was possible. The intendants were charged with adjudicating disputes and keeping peace in the villages, and, more fundamentally, with managing community resources.[15] The distribution of community lands and funds was made the explicit prerogative of the intendants. The Bourbons were not willing to leave these vital matters in the hands of native authorities (or of local prelates, for that matter). The crown sought to enhance the political leverage of the intendants so that they could shield Andean villages from outside threats and facilitate the extraction of surpluses from them. The royal mandate was to distribute community lands more equitably, but behind it was the threat of heavier taxation and mita recruitment. Compared to the crude tactics of Paula Sanz, the reformist strategy of extraction probably seemed more prudent and effective.

Francisco de Viedma was one of the few intendants who took up the challenge to implement land reform in the Indian communities. From the beginning of his term, he expressed concern about the extreme imbalances in community land distribution and tribute categories. As noted in chapter 3, the first Indian population census taken after the Indian uprisings revealed that landholding originarios made up only about 15 percent of the village population. The overwhelming majority of Indians were dependent leaseholders, or at least so they claimed to the tribute collectors. Viedma's tour of the villages alarmed him further, for he suspected that caciques like the Liro de Córdovas of Tapacarí were controlling the distribution of community lands in their own interests.[16] The decay of communal landholding was even more advanced in the valley pueblos of Sipesipe, El Paso, and Tiquipaya, where Indians hardly outnumbered mestizos and creoles any longer. Thus, the intendant advocated the restoration of the corporate village much along the lines of Toledo's blueprint. He hoped to distribute lands more democratically among village Indians, with little regard for their cultural or social links to their communities. The result would be the passage of landless forasteros into the status of landholding originarios. Viedma justified his plan on fiscal and moral grounds: by generating "more tribute monies . . . the land reform would allow the Indians to break their

15 J. Fisher, *Government and Society in Colonial Peru*, chap. 4; Lynch, *Spanish Colonial Administration*, chap. 8.

16 Viedma, *Descripción geográfica*, 182; see also chap. 4.

bonds of slavery and escape the misery they suffer as dependents of the few originarios who have land."[17] State intervention would reverse the process of class differentiation in the villages and guarantee the means of subsistence to a servile Indian peasantry. Viedma glossed over the fact that the reform would subjugate originario peasants more directly to state obligations.

As is so often the case with such efforts, the intendant's land reform fell far short of its goals. The 1793 padron revealed that the number of originarios in Cochabamba increased by 79 percent since 1786, from 339 to 607 (see table 20). Yet forasteros still outnumbered originarios by more than three to one. Moreover, the impact of the land reform was uneven. Land was widely redistributed in Sipesipe, El Paso, and Tiquipaya, but in the cabecera pueblo of Tapacarí, where land was most concentrated among the originario population, the reform was less effective.[18] Perhaps Viedma was unwilling to challenge the power and authority of the Liro de Córdova clique that still ruled Tapacarí. After all, that village had erupted in 1781, and its rebels had divided the province into two parts for several months. Viedma may have felt that he could not afford to dislodge the caciques and

Table 20. Composition of Tributaries in Pueblos Reales of Cochabamba, 1786 and 1793

	1786			
			Originarios	
Pueblo Real	*Total Number of Tributaries*	*Forasteros*	*Number*	*Percentage*
Tapacarí	1,465	1,296	169	11.5
Sipesipe	381	316	65	17.1
El Paso	219	190	29	13.2
Tiquipaya	424	348	76	17.9
Total	2,489	2,150	339	13.6
	1793			
Tapacarí	1,468	1,268	200	13.6
Sipesipe	420	264	156	37.1
El Paso	236	128	108	45.8
Tiquipaya	433	290	143	33.0
Total	2,557	1,950	607	23.7

Sources: AGN, Sala 13, Padrones, 18.2.1, Leg. 46; 18.2.2, Leg. 47; and 18.2.5, Leg. 150.

17 Viedma, *Descripción geográfica*, 64.

18 See chap. 4, and Sánchez-Albornoz, *Indios y tributos*, 180-185.

risk losing their loyalty and collaboration at a moment when heavier taxation required strong rule and the financial bonding of tribute dues. In any event, it is ironic that the Liro de Córdovas emerged from the reform with more material wealth rather than with less. Records show that they were granted royal licenses to build and operate grain mills in the Tapacarí River valley in the late 1790s.[19] Evidently, the land reform was adjusted to local circumstances. Egalitarian distribution may have been the ideal, but it was applied only where royal interests so dictated.

Land redistribution was not the only mechanism by which Viedma tried to alter the social hierarchy of the Indian villages. He wanted to reverse the centuries of pauperization of the villages by building up their capital stock and then purposefully managing the dispensation of the funds. His main project was Tapacarí. Community funds would be obtained from two sources: interest on outstanding mortgage loans, which had accumulated over many years of delinquent payment; and the sale of wheat cultivated on communal lands.[20] Viedma was not specific about which lands would be earmarked for communal production or about the role that the caciques would play in the communal efforts to rebuild the municipal treasury. On the contrary, what is striking about his proposal is the implicit separation of the village elite from the proposed reforms. Viedma apparently wanted to intervene directly in the village economy to ensure that surplus harvests were marketed for the benefit of the community as a whole.

Viedma therefore, proposed the establishment of a "neutral" administrative body (composed of himself, two treasurers, a member of the cabildo, and the royal protector of Indians) to oversee the use of the communal funds. In his view, the funds were to serve three purposes. First, they would underwrite tribute deficits. The state would no longer be so dependent upon the personal assets of the caciques to post bond for the value of tribute, nor would cobradores find themselves in debt following their rounds of tribute collection. Second, the community would spend a portion of its monies for the pur-

19 In 1798, for example, Matías Quispe won a royal license to build two grain mills on the outskirts of the pueblo real, in recognition of his "punctual and efficient" handling of tribute collection. AGN, Sala 9, Tribunales, 37.3.2, Leg. 124, Exps. 18 and 27 (1798).

20 AGI, Charcas, Leg. 436, "Instrucción que forma . . . Francisco de Viedma para el gobierno de los monte-píos," July 20, 1798, AGI, Charcas, Leg. 436. (See also table A-4).

chase of basic goods (mules, iron, tools, and cloth) at wholesale prices for resale to peasant households, eliminating the fees of middlemen.[21]

Finally, the funds would be used to restore a measure of community welfare to Tapacarí. They could be allocated to purchase supplies for departing mitayos or to make loans to peasant families in stress. Although he never conceptualized his plan in such terms, Viedma was proposing to take over the traditional responsibility of the ethnic elite to tend to the well-being of all community members. The traditional basis of cacique legitimacy had long disintegrated in Tapacarí, as hierarchical relations were no longer governed by Andean ideals of reciprocity and redistribution (see chapter 4). Viedma felt it was incumbent upon the state to shield village peasants from their own native overlords as well as from outsiders. Tapacarí's new *monte-pío* (pious works) would serve as a halfway house of charity and insurance, providing the needy with emergency resources and underwriting the value of communal tribute. The Bourbon state would undertake to restore the traditional rights of community members to a minimum of subsistence security as long as their caciques met their obligations to the state.

The issue of legitimate Andean rule in the villages, which had been raised in the middle of the eighteenth century by the eruption of feuds and the pressures of the repartimiento (see chapter 4), continued to vex Viedma and other intendants. In Tapacarí, as seen earlier, there was a prolonged political struggle between the Condoris and the Liro de Córdovas over the right to moiety rule. The intendants were unwilling to leave the question of cacique legitimacy to the ad hoc decision making of the audiencia. Furthermore, barely a decade had passed since the rebellions, and the state needed to monitor closely the succession to power in the villages. The Ordinance of Intendants, enacted in 1782, restored many of the Toledan regulations governing the accession to and transmission of ethnic authority. For example, members of the village hierarchy (alcaldes, cobradores, etc.) were to be elected by natives in the community, and the position of cacique was to go only to members of a noble line-

21 The Ordinance of Intendants (1782) outlawed the repartimiento de mercancías, and at the same time authorized the establishment of government-run shops in which Indians could purchase goods at regulated prices and on credit. The law was opposed by most intendants; only Viedma and the intendant of Paraguay took concrete measures to implement it. See Lynch, *Spanish Colonial Administration*, 196-199.

age.[22] But whereas in Toledo's day noble lineages produced numerous heirs, in the 1790s many villages could not come up with direct descendants of noble ancestors. Viedma complained that "the decadence of the Indians and the lack of legitimate succession is the cause of confusion and chaos [in selecting caciques]."[23] Without caciques of noble lineage to inherit the staff of office, it was left to the subdelegado to select candidates for the cacicazgo. Sometimes, the local authority appointed a native; on other occasions, subdelegadoes nominated two or three "appropriate candidates" from among whom the village could elect one. According to Viedma, local Spanish authorities employed various means of maneuvering certain individuals into positions of power in the village hierarchy, although the crown tried to limit this by stipulating that colonial authorities could appoint caciques interinos or "governors" only if no legitimate heir could be identified.[24]

Royal authorities were also granted the power to intervene in villages where the cacicazgo was in dispute among blood relatives of a former cacique. The members of a parcialidad may have had the right to choose a cacique from among several claimants, but the intendant or the subdelegado had the right to pass judgment on the "eligibility" of the candidates, thus preserving a mechanism by which colonial authorities could manipulate the ethnic hierarchy of villages. An heir to the cacicazgo was also supposed to prove himself fluent in Spanish and skilled in agriculture and crafts.[25] In practice, however, very little had changed since the middle of the eighteenth century. Local royal authorities sought candidates who were close kin to the former cacique and who were wealthy enough to underwrite their moiety's tribute dues. In an age of heavier taxation, this latter qualification was especially important, lest the subdelegado find himself in arrears to the royal exchequer. In the 1790s, the subdelegado of Arque explained to the judges of the audiencia that

22 These matters were dealt with in arts. 10 and 11 of the ordinance. See also "Exp. sobre los indios que deben elegir sus alcaldes," ANB, EC no. 245 (1796), and "Exp. sobre los indios alcaldes en Carangas," ANB, EC no. 247 (1796).

23 "Exp. de elecciones de caciques interinos de Capinota," ANB, EC no. 72 (1796).

24 "Exp. por Clemente Choque sobre el dueño del cacicazgo," ANB, EC no. 48 (1796), f. 15.

25 "Exp. con la nomina de las elecciones de alcaldes indios," ANB, EC no. 136 (1794); "Confirmación de indios de la elección de alcaldes de Oruro, año de 1795," ANB, EC no. 24 (1795), f. 6.

he appointed caciques only if they could guarantee the entire tribute quota;[26] and in court battle in Santiago de Berenguela, a creole litigant admitted that an Indian had been named sole candidate for the cacicazgo because "he is the legitimate grandson of Don Diego Condorena and because he could underwrite the royal tribute debt for the value of 12,000 pesos."[27] In spite of the royal proclamations to the contrary, material assets still outweighed kinship and service to the community in the selection of native candidates for the village hierarchy.

Another important attribute for a cacique was proven loyalty to the crown. The litmus test was the Indian's behavior during the 1781 rebellions. Rebel leaders had been executed, but in the lingering climate of fear and suspicion, the slightest indication that a prospective cacique had sympathized with the insurgents could be disabling. Subdelegados could rule out a candidate because of a report of suspicious behavior a decade earlier. Intravillage disputes over the cacicazgo sometimes led to accusations of sedition during the general uprisings. One such case occurred in Capinota during the mid-1790s, when Ygnacio Condo challenged the subdelegado's choice of a distant cousin, Guillermo Condo, as cacique.[28] Ygnacio claimed to be the legitimate heir upon his father's death in 1782. However, because he was too young at the time, the cacicazgo passed to his uncle, Tomás Condo. In the meantime, Ygnacio served as a mitayo and then as a principal. When his uncle died, the cacicazgo was passed to his cousin, the cacique of Anansaya and an enemy of his family. Ygnacio declared that Guillermo, his father, and a brother had been traitorous in 1780 and 1781, having traveled through villages inciting Indians to rebel, in alliance with the Chayanta rebel leader, Tomás Catari. Ygnacio's own father, a cacique at the time, had remained loyal and fled to the city of Cochabamba to hide from the rebels. Ygnacio's story was disputed by his cousin, and the subdelegado ruled in Guillermo's favor. The trial reveals how the legacy of rebellion and war could feed into ethnic rivalries and power struggles at a time when the state was trying to control the village hierarchy.

The basic purpose of the reforms of the late eighteenth century

26 "Exp. sobre que don Augustín Jascata hace renuncia del cargo de cacique . . . de Capinota," ANB, EC no. 158 (1808).

27 "Exp. por Nicholás Condorena sobre el derecho al cacicazgo de . . . Santiago de Berenguela," ANB, EC no. 158 (1799).

28 "Exp. sobre que don Augustín Jascata hace renuncia del cargo de cacique . . . de Capinota," ANB, EC no. 158 (1808).

was to resurrect, in modified form, the extractive model of exploitation that Toledo had introduced into the Andes some two centuries earlier. The Bourbons sought to rebuild the twin pillars of that model, the institutions of tribute and the mita, and to initiate a new cycle of taxation. But there was much to be done at the village level before the apparatus of extraction could function. If the state was once again to enforce the extraction of tribute and the flow of migrants to the silver mines of Potosí, it would have to protect the subsistence base of Andean communities much more diligently than it had in the recent past. The abolition of the repartimiento de mercancías and the displacement of the corregidores were important first steps. Further, as in Toledo's day, the intendants were ordered to intervene in the internal affairs of the villages and to mediate the relations between caciques and peasants. The state was to penetrate to the very heart of the community to alleviate the social ills that had resulted from almost two centuries of neglect and abuse.

But if the Bourbons' reforms looked very much like Toledo's ordinances, the social landscape of the Indian villages was not at all the same. The villages were sharply differentiated in their degree of self-sufficiency, cultural cohesiveness, and adherence to traditional norms governing relations of production. Many villages in Alto Perú had proved relatively resilient in maintaining their unity and cultural integrity against the forces of attrition and fragmentation.[29] But colonialism had sapped the internal resources and broken down the moral fiber of many other villages. In Cochabamba, the decay of communal traditions in the pueblos reales put to test the effectiveness of the Bourbons' social reforms.

For all his ambition and innovation, Viedma's administration had little impact on village society. His land reform did no more than paper over class divisions and increase the tribute rates of many former forasteros. It did not release peasants from subservience to prosperous, powerful, landholding Indians. Furthermore, Viedma's call for the payment of outstanding interest on the mortgage loans that had been issued by the villages could not be enforced. Heavily indebted landowners objected to making interest payments on loans contracted by their grandfathers or great-grandfathers. The regulations on cacique succession were manipulated by subdelegados,

29 Indeed, many communities had not only maintained their self-sufficiency but had even flourished by marketing wheat at Potosí and by preserving the tradition of dual residence in puna and valley zones. See Platt, *Estado boliviano y ayllu andino*, chap. 1.

much as corregidores had done earlier (see chapters 3 and 4). Even the intendant's efforts to shield the villages from coercive mercantile practices proved ineffective.[30]

In short, Viedma's reforms failed. Yet the tragedy of the Bourbon decades lay not so much in the failure of the state to redistribute community resources more equitably or to protect the villages from exploitation, but rather in its spectacular success in draining revenue from the native subjects. Where the social reforms failed, the fiscal reforms launched a new cycle of extraction that left the villages more impoverished than ever.

The Bankruptcy of Reform

Beginning in the 1770s, the Bourbons took systematic measures to generate more tax revenue in the Andes. The creation of the viceroyalty of La Plata was but one administrative change that decade designed to curtail contraband and siphon off more revenue from the colony. Tribute and taxes on mining were still the major sources of royal income in the southern Andes, but the state was turning increasingly to other sources. By the first decade of the nineteenth century, the financial burden of empire was beginning to weigh heavily on the merchant, mining, and landholding elites.

From the imperial point of view, the need to increase revenue from the colonies arose out of the desire to strengthen royal authority over them and to deter mercantile and military encroachment by England and her ally, Portugal. To increase revenue required in turn that the colonial economy be stimulated in ways that were not detrimental to the economic interests of the metropolitan elite. An overhaul of the fiscal system was also in order. It was in this last area of reform that the Bourbons achieved their greatest success in the viceroyalties of Peru and La Plata.[31]

30 These problems were not peculiar to Cochabamba, of course. Elsewhere in Peru, as Fisher has pointed out, "many subdelegates, especially in the sierra, continued the repartimientos and other abuses, and the intendants, as a result of indifference or impotence, or both, failed to check their activities." J. Fisher, *Government and Society in Colonial Peru*, 91. The problem of corruption was widely discussed in the 1780s by several intendants. They pointed to the lack of suitable candidates for the low-prestige post of subdelegado. In 1784, the bishop of Santa Cruz deplored the unsuitable character of most subdelegados in the Cochabamba region. Rather than "professionalize" this level of the bureaucracy, the crown granted the post to local landlords and petty officials with appropriate connections. Lynch, *Spanish Colonial Administration*, 76-77.

31 Fisher notes that "the general condition of the [Peruvian] viceregal exchequer

The need for increased revenue became particularly acute with the creation of the viceroyalty of La Plata in 1776. The sparse settlement of the pampas and the lack of economic activity except for cattle ranching and the export of hides made the extensive zone south of Tucumán a relatively unprofitable region. Without tax revenues from the northern provinces of Alto Perú, the new viceroyalty would have been economically unviable. Indian tribute and taxes on trade and silver mining were the main sources of the cash needed to pay the high cost of maintaining a bureaucracy and of protecting the Atlantic coastline from Portuguese and British interlopers.[32]

Even in times of peace, Buenos Aires drained funds from the interior provinces. In 1790, for example, Potosí transferred 818,768 pesos to the viceregal treasury at Buenos Aires.[33] Part of that money originated in Potosí itself—from mining taxes, tribute, and customs duties. Another part probably derived from revenue raised in the subordinate territories of La Paz, Cochabamba, and La Plata, which the Potosí authorities collected and transmitted to Buenos Aires.[34] Cochabamba was not the highest revenue producer in the viceroyalty. Potosí, with its mining taxes; La Paz, with its high tribute revenues (more than twice those of Cochabamba in 1790, and 80 percent of La Paz's total tax revenues in that year); and Buenos Aires, with its rich returns from customs duties, all generated more income for the state. But together, the four intendancies of Alto Perú supported the import-export trade of the port of Buenos Aires and helped to offset the annual deficits in the Buenos Aires treasury. In 1790, this deficit amounted to 123 percent of income that year; the revenue received from the interior provinces reduced it to 108 percent of income.[35]

---

improved considerably between 1782 and 1787.": J. Fisher, *Government and Society in Colonial Peru,* 118. Lynch argues that, while the overhaul of the fiscal machinery was only partly successful in the viceroyalty of La Plata, "it gave a unified and vigorous stimulus to honesty and efficiency": *Spanish Colonial Administration,* 131.

32 In 1790, mineral taxes generated 1,102,642 pesos (32 percent of the total revenues 3.4 million pesos that year); commercial imposts, 749,617 pesos (22 percent); and tribute, 562,528 pesos (16 percent). Herbert Klein, "Structure and Profitability of Royal Finance in the Viceroyalty of the Río de la Plata in 1790," *Hispanic American Historical Review* 53 (1973): 444. Klein estimates that at least two-fifths of royal expenditures went to maintain the viceroyalty's bureaucracy. Ibid., 455.

33 Ibid., 451.

34 Ibid., 463.

35 Ibid., 453.

Yet even with that help, the viceregal treasury was in a chronic state of indebtedness. In 1790, almost 40 percent of all viceregal expenditures went to maintain the bureaucracy. In fact, the viceroyalty was barely able to pay for its own maintenance and military security. Although it was the second largest taxation zone in the entire empire after New Spain, the viceroyalty of La Plata nevertheless remitted little income to Madrid. Although the royal revenues generated in the viceroyalty of La Plata were more than 20 percent of the revenues raised in New Spain, the southern viceroyalty sent to the mother country tax monies that amounted to only about 6 percent of Mexico's remittances. The tax revenue from the interior provinces of Alto Perú was therefore crucial for the maintenance of this Spanish colony.[36]

Why, then, were the Bourbons so determined to increase royal income in the southern zone if so little revenue actually reached the metropolis? Part of the reason lies in Spain's need to defend the Atlantic coast, as part of the struggle against England in the New World, and to close the river basin area to British and Portuguese contraband trade. This was particularly important because La Plata was a potential market for Catalan textiles and other metropolitan goods. In other words, to the people of Alto Peru, higher taxes would mean increased commercial competition from Spanish manufacturers.

The advent of new taxes and fiscal policies had far-reaching effects on the economy and society of Cochabamba. Shortly before the creation of the intendancy, royal administrators had begun to reorganize the provincial treasuries of Alto Perú. Previously, the Potosí treasury had served as the central treasury for all of the provinces of Alto Perúa. Royal income from Cochabamba flowed into that *caja principal*, which then remitted a portion of the revenue to the viceregal treasury in Lima. In 1773, the crown established two other treasuries in Charcas: one in La Plata and the other in Cochabamba. Three years later, with the creation of the viceroyalty of La Plata, the treasury at Buenos Aires became the *tribunal mayor de cuentas*, or principal accounts office, although Potosí's treasury continued to be the central accounting office for Alto Perú. There was also a network of subsidiary treasuries (*cajas surbordinadas*) throughout the Viceroyalty, each of which sent its accounts and part of its income to either Potosí or Buenos Aires. Cochabamba was one such caja subordinada, sending its excess revenue to Potosí.[37]

36 Ibid., 456.

37 On the fiscal reforms under the Bourbons, see Klein, "Structure and Profita-

Extant records of these treasuries show that gross royal income in Cochabamba increased five and a half times between 1757 and 1809 (see figure 14). Part of that increase reflected the fact that after the establishment of Cochabamba's treasury in 1773, the province of Mizque remitted its revenue there. But Mizque's economy was in decay and its tributary population was small, so the province could not have been an important revenue producer. The increase in Cochabamba's revenue derived mainly from improved methods of collection, additional taxes that weighed more heavily upon the elite, and the increase of tributary population in the central valleys. After 1780, royal authorities levied a 6 percent ad valorem tax (alcabala) on the sale of goods, local tribute collection was systematized, and the state imposed a host of new taxes on commercial activities. Despite poor harvest conditions in the early 1780s, the state extracted an increasingly large surplus from the province.

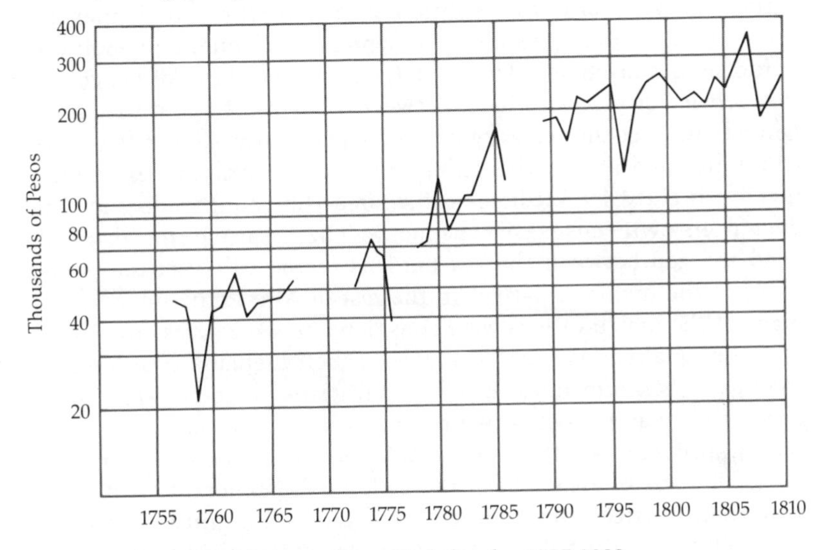

Figure 14 Gross Royal Income from Cochabamba, 1757-1809
Sources: See table A-6, and AHMC, Leg. 1175 (1757-1767).
Note: Gross royal income includes uncollected taxes and residual income from previous years.

bility,"441-443; Lynch, *Spanish Colonial Administration*, chap. 6; Guillermo Céspedes de Castillo, "Reorganización de la hacienda virreinal peruana en el siglo XVIII," *Anuario de historia del derecho español* 23 (1953): 329-369; and Pedro Santos Martínez, *Historia económica de Mendoza durante el virreinato, 1776-1810* (Madrid: Universidad Nacional de Cuyo, 1961), chap. 6. For the instructions on account keeping published by the crown in 1784, see "Nuevo método de cuenta y razón para la real hacienda en las Indias," reprinted in *Revista de la Biblioteca Nacional* (Buenos Aires) 4 (1940): 267-318.

The effect of the fiscal reforms on tribute was particularly dramatic. Tribute revenue rose from an annual average of less than 50,000 pesos between 1780 and 1784 to an annual average of almost 100,000 pesos in the quinquennium 1800-1804, though it subsequently declined as a result of the famine of 1804 (see table A-6). From the imperial perspective, this increase was the most notable achievement of Viedma's administration. Ever since the 1730s, royal agents had tried to increase tribute revenue in the Cochabamba valleys. Forasteros were made liable for tribute in that decade, but authorities were notably unsuccessful in collecting the tax (see chapter 3). Viedma's feat in managing to wring substantially more tribute money out of the Cochabamba peasantry was not a minor one, since tribute made up more than 40 percent of the total income of the provincial treasury (see table A-6).

The effect of the tax reforms on the peasantry was quite different. Only a few years after the abolition of the repartimiento de mercancías, tribute obligations began to depress the economic conditions of forastero households. The more rigorous procedures of tax collection left fewer places to hide. Between 1786 and 1808, royal agents fanned out over the territory on four separate occasions to hunt for tributaries and prospective tributaries. In Cochabamba, tax collectors were aided by Viedma, who toured the countryside and conducted his own census (see chapter 5). The fiscal reforms also widened the gap between the tax burdens of the valley peasants and those of the highland natives in the rest of Alto Perú. Since the Indians of the maize valleys were considered to have access to acreage of higher quality than that available to their highland counterparts, they paid premium rates. Landless forasteros of Cochabamba were expected to pay six pesos two reales a year—more than most landholding originarios of the puna paid.[38] This was the reason why the Carangas Indians of Sicaya, near the valleys of Capinota, fought to retain their vertical ties to their highland community of Toledo; although the quality of the land there was poorer than that in most valley areas of Cochabamba, their status as originarios would have meant lower tax rates (see chapter 4).

Alcabalas, the taxes on trade and commerce, constituted about 15

38 A visitador who made an inspection of Cochabamba in 1793 noted that forasteros were not supposed to pay more than seven pesos in tribute each year and that in most provinces of Alto Perú they paid only five pesos, except in Potosí, where they often paid seven. "Informe de la contaduría de retasas sobre la revisita del partido de Santa Cruz," Feb. 25, 1793, RAH, ML, 9/1733, tomo 78, ff. 170-172.

percent of royal income from the province. The "royal ninth" (*real noveno*), a tax of 11 percent levied on tithes, was an important source of revenue (see table A-6), but it was the alcabalas that were the heaviest burden on producers and traders. As part of the Bourbon reforms, tax farming was replaced with methods of direct collection, toll houses were established along the river trade routes of Arque and Tapacarí, and in 1780 the rate of alcabalas was raised to 6 percent from its previous level of 4 percent. Alcabala revenues increased sharply in the 1770s and again in the late 1780s, after the region had recovered from the rebellions. This was a period of relatively sluggish trade and generally stagnant prices, so the increased revenue from alcabalas simply reflected the higher rate and the stricter enforcement. In 1774 and again in 1780, wealthy merchants and rural craftsmen briefly united in opposition to the reforms, and there were some incidents of mob action (see chapter 5).[39]

By 1800, the region's population had endured twenty-five years of tax reforms. The overhaul of the fiscal machinery and the establishment of a provincial treasury in Cochabamba had produced spectacular results. But it also imposed relentless pressure on most people and drained the region of scarce capital at a time when Viedma was trying to rejuvenate its economy. Above all, increased tribute income—the main source of royal revenue in Cochabamba—cut into the subsistence production of peasants, even as the regional economy began to deteriorate after the turn of the nineteenth century. In good times and bad, the peasant family had to meet its obligations to the state. Spanish absolutism made no concessions to human misfortune, even when drought struck and famine stalked the arid land.

Early in 1805, Viedma wrote despairingly to the consulado of Buenos Aires:

> We have had a serious shortage of water during the last five years, especially in the past year. There are not voices to express the calamity and hunger that the miserable Indians and mestizos suffer, such that they must beg to live. Agriculture, the only livelihood of these people, has not yet yielded its fruits. The tocuyo trade has decayed, and public works have ceased due to a

39 "Testio. del procurador gral . . . ," AGI, Charcas, Leg. 505 (1794). See above, chap. 5, no. 90. There was much contemporary debate over the exemption of Indian traders from alcabala levies; see "Exp. del recurso hecho por Don Manuel Maruri c/ el gob. de Potosí sobre que no le embarase el cobro de dhas alcabalas de los indios . . . ," ANB, Minas, tomo 149, no. 81; "Documento sobre la exención de la alcabala que debe gozar los indios," ANB, EC no. 141 (1779).

> shortage of capital. Everything is lamentable. People wander in masses, begging in the towns and countryside. They eat roots of withered grass in order to survive. . . . [They] are wandering corpses, and many collapse, dead from starvation.[40]

Viedma's description could have applied to any region of Alto Perú. Authorities reported that the highland peasants suffered even more acutely, particularly near the salt pans of Lake Poopó, where even in good years the arid altiplano yielded only quinoa and bitter potatoes. They reported an increase in mortality rates, the extermination of livestock, and the total loss of the harvest, including next year's seeds. Everywhere, people had turned to begging and scavenging, eating wild roots and wood in their quiet desperation.[41]

This crisis pierced the veil of Bourbon "enlightenment" and revealed the imperatives of imperial rule. In 1805, in the midst of human misery, an executive order to all intendants, caciques, and alcaldes demanded that they account for the decline of tribute revenues and the delay in the remittances. Local authorities were reminded that tributes were due promptly on January 25 (the Christmas installment) and June 25 (following collection on San Juan's Day). No excuse was acceptable, neither natural calamity nor human deprivation.[42]

The subsistence crisis of the first decade of the nineteenth century broke the peasant family economy, fragmented Andean communities, and destroyed regional economies. Revenue from tribute and economic activity plummeted as a result. In Cochabamba, royal income from tribute, alcabalas, and novenos reales declined after 1804 and did not recover for the rest of the decade. Tribute dropped sharply, from 465,368 pesos in the 1800-1804 period to 277,560 pesos in the 1805-1809 period. Where tribute had represented almost half of all royal income in Cochabamba during the earlier period, it represented only 36 percent in the later one (see table A-6). As tax revenue from economic activity and tribute dried up, the provincial treasury, in a search for other sources of income, even taxed the upper classes (see below). Nevertheless, the treasury's net income

40 AGN, Sala 13, Cajas Reales, 5.8.7, Jan. 13, 1805.

41 "Exp. de yndios de Carasa solicitando el convento de San Augustín les rebajen el arriendo por la calamidad del año, AHMC, Leg. 1099 (1804); AGN, Sala 9, Intendencia, 5.8.7, Feb. 15, 1804, and Feb.-Mar., 1805. See also chap. 6.

42 "Exp. sobre que los caciques cobradores pasen a pagar sus cobranzas a la tesorería," ANB, EC no. 198 (1805).

dropped sharply after 1802, and between 1804 and 1808, royal expenditures outstripped royal income. Moreover, the treasury was sending a larger and larger proportion of its revenue out of the region, to the superordinate treasures of Buenos Aires and Potosí and, after 1803, to the newly established treasury of Santa Cruz. What was more ominous, tax collections were lagging. Uncollected tax liabilities nearly doubled between 1795-1799 and 1800-1804 and increased by another 50 percent in the next five-year period. The amount of uncollected taxes averaged 32,494 pesos a year between 1805 and 1809.[43] Just when Buenos Aires was draining off more royal income from Cochabamba, more and more people were simply evading the tax collectors.

The growing burden of imperial finance reflected the militarization of colonial society during the first decade of the nineteenth century. The royal revenue itemized as *otras tesorerías* (other treasuries), in the debit column of the ledger, was earmarked for expenses outside the province. The precise destination of these funds cannot be traced, but most of them probably went to defray military costs in the River Plate region. It is surely no accident, for instance, that a huge increase in otras tesorerías, from approximately 92,800 pesos in 1806 to 141,900 pesos in 1807, followed immediately upon the British invasion of Buenos Aires.[44] Intensified efforts to militarize the intendancies of Alto Perú also absorbed more royal revenue in this decade. Royal expenditures on military salaries, for example, rarely surpassed 4,000 pesos annually before 1800, but in 1807 and again in 1809, they were about 79,000 pesos.[45]

In 1807, the provisional junta of the royal treasury in Cochabamba met to organize the "war effort." The junta planned to stockpile supplies of wood, iron, gunpowder, and other materials needed for the local production of weaponry.[46] Although the intendancy of Santa Cruz de la Sierra was buried in the interior of the colony, hundreds of miles from Buenos Aires, its uncharted eastern frontier bordered Portuguese territory and thus was a point of penetration for both the

43 AGN, Sala 13, Cajas reales 27.4.4, Leg.236 (1795); 5.5.3, Leg. 18 (1796); 27.5.2, Leg. 240 (1797); 27.5.4, Leg. 241 (1798); 27.6.1, Leg. 243 (1799); 5.6.1, Leg. 22 (1800); 5.6.2, Leg. 23 (1801); 5.6.3, Leg. 24 (1802); 5.6.4, Leg. 25 (1803); 5.7.1, Leg. 28 (1804); 5.7.3, Leg. 30 (1805); 5.8.1, Leg. 34 (1806); 5.8.4, Leg. 37 (1807); 5.9.1, Leg. 40 (1808); 5.9.5, Leg. 44 (1809).

44 AGN, Sala 13, Cajas reales, 5.8.1, Leg. 34 (1806), and 5.8.4, Leg. 37 (1807).

45 AGN, Sala 13, Cajas reales, 5.8.4, Leg. 37 (1807), and 5.9.5, Leg. 44 (1809).

46 AGN, Sala 9, Intendencia, 5.9.1, Sept. 4, 1807.

Portuguese and their British allies. Emergency measures were called for if the intendancy was to be protected from the "heathen enemy."

That meant, essentially, that more royal revenue had to be squeezed out of the local population. For the first time, religious institutions, wealthy merchants, and landowners in the central valleys of Cochabamba were taxed. The region's monasteries, convents, and cofradías were required to pay 15 percent on the value of interest on loans and on the sale of their properties.[47] In 1808, as Napoleon's armies swarmed over the Iberian peninsula, the treasury forced the region's monasteries to "lend" it cash, in the amount of 19,462 pesos.[48] Persons inheriting property worth more than 2,000 pesos had to pay either 2 or 4 percent of the value of their inheritance, depending on their relationship to their benefactor.[49] Other vecinos found themselves cajoled or coerced into lending money to the government.[50] As it turned out, these fiscal pressures came at the beginning of a long period of insurgency that would plunder and exhaust the regional economy until the last vestiges of Spanish imperial rule were finally destroyed in 1824 and 1825.

The crisis years between 1804 and 1808 closed the chapter of Bourbon reforms in Alto Perú and initiated the long period of insurgency that culminated in Independence. In the Cochabamba region, the social impact of two decades of reform was contradictory. On the one hand, class antagonisms were intensified. Agrarian class relations deteriorated sharply, as large numbers of rural people were struck by famine and destitution. Class polarizations were never so nakedly exposed as in 1804, when tithe dealers paid record prices to capitalize on the scarcity and soaring prices of maize and wheat. Peasants saw tithe speculators and large landowners feeding on their misfortune. Crop failures eliminated the smallholders as sellers in the

47 AGN, Sala 13, Cajas reales, 5.7.3, Leg. 30 (1805), and 5.8.4, Leg. 37 (1807). This measure was applied to the entire colony. See Brian Hamnett, "The Appropriation of Mexican Church Wealth by the Spanish Bourbon Government: The 'Consolidation of Vales Reales,' 1805-1809," *Journal of Latin American Studies*, 1 (1969): 86-91.

48 AGN, Sala 13, Cajas reales, 5.9.1, Leg. 40 (1808).

49 Ibid.

50 In early 1807, Cochabamba's largest merchant, Francisco Ventura Valiente, donated five hundred pesos for "extraordinary expenses in the defense of the capital" against the British invaders. He also supplied one thousand varas of tocuyos for bandages. AGN, Sala 9, Intendencia, 5.9.1 (1807).

marketplace and brought a temporary restoration of agrarian monopoly to landowners, merchants, and diezmeros. Social tensions in the region were compounded by the collapse of the tocuyo trade after 1802, for not only did the collapse hurt the artisans and merchants involved in the textile industry, but the bonanza that preceded it had concentrated wealth in the hands of a few merchants able to capitalize on the long-distance overland trade. Artisans were marginalized from the wholesale trade, and many fell into debt and dependence upon merchant-creditors (see chapter 7). During the years ushering in the nineteenth century, the terms of exchange shifted against the plebe and peasantry.

On the other hand, the great disparity between the ideals of reform and the harsh reality of reform left a bitter legacy that turned most people in the region against the Bourbon state. The disillusionment with imperial rule gave the region's wealthy and poor something in common that was potentially explosive. The Andean inhabitants of the pueblos reales saw that the reforms had failed to restore the economic autonomy of their villages or correct the extreme imbalances in the internal distribution of communal resources. Instead, they faced a more coercive, extractive state apparatus, and one without the power or willingness to provide the patronage that the Toledan state had offered in return for tribute and mitayos. Worse still from their point of view was the moral ignominy of a colonial state that demanded more tribute during the worst famine in memory. Meanwhile, class privilege offered less and less immunity from royal taxation. The wealthy were being ferreted out as sources of income with which to meet military needs. But even before the Napoleonic invasion of Spain, the regional elite had begun to see false promises in the economic reforms proposed by their innovative intendant. Promises of frontier colonization and industrial growth disintegrated before royal opposition and regional rivalry. By 1804, the horizons of potential entrepreneurs had narrowed and disillusionment had set in. There seemed to be no road out of the region's economic quagmire, after all.

Thus, while the conjuncture of economic crisis and growing disillusionment did not forge a popular movement or unite landowners and peasants, it may have created a common ground. But then, for a short period between 1810 and 1812, extraordinary circumstances would unite the rich and the poor in an insurgency movement against royal troops. Creole landowners struck out from Cochabamba to defeat the royalists in the town of Aroma, on the altiplano, while in the heartlands of the region, Andean and cholo peasants brandished primitive arms and tools against the invading Spanish cavalry. Fragile bonds of solidarity momentarily turned the region of Cochabamba into a symbol of anticolonialism and the center of Alto Perú's struggle for independence.[51]

To end the story of agrarian conflict and change in colonial Cochabamba on this note would, perhaps, create false expectations. Class tensions and contradictions were not subsumed for long in the decolonization movement. Populist myths concerning participation in the independence struggles in Cochabamba tend to obscure the class conflicts that surfaced again after fifteen years of intermittent fighting had finally brought victory. The war brought many changes, particularly in the composition of the landowning elite and the ownership of valley lands. But it did not shatter the agrarian class structure or release the peasantry from the burdens of heavy taxation. On the contrary, the new state was built on the fiscal foundations of the old, and a new cycle of tributary extractions was set in motion.

But if the creole state resurrected, in an altered form, a political economy of colonialism, it also inherited a refractory peasantry in the maize valleys, who historically had demonstrated the limits of state power. That had happened, dramatically, in the tribute rebellion of 1730. But more often, peasants had shaped the contours of class society in the region, and confronted the injustices of colonialism, in their everyday activities, prosaically rather than heroically. The local tradition of resistance was not one of visible, collective action guided by native or class ideology. Rather, peasant defiance was expressed in minor acts of resistance, such as slipping through the interstices of the tribute system. Over time, these silent strategies of "passive resistance" had challenged the model of colonial exploitation based on caste and turned the Cochabamba region into a symbol of its erosion. When the creole state tried in the 1830s to impose that model once again, it encountered the limits of its capacity to discipline the valley peasants. The legacy of peasant resistance threatened the continuity of the neocolonial order.

51 Guzman, *Cochabamba*, pp. 126-129; Charles Arnade, *The Emergence of the Republic of Bolivia* (Gainesville: University of Florida Press, 1957), 32-37; and René Arce, *Participación popular en la independencia de Bolivia* (La Paz: Colegio Don Bosco, 1979).

CHAPTER NINE

Colonial Legacies and Class Formation

Like so many social historians, I often searched, while in Bolivia, for visible links to the colonial past in contemporary rural society. I was eager to find material artifacts that would make rural colonial society seem less abstract and textureless. Such vestiges of the past were not hard to find. During a hike early one Sunday morning into the quebradas of Sacaba, I came upon an ancient grain mill, owned and worked by a local peasant and his young son. A walk on the outskirts of the city of Cochabamba led to a half-eroded hacienda, now inhabited by poor migrant families; it was an estate registered in the eighteenth-century notarial books I had been working with. An eight-hour truck ride up the Tapacarí riverbed deposited me in San Augustín de Tapacarí, a village of thatched-roof huts, perched precariously on a hillside at the confluence of rivers, that once claimed to be the province's most important pueblo real and a major trade route to the western altiplano.

But I found more vital and vivid legacies of the past in the small peasant enterprises and weekly ferias that still thrive in the central valleys. The presence of the colonial past is to be found, for example, in Cliza's marketplace on Sunday, where thousands of peasants congregate from dawn until midday, haggling in Quechua over the prices of sheep, potato seed, and coca. It is also to be found in the peasant families of Punata, who are cultivators, peddlers, and chicha-makers; and in peasant households such as the one I visited in Sacaba, where the household head weaves bayeta, and his wife markets it, when agricultural work does not occupy them. Contemporary scenes of a robust peasant economy, based on *producción parcelaria* (small-scale agriculture) and a strong commercial orientation, are not byproducts of the 1953 agrarian reform. They harken back to colonial times. As we saw, a distinct peasant economy began to assume form and force in the later part of the eighteenth-century, emerging from, and accelerating, the fragmentation of rural property units and the erosion of the economic power of landowners.

But there is a darker scene, far from the valleys, that also stands as mute testimony to the historical evolution of agrarian class relations in eighteenth and nineteenth-century Cochabamba. Today, in the mine shafts of San José, on the outskirts of Oruro, and in the tin mines of Siglo XX-Uncía, a large number (perhaps a majority) of the workers are the sons or grandsons of Cochabamba peasants. In the early twentieth century, these migrant peasants from the valleys composed the body of an incipient industrial proletariat that extracted crude ore from the new or "modernized" mines that fed the industrialized nations with the tin, tungsten, lead, and copper that they craved.

These are contrasting images: an enterprising peasant family that combines agriculture, craft production, commerce, and occasional day labor, and a mine worker whose father severed his roots in the land and cast his fate with the demons of the industrial underworld. The contrast would seem a contradiction in historical terms, one that feeds into the on-going debate over the impact of capitalism on Latin American peasantries.[1] On the one hand, the region may be seen as a symbol of the resilience and resourcefulness of a peasantry that is famous for its diversified economy. Even today, there is little agrarian capitalist enterprise in Cochabamba; small-scale peasant and artisan production still reigns supreme. It is the petty commod-

1 The basic issue in the debate is whether the peasant economy has the capacity to survive and reproduce itself under dependent capitalism, or will gradually disappear as capitalist relations penetrate the countryside. The two principal schools of thought revolve around the early debates over the transition to capitalism in the Russian countryside. Latin American exponents of "peasantization" are influenced by the principal work of A. V. Chayanov, *The Theory of the Peasant Family Economy*, ed. and trans. D. Thorner, B. Verblay, and R.E.F. Smith (Homewood, Ill.: Irwin, 1966); those who argue that peasants tend to become proletarians usually take, as their conceptual point of departure, V. I. Lenin, *The Rise of Capitalism in Russia* (Moscow: Progress, 1974). Much of this controversy is cast in terms of "articulating modes of production" and the relative importance, functional symbiosis, and inherent historical tendencies of interpenetrating modes of production. See Foster-Carter, "Modes of Production Controversy." For summaries of the issues and debate as they relate to Latin America, see Alain de Janvry, *The Agrarian Question and Reformism in Latin America* (Baltimore: The Johns Hopkins University Press, 1981), esp. chap. 3; Alain de Janvry and L. A. Couch, "El debate sobre el campesinado: Teoría y significación política," *Estudios rurales latinoamericanos* 2 (1979): 282-295; and Richard L. Harris, "Marxism and the Agrarian Question in Latin America," *Latin American Perspectives* 5 (1978): 2-26.

ity producer who supplies the towns and cities across the region.[2] From a short-term regional perspective, the historical resilience of the peasant class looms large. Yet, on the other hand, the region expelled peasants into the capitalist export sector; they became the main source of a dispossessed labor force in mining around the beginning of the twentieth century. The decomposition of the peasantry spawned a nascent industrial proletariat.

From a long-term historical perspective, these apparently contradictory tendencies—the social reproduction of the peasantry and its simultaneous erosion—are simply two aspects of the process of advancing social differentiation within the peasant class. As throughout the colonial past, so also in the postindependence period, peasants were both protagonists in their struggle for a livelihood and for just terms of exchange and also the objects, often the victims, of historical forces and ecological pressures that threatened their precarious existence and often forced them to surrender to the harsh terms of the labor market. In some cases, migration to wagework in the mines brought supplementary income that strengthened the viability of the peasant family economy. But in countless other cases, valley peasants and rural laborers succumbed to the emerging industrial regime out of desperation. For many rural cultivators, the erosion of sources of subsistence during the nineteenth-century was the most important legacy of colonialism. It was this legacy that created, out of those at the bottom of the rural social heap, an industrial proletariat.

In the following pages, by way of conclusion, I will gather together the various strands of the preceding analysis of class formation under colonial rule in the Cochabamba region. I will then turn to explore the contradictory processes of social differentiation within the Cochabamba peasantry, as it confronted a neocolonial order and then the penetration of foreign capital in the late nineteenth century.[3]

2 Jorge Dandler Hanhart, "Diversificación, procesos de trabajo, y movilidad espacial en los valles y serranías de Cochabamba," in Harris, Larson, and Tandeter, *Participación indígena*, 639-682. Dandler's research on the peasant family economy in different zones of the region of Cochabamba is part of a team project under the auspices of the Centro para el Estudio de la Realidad Económica y Social (CERES).

3 The aim of this chapter is heuristic: to broadly interpret regional agrarian change in the nineteenth and twentieth centuries and to suggest future directions of research for testing these interpretations. For many of the ideas explored in this chapter, I am indebted to Tristan Platt and Ramiro Molina Barrios, for

Historical Roots of Agrarian Classes

As this study has shown, the origins of agrarian class formation date to the early colonial period. During the later part of the sixteenth century, a class structure based upon the private control of land and the expropriation of surplus from economically dependent peasants took root in the valleys. The development of this precapitalist agrarian order, however, was neither an inevitable nor an irrevocable response to the European invasion and the incursion of market forces. The early European colonizers were extraordinarily successful in their efforts to impose control over Indian land and labor in the valleys, but in many surrounding regions, particularly in the highlands and across the altiplano, the advance of private landownership and class relationships did not occur until the later part of the nineteenth-century. Andean ethnic groups continued to have collective access to land in exchange for some degree of compliance to the tributary demands of the colonial state.

In the Cochabamba region, a peculiar configuration of conditions made it possible for Europeans to overcome Andean resistance and establish a firm foothold in the valleys by the 1570s and 1580s. The precolonial heritage of Inca rule and mitmaq settlement in the region impeded the ability of Andean peoples to forge ethnic alliances and block European encroachment following the Spanish Conquest. On the one hand, the Cochabamba valleys afforded fertile niches for ethnically diverse mitmaq colonies scattered throughout the region. Cochabamba was an ethnic frontier area, where pockets of Aymara peoples extended the vertical archipelagos of their powerful altiplano kingdom into the eastern reaches of the maize valleys and beyond into the tropical lowlands. It sheltered a mélange of ethnic settlements, both mitmaq and autochthonous, that coexisted uneasily with each other until the arrival of the Europeans. On the other hand, the Valle Bajo was annexed directly by the Incas and turned into a principal granary of Tawantinsuyu. Under a highly centralized, elaborate organization of labor prestation, both permanent and transient ethnic groups cultivated maize for the Incas.

This combination of centralized Incaic rule and atomized ethnic settlement in the valleys created a precarious situation, which the Europeans began to exploit in the 1540s and 1550s. The military phase of the conquest seemed to shatter the Incaic agrarian regime,

allowing me to read parts of their study (in manuscript form), *Qollaruna: El origen social del proletariado del estaño* (forthcoming).

as the transient laborers fled upland, leaving a few Incaic lords beholden to encomenderos for their status as Indian intermediaries and their continued authority to rule (at a local level). Among the mitmaq colonies, there could be no unified ethnic resistance to Spanish penetration. The conquest had upset the delicate balance of power that had obtained among the diverse Aymara and Quechua-speaking ethnic groups in the region. In the transition to colonial rule, highland-based Aymara polities struggled to recover traditional rights to valley lands. Many of those Indians who remained in the Valle Bajo after the collapse of the Inca state were thrown on the defensive against the aggressive pursuits of highland Indians. To defend their hold over valley resources and their authority over Indians, local caciques (as the Europeans now called them) sought legitimacy and protection from their new European overlords. In the absence of political and moral consensus and ethnic solidarity, valley Indians became extremely vulnerable to Spanish exploits. This became increasingly clear in the 1570s, 1580s, and 1590s, when they realized that Spanish chacareros, not Aymara lords, posed the gravest threat to their existence. But by then, the balance of forces had tipped in favor of a growing number of aggressive landowners.

The emergence of class relationships in the region, however, cannot be understood simply in terms of Andean and European alliances and conflicts at the regional level. The consolidation of the colonial system of exploitation, based primarily upon modes of indirect rule, set in motion deeper currents of socioeconomic change in the region. As it centralized power in the 1570s and 1580s, the colonial state became the principal claimant of the labor of its Andean subjects. On an ideological level, the colonial state tried to establish its authority among Andean lords by granting them certain privileges and legitimating certain "customary rights and obligations" of all Andean peoples who lived in state-sanctioned villages. Most important, the state validated their collective right to a minimum degree of subsistence security, at the same time that it rationalized Indian settlement and land tenure in ways that would facilitate tribute collection. This was part of the Toledan system of indirect rule in the southern Andes that was designed to subsidize both the colonial bureaucracy and the mining industry at Potosí. In the short term, the power of the colonial order seemed impressive. Between 1570 and 1620, the southern Andes became the premier source of the commodity money for an expanding world market economy, and Potosí became a commercial magnet and a source of circulating medium that stirred up the regional economies of the Andes. Both indigenous and Spanish areas of settlement were drawn into the expanding orbit of Potosí's market.

Mercantile forces therefore played a fundamental role in the transformation of social relations and the development of agrarian classes in Cochabamba. Spanish chacareros, driven by the commercial opportunities emanating from Potosí, organized agricultural production for export to the mines. They attracted Indians from nearby pueblos reales and employed them as jornaleros, sharecroppers, and tenants. As time went on, many landowners reinforced their hold over a servile labor force of yanaconas. The creation of a dependent rural labor force thus accompanied the growth of livestock ranches, the spread of wheat fields, and the intensive production of maize on irrigated lands (with techniques inherited from the Incas). These developments signaled the formation of a regional economy responsive to the inflationary market in food crops created by the silver bonanza. But, it is worth underscoring, the penetration of the market in this part of the Andes was not the causal determinant of Cochabamba's early agrarian transformation. The advent of commercial capitalism in the southern Andes was neither inexorable nor sufficiently powerful to destroy traditional forms of Andean social organization in all areas. Nor was the power of the colonial state a determining force capable of transforming Andean lifeways. Theoretically, it established some mechanisms to preserve the economic autonomy of ethnic groups at the level of ayllu or village. That the Cochabamba region departed so radically from its precolonial social patterns during Potosí's second cycle of silver production in the late sixteenth century was in part the consequence of Andean ethnic fragmentation (intrinsic to mitmaq settlement patterns) and of the political vacuum left by the collapse of Inca control over valley lands. In contrast, throughout nearby highland regions, most Indians retained some degree of collective economic control over land and labor prestations.

On the other hand, Cochabamba was certainly not unique. In other areas along the eastern valleys and slopes of the cordillera, similar circumstances eroded the power of Andean groups before the advance of Spanish landowners. Europeans took advantage of splintered and weak ethnic settlements in the valleys of Larecaja, Chuquisaca, Tomina, and other kichwa areas to expropriate choice lands in temperate climes. Even farther afield, in the regions of Huamanga and Arequipa, for example, strong parallels may be drawn. But in each area, the precolonial heritage was different; the particular configuration of ethnic settlements was specific to the region;

and the social dynamics and consequences of struggle between Andeans and Europeans varied. Cochabamba was perhaps an extreme case of weak Andean resistance to European settlement; the strong Inca presence there had created a brittle, hierarchical social order that could not survive the initial military defeat. The origins, if not the evolution, of early agrarian class formation in Cochabamba therefore were rooted as much in the precolonial past as in the expansion of an internal market that incorporated the southern Andes into the world economy.

Over the course of the seventeenth and eighteenth centuries, the evolution of agrarian classes in the region took on a dynamic of its own. Potosí's mercantile power faded with time, and, over the long term, Cochabamba was increasingly subject to pressures that reflected the failure of the Toledan model of colonial rule in Alto Perú. The region's large forastero and mestizo population was only the most visible sign of the erosion of the state-organized extractive system. It was this group of forastero and mestizo peasants that eventually had the greatest impact upon the agrarian class structure in the valleys. Through their prosaic pursuits of a livelihood, peasant families created the elements of a viable, alternative economy within the institutional confines of the hacienda system of landholding and labor control. In so doing, they slowly and almost silently began to alter the contours of the regional economy and society during the late colonial and postcolonial periods.

The analysis of the emerging peasant economy in eighteenth-century Cochabamba situated the dynamics of regional class relations in the broader context of economic stagnation and decline and fragmented political rule. Although Potosí's output began to recover modestly in the second half of the century, following a secular slide, its power as a market for the wheat and maize products of the valleys remained weak and erratic. Furthermore, most staple prices declined or stagnated during this period, and Cochabamba's landlords confronted aggressive commercial competition from the ayllus of Chayanta, which virtually captured the wheat trade to Potosí in the late part of the century. The diminished scope, stability, and intensity of interregional trade in grains had come to transform the economic logic of commercial agriculture in eighteenth-century Cochabamba. Increasingly, demesne agriculture depended upon cyclical harvest failures and shortages to force up prices. Landlords with large grain reserves, tithe speculators, and cultivators who controlled permanently irrigated bottomlands all found themselves in position to capitalize on drought. Mercantile accumulation pivoted on scarcity, which both created need and eliminated small-scale producers from the marketplace.

But those moments of calamity and profit were infrequent. In the intervals, landlords sought short-term solutions to the cumulative pressures of market contraction, capital shortage, debt, and property fragmentation. One apparent solution was found in a rentier strategy. Increasingly, landlords parceled out hacienda resources to their tenants in a multiplicity of forms. Tenants were enmeshed in a web of obligations, in return for which they might cultivate leaseholds, share common pasture, collect firewood, or sharecrop potato or maize fields. As a result, property rights often corresponded only loosely to the mosaic of de facto landholding rights and the way the land was worked. Haciendas came to be internally colonized by a growing population of arrenderos. Over the longer term, landlord adjustments to secular decline created an opportunity for peasants to reconstitute a subsistence economy within the confines of the estate. Sooner or later, as custom became entrenched, the expansion of peasant smallholding on estate lands encroached on the power of landlords to determine the disposition or use of their resources and sometimes even the terms of exchange with their tenants.

In the shifting balance of class forces, peasant smallholders devised creative solutions to the problems of subsistence insecurity, involving a shrewd manipulation of available resources, human reciprocities, and market initiatives.[4] Andean forms of labor-sharing, barter, and insurance all served to support traditional social relations of production. But so, too, did commercial enterprise. The particular weight or balance of market and nonmarket strategies at any given time depended on a peasant family's particular equilibrium of resources and needs. In the drier highlands, peasants living on haciendas usually tried to assemble parcels of land in different ecological zones. Crop diversification, to spread risk and extend the family's

4 Dandler Hanhart, "Diversificación," and the presentations at the weeklong CERES seminar, "Valles y serranías de la región de Cochabamba," (Cochabamba, July 29-August 2, 1981). See also similar analyses of the "open" family economy in the Montaro and Yanamarca valleys of central Peru, in Norman Long and Bryan R. Roberts, eds., *Peasant Cooperation and Capitalist Expansion in Central Peru* (Austin: University of Texas Press, 1978); Norman Long and Bryan R. Roberts, *Miners, Peasants, and Entrepreneurs: Regional Development in the Central Highlands of Peru* (Cambridge: Cambridge University Press, 1984); and Florencia Mallon, *The Defense of Community in Peru's Central Highlands: Peasant Struggle and Capitalist Transition, 1860-1940* (Princeton: Princeton University Press, 1983), 209 ff.

reach across complementary agricultural zones, cast their subsistence strategies in traditional Andean terms. In the valleys, the recreation of "micro-verticality" to diversify crops and diminish risk was less viable. In fact, in the Valle Bajo, where permanent irrigation often yielded two maize harvests a year, peasants concentrated on one crop and hired extrafamilial hands to harvest it. In the drier valley of Cliza, peasants diversified from maize into livestock and potatoes. But in both valleys, small-scale, intensive agriculture was usually insufficient to support a household, so peasants engaged in a host of nonagricultural activities. They sold crops both locally and in distant marketplaces, and, more important, they created a network of retail markets where staple commodities were traded in kind or for cash. The ferias were arenas of "horizontal exchange" among members of the same class, rather than urban colonial marketplaces where the logic of commercial capitalism governed exchange.

In terms of both production and exchange, therefore, we see the dim outlines of a peasant economy in formation during the late colonial period. It was composed of dependent smallholders, most of whom still had no title to land but were gradually wresting control over productive resources and nibbling away at the edges of demesne agriculture. Peasants were turning into artisans, traders, and sometimes petty usurers. On a regional scale, they were creating an incipient rival economy that narrowed the commercial opportunities and conditioned the mercantile tactics of Cochabamba's landed elite. Already by the late eighteenth-century, the valley peasantry was a force to be reckoned with.

Yet the very historical processes that gave substance and form to this distinctive peasant class, that deepened the interpenetration of subsistence and commercial activities, also placed intrinsic limits on its economic autonomy. However shrewd and flexible peasant families might be in their livelihood strategies, and however much they tried to balance their subsistence requirements against reciprocal obligations to kinsmen or neighbors, they lived and worked outside the cultural and material context of Andean village society. They may have practiced reciprocities, but those practices were embedded in a class context. In their daily pursuit of a livelihood or their struggle against the enduring injustices and humiliations of being Indian in colonial society, or living in the shadow of a patrón, most valley peasants faced the world alone. They did not have recourse to the material and ideological traditions of Andean communities to defend themselves against the incursion of outside claimants, the arbitrary demands of a landlord, or the ravages of natural disaster. There was no communal tradition of group self-sufficiency, reciprocity, and distribution to buffer the peasant household against subsistence threats or to contain class forces. Valley peasants had no means of calling upon the moral economy of their ancestral kin and ethnic groups to collectively confront the outside world whenever it turned hostile. In short, the absence of a strong ethnic heritage in the valleys left most peasants without economic autonomy or symbolic integrity.[5]

The relative weakness and vulnerability of valley peasants eking out a subsistence outside the ayllu context is especially evident when judged against Andean ideals of self-sufficiency, reciprocity, and collectivity. As was discussed in chapters 3 and 4, those ideals had ceased to govern or mediate social relations in many Andean villages by the early seventeenth-century. Indeed, Andean migration into the Cochabamba valleys during the seventeenth century was one important consequence of the strains and distortions of village life under the impact of colonial rule. In the Cochabamba region, village society organized around the reducciones had decayed considerably by the eighteenth century.

Yet, at base, this judgment of the vulnerability of valley peasants to the corrosive forces of class, state incursion, and subsistence threat is not made against some utopian ideal. It is set in the specific conditions of life and work in the ayllus of the neighboring province of Chayanta at the end of the colonial period. Among the six ayllus of Chayanta—once the locus of powerful ethnic groups who served as the Inca's privileged warriors—the communal tradition and segmentary organization continued to thrive. Platt's study of these ayllus during the nineteenth century reveals the extent to which they had preserved their unity, group self-sufficiency, and traditional moral economy.[6] The material foundations of their communal tradition rested on their dual-residency patterns. The ayllus controlled lands in the puna and in the valley, extending their reach across several ecological tiers of the vertical landscape. Through kinship and reciprocity, the communities enjoyed almost the full gamut of Andean agriculture: they had access to both the tuber staples of the highlands and the maize agriculture of the valleys. The vertical dis-

5 For similar discussions in different contexts, see Scott, *Moral Economy of the Peasant*, 40-43; and Mallon, *Defense of Community*, 330 and 342.

6 Platt, *Estado boliviano y ayllu andino*, chap. 1 and 2 and "Role of the Andean Ayllu." See also O. Harris, "Labor and produce."

position of family labor between puna and valley, the patterns of transhumance, and the intricate networks of reciprocity were all coordinated by village norms, customs, and ceremonial/agricultural calendars.[7] To be sure, the ayllus did not exist in an egalitarian paradise. Conflicts, rivalries, and processes of social differentiation marred village life and had to be channeled in nondestructive ways. But the ayllus did manage to harness commercial forces without allowing them to destroy the internal social fabric of communal life. They ensured a subsistence niche to all their members, and they protected their collective interests against outside threats. In short, they faced the world, for the most part, as ethnic collectivities.

Beyond Colonialism

The dissolution of the colonial state and the transition to republican rule in Bolivia posed a major threat to the peasants of Chayanta and other highland regions where the ayllu had adapted and reproduced itself under colonial rule. In the aftermath of war, as President Andrés Santa Cruz tried to shape the new government in the late 1820s, there were plans to abolish tribute and, in effect, end the ideological basis for ayllu landholding. Eventually, the mining recession and the fiscal crisis of the fledgling national government forced the state to fall back on the institution of tribute as its main source of revenue. Reestablished in 1831 (and abolished only much later, in 1882), tribute levied upon Indians made up about 60 percent of government revenues by the middle of the nineteenth century.[8] In real and symbolic terms, state-sponsored extraction served as the mainstay of the new republic until the mining industry once more began to grow. There were monetarist devices for providing governmental revenues during this period as well. In 1830, the state issued a debased silver currency (*moneda feble*) as a temporary solution to its chronic financial deficit. This political economy, however shaky and unstable in the 1830s and 1840s, had many affinities with the former colonial state. It was grounded in mercantilist ideology, tempered by

7 See the sources cited in n. 6. On the role of "ethnic time," tribute, and market participation among the ayllus of Lipez, see Tristan Platt, "Calendarios tributarios e intervención mercantil: La articulación estacional de los ayllus de Lipez con el mercado minero potosino (siglo XIX)," in Harris, Larson, and Tandeter, *Participación indígena*, 471-558.

8 Sánchez-Albornoz, *Indios y tributos*, 217, and Herbert S. Klein, *Bolivia: The Evolution of a Multi-Ethnic Society* (Oxford: Oxford University Press, 1982), 105.

its neocolonial dependence upon tribute. In its policies of official and de facto protectionism, it also shielded Bolivia's internal economy from foreign commercial penetration.[9]

The strong continuities of the republican state with colonial policies toward tribute and corporate landholding preserved the ideological underpinnings of traditional state-peasant relations. All across highland Bolivia, wherever the ayllu thrived, Andean peoples viewed the restoration of tribute as legal confirmation of their collective right to hold land. It served as symbolic endorsement by the state that their way of life might still be preserved, even as other things changed.[10] Indeed, the people of Chayanta sought to maintain their tribute obligations to the state, for tribute simply represented one side of the traditional, asymmetrical "pact of reciprocity" that had always governed relations between the ayllus and the state. In return for tribute, the Chayanta peoples received state sanction that legitimated and preserved their economic autonomy and cultural heritage. Furthermore, their collective control over village resources and their traditional role in the wheat market gave those ayllus considerable leeway in coping with tribute burdens. Ethnic leaders spread the burden, made internal adjustments in tribute categories, and marketed communal harvests to mitigate the pressures of tribute and rationalize the allocation of community resources to meet their tribute obligations.[11] These ayllus had advantages in their ecological endowments and cultural cohesion, but recent research documents the survival of ayllus across much of highland Bolivia at least until the advent of free-market policies in the late nineteenth century.[12] Not only did Andean communities persist well into the century; they even experienced population growth (although tributary popu-

9 Platt (*Estado boliviano y ayllu andino*, chap. 1) argues that traditional patterns of interregional wheat trade survived the transition to republican rule largely because of the protectionist effects of currency devaluation and the high costs of overland transport from the coast. It also appears that, after the first rush of English traders onto the scene in the late 1820s, foreign competition in textiles somewhat receded. In any event, the artisanal production of cotton cloth in Cochabamba was not eliminated. See Brooke Larson, *Explotación agraria*, chap. 5.

10 Sánchez-Albornoz, *Indios y tributos*, p. 204.

11 Platt, *Estado boliviano y ayllu andino*, chap. 2.

12 Erwin P. Grieshaber, "Survival of Indian Communities in Nineteenth-Century Bolivia" (Ph.D. diss., University of North Carolina, 1977), and "Survival of Indian Communities in Nineteenth-Century Bolivia: A Regional Comparison," *Journal of Latin American Studies* 12 (1980): 223-269.

lation rose in most highland provinces of Bolivia between the census years of 1838 and 1877).[13]

In the Cochabamba region, where the communal tradition was historically weak and private modes of surplus extraction had predominated since early colonial times, the patrimony of a colonial or neocolonial state had little meaning. The state had no moral power to grant land to its forastero tributaries inhabiting hacienda lands. At most, judicial institutions might serve a mediating function in peasant-landlord conflicts over rent. But in general, tribute represented naked extraction to the valley smallholder. Historically, the incursion of the state had long since upset the social equilibrium in the valleys; caste had decayed and forasteros were hardly distinguishable from cholo or mestizo peasants.

When the republican government of Bolivia resurrected the tribute institution in 1831, only a century had passed since the tax rebellion in Cochabamba. That uprising of valley mestizos against tribute levies had precluded, for almost fifty years, the systematic collection of head taxes in the province. The Bourbons had finally generated more tribute during the two decades (1786-1808) of fiscal reorganization. But tribute was still not an accepted institution. In fact, heavier taxation had coincided with a period of regional economic decline and ultimately a famine. The intrusive Bourbon state had produced penury and painful memories among the valley peasants.

Much had changed since then. Peasants of the central valleys had experienced fifteen years of warfare, during which they had tasted the fruits of victory for a while. Their protonational sentiment and participation in the independence movement had raised expectations about a new social order that would finally shatter the institutions of mita and tribute. They suspected, moreover, that a republican state would be unable to single out the forasteros from the mixed-blood population in a countryside where almost everyone spoke Quechua. The legend and memory of Calatayud warned against state infringement on the perceived rights of cholos and mestizos in Cochabamba.

A phenomenological analysis of peasant perceptions of the creole state and the injustice of the new tribute system awaits the inquiries of another historian. But the forms and effects of peasant resistence to republican tribute can perhaps be seen in the census records. Un-

13 Grieshaber, "Survival of Indian Communities" (1977) and "Survival of Indian Communities" (1980); Platt, *Estado boliviano y ayllu andino*, 62-70; Klein, "Peasant Response to the Market."

like the case in the highlands, the tributary population of Cochabamba was vanishing during the middle decades of the nineteenth-century. The number of tributaries declined by 38 percent between 1838 and 1877, from 11,067 to 6,828.[14] Some of that decline was produced by excess deaths caused by an epidemic around 1856, but some of it was due to peasant flight and "passing" into the ranks of cholos and mestizos. In areas like the Cercado and the Cliza valley, where racial and cultural amalgamation was most extensive, the decline of tributary population was sharpest[15]; and the drop in tributaries living outside the five pueblos reales was steeper than the decline within the villages.[16]

It is not clear either how Indians evaded the new tribute regime or the extent to which the creole state disrupted the equilibrium of peasant households in the valleys in the nineteenth century. In the 1830s and 1840s, peasant defiance in the valleys did not take the form of collective action. Resistence was expressed individually and silently, in the clandestine actions of peasants who somehow shed their ascriptive ethnic status. The forasteros slowly vanished, as mestizaje spread.[17] But the sharp divergence between the success of

14 Grieshaber, "Survival of Indian Communities" (1977), 138, 140, and 142; "Survival of Indian Communities" (1980), 236 and 244. Grieshaber's work was based upon the following Indian census records of Cochabamba, housed in the ANB: Arque, no. 5 (1850); Ayopaya, no. 13 (1844); Cercado, no. 21 (1850); Cliza, no. 23 (1831), nos. 24 and 25 (1846), and no. 26 (1850); Punata, no. 30 (1867); Tapacarí no. 31 (1828), nos. 32 and 33 (1844), no. 34 (1851), and nos. 35 and 36 (1867); Tarata, no. 37 (1872); and Cochabamba, no. 40 (1834) and no. 41 (1844).

15 Tributary population declined by 78 percent in Cliza and 75 percent in the Cercado, compared to the overall decline of 38 percent. For sources, see n. 14.

16 Hacienda tributaries declined from 4,284 in 1838 to 1,843 in 1877 (a 57 percent decrease). Pueblo real tributaries dropped from 6,783 in 1838 to 4,985 in 1877 (a 19 percent decrease). These estimates are Grieshaber's (see n. 14). It is difficult to assess overall Indian population trends, however, since census-takers often failed to register women and children after about midcentury: Klein, "Peasant Response to the Market," 116.

17 It is suggestive that the two complete censuses of the region (Viedma's, in 1788, and the Bolivian state's, in 1900) show that in roughly the area occupied by the colonial province of Cochabamba, total population increased from about 125,000 to 248,000, while the proportion of "whites" increased slightly (from 16 to 18 percent), and that of "Indians" decreased from 45 to 23, whereas "mestizos and cholos" increased from 33 to 51 percent. (The residual category of "others" increased from 5 to 7 percent.) Contemporaries talked about the gradual "whitening" of the rural population, as Indians declined and the "whiter" mixed blood population expanded. See chap. 5, esp. Table 13, and, for 1900, Federico

the tributary regime in the highlands and its failure in the valleys points to different peasant perceptions of the moral authority of the republican state. Compliance in the highlands and resistance in the valleys can be understood only in the light of the different social legacies of colonial rule. For many highland ayllus, tribute symbolized state protection of communal lands even after the independence wars were won. But in the Cochabamba valleys, the primacy of agrarian class relationships had marginalized the patron-state and undermined its ability to extract tribute. It had nothing to offer the peasant family that was eking out a precarious existence outside the village context.

In the 1870s and 1880s, the neocolonial, mercantilist regime gave way to a new political economy of the free market. As Mitre has shown, those decades were a historical watershed that reintegrated Bolivia into the world market economy as both a mineral producer and a market for imported food crops.[18] Silver mining entered a phase of rapid growth between 1873 and 1895, which paralleled in volume of output the second silver cycle of Toledo's times.[19] New mines in Huanchaca and Colquechaca disgorged silver, and they called for a more highly skilled, stable labor force, anchored to the site of production, to work its machines and meet the regimented work schedules. Other, smaller, preindustrial mines required only seasonal or unskilled workers who worked on a contract basis. The labor requirements of the new mines continued to grow after the turn of the century, as tin replaced silver and industrial metals became profitable to export.

The modernized silver industry depended on railroads to carry crude ore to the Pacific coast and overseas, and at the same time the rails opened the interior of Bolivia to Chilean wheat imports and other foreign staples. Rails linked the port of Antofagasta to Pulacayo and Uyuni in 1889 and advanced across the altiplano to Oruro in 1892. By the turn of the century, railroads had created an alternative circuit of trade revolving around the exportation of crude ore and the importation of wheat.[20] In 1890, the consumers of La Paz

---

Blanco, *Diccionario geográfico de la República de Bolivia*, 4 vols. (La Paz: Oficina Nacional de Inmigración, 1901), vol. 2.

18 Antonio Mitre, *Los patriarcas de la plata: Estructura socioeconómica de la minería boliviana en el siglo XIX* (Lima: Instituto de Estudios Peruanos, 1981).

19 See Klein, *Bolivia*, 298-299 (table 2).

20 J. Valerie Fifer, *Bolivia: Land, Location, and Politics since 1825* (Cambridge: Cambridge University Press, 1972), 66-70.

could purchase Chilean wheat for less than they paid for wheat hauled over the mountains by mule from Cochabamba.[21] Contemporary observers worried about the impact of the new imports on Bolivia's small-scale, primitive industries. In the marketplace that sprang up near railroad junctions, foreign imports displaced tocuyos and flour from Cochabamba, the bayetas from Oruro, and sugar from Santa Cruz.[22] Small-scale traditional trade networks survived where foreign imports did not reach or where popular patterns of consumption (of maize, for example) still depended on internal sources of supply. But the advent of rail transportation reoriented the western altiplano to the world market, away from the eastern valleys and serranías that had traditionally provisioned them.[23]

The final element in the historical watershed was the state's "project of national integration." As the silver oligarchy consolidated its control over the national government, the ideology of capitalism provided new guideposts for state policy.[24] To unfetter the economy, shift the tax base to productive enterprise, and unlock the nation's human and natural resources, the state reversed its policy toward communal landholding and tribute and began to enforce the commodification of ayllu lands. Between 1874 and 1882, communal property and tribute were legislated out of existence. At the same time, a tax was levied on the assessed value of land to replace the tithes and *primicias* (taxes on Indian crops and livestock). Thus, there was no relief from taxation for native landholders. But more than ever before, the ayllus were vulnerable to market forces. Communal landholding was forsaken by the liberal state for the ideals of a free market economy. In many areas near La Paz, the enforcement of the 1874 Law of Expropriation unleashed commercial forces and accelerated the advance of latifundios across the altiplano.[25]

21 Mitre, *Patriarcas*, 176; Grieshaber, "Survival of Indian Communities" (1977), 228.

22 Platt and Molina Barrios, *Qollaruna*, 5.

23 Ibid., 8; Platt, *Estado boliviano y ayllu andino*, 68-70.

24 Platt, *Estado boliviano y ayllu andino*, chap. 3; Herbert S. Klein, *Politics and Political Change in Bolivia* (Cambridge: Cambridge University Press, 1969), chaps. 1 and 2; and Marie-Danièle Demelas, "Darwinismo a lo criollo: El darwinismo en Bolivia, 1880-1910," *Historia boliviana* 1 (1981): 55-82.

25 Silvia Rivera, "La expansión del latifundio en el altiplano boliviano," *Avances*, no. 2 (1978): 95-118. For a critical assessment of Rivera's argument, see Gustavo Rodríguez Ostría, "Expansión del latifundio o supervivencia de las comunidades indigenas? Cambios en la estructura agraria boliviana del siglo

But the tradition of communal solidarity in some areas of Bolivia, such as Chayanta, proved stronger than the land reform. The state threatened in Chayanta what Platt described as "an entire social and cultural order in which the Andean ecology, production and marketing calendars, residence patterns, and tributation to the state all meshed into a rhythm of social activity,"[26] and the ayllus responded violently. What began as an attack on a local tax collector, a regional representative of the state, eventually escalated into a series of uprisings that culminated in the so-called "Caste War" of 1899. This was followed by the elaboration of a program of "cultural liberation and ethnic revindication" that recalled the rebellions of 1781.[27] For the moment, state efforts to fragment the ayllus were thwarted in this corner of the Andes.

The policies of the state had entirely different social consequences for rural society in the Cochabamba valleys. There, the threat did not lie in the state's *ex-vinculación* laws forbidding communal landholding, and it did not provoke ethnic resistance to the commodification of village lands. On the contrary, the valley pueblos reales (Sipesipe, El Paso, and Tiquipaya) were broken up into parcels of land that were put on the market as early as 1878.[28] Neighboring hacendados purchased some of these parcels, but more often they were sold to peasants and artisans who purchased, on average, less than a hectar each. Between 1886 and 1894, about 60 percent of village land passed into the hands of small-scale cultivators. The easy transition to legalized private landholding and the dissolution of those pueblos reales after four centuries are evidence of the long process of internal decay of community life and norms in the villages. Long before republican laws sanctioned the privatization of village land, the pueblos reales had fragmented into de facto smallholdings, cultivated by a growing number of mestizos.

In contrast to the quiescence of the valley peasantry, the landowning elite reacted strongly against the policies of taxation and free trade. They felt themselves the victims of the new property taxes (*catastros*) that shifted more of the tax burden to the creoles. The new taxes cut into their returns on commercial agriculture and dis-

---

XIX," *Serie: Historia*, Working Paper no. 1, Instituto de Estudios Sociales y Económicos (IESE), Universidad Mayor de San Simon (Cochabamba, 1983).

26 Tristan Platt, "Liberalism and Ethnocide in the Southern Andes," *History Workshop*, no. 17 (1984): 12.

27 Ibid., 15. See also Platt, *Estado boliviano y ayllu andino*, chap. 4.

28 Rodríguez Ostría, "Expansión del latifundio," 11.

couraged land concentration and improvement. Moreover, in the 1920s, levies on the production of chicha depressed local demand. People turned to contraband liquors, and maize, the staple and symbol of valley agriculture since time immemorial, thus lost a large part of its market. To the landowners, however, the weight of taxes was minor compared to the impediments to interregional trade. The free-trade policies of the state represented "a protectionist policy in favor of other countries, and against Bolivia, for imported foodstuffs like wheat flour."[29] Not only did the importers pay but a modicum of tax; they also enjoyed relatively low freight costs. It was a common joke that Buenos Aires was closer to Europe than Cochabamba was to Santa Cruz. The valley landowners felt a growing economic isolation from the rest of Bolivia, especially the markets of the altiplano. The region was situated in the geographic center of the populated backbone of the nation, and yet it was cut off from the markets of La Paz, Oruro, and the mines. Who could afford freight costs to haul wheat, when imported grains were both superior in quality and cheaper? The landlords also were shut out of the subsistence marketplaces and traditional circuits of trade among valley cultivators and highland traders. The surviving large estates demanded a large volume of monetarized transactions, if such deals depended on periodic crop failures and high grain prices. However, the traditional cyclical rhythm of mercantile accumulation by large valley landlords was broken by the advent of foreign competition and cumbersome taxes.[30]

29 Octavio Salamanca, *La crisis en el departamento de Cochabamba* (Cochabamba: Ilustración, 1927), 36.

30 In 1901, Blanco noted that the interregional trade of Arque, where once "the Indians of . . . La Paz and . . . Puno came to buy large quantities of wheat and maize.," had "lost all its importance since the introduction . . . of flour from Chile which, in spite of its inferior quality, is preferred for its low price." Blanco, *Diccionario geográfico*, 2: 10. Many of Cochabamba's large landlords responded to the foreign competition by shifting from wheat to maize production. Until 1917, most maize was produced for the manufacture of chicha, but then, with the arrival of the railroad, hacendados discovered new commercial opportunities in the production of maize alcohol. During the 1920s, the region's maize production continued to increase as more of the crop was turned into alcohol. By 1927, however, the supply of grain alcohol outstripped the demand. Furthermore, government toleration of contraband trade in imported alcohol, stiffer taxes on maize and chicha, and increasing freight costs combined to drastically reduce the margin of returns on large-scale agriculture. For more detailed discussion, see Ricardo Azogue Crespo, Gustavo Rodríguez, and Humberto Bolares,

The landlord view was perhaps best expressed by the hacendado and essayist Octavio Salamanca. In 1927, Salamanca published an essay criticizing the national government for its destructive and unjust policies toward agriculturalists in the valley. Though he claimed to speak for all cultivators, both large and small, his assessment of the agrarian problem reflected his class biases. It was his opinion that the 50 percent increase in taxes during the previous five years was devastating to large landowners. Over the same period, maize consumption had fallen sharply, depressing prices. The "scissors" effect of higher fixed costs and declining prices was destroying the valley hacienda. The shortage of credit and capital in the region exacerbated the problem, since it meant that landowners could not obtain the loans they needed to cover short-term deficits and tide them over until times improved. Just as peasants in the valleys once dreaded the arrival of the tribute census taker, now landlords feared the property-tax assessor. Indeed, the property tax affected the rich more than the poor, for large landowners could not elude it as easily as smallholders could. That, at least, is what Salamanca seemed to suggest when he said that "practically all taxes are paid by the whites."[13] Thus, the state's assault on "white landowners" threatened to undermine the very foundations of class society in the valleys and to doom the hacienda to extinction.

There was another dimension, however, to the agrarian problems in Cochabamba during the early twentieth century, having to do less with the state or the market than with the internal dynamics of class. More than ever before, landlords were being squeezed from below by peasant smallholders. Across the central valleys, peasants were purchasing parcels of land. Estates were in an advanced state of fragmentation. In a pamphlet published in 1931, Salamanca estimated that, out of the province's total population of some 400,000 people, about 120,000 owned urban and/or rural property. Salamanca believed that one half of them "are those whom we call Indians, because they cultivate the land, . . . but who are really mestizos and cholos."[32] The advance of peasant proprietorship was so rapid that Salamanca believed that the old hacendado families were being "dispossessed" of their estates. In the cantón of Colcapirgua, for exam-

"Cochabamba: El proceso histórico de su constitución como región, 1900-1930," part 3 *Los Tiempos*, Jan. 23, 1986, pp. 2-3.

31 Salamanca, *Crisis en el departamento de Cochabamba*, 38.

32 Octavio Salamanca, *El socialismo en Bolivia* (Cochabamba: Bolívar, 1931), 185-186.

ple, there were 2,000 small properties. Only sixteen haciendas had survived, and the largest counted only seventeen tenants. In the Cliza valley, the so-called piqueros (owners of small amounts of property) were proliferating, as more and more peasants invested their meager savings in land titles.[33] Here, then, was another aspect of the state of affairs in agriculture: the consolidation and legitimation of peasant smallholdings at a time of depressed agricultural profits. The incursion of the peasants into the legal structure of property holding threatened to destroy the material and ideological basis of agrarian exploitation that had governed class relations in the valleys for four centuries.

But how, in a period of depressed markets and heavy taxes, did peasants manage to acquire land? Salamanca showed the methods that were used. While he idealized the "harmonious" relations between landlords and tenants in the valleys, he also believed that landlords bargained over the terms of rent from a weak position. Tenants, he argued, were in a favorable position to acquit themselves of their labor obligations and to concentrate on the cultivation of potato or maize lands. They also sharecropped large tracts of hacienda land and surrendered only half of the crop to their landlords. Thus, in Salamanca's view, even colonos were able to accumulate money to purchase small plots of land. It was common for tenants to continue leasing hacienda land while they acquired parcels of their own until they had finally established economic independence.[34] Salamanca's analysis reveals more about the class outlook of beleaguered landlords than it does about the conditions of tenancy, for it shows how weak some hacendados seemed to consider themselves to be before the advance of their own tenantry.

Salamanca particularly admired the ability of peasant families to blend subsistence and commercial activities. Against the somber picture of hacendados abandoning their enterprises, his description of a buoyant peasant economy stands out in bold relief. He had obviously observed the myriad facets of the economy in the valleys:

> Recall that at least half the landowners are mestizos. . . . They do not abandon their properties . . . but as land alone does not yield enough to satisfy their basic needs, they engage in com-

33 Ibid. Evidence of widespread *piquería* in parts of the Cliza valley is found in Olen, *Cantón Chullpas*, and in oral testimony of peasants in Tiraque and Chillichi (personal communication by anthropologists María Lagos and Bryan Anderson, respectively).

34 Salamanca, *Socialismo en Bolivia*, 187-188.

merce. While the men work in the fields or work for wages in a nearby city, the women shepherd the flocks, spin, weave, make *huiñapo* and chicha, sell fruits, and trade their products in the mines and cities of the altiplano.[35]

These activities generated small amounts of capital, which the women carefully hoarded, away from their men who might squander it in the chicherías. Here, then, in the delicate equilibrium of the peasant household as a unit of production and consumption lay the source of petty capital accumulation, "in these savings lies the explanation for the enormous territorial subdivision of the valleys," concluded Salamanca.[36]

Salamanca was acutely aware of the threat that a robust peasant economy presented to the local property structure. He focused on the ability of peasant households to gain freedom from rent as they acquired properties. But historically, processes of social differentiation are never one-sided or unilinear. Peasant prosperity could easily be reversed by a natural or personal calamity. Even "independent" smallholders rarely lived much above the threshold of subsistence insecurity. Ominously, there was, during the late nineteenth and early twentieth centuries, growing population pressure on productive resources in the central valleys. The subdivision of valley lands reflected not only enhanced peasant purchasing capacity, but also the growing hunger for forest, water, and fertile land. Between the Viedma census of 1788 and the first complete regional census in 1900, the population had almost doubled.[37] Salamanca commented on the shrinking supply of good valley land, the problem of erosion,

35 Ibid., 188. (*Huiñapo* referred to the balls of fermented dough used to make chicha.) More than twenty years earlier, in 1907, the *Círculo comercial cochabambino* had made note of the preponderance of small-scale traders in the export of maize, chicha, flour, potatoes, vegetables, and other products to the altiplano towns. It estimated that 75 percent of this commerce was controlled by "people of the village and the countryside." Most of them came from the area around Punata, Cliza, and Tarata in the Cliza valley. (Cited in Azogue Crespo Rodríguez, and Bolares, "Cochabamba," 2.) For a study of the contemporary peasant family enterprise in one subregion, see Francis R. Cajka, "Peasant Commerce in the Serranías of Cochabamba, Bolivia" (Ph.D. diss., University of Michigan, 1979).

36 Salamanca, *Socialismo en Bolivia*, 189. For a brief discussion of the internal decomposition of haciendas in the Cliza valley prior to the 1953 agrarian reform, see Jorge Dandler Hanhart, "El desarrollo de la agricultura, políticas estatales, y el proceso de acumulación en Bolivia" (typescript, 1981), 45-56.

37 See n. 17 above.

and the increasing density of population.[38] In particular, the problem of deforestation had worsened since the turn of the century, when the increase in chicha production began to require greater quantities of charcoal. Thus, the spread of peasant proprietorship was also accompanied by signs of ecological deterioration, fractionalization of output, and pauperization of many smallholders. Bits and pieces of land were bought and sold, but this did not lead to an even distribution of resources. Smallholders often bequeathed their parcels of land to their children, dispersing them among many heirs. While some families accumulated a few worldly possessions, some pack animals, a patch of potato land here and of maize land there—perhaps as they continued to work on the landlord's demesne—others slipped into the ranks of landless laborers, squatters, or subtenants. Among the peasantry, land tenure relations became increasingly stratified.[39]

As the process of social differentiation advanced, it created more precarious conditions for peasants who could neither purchase land nor secure the customary patronage of their landlords who were now increasingly looking to "sell out." A group of "redundant" laborers was beginning to emerge that found no secure subsistence niche in the region. Across the valleys around the turn of the century, therefore, labor arrangements became more intricate and elaborate. In much the same way that Geertz describes for Indonesia,[40] the laboring poor in Cochabamba entered into a great variety of labor agreements—leasing, subcontracting, pawning, jobbing, and wage work. More and more, they turned to the tertiary sector.[41] Where that failed to provide a livelihood, they set off to find work in the mines and salt fields beyond the western cordillera. Over the course of a century, the cumulative effects of the region's economic involution had created conditions favorable to the expulsion of poor peasants and day laborers into the expanding export sector, once wage work was available.[42]

38 Salamanca, *Socialismo en Bolivia*, 187.

39 Two earlier studies of Cliza describe cross-sections of rural society and show the various strata of tenants, squatters, and piqueros in the 1930s and 1940s: Olen, *Cantón Chullpas*, and Patch, "Social Implications," 22-29.

40 Geertz, *Agricultural Involution*, 99.

41 A report issued in 1907 estimated that 50 percent of the labor force in Punata, Cliza, and Tarata were arrieros. That may be an exaggeration, but the observation underscores the prevalence of nonagricultural activities among the "part-time" peasants in the Cliza valley. See Azogue Crespo, Rodríguez, and Bolares, "Cochabamba," 2, and Dandler Hanhart, "Diversificación," 20-21.

42 Platt and Molina, Barrios (*Qollaruna*, 28-30) speculate that peasant migration

The outlines of patterns of migration out of the valleys around the turn of the century have only recently come to light, especially in the research of Platt and Molina Barrios.[43] Their analysis of mining-company records on the work force of the largest tin mine in Bolivia, Llallagua-Uncía, reveals a preponderance of mine workers from the Cochabamba valleys. This confirms Harris and Albó's briefer study of industrial mine workers, in which they noted the large-scale migration of Cochabamba peasants and former peasants to mines in Norte Potosí (as Chayanta was now called).[44] The influx of valley peoples into the mining camps created "islands" of Quechua-speaking cholos and mestizos in the heart of Chayanta. Where the peasants of Chayanta resisted proletarianization and continued to this day to work in the mines only temporarily and under limited conditions,[45] Cochabamba migrants often cast their fate with the mines and forged the new industrial proletariat of tin mining.

The predominance of Cochabamba miners in Llallagua-Uncía was already evident in the 1920s, the decade of Cochabamba's so-called "agrarian crisis." But the exodus had actually began much earlier, probably sometime in the 1880s and 1890s, well before the development of the tin mines. To date, there has been little research on the westward migratory movement from the valleys, but several contemporary observations and the study of Platt and Molina Barrios provide important clues to the early wave.[46]

During the thirty-year boom (1880-1910) in nitrate production in Bolivia's "lost lands" of the Atacama desert, poor peasants left the

from Cochabamba followed upon a period of subsistence crisis in the peasant economy. They suggest that part of the deterioration in the standard of living was due to the contraction in demand for the foodstuffs that valley peasants had traditionally traded to highland peoples. Yet Salamanca (*Socialismo en Bolivia*, 187-188) mentions peasant commerce in the mines as one important source of petty accumulation, and Platt and Molina Barrios (*Qollaruna*, 20) themselves show that Cochabamba products continued to be sold in the marketplace of Uncía. The evidence is clearly still too preliminary and fragmented to permit more than speculation about the intensity or causes of the crisis in the peasant economy.

43 Platt and Molina Barrios, *Qollaruna*, esp. chap. 2.

44 Olivia Harris and Xavier Albó *Monteras y guardatojos. Campesinos y mineros en el norte de Potosí* (La Paz: Centro de Investigación y Promoción del Campesinado, 1975), 22, 26-27.

45 Ricardo Godoy, "From Indian to Miner and Back Again: Small-scale Mining in the Jukumani Ayllu, Northern Potosí, Bolivia," (Ph.D. diss., Columbia University, 1983); Harris and Albó, *Monteras*, 84; Platt and Molina Barrios, *Qollaruna*, 30-31; and Harris, "Labor and produce," 91-93.

46 Platt and Molina Barrios, *Qollaruna*, 25-26.

valleys for the mines. On the barren coast of Chile, they extracted nitrate for export to Europe and North America, where it was used for explosives and fertilizer.[47] In 1907, a report on the agriculture in Cochabamba expressed alarm at the growing number of impoverished peasants who had been forced to abandon their parcels of land and move to the Chilean coast: "So numerous are those who emigrate from Cochabamba that, within a few years, they will represent the industrial progress of a fatherland that is not theirs."[48] Two years later, a local newspaper, *El heraldo*, again reported widespread movement out of the region. The editor considered the cause to be the depressed level of agricultural prices and the glutted grain market, and he estimated that several thousand people had left the valleys since the beginning of the decade.[49]

When job opportunities on the coast dried up shortly before the First World War, and even more so afterward, Cochabamba's laborers began to return to Bolivia. In 1911 and 1914, local newspapers in Uncía and Oruro noted, with some anxiety, the flood of Cochabambinos and other Bolivians returning from the nitrate fields.[50] Some may have hoped to purchase land in the valleys, but many others now felt themselves to be permanent wageworkers and sought work in the new tin industry. From white saltpeters to black mines: they moved from an extractive industry on the wane to one just beginning to expand. It did expand over the next decade, but it did not do so enough to absorb these additions to the labor force. The swelling supply of valley migrants seeking wage work on the altiplano was beginning to outpace demand during the second and third decades of the twentieth-century.[51]

47 Fifer, *Bolivia*, 73-74. The "lost lands" were the coastal territories ceded to Chile after Bolivia's defeat in the War of the Pacific (1879-1883).

48 José Aranibar, "Proprietarios, conductores, y clase menesterosa al frente de los años agrícolas," *Boletín agrícola del Ministerio de Colonización y Agricultura*, no. 18 (1907), 101. (I am grateful to Gustavo Rodríguez for bringing this article to my attention.)

49 Cited in Azogue Crespo, Rodríguez, and Bolares, "Cochabamba," 2.

50 See Platt and Molina Barrios, *Qollaruna*, 24-25.

51 Platt and Molina emphasize this oversupply of labor, which was a circumstance favorable to the early phase of mining industrialization in Bolivia. In sharp contrast, the Cerro de Pasco mining company of the central sierra of Peru suffered from a chronically inadequate and unstable labor force (because of the low wages). In Bolivia, there was less of a need to "break" the peasant subsistence sector, wage caste war against the ayllus of Chayanta, or deploy coercive

Peasants into miners: however dramatic the transformation seemed to be in this particular region in the early twentieth-century, peasant ties were never completely cut. Furthermore, repercussions of these waves of migration were felt everywhere in the valleys. Directly or indirectly, through kin, neighbors, or landlords, peasants were drawn into the industrial orbit of the mines even if they never set eyes on the bleak encampments of Llallagua-Uncía or San José. Stories and rumors about the conditions of life and work in the mines began to filter back to the valley. Peasants had cousins and friends who, after only seven or eight years in the shafts, began to vomit up pieces of their blackened lungs in a slow agony of death. They heard gruesome reports of a massacre of mineworkers in Uncía in 1923. But they also heard about bold protests of miners during the 1920s. A sense of militancy, forged around an emerging class identity and solidarity, was in the air. While many peasants in Cochabamba may not have quite understood the circumstances of the brutal struggle in the distant mines, a growing number of smallholders in Cliza and the Valle Bajo began to appreciate the force and meaning of class conflict.[52] The mines were beginning to cast a new, more ominous shadow across the valleys. Cochabamba peasants themselves would soon begin to mobilize for social justice, preparing the ground for revolution and reform just a few years hence.

On the temporal horizons that stretch into the past, opening generous expanses of historical time, historians can always find the social continuities or discontinuities they seek. The *longue durée* per-

mechanisms of labor recruitment such as *enganche* (though it did function in Bolivia). For comparison with Peru, see especially Mallon, *Defense of Community*, chaps. 5 and 6; Adrian DeWind, *Peasants Become Miners: The Evolution of Industrial Mining Systems in Peru* (New York: Garland, 1987); and Long and Roberts, *Miners*.

52 On the development of class ideologies and the political mobilization of miners, see especially June Nash, *We Eat the Mines and the Mines Eat Us: Dependency and Exploitation in Bolivian Tin Mines* (New York: Columbia University Press, 1979). On the influence of mining politics on valley peasants, see Harris and Albó, *Monteras*, 26-27 and 37ff.; Jorge Dandler Hanhart, *El sindicalismo campesino en Bolivia: Los cambios estructurales en Ucureña* (México City: Instituto Indigenista Interamericano, 1969); and Jorge Dandler Hanhart, "Politics of Leadership, Brokerage, and Patronage in the Campesino Movement of Cochabamba, Bolivia" (Ph.D. diss., University of Wisconsin, 1971). See also James Kohl, "The Cliza and Ucureña War: Syndical Violence and National Revolution in Bolivia," *Hispanic American Historical Review* 62 (1982): 607-628, and Andrew Pearse, "Peasants and Revolution: The Case of Bolivia," *Economy and Society* 1 (1972): 255-279, 399-424.

spective of social reality in preindustrial Europe over three or four centuries leaves the strong impression that the structure of social relationships in the countryside was resistant to crises, shocks, and internal contradictions. From this perspective, the historian may invoke the power of geography, culture and civilization, economy and state, class or colonial relationships, or attitudes (*mentalités*) as structural constraints that slowed the tempo of historical change over the long term. Cast in this Braudelian framework, human societies seem to be endowed with a permanence and coherence that are almost impervious to human action. "Some structures . . . become stable," writes Braudel, "[and] get in the way of history, hinder its flow, and in hindering it shape it."[53]

Yet that same contemplation of a vast sweep of time can bring into focus a different historical landscape, one marked by discontinuities and change. From far above the surface of political events and short-term economic fluctuations, a long-term vision of history brings to light the sharp outlines of economic and social trends that move together or at odds with each other, shaping time in the image of cycles and intercycles and occasionally punctuating it by the force of a structural crisis. Such a vision, following the movement of several simultaneous tendencies imbues history with motion, ebb and flow, contradiction and change. It locates within social structures the elements of their own disequilibrum and the potential for their transformation; it reveals the fragility of the basis of economic life; and it grants the power of human agency to people trapped inside enduring social relationships that seem eternal. The trans-conjunctural perspective may be primarily economic, which traces cyclical time and charts the shifting direction or tempo of secular trends that produced significant social consequences. Or it may focus on human relationships that both condition and were conditioned by the larger political and economic environment. Through this conceptual lens, long-term history makes visible the power of people to alter social structures and shape their own world, even if they did so unconsciously and "not always as they wanted." Social history that widens the scope of historical time into several centuries can still chart the currents and eddies of structural change, insurrectional threats to the social order, and shock waves that reverberate through seemingly static or brittle social and mental structures. In so doing, it brings to light precisely the impermanence, sometimes the evanescence, of

53 Fernand Braudel, *On History* (Chicago: University of Chicago Press, 1980), 130.

social structures and relationships that otherwise seem carved in stone.

This long-term perspective on agrarian conflict and change in the Cochabamba region has found deep currents of socioeconomic change amidst striking continuities. In spite of the strong presence of Europe in the region since the sixteenth-century, the enduring influence of mining on the regional economy, and Cochabamba's continued importance as a food producer for western highland Alto Perú, the social organization and texture of rural life and the region's functional role in the economic totality were full of historical motion and subject to conjunctural pressures. The presence of historical change in continuity is best illustrated by Bolivia's two major mining cycles. In the first, in the late sixteenth-century, the valleys were closely integrated into the silver export industry and were indirectly subjected to the imperatives of the world market and the logic of mercantile capitalism. Cochabamba's nexus to the mines was maize and wheat, and its emergent role as the region's granary conditioned, in some measure, the mercantilization of productive relations, based on servile labor. In the silver cycle of the late nineteenth-century, the regional economy once more became closely tied to the mining sector, but its role as food producer during the era of mercantile capitalism had diminished. Cochabamba had become primarily an exporter of people, who no longer could cling to the husk of a penurious peasant existence.

Where the origins of Cochabamba's agrarian class society in the sixteenth century lay in the peculiar legacies of Incaic rule and the imperatives and contradictions of mercantile colonialism, the subsequent evolution of agrarian class relations within the region created the social conditions for the emergence of an incipient proletariat for the nitrate fields and tin mines outside it around the turn of the twentieth century. Cochabamba, once the region of refuge for Andean migrants seeking respite from the pressures of colonialism, became a region of flight, where the pressures and tensions of class forced peasants to submit to the degradation and dangers of mining. Out of the ebb and flow of class conflict and the historical processes of social differentiation, the region had turned from an exporter of grains in the late sixteenth-century to an exporter of people in the late nineteenth-century.

Appendix

Table A-1. Annual Average of Tithes in the Archbishopric of Charcas (La Plata) from 1599 to 1607, by District

District	*Pesos Corrientes*	*Percentage*
Cochabamba	15,222	15.9
Yotala	11,007	11.5
Pitantora	9,756	10.2
Tomina	8,021	8.4
Matacas	7,442	7.8
Mizque	6,098	6.4
Paspaya, Pilaya	5,844	6.1
Oroncoto	5,784	6.0
Alcantari	5,183	5.4
Poopó	4,241	4.4
Guata	3,607	3.8
Potosí	3,152	3.3
Tarija	2,735	2.9
Moxtoro	1,923	2.0
Terrado	1,754	1.8
Soroche, Pocopoco, Luxe, Tarabuco, and Yocala	1,676	1.8
Potolo	236	0.2
Atacama, Chucuito	102	0.1
Chacras of Cochabamba, Paria, and Carangas	1,023	1.1
Chacras of La Plata province	855	0.9
Total	95,661	100.0

Source: "Diezmos del arzobispal de la Plata, 1599-1607," AGI, Charcas, Leg. 153.

Table A-2. Indian Population of Cochabamba Province, 1683-1850

Year	*Total Indian Population*	*Tributary Population*
1683	26,420[a]	6,735
1737	—	5,484[b]
1752	26,531	5,778
1786-1787	58,402	10,773
1792-1793	57,580	8,760
1804-1808	59,277	11,718
1850	46,587[c]	6,046[d]

Sources: For 1683, AGN, Sala 13, Padrones, 18.1.1, Leg. 41, and 18.1.3, Leg. 43. For 1737, AGN, Sala 13, Padrones, 18.1.5, Leg. 45. For 1752, José Antonio de Velasco, *Memorias de los virreyes que han gobernado el Perú*, vol. 4, appendix, pp. 9-11. For 1786-1787, AGN, Sala 13, Padrones, 18.2.1, Leg. 46; 18.2.2, Leg. 47; and 18.2.3, Leg. 48. For 1792-1793, AGN, Sala 13, Padrones, 18.2.3, Leg. 48; 18.2.4, Leg. 49; and 18.2.5, Leg. 50. For 1804-1808, AGN, Sala 13, Padrones, 18.3.3, Leg. 53, and 18.4.4, Leg. 54. For 1850, ANB, Padrones, Cochabamba.

[a] Does not include non-tribute-paying Indians in the parish of Caraza.

[b] Does not include tributary population of the district of Ayopaya, which probably numbered about 400.

[c] Does not include Indian population of Sacaba, and population of Ayopaya is based on the 1844 census.

[d] According to the *Tribunal General de Valores*, tributary population of Cochabamba in 1856 was 9,437 (personal communication from Nicolás Sánchez-Albornoz).

Table A-3. Indian Population of Cochabamba Province, by Partido, Selected Years from 1683 to 1871

Year	*Total Indian Population*	*Number of Tributaries*	*Number of Ausentes*	*Ausentes as a Percentage of Tributaries*
		Partido of the Cercado		
1683	1,170	311	—	—
1737	1,516	254	—	—
1786	4,182	893	25	2.8
1792	4,421	866	75	8.7
1802	4,273	850	242	28.5
1850	3,224	507	329	64.9
		Partido of Sacaba		
1683	866	209	—	—
1737	—	211	—	—
1787	3,805	673	12	1.8
1791	3,397	592	59	10.0
1797	4,577	706	152	21.5
1804	3,194	533	102	19.1
		Partido of Tapacarí		
1683	5,693	2,161	—	—
1737	—	1,573	—	—
1786	14,766	3,089	113	3.7
1793	15,584	3,144	257	8.2
1798	16,806	3,315	480	14.5
1804	15,820	3,032	724	23.9
1844	18,240	3,477	762	21.9
1851	16,845	3,389	897	26.5
		Partido of Cliza		
1683	3,581	812	—	—
1737	7,478	1,382	—	—
1786	16,227	2,769	38	1.4
1792	16,355	2,769	38	1.4
1797	17,553	3,098	558	18.0
1803	17,345	3,519	368	10.5
1805	—	2,763	584	21.1
1831	—	1,566	—	—
1846	7,344	956	1,310	137.0
1850	4,487	718	1,567	218.2
		Partido of Arque		
1683	2,922[a]	1,079	—	—
1737	—	1,506	—	—
1787	14,906	2,488	—	—
1792	14,722	2,504	513	20.4
1798	15,088	2,932	322	11.0
1804	12,913	2,692	505	18.8
1850	13,861	2,783	1,989	71.5

Table A-3. Indian Population of Cochabamba Province, by Partido, Selected Years from 1683 to 1871 (*cont.*)

Year	*Total Indian Population*	*Number of Tributaries*	*Number of Ausentes*	*Ausentes as a Percentage of Tributaries*
		Partido of Ayopaya		
1683	9,759	2,163	—	—
1737	—	558	—	—
1787	5,420	845	111	13.1
1792	5,700	973	209	21.5
1807	6,214	1,172	259	22.1
1844	5,670	1,032	112	10.9
1871	—	513	—	—

Sources: See table A-2.

[a] Does not include non-tribute-paying Indians in the parish of Caraza.

Table A-4. Debts of Hacendados to Pueblos Reales of Cochabamba, 1776

Lending Community	*Property Mortgaged*	*Original Owner*	*Present Owner*	*Date of Original Mortgage*	*Principal of Loan (pesos)*	*Total Outstanding Debt (pesos)*
Pocona (Mizque)	Chuchupunata (Cliza)	Francisco de Medrano	?	1590	5,980	?
Sipesipe	Sununpaya (Cliza)	Juan Sánchez Macías	Francisco Saavedra	1586	1,200	1,001
Santiago de Cotagaita (?) (Mizque?)	mills of hacienda Pocoata (Cliza)	Fernando de Soria	?	1676	1,400	5,950
Sipesipe	Coñacoña, Guaicanaio	Pedro Maldonado	?	1549	300	772
Sipesipe	Calacala, Queroquero[a]	Francisco de Ynojosa; Juan Osorio	?	1576	198	300
Sipesipe	Queroquero[a]	Alonso de Escobar	?	1594	600	5,430
?	Queroquero[a]	Cristóbal de Arébalo y Diego Perea		1584	100	955
Sipesipe	Colcapirgua	Juan Sánchez Macías	?	1586	100	945
?	Samaca, Motefato	Andrés de Rivera	?	1579	180	?
Sipesipe	"unas haciendas"	Pedro de Baraona	?	?	426	?
Sipesipe	?	Francisco de Ynojosa; Juan de la Reinaga	Miguel de Rosales	1567	229	?

Source: "Testimonio de la nómina general de deudores de la Caxa Gral. de censos de comunidades de Indios . . . de la real audiencia de . . . Charcas, año de 1776," document no. C2518, BN.

[a] There were three different haciendas bearing the name of Queroquero.

Table A-5. Viedma's Reports on Grain Prices and Planting and Harvest Conditions in Cochabamba, 1784-1808

Year	*Months*	*Price (reales per fanega)*		*Planting and Harvest Conditions*
		Wheat	*Maize*	
1784	Sept.-Dec.	58	—	Poor harvest; flooding
1785	Jan.-Apr.	32	20	Abundant rain followed by dry planting season; good yield foreseen
	May-Aug.	32	16-20	
	Sept.-Dec.	25	16	
1786	Jan.-Apr.	14-17	16	At beginning of harvest, sufficient grain to supply local population for two years; little grain exported; planting late, poor harvest foreseen
	May-Aug.	19-20	16-20	
	Sept.-Dec.	19-20	20	
1787	Jan.-Apr.	16	20	Little rain, but previous year's harvest kept most agricultural prices from rising drastically; conditions favorable for planting; good harvest expected for next year
	May-Aug.	25	22	
	Sept.-Dec.	26	24	
1788	Jan.-Apr.	20	22	Too much rain; much maize seed rotted in moist soil
1790	Jan.-Apr.	16	20	
1792	Jan.-Apr.	20	24	Little rain; good harvest expected only for irrigated crops; grain supply sufficient for local population due to abundant grain supplies from past years
1793	July-Dec.	—	—	Poor harvest; prices stable because of abundant grain stored from past harvests
1794	Jan.-Apr.	12	16	Heavy rains; good harvest
	June-Sept.	12	16	
1795	Jan.-Apr.	12	16	Abundant harvest
	June-Dec.	12	16	
1796	Jan.-June	12	14	Good harvest
1797	July-Dec.	—	28	Poor maize harvest, but scarcity avoided by grain stored in municipal granary
1798	Jan.-June	12	22	Abundant rainfall; heavy yields
1799	July-Dec.	28	24	Poor harvest, but little scarcity; prices slightly higher than usual
1800	July-Dec.	32	24	Serious shortage of water; drought destroyed much of wheat crop
1804	July-Dec.	132	112	Second successive year of drought, worst in history of Cochabamba; almost all crops lost; severe famine
1806	Jan.-June	40-48	32	Poor weather, but prices have declined; good harvest foreseen
	July-Dec.	40	32	
1807	July-Dec.	60	28	Little rainfall; planting delayed; poor harvest expected; prices slightly higher
1808	July-Dec.	32	24	Hot and dry weather; planting delayed; poor harvest foreseen

Sources: AGN, Sala 9, Intendencia, 5.8.3, Leg. 2; 5.8.4, Leg. 3; 5.8.5, Leg. 4; 5.8.6, Leg. 5; 5.8.7, Leg. 6; 5.9.1, Leg. 7; and 5.9.2, Leg. 8.

Table A-6. Sources and Amounts of Royal Income in Cochabamba, by Quinquennium, 1775-1809

	1775-1779[a]		*1780-1784*		*1785-1789*[b]	
	Amount (pesos)	*Percentage*	*Amount (pesos)*	*Percentage*	*Amount (pesos)*	*Percentage*
Indian tribute	122,578	49.3	241,809	44.7	202,899	44.0
Alcabalas	64,302	25.9	110,610	20.5	76,883	16.7
Reales novenos	11,999	4.8	29,359	5.4	20,551	4.5
Taxes on bureaucratic offices and salaries	40,152	16.2	109,863	20.3	90,331	19.6
Civil offices and salaries						
Sale of offices	4,493	1.8	5,025	0.9	6,133	1.3
Income tax	—	—	—	—	78	<0.1
Pension fund	—	—	273	<0.1	675	0.2
Military offices and salaries						
Fund for invalids	126	<0.1	572	0.1	260	<0.1
Pension fund	2,393	1.0	21,176	3.9	8,635	1.9
Ecclesiastical offices and salaries						
Inheritance tax	—	—	—	—	23,539	5.1
Tax on vacant higher-clergy posts	3,571	1.4	18,373	3.4	2,523	0.6
Tax on vacant lower-clergy posts	24,249	9.8	56,923	10.5	31,515	6.8
Income tax	1,496	0.6	2,802	0.5	12,948	2.8
One-month tax on clerical salaries	1,828	0.7	1,917	0.4	1,557	0.3
5-percent tax on clerical salaries	1,996	0.8	2,802	0.5	1,075	0.2
Surtax	—	—	—	—	1,393	0.3
State monopolies	3,792	1.5	13,960	2.6	7,742	1.7
Tobacco	—	—	—	—	—	—
Mercury	—	—	—	—	568	0.1
Playing cards	—	—	—	—	—	—
Stamped paper	3,792	1.5	13,960	2.6	7,174	1.6
Miscellaneous	5,651	2.3	34,895	6.5	62,511	13.6
Real hacienda en común	494	0.2	600	0.1	1,297	0.3
Otras tesorerías	455	0.2	—	—	—	—
Tax on possessions of deceased persons	—	—	—	—	301	<0.1
Tax on Jesuit property	—	—	23,276	4.3	53,630	11.6
Tax on sale of lands and titles	—	—	821	0.2	2,350	0.5
Fines	100	<0.1	150	<0.1	44	<0.1
Military defense tax	—	—	5,449	1.0	—	—
Alcances de cuenta	—	—	110	<0.1	171	<0.1
Diversos	4,602	1.9	4,489	0.8	4,718	1.0
Total	248,474	100.0	540,496	100.0	460,917	100.1

Sources: AGN, Sala 13, Cajas reales, 5.2.5, Leg. 1 (1775 and 1776); 5.2.6, Leg. 2 (1777 and 1778); 5.3.1, Leg. 3 (1779 and 1780); 5.3.2, Leg. 4 (1781 and 1782); 27.1.1, Leg. 218 (1783); 5.3.3, Leg. 5 (1784); 5.3.4, Leg. 6 (1785); 5.3.5, Leg. 7 (1786); 27.2.2, Leg. 224 (1787); 27.2.3, Leg. 225 (1788); 5.4.3, Leg. 11 (1789); 27.3.2, Leg. 229 (1790 and 1791); 5.4.6, Leg. 14 (1792); 27.3.3, Leg. 230 (1793); 27.4.3, Leg. 235 (1794); 27.4.4, Leg. 236 (1795); 5.5.3, Leg. 18 (1796); 27.5.2, Leg. 240 (1797); 27.5.4, Leg. 241 (1798); 27.6.1, Leg. 243 (1799); 5.6.1, Leg. 22 (1800); 5.6.2, Leg. 23 (1801); 5.6.3, Leg. 24 (1802); 5.6.4, Leg. 25 (1803); 5.7.1, Leg. 28 (1804); 5.7.3, Leg. 30 (1805); 5.8.1, Leg. 34 (1806); 5.8.4, Leg. 37 (1807); 5.9.1, Leg. 40 (1808); and 5.9.5, Leg. 44 (1809).

1790-1794		*1795-1799*		*1800-1804*		*1805-1809*	
Amount (pesos)	*Percent-age*	*Amount (pesos)*	*Percent-age*	*Amount (pesos)*	*Percent-age*	*Amount (pesos)*	*Percent-age*
437,495	52.8	460,314	48.5	465,368	49.4	277,560	29.8
141,533	17.1	136,242	14.3	126,835	13.5	93,299	10.0
43,451	5.2	27,749	2.9	43,713	4.6	26,049	2.8
93,181	11.2	145,836	15.4	129,161	13.7	92,783	10.0
4,570	0.6	983	0.1	3,183	0.3	2,426	0.3
2,902	0.3	1,886	0.2	2,037	0.2	2,183	0.2
4,687	0.6	9,594	1.0	8,966	1.0	2,636	0.3
4,744	0.6	3,940	0.4	3,510	0.4	5,981	0.6
6,636	0.8	26,179	2.8	2,966	0.3	1,779	0.2
—	—	—	—	3,925	0.4	9,596	1.0
7,857	0.9	46,131	4.9	9,832	1.0	43,204	4.6
23,490	2.8	33,722	3.5	81,356	8.6	16,784	1.8
19,324	2.3	1,616	0.2	—	—	428	<0.1
3,926	0.5	2,907	0.3	526	<0.1	2,582	0.3
6,033	0.7	4,582	0.5	6,374	0.7	3,855	0.4
9,012	1.1	14,296	1.5	6,486	0.7	1,329	0.1
38,690	4.7	32,781	3.5	58,824	6.2	22,388	2.4
—	—	20,000	2.1	36,800	3.9	6,000	0.6
27,571	3.3	818	<0.1	—	—	—	—
—	—	—	—	—	—	534	<0.1
11,119	1.3	11,963	1.3	22,024	2.3	15,854	1.7
75,001	9.0	147,128	15.5	117,791	12.5	419,059	45.0
20,984	2.5	78,188	8.2	74,542	7.9	239,089	25.7
602	<0.1	14,779	1.6	8,696	0.9	156,204	16.8
4,783	0.6	2,262	0.2	906	<0.1	—	—
—	—	—	—	—	—	—	—
5,944	0.7	1,797	0.2	220	<0.1	123	<0.1
261	<0.1	285	<0.1	117	<0.1	113	<0.1
20,544	2.5	27,607	2.9	13,064	1.4	509	<0.1
517	<0.1	4,978	0.5	1,771	0.2	1,324	0.1
21,366	2.6	17,232	1.8	18,475	2.0	21,697	2.3
829,351	100.0	950,050	100.1	941,692	99.9	931,138	100.0

Note: Discrepancies in totals of percentages due to rounding.
[a] Except 1777, data for which are missing.
[b] Except 1787 and 1788, data for which are missing.

Glossary

alcabala	ad valorem tax (6 percent after 1780) on the sale of slaves, real estate, tithes, and many commodities
alcalde	mayor; member of the *cabildo*; royal official who administered a rural district (*partido*), often after purchasing the office (replaced by *subdelegado* in 1784)
arancel	a royal proclamation regulating prices, rent, wages, etc.
arrendatario	person, usually a creole, who leased a hacienda, mill, or large tract of land, with its tenantry, for a stipulated rent over a period of several years
arrendero	a tenant, usually an Indian or mestizo, who cultivated land on a hacienda and paid rent in labor, kind, and/or money
arriero	muleteer
arroba	a measure of weight, equivalent to about twenty-five pounds
asignación	assignment of landholding rights to *originarios* in an Indian village
ausente	a missing or absent tributary
ayllu	formally, an endogamous lineage claiming descent from a common ancestor; in practice, the basic kin unit of Andean native society, which held title to land, organized cooperative labor teams, and performed other collective functions
azoguero	owner of a silver refinery (literally, "mercury man," so called because mercury was used in refining silver)
bayetas	rough unbleached woolen cloth
cabecera	the principal village of a *pueblo real*
cabecera del valle	the highest part of a valley, where lands were usually irrigated
cabildo	municipal council
cacicazgo	Indian chieftainship

caja de comunidad	treasury of an Indian pueblo, which was supposed to finance tribute deficits as well as supply mortgage capital to Spaniards acquiring land
caja real	royal treasury
cajón	a tank for refining silver by amalgamation, large enough to hold fifty *quintales* of milled ore
capellanía	an ecclesiastical benefice, which yielded 5 percent annually on the principal
carga	a measure of volume, equivalent to about six bushels
censo	a loan or credit guaranteed by collateral, usually land, bearing 5 percent interest
censo en compra	a mortgage loan negotiated at the time of purchase of land
censualista	a person or association providing a *censo*
chácara	a small estate or grain farm; also, in the eighteenth century, *chacra* (from the Quechua word *chajra*, farming, sowing, land)
chicha	Andean alcoholic beverage, usually made from maize
cholo	in the eighteenth century, a person formally defined as being "three-quarters Indian and one-quarter white"; later, a person of mixed Andean and European ancestry generally
chuño	"freeze-dried" potatoes, processed in high-altitude zones with extreme diurnal temperatures, making it possible to preserve them over a long period of time
cobrador	*originario* assigned by a cacique to collect tribute in an Indian village
composición de tierras	royal inspection and validation of land titles
corregidor	Spanish magistrate and administrator of a district (*corregimiento*); the post was abolished in the early 1780s
corregidor de indios	magistrate in charge of a rural Indian district
diezmo	one-tenth; tax levied on grain
efectos de Castilla	European (mainly Spanish) imported goods
efectos de la tierra	goods imported from other colonial provinces
encomendero	Spanish colonizer who was granted by the crown the right to collect tribute from one or more native communities and was expected, in return, to protect the welfare of the inhabitants

estancia	a highland property where grazing was usually combined with potato cultivation
fanega	a measure of volume that varied by region but was generally equivalent to about 1.6 bushels
fanegada	a measure of land area that varied by region and by soil fertility but generally referred to the amount of land needed to sow one fanega of seed
feria	open-air weekly retail marketplace
forasteros	Indians living in a community other than that of their original kin group and having no landholding rights in the host community (distinguished from *originarios*); in Cochabamba, they lived in Spanish towns and on Spanish haciendas as well as in *pueblos reales*
huaca	Andean deity believed to take the form of a mountain peak, rock, cave, water, or other natural object
kajcha	a silver thief, usually a *minga* who scavenged silver ore on weekends and sold it
kichwa	temperate valley zone where maize was the principal crop during Incan times
kuraka	Andean ethnic lord (the term was later replaced by the Spanish term "cacique")
legua	a measure of length, roughly the distance a horse could walk in an hour (approximately 2.5-3 miles)
maica	irrigated maize land
minga	wageworker in the mines
mit'a	literally, in Quechua, a turn at some task; more generally, the Andean system of rotating turns of service in the performance of community labor or the rendering of service to the Incan emperor
mita	colonial institution of rotation draft labor, particularly for work in the silver mines of Potosí (from the Quechua term *mit'a*)
mita de agua	an irrigation system that delivered water to designated properties, usually those of hacendados, for a specified number of hours a week or month
mitayo	an Indian laborer serving in the *mita*
mitimaes	Indian colonizers sent by their ethnic group to cultivate land in different ecological zones and at some distance from their homeland; also, Indians sent by the Incas to colonize recently conquered territories
mittayoc	seasonal migrant laborer who cultivated maize on Incan lands
obraje	primitive textile factory or workshop

obras pías	works of charity, usually sponsored by the Spanish crown
originarios	Indians still living with their original kin group and having the rights and responsibilities of *ayllu* membership (distinguished from *forasteros*)
parcialidad	moiety of an Indian village, usually composed of two sections, Anansaya (the upper half) and Urinsaya (the lower half)
partido	subdivision of a *corregimiento*; an administrative district composed of several parishes
peara (de mulas)	the load of goods carried by a "standard" mule train, usually consisting of ten mules
peso corriente	a silver coin weighing one ounce; the standard monetary unit for ordinary transactions, subdivided into eight reales
peso ensayado	the standard monetary unit of account in the early colonial era, subdivided into twelve reales
primicias	literally, "first fruits"; a tax levied on Indian crops and livestock
provincias obligadas	provinces from which *mitayos* were recruited
pueblo real	Spanish term for an Indian district, including a principal (*cabecera*) village and its surrounding rural settlements; there were five *pueblos reales* in eighteenth-century Cochabamba (Tapacarí, Sipesipe, El Paso, Tiquipaya, and Capinota)
puna	cold, dry lands at altitudes of 12,000 feet or more
quebrada	mountain gorge through which a stream flows down to the central valleys
quintal	a measure of weight, equal to four *arrobas*
quinto	the "royal fifth"; a tax levied on the silver extracted from the mines of Potosí
ramo	treasury account
real noveno	the "royal ninth"; a tax of 11 percent levied on tithes, which in turn were based on the estimated value of a region's agricultural production in a given year
reducción	forced resettlement program of Viceroy Toledo to bring dispersed Andean groups together into nucleated villages of Spanish design in order to facilitate state control and collection of tribute
repartimiento de mercancías	forced distribution of merchandise to Indians, usually on credit, by a *corregidor* or his agent
reservados	old and disabled men who were exempt from tribute and mita duty
residencia	judicial review of the conduct of a *corregidor* or other official at the end of his term in office

subdelegado	highest appointed official of a *partido*
temporal	dry land where wheat was usually cultivated
tocuyero	a weaver of *tocuyos*
tocuyos	rough unbleached cotton cloth
vara	a measure of length, approximately equivalent to thirty-three inches
veintena	one-twentieth; tax levied on wheat sown on Indian lands
viche	an area of land, equivalent in the Cochabamba region to about one-sixth of a *fanegada*
yanacona	a retainer who served the Incan emperor or an ethnic lord as a life-long servant
yanacona colonial	an Indian servant, miner, or agricultural laborer removed from his ayllu and bound to a Spanish overlord
yanaconaje	institution of personal servitude (see *yanacona* and *yanacona colonial*)
yungas	low-altitude tropical lands, generally on the eastern slopes of the Andes; specifically, in Alto Perú, the coca-producing region bordering the province of La Paz; also, the people inhabiting such regions

Bibliography

Manuscript Collections

BOLIVIA

Archivo Nacional de Bolivia, Sucre (ANB)

A superb repository of documents for the audiencia of Charcas and for Bolivia during the nineteenth century, this archive provides both fine-grained descriptive materials on the Cochabamba region and indispensable sources on mining, government, the Indian population, and the political culture of the dominant elites during the colonial period. Under the direction of Gunnar Mendoza, the archive's holdings have been meticulously catalogued and indexed. The major categories of documentary sources consulted for this study are listed below.

Sección de Tierras e Indios

Expedientes y correspondencia (EC) consist of royal edicts, civil and criminal court records, petitions, grievances, inspector's reports, and other documents. They are exceptionally rich sources for the study of Andean society, land transactions and disputes, and government policy. Included among the documents in this category are:

"Visita y composición de tierras y estancias en Cochabamba." 1748. EC no. 100.

"Juicio en grado de apelación sobre los capítulos que se lee a Don Juan Guillermo Liro de Córdova, por el indio Blas Condori, sobre tierras en el pueblo de Tapacarí." 1753. 136 ff. EC no. 46.

"Real provisión del cobrador de tributo de Sipesipe, con petición que el cacique exije el padrón . . ." 1754. EC no. 25.

"Informaciones hechas . . . sobre el número de indios mitayos . . . que se deben marchar a Potosí." 1755. EC no. 23.

"Quejas al rey de indios de Tapacarí, Mojosa, Yaco, y Cavaxi . . .

sobre los execivos [*sic*] derechos que se les cobra en sus entierros, matrimonios . . ." 1761. EC no. 31.

"Indios de Cochabamba sobre el pretender de sujetarlos a servidumbre de yanaconazgo en la hacienda de la Laguna." 1772. EC no. 216.

"Diligencias e averiguaciones de los bienes sustraidos a los caciques de Tapacarí." 1781. EC no. 36.

"Cuaderno de cuentas de las cosechas de las sementeras de caciques de Tapacarí." 1782. EC no. 84.

"Exp. sobre las elecciones de caciques interinos de Capinota." 1796. EC no. 72.

"Exp. sobre el remate de alcabalas de harinas de trigo y maíz." 1803. EC no. 3.

Sección de la audiencia de Charcas

Expedientes and correspondencia deal with such issues as taxes and treasury administration, corruption among colonial authorities, tithes and other ecclesiastical concerns, conditions of bridges and roads, disputes over land sales, commerce, and grain shortages. Similar to the expedientes concerned with Indian affairs, these records are full of rich detail about aspects of regional society. For a sample of the material on Cochabamba in the late colonial period, see EC no. 32, 37, 49, 72, and 79.

Mano de obra—Minería

This manuscript collection provides information on the export of labor and goods to Potosí from outlying rural districts and on all aspects of mining society.

Padrones de indios

This archive contains a series of Indian census records of Cochabamba for the following partidos and years: Argue, 1850; Ayopaya, 1844; El Cercado, 1850; Cliza, 1831, 1846, and 1850; Punata, 1867; Tapacarí, 1828, 1844, 1851, and 1867; Tarata, 1872; and Cochabamba, 1834 and 1844. These records, particularly several *catastros*, provide information about Indian landholding patterns in the region.

Administración de Mariscal Sucre

Catalogued under Sucre's Ministry of the Interior (MI) is rich information on monastic wealth in the region around the time of independence. See especially MI, vol. 1, no. 7, and vol. 2, no. 9.

Escrituras públicas (EP)

Of special interest are the books kept by three royal notaries—Juan Luís Soto, Gáspar de Rojas, and Lázaro de Aguila. They recorded transactions of all kinds, and their books reveal the intensity and variety of trade and commerce at Potosí during the early years after its founding in 1545.

Archivo Histórico Municipal de Cochabamba, Cochabamba (AHMC)

The municipal archive of Cochabamba was closed to the public at the time of my arrival in the city in 1974, because the documents were unorganized and uncatalogued. However, with the help of numerous people who appreciated the importance of archival research and who wrote letters, made phone calls, and campaigned on my behalf for the better part of two months, I was able to gain access to the archive, and shortly afterward I was joined by several local historians. Since then, the archive, which is housed in the Palacio de la Cultura in downtown Cochabamba, has been opened to the public.

The citations of material from this archive refer to the original number on the outside of the legajo (file) in which the document was found. The archive is currently being organized and many of the documents have been catalogued, so that citations in this text may not correspond to the new archival designations. However, I have identified most documents by a short, descriptive title and a date as well as by a legajo (Leg.) number.

The files include local trial records, complaints, wills, inventories, and petitions that provide microscopic views of rural life, commercial transactions, inheritance patterns, kinship ties, credit and debt relations, land tenure patterns, rent payments, tithe transactions, and myriad other facets of local society. Absent were the cabildo records. Apparently, manuscript copies of the libros de cabildo are not extant, although excerpts have been published in the *Digesto de ordenanzas*. Another disappointment was to discover that the records of the Monastery of Santa Clara apparently had been destroyed.

Archivo de la Biblioteca de la Universidad Mayor de San Andrés, La Paz

"Ynformación sumaria producida sobre las alteraciones de la provincia de Cochabamba en 1781." No. 97, 1781.

PERU

Biblioteca Nacional, Lima (BN)

"Testimonio de la nómina general de deudores de la Caxa Gral. de censos de comunidades de Indios . . . de la real audiencia de . . . Charcas, año de 1776." Document no. C2518.

ARGENTINA

Archivo General de la Nación, Buenos Aires (AGN)

As is well known, the AGN houses abundant documentary material on Alto Perú, particularly during the period of the viceroyalty of La Plata (1776-1810). The documents are catalogued by year, subject, and place.

Sala 13 (Cajas reales)

These treasury records include royal customs house records (*Guías y cuentas de alcabalas*) and Indian census records (*Padrones*); for Cochabamba, they span the years from 1773 to 1809, with only three annual records missing. The cajas reales consist of bound volumes, *Cuentas mayores de caja* and *Cuentas mensuales de caja*, which respectively include yearly and monthly entries of tax income and expenditures. In addition, unbound volumes, *Relaciones juradas*, available for only some of the years, give more detailed breakdowns of royal income and expenditures. The treasury records also include separate accounts of royal income from alcabalas—the tax on sales of most goods, real estate, and slaves, and the auction price of tithes. These records list the types, volume, and unit market value of goods imported into the province, and usually the merchants involved in the transactions and the origin of the merchandise (or sometimes a previous custom house where registered). They also record the value of tithes for each parish in the province each year and the 6 percent ad valorem tax that tithe collectors paid on their tithe investment. Treasury accounts consulted were 5.2.5, Leg. 1, through 5.9.7, Leg. 46. The unbound treasury and alcabala records for the region are found in Contaduría, Cuerpo 27, Legs. 218-250.

The padrones of Cochabamba are located in 18.1.1, Leg. 41 (1683), through 18.3.4, Leg. 54 (1804-1808). (See appendix tables A-1 and A-2.) The earliest Indian census found for Cochabamba in this archive dates from 1618-1619: 17.10.4, Leg. 40, books 1 and 2.

Sala 9 (Intendencia, Justicia, Criminales, Consulado, etc.)

There is abundant and varied material pertaining to the economy, society, and governance of the intendancy of Santa Cruz de la Sierra (which incorporated the old corregimiento of Cochabamba) in these sections of the AGN. An important series of reports are the trimester and semester records kept by the intendant, Francisco de Viedma, on harvest conditions, crop prices, and grain supplies for the years from 1784 to 1808 (see Intendencia, 5.8.2 through 5.9.2). Extensive records on the royal tobacco monopoly exist, as well as varied materials on such problems as Viedma's efforts at administrative and economic reform, expropriated properties of the Jesuits, the cost and recruitment of militiamen, royal taxes on grain mills and real-estate transfers, the difficulties of tribute and alcabala collection, contraband trade, tocuyo exports, shortages of pack animals, cabildo members, merchants and shopkeepers, and the appointment, responsibilities, and corrupt practices of subdelegados.

SPAIN

Archivo General de Indias, Seville (AGI)

Among the important documents on Alto Perú in this collection, particularly valuable are several early treasury records on tithes (see Charcas, Leg. 153, Diezmos del arzobispal de la Plata, 1599-1607) and on tribute on the yanacona population of Alto Perú (see Contaduría, Leg. 1818, Jan. 31, 1666). There is abundant correspondence concerning the bishopric of Santa Cruz (Charcas, Legs. 152, 153, 219, 375, 387, 388, 407, 408, 409, and 410). On the tax rebellion of 1730-1731 in Cochabamba, see Charcas, Legs. 343 and 344. On the conflicts in the pueblo real de Tapacarí and complaints about the corregidor, Bartolomé Fiorilo Pérez, in the middle years of the eighteenth century, see Charcas, Legs. 367 and 436. Numerous other documents on Cochabamba, which contain information on aspects of rural Indian society and protests carried up through the audiencia of La Plata to Madrid, are catalogued in the sections of Charcas and Justicia.

Real Academia de Historia, Madrid (RAH)

Colección Mata Linares (ML)

The most important sources for this study are the series of reports written by Francisco de Viedma, José Gómez Merino, Pedro Canals, Lázaro de Rivera, Tadeo Haenke, Francisco de Paula Sanz, and others on aspects of the region's economy and potential development. These reports, contained in this collection, were part of the Bourbon effort to promote commercial agriculture, improve road conditions, systematize tax collection, and so on (see chapter 7). There is also in this collection a wealth of documentary material on the Yuracaree, Moxo, and Chiquito settlements in the tropical lowlands and on the controversy over whether to transfer the seat of the bishopric of Santa Cruz to the city of Cochabamba.

ENGLAND

British Library, London

United Kingdom. Foreign Office 61/12. John B. Pentland, *Report on the Bolivian Republic. 1827. Microfilm.*

Published Documents

Acosta, José de. *The Natural and Moral History of the Indies*. 1590. Reprint. London: Hakluyt Society, n.d.

Amat y Juniente, Manuel de. *Memoria de gobierno*. Edited by Vicente Rodríguez Casado and Florentino Pérez Embid. Seville: Escuela de Estudios Hispanoamericanos, 1947.

Arzáns de Orsúa y Vela, Bartolomé. *Historia de la villa imperial de Potosí*. Edited by Lewis Hanke and Gunnar Mendoza. 3 vols. Providence: Brown University Press, 1965.

Arce, René, ed. "Un documento inédito de Pedro Vicente Cañete [y Domínguez] en torno a la controversia de la nueva mita de Potosí." In *Estudios bolivianos en homenaje a Gunnar Mendoza*, edited by Martha Urioste de Aguirre, 119-124. La Paz, 1978. Mimeograph.

Barriga, Victor M. *Memorias para la historia de Arequipa*. 4 vols. 1786-1791. Reprint. Arequipa: La Colmena, 1941-1952.

Blanco, Federico. *Diccionario geográfico de la República de Bolivia*. 4 vols. La Paz: Oficina Nacional de Inmigración, 1901.

Bueno, Cosme. "Descripción de las provincias pertenecientes al arzobispado de La Plata." [1740s.] In *Colección de documentos literarios del Perú*, 11 vols. Edited by Manuel de Odriozola. Vol. 3. Lima: A. Alfaro, 1872.

Cabeza de Vaca, Diego, et al. "Descripción y relación de la ciudad de La Paz." [1590s.] In Marcos Jiménez de la Espada, ed., *Relaciones geográficas de Indias: El Perú*. Madrid: Atlas, 1965.

Cañete y Domínguez, Pedro Vicente. *Guía histórica, geográfica, física, civil, y legal del gobierno e intendencia de la provincia de Potosí*. 1789. Reprint. Potosí: Colección de la Cultura Boliviana, 1952.

Capoche, Luís. *Relación general de la villa imperial de Potosí*. 1585. Reprint. Madrid: Atlas, 1959.

Cieza de León, Pedro de. *The Incas*. 1553. Edited by Victor W. von

Hagen and translated by Harriet de Onís. Norman: University of Oklahoma Press, 1976.

Cobo, Bernabé. *Historia del nuevo mundo.* 1653. Reprint. Madrid: Atlas, 1956.

Dalence, José María. *Bosquejo estadístico de Bolivia.* 1846. Reprint. La Paz: Editorial Universidad Mayor de San Andrés, 1975.

"Descripción de la villa y minas de Potosí, año de 1603." In Jiménez de la Espada, *Relaciones geográficas,* 372-385.

Díez de San Miguel, Garci. *Vista hecha a la provincia de Chucuito en 1567.* Edited by Waldemar Espinosa Soriano. Lima: Casa de la Cultura del Perú, 1964.

Digesto de ordenanzas, reglamentos, acuerdos, decretos de la municipalidad de Cochabamba. 3 vols. Cochabamba: Heraldo, 1900.

Escalona Agüero, Gaspar de. *Gazofilacio real del Perú.* 1647. Reprint. La Paz: Estado, 1941.

Espinoza Soriano, Waldemar, ed. "El memorial de Charcas: Crónica inédita de 1582." *Cantuta: Revista de la Universidad Nacional de Educación* (Chosica, Peru), 1969: 1-35.

Fuentes, Manuel A., ed. *Memorias de los virreyes que han gobernado el Perú durante el tiempo del colonaje español.* 4 vols. Lima: Felipe Bailly, 1859.

Haenke, Tadeo. "Memoria sobre el cultivo del algodón y el fomento de sus fábricas en esta América." In *Telégrafo mercantil,* AGN, tomo 2, no. 36, 1801.

———. *Su obra en los Andes y la selva boliviana.* 1799. Reprint. Cochabamba: Amigos del libro, 1974.

Jiménez de la Espada, Marcos, ed. *Relaciones geográficas de Indias: El Perú.* [1580s-1590s.] Reprint. Madrid: Atlas, 1965.

Juan y Santacilia, Jorge, and Ulloa, Antonio de. *Discourse and Political Reflections on the Kingdoms of Peru.* Edited and translated by John J. TePaske and Besse A. Clement. Norman: University of Oklahoma Press, 1978.

Levillier, Roberto, ed. *La audiencia de Charcas: Correspondencia de presidentes y oidores.* 3 vols. Madrid: J. Pueyro, 1918-1922.

———, ed. *Gobernantes del Perú: Cartas y papeles, siglo XVI.* 14 vols. Madrid: Sucesores de Rivadeneyra, 1921-1926.

Lizárraga, Reginaldo de. *Descripción breve de toda la tierra del Perú, Tucumán, Río de la Plata, y Chile.* 1609. Reprint. Madrid: Atlas, 1968.

López y Velasco, Juan. *Geografía y descripción universal de las Indias.* 1574. Reprint. Madrid: Atlas, 1971.

Matienzo, Juan. *Gobierno del Perú.* 1567. Reprint. Buenos Aires: Cía. sud-americana de Billetes de Banco, 1910.

Messía Venegas, Alfonso. "Memorial al virrey Luís de Velasco." 1603. In Rubén Vargas Ugarte, ed., *Pareceres jurídicos en asuntos de Indias (1601-1718)*, 94-115. Lima, 1951.

Moreno, Gabriel René. *Catálogo del archivo de Mojos y Chiquitos.* 1888. Reprint. La Paz: Instituto Boliviano de Cultura, 1976.

"Nuevo método de cuenta y razón para la real hacienda en las Indias." *Revista de la Biblioteca Nacional* 4 (1940): 267-318.

Orbigny, Alcides d'. *Viaje a la América meridional . . . realizado de 1826 a 1833.* Reprint. 4 vols. Buenos Aires: Futuro, 1945.

Pease, Franklin, ed. "Una visita al obispado de Charcas." 1590. *Humanidades,* no. 3 (1969): 89-125.

Polo de Ondegardo, Juan. "Informe . . . al Lic. Briviesca de Muñatones sobre la perpetuidad de las encomiendas en el Perú." 1561. *Revista histórica* 13 (1940): 125-196.

———. "Relación de los fundamentos acerca del notable daño que resulta de no guardar a los indios sus fueros." 1571. In *Colección de documentos inéditos relativos al descubrimiento, conquista, y organización de las antiguas posesiones españolas de América y Oceanía . . .* vol. 17 of 42. Madrid: Imprenta del Hospicio, 1872.

Poma de Ayala, Felipe Guaman. *El primer nueva corónica y buen gobierno.* 3 vols. 1615. Edited by John V. Murra and Rolena Adorno. Mexico City: Siglo XXI, 1980.

Repartimiento de tierras por el Inca Huayna Capac. 1556. Reprint. Cochabamba: Universidad de San Simon, 1977.

Romero, Carlos A., ed. "Libro de la visita general del virrey Francisco de Toledo, 1570-1575." *Revista histórica* 7 (1924): 115-216.

Santillán, Hernando de. "Relación del origen, descendencia, política, y gobierno de los Incas. . . ." 1563-1564. In *Colección de libros y documentos referentes a la historia del Perú,* vol. 9. Ser. 2, 11 vols. Lima: San Martí, 1927.

Solórzano Pereira, Juan de. *Política indiana.* 5 vols. 1647. Madrid: Compañía Ibero-americana, 1930.

Titu Cusi Yupanqui, Diego de Castro. *Relación de la conquista del Perú.* 1570. Reprint. Lima: Biblioteca Universitaria, 1973.

Vargas Ugarte, Rubén, ed., *Pareceres jurídicos en asuntos de Indias (1601-1718).* Lima, 1951.

Vázquez de Espinosa, Antonio. *Compendio y descripción de las Indias occidentales.* 1630. Reprint. Madrid: Atlas, 1969.

Viedma, Francisco de. *Descripción geográfica y estadística de la provincia de Santa Cruz de la Sierra.* 1788. Reprint. Cochabamba: Amigos del Libro, 1969.

Villava, Victorián de. "Discurso sobre la mita de Potosí." 1793. In *Vida y escritos de Victorián de Villava,* edited by R. Levene. Buenos Aires: Peuser, 1946.

"Visita a Pocona." 1557. *Historia y cultura* (Lima), no. 4 (1970): 269-308.

Books, Articles, and Pamphlets

Abercrombie, Thomas. "The Politics of Sacrifice: An Aymara Cosmology in Action." Ph.D. diss., University of Chicago, 1986.

Albó, Xavier, and Mauricio Mamani. "Esposos, suegros, y padrinos entre los Aymaras." In *Parentesco y matrimonio en los Andes,* edited by E. Mayer and R. Bolton, 283-326. Lima: Universidad Católica, 1980.

Anderson, Perry. *Lineages of the Absolutist State.* London: New Left Books, 1974.

———. *Passages from Antiquity to Feudalism.* London: New Left Books, 1974.

Aranibar, José. "Proprietarios, conductores, y clase menesterosa al frente de los años agrícolas." *Boletín agrícola del Ministerio de Colonización y Agricultura,* no. 18 (1907): 98-102.

Arnade, Charles. *The Emergence of the Republic of Bolivia.* Gainesville: University of Florida Press, 1957.

Arce, René. *Participación popular en la independencia de Bolivia.* La Paz: Colegio Don Bosco, 1979.

Assadourian, Carlos Sempat. "Potosí y el crecimiento de Córdoba en los siglos XVI y XVII." Typescript. Published in *Cuadernos de historia social y económica* 8 (1971): 1-19.

———. "Integración y desintegración regional en un espacio colonial: Un enfoque histórico." In Assadourian, *Sistema economía colonial,* 109-134.

———. "La producción de la mercancía dinero en la formación del mercado interno colonial; el caso del espacio peruano, siglo XVI." In Florescano, ed., *Ensayos sobre el desarrollo económico,* 223-292.

———. *El sistema de la economía colonial: Mercado interno, regiones, y espacio económico.* Lima: Instituto de Estudios Peruanos, 1982.

———. "Dominio colonial y señores étnicos en el espacio andino." *HISLA,* no. 1 (1983): 7-20.

Azogue Crespo, Ricardo, Gustavo Rodríguez, and Humberto Solares. "Cochabamba: El proceso histórico de su constitución como región, 1900-1930," part 3. *Los tiempos*, Jan. 23, 1986, pp. 2-3.

Bakewell, Peter J. *Silver Mining and Society in Colonial Mexico: Zacatecas, 1546-1700*. Cambridge: Cambridge University Press, 1971.

———. "Registered Silver Production in the Potosí District, 1550-1735." *Jahrbuch für Geschichte von Staat, Wirtschaft, und Gesellschaft lateinamerikas* 12 (1975): 67-103.

———. "Technological Change in Potosí: The Silver Boom of the 1570's." *Jahrbuch für Geschichte von Staat, Wirtschaft, und Gesellschaft lateinamerikas* 14 (1977): 55-77.

———. *Miners of the Red Mountain: Indian Labor at Potosí, 1545-1650*. Albuquerque: University of New Mexico Press, 1984.

Baraona, Rafael. "Una tipología de haciendas en las sierra ecuatoriana." In *Reformas agrarias en América latina*, edited by O. Delgado, 688-694. México City: Fondo de Cultura Económica, 1965.

Barnadas, Josep M. *Charcas, 1535-1563: Orígenes de una sociedad colonial*. La Paz: Centro de Investigación y Promoción del Campesinado, 1973.

———. *Los Aymaras dentro de la sociedad boliviana*. La Paz: Centro de Investigación y Promoción del Campesinado, 1976.

———. "Las reducciones jesuitas de Mojos." *Historia boliviana* 4 (1984): 135-166.

Bastien, Joseph W. *Mountain of the Condor*. St. Paul, Minn.: West Publishing, 1978.

Bauer, Arnold J. "Chilean Rural Labor in the Nineteenth Century." *American Historical Review* 76 (1971): 1059-1082.

———. "The Church and Spanish American Agrarian Structure, 1765-1865." *Americas* 28 (1971): 78-98.

———. *Chilean Rural Society from the Spanish Conquest to 1930*. Cambridge: Cambridge University Press, 1975.

———. "Rural Workers in Spanish America: Problems of Peonage and Oppression." *Hispanic American Historical Review* 59 (1979): 34-63.

Bennett, Wendell C. "The Andean Highlands: An Introduction." In *The Handbook of South American Indians*, 7 vols., edited by J. Steward, 2: 1-60. Washington, D.C.: Smithsonian Institution, 1946.

Berkhofer, Robert F. *The White Man's Indian*. New York: Knopf, 1978.

Block, David. "Links to the Frontier: Jesuit Supply of Its Moxos Missions, 1683-1767." *Americas* 37 (1980): 161-178.

Bonifaz, Miguel. "El problema agrario indígena en Bolivia durante la época republicana." *Revista de estudios jurídicos, políticos, y sociales* 8 (1947): 70-75.

Borah, Woodrow. *New Spain's Century of Depression.* Berkeley and Los Angeles: University of California Press, 1951.

Borde, Juan, and Mario Góngora. *Evolución de la propiedad en el Valle del Puangue.* 2 vols. Santiago: Editorial Universitaria, 1956.

Bouysse-Cassagne, Thérèse. "Tributo y etnías en Charcas en la época del Virrey Toledo." *Historia y cultura* (La Paz) 2 (1976): 97-114.

———. "L'espace aymara: Urco et uma." *Annales E.S.C.* 33 (1978): 1057-1080.

Boyer, Richard. "Mexico in the Seventeenth Century: Transition of a Colonial Society." *Hispanic American Historical Review* 57 (1977): 455-478.

Bradby, Barbara. " 'Resistance to Capitalism' in the Peruvian Andes." In Lehmann, ed., *Ecology and Exchange,* 97-122.

Brading, David. *Miners and Merchants in Bourbon Mexico, 1763-1810.* Cambridge: Cambridge University Press, 1971.

———. "Estructura de la producción agrícola en el Bajío, 1700 a 1850." In *Haciendas, latifundios, y plantaciones en América latina,* edited by E. Florescano, 105-131. Mexico City: Siglo XXI, 1975.

———. *Haciendas and Ranchos in the Mexican Bajío: León, 1700-1860.* Cambridge: Cambridge University Press, 1978.

———. "El mercantilismo ibérico y el crecimiento económico en la América latina del siglo XVIII." In Florescano, ed., *Ensayos sobre el desarrollo económico,* 293-314.

Brading, David, and Harry Cross. "Colonial Silver Mining: Mexico and Peru." *Hispanic American Historical Review* 52 (1972): 545-579.

Braudel, Fernand. "European Expansion and Capitalism, 1450-1650." In *Chapters in Western Civilization,* 2 vols., edited by the Contemporary Civilization Staff of Columbia College, 1: 245-288. New York: Columbia University Press, 1961.

———. *On History.* Chicago: University of Chicago Press, 1980.

Braudel, Fernand, and F. Spooner. "Prices in Europe from 1450 to 1750." In *The Cambridge Economic History of Europe,* 7 vols., edited by E. E. Rich and C. H. Wilson, 4: 378-486. Cambridge: Cambridge University Press, 1967.

Brenner, Robert. "Agrarian Class Structure and Economic Development in Pre-Industrial Europe." *Past and Present* 70 (1976): 30-75.

———. "The Origins of Capitalist Development: A Critique of Neo-Smithian Marxism." *New Left Review* 104 (1977): 25-92.

Browman, David. "El manejo de la tierra árida del altiplano del Perú y Bolivia." *América indígena* 40 (1980): 143-159.

Brush, Stephen B. "Man's Use of an Andean Ecosystem." *Human Ecology* 4 (1976): 147-166.

Buechler, Rose Marie. "Technical Aid to Upper Peru: The Nordenflicht Expedition." *Journal of Latin American Studies* 5 (1973): 37-77.

———. "Mining Society of Potosí, 1776-1810." Ph.D. diss., University of London, 1974.

———. "El intendente Sanz y la 'mita nueva' de Potosí." *Historia y cultura* (La Paz), no. 3 (1977): 59-95.

Burkholder, Mark A. "From Creole to *Peninsular*: The Transformation of the Audiencia of Lima." *Hispanic American Historical Review* 52 (1972): 395-415.

Byrne de Caballero, Geraldine. "La arquitectura de almacenamiento en la logística incáica." *Diario*, Nov. 30, 1975, p. 2.

Caillet-Bois, Ricardo. "Un ejemplo de la industria textil colonial." *Boletín del Instituto de Investigaciones Históricas* 14 (1938): 19-24.

Cajka, Francis R. "Peasant Commerce in the Serranías of Cochabamba, Bolivia." Ph.D. diss., University of Michigan, 1979.

Camacho Saa, Carlos. *Minifundia, Productivity, and Land Reform*. Madison, Wis.: Land Tenure Center, 1966.

Campbell, Leon G. *The Military and Society in Colonial Peru, 1750-1810*. Philadelphia: American Philosophical Society, 1978.

———. "Recent Research on Andean Peasant Revolts, 1750-1820." *Latin American Research Review* 14 (1979): 3-49.

Carmagnani, Marcello. "La producción agropecuaria chilena: Aspectos cuantitativos (1680-1830)." *Cahiers des Amériques latines*, no. 3 (1969): 3-21.

———. *Formación y crisis de un sistema feudal*. Mexico City: Siglo XXI, 1976.

Centro de Estudios de la Realidad Económica y Social. *Programa de investigación sobre la economía y desarrollo regional de Cochabamba*. La Paz: CERES, 1981. Mimeograph.

Céspedes del Castillo, Guillermo. "Lima y Buenos Aires: Repercusiones económicas y políticas de la creación del virreinato de La Plata." *Anuario de estudios americanos* 3 (1946): 667-874.

———. "La visita como institución indiana." *Anuario de estudios americanos* 3 (1946): 984-1025.

———. "Reorganización de la hacienda virreinal peruana en el siglo XVIII." *Anuario de historia del derecho español* 23 (1953): 329-369.

Chaunu, Huguette, and Pierre Chaunu. *Séville et l'Atlantique, 1504-1650.* 8 vols. Paris: S.E.V.P.E.N., 1955-1959.

Chayanov, A. V. *The Theory of the Peasant Family Economy*, ed. and trans. D. Thorner, B. Verblay, and R.E.F. Smith. Homewood, Ill.: Irwin, 1966.

Chevalier, François. *La formation des grands domaines au Mexique: Terre et société aux XVIe–XVIIe siècles.* Paris: Institut d'Ethnologie, 1952.

Choque, Roberto. "Pedro Chipana: Cacique comerciante de Calamarca." *Avances* no. 1 (1978): 28-32.

Coatsworth, John. "The Limits of State Absolutism: The State in Eighteenth-Century Mexico." In Spalding, ed., *History of Colonial Latin America*, 25-52.

Cobb, Gwendoline Ballantine. "Supply and Transportation for the Potosí Mines, 1545-1640." *Hispanic American Historical Review* 29 (1949): 25-45.

Cole, Jeffrey A. "An Abolitionism Born of Frustration: The Conde de Lemos and the Potosí Mita, 1667-1673." *Hispanic American Historical Review* 63 (1983): 307-334.

———. "Viceregal Persistence versus Indian Mobility: The Impact of the Duque de la Plata's Reform Program on Alto Perú, 1681-1692." *Latin American Research Review* 19 (1984): 37-56.

———. *The Potosí Mita, 1573-1700: Compulsory Indian Labor in the Andes.* Stanford, Calif.: Stanford University Press, 1985.

Coleman, D. C., ed. "Eli Heckscher and the Idea of Mercantilism." *Scandinavian Economic History Review* 5 (1957): 3-25.

———. *Revisions in Mercantilism.* London: Methuen, 1969.

Collier, George, Renato Rosaldo, and John Wirth, eds. *The Inca and Aztec States, 1400-1800.* New York: Academic Press, 1982.

Cook, Noble David. "La población indígena en el Perú colonial." *Anuario del Instituto de Investigaciones Históricas*, no. 8 (1965): 73-105.

———. *Demographic Collapse: Indian Peru, 1520-1620.* Cambridge: Cambridge University Press, 1981.

———, ed. *Tasa de la visita general de Francisco de Toledo*. Lima: Universidad Nacional Mayor de San Marcos, 1975.

Cornblit, Oscar. "Society and Mass Rebellion in Eighteenth-Century Peru and Bolivia." In *St. Anthony's Papers*, no. 22, edited by R. Carr, 9-44. Oxford: Oxford University Press, 1970.

Costeloe, Michael. "The Administration, Collection, and Distribution of Tithes in the Archbishopric of Mexico, 1800-1860." *Americas* 23 (1966): 3-27.

Crahan, Margaret. "The Administration of Don Melchor de Rocafull, Duque de la Palata, Viceroy of Peru, 1681-1689." *Americas* 4 (1971): 389-412.

Crespo Rodas, Alberto. "La mita de Potosí." *Revista histórica* 12 (1955-1956): 158-162.

Cushner, Nicolas. *Lords of the Land: Sugar, Wine, and the Jesuit Estates of Coastal Peru, 1600-1767*. Albany: State University of New York Press, 1980.

Dandler Hanhart, Jorge. *Local Group, Community, and Nation: A Study of Changing Structure in Ucureña, Bolivia, 1935-1952*. Madison, Wis.: Land Tenure Center, 1967.

———. *El sindicalismo campesino en Bolivia: Los cambios estructurales en Ucureña*. Mexico City: Instituto Indigenista Interamericano, 1969.

———. "Politics of Leadership, Brokerage, and Patronage in the Campesino Movement of Cochabamba, Bolivia." Ph.D. diss., University of Wisconsin, 1971.

———. "El desarrollo de la agricultura, políticas estatales, y el proceso de acumulación en Bolivia." 1981. Typescript.

———. "Diversificación, procesos de trabajo, y movilidad espacial en los valles y serranías de Cochabamba." In Harris, Larson, and Tandeter, *Participación indígena*, 639-682.

Davies, Keith. *Landowners in Colonial Peru*. Austin: University of Texas Press, 1984.

Demelas, Marie-Danièle. "Darwinismo a lo criollo: El darwinismo en Bolivia, 1880-1910." *Historia boliviana* 1 (1981): 55-82.

Desdevises du Dezert, Georges. "Les missions des Mojos et des Chiquitos de 1767 à 1808." *Revue hispanique* 43 (1918): 365-430.

DeWind, Adrian. *Peasants Become Miners: The Evolution of Industrial Mining Systems in Peru, 1902-1974*. New York: Garland, 1987.

Dobyns, Henry. "An Outline of Andean Epidemic History to 1720." *Bulletin of the History of Medicine* 37 (1963): 493-515.

Dollfus, Olivier. *El reto del espacio andino*. Lima: Instituto de Estudios Andinos, 1981.
Dupré, George, and Pierre-Philippe Rey. "Reflections on the Pertinence of a Theory of the History of Exchange." *Economy and Society* 2 (1973): 131-163.
Duviols, Pierre. "La represión del paganismo andino y la expulsión de los moriscos." *Anuario de estudios americanos* 28 (1971): 201-207.
Espinoza Soriano, Waldemar. "El alcalde mayor indígena en el virreinato del Perú." *Anuario de estudios americanos* 17 (1960): 183-300.
Estiada, Teodomiro. *Pequeña monografía del Departamento de Cochabamba*. Oruro: Tribuno, 1904.
Farriss, Nancy. *Mayan Society under Colonial Rule*. Princeton: Princeton University Press, 1984.
Febres Villarroel, Oscar. "La crisis agrícola en el Perú en el último tercio del siglo XVIII." *Revista histórica* 27 (1964): 102-199.
Fifer, J. Valerie. *Bolivia: Land, Location, and Politics since 1825*. Cambridge: Cambridge University Press, 1972.
Fioravanti-Molinié, Antoinette. "Multi-Levelled Andean Society and Market Exchange: The case of Yucay (Peru)." In Lehmann, ed., *Ecology and Exchange*, 211-230.
Fisher, F. J. "Commercial Trends and Policy in Sixteenth-Century England." *Economic History Review*, 1st ser., 10 (1940): 95-117.
Fisher, John. *Government and Society in Colonial Peru: The Intendant System, 1784-1814*. London: Athlone, 1970.
———. *Minas y mineros en el Perú, 1776-1824*. Lima: Instituto de Estudios Peruanos, 1977.
Fisher, Lillian Estelle. *The Last Inca Revolt, 1780-1783*. Norman: University of Oklahoma Press, 1966.
Florescano, Enrique. *Precios del maíz y crisis agrícola en México, 1708-1810*. Mexico City: Colegio de México, 1969.
———. *Origen y desarrollo de los problemas agrarios de México, 1500-1821*. Mexico City: Era, 1976.
———. "The Formation and Economic Structure of the Hacienda in New Spain." In *The Cambridge History of Latin America*, 5 vols., edited by Leslie Bethell, 2: 153-188. Cambridge: Cambridge University Press, 1984.
———, ed. *Ensayos sobre el desarrollo económico de México y America latina*. Mexico City: Fondo de Cultura Económica, 1979.
Flores Galindo, Alberto. "Buscando un Inca." Paper presented at the

Social Science Research Council/University of Wisconsin Conference on Resistance and Rebellion in the Andean World, 18th-20th Centuries, Madison, Wis., Apr. 26-28, 1984.
———, ed. *Túpac Amarú II: 1780.* Lima: Retablo de papel, 1976.
Flores-Ochoa, Jorge A. *Pastoralists of the Andes.* Philadelphia: Institute for the Study of Human Issues, 1979.
Foster-Carter, Aidan. "The Modes of Production Controversy." *New Left Review* 107 (1978): 47-78.
Gade, Daniel W., and Mario Escobar. "Village Settlement and the Colonial Legacy in Southern Peru." *Geographical Review* 72 (1982): 430-449.
Garavaglia, Juan Carlos. "Un capítulo del mercado interno colonial: El Paraguay y su región (1537-1682)." *Nova Americana* 1 (1978): 11-56.
Gardner, Richard L. "Price Trends in Eighteenth-Century Mexico." *Hispanic American Historical Review* 65 (1985): 279-326.
Geertz, Clifford. *Agricultural Involution: The Processes of Ecological Change in Indonesia.* Berkeley and Los Angeles: University of California Press, 1963.
Glave, Luís Miguel. "Trajines: Un capítulo en la formación del mercado interno colonial." *Revista andina* 1 (1983): 9-76.
Glave, Luís Miguel, and María Isabel Remy. *Estructura agraria y vida rural en una región andina: Ollantaytambo entre los siglos XVI y XIX.* Cuzco: Centro de Estudios Rurales Andinos "Bartolomé de las Casas," 1983.
Godoy, Ricardo. "From Indian to Miner and Back Again: Small-Scale Mining in the Jukumani Ayllu, Northern Potosí, Bolivia." Ph.D. diss., Columbia University, 1983.
Golte, Jürgen. *La racionalidad de la organización andina.* Lima: Instituto de Estudios Peruanos, 1980.
———. *Repartos y rebeliones: Túpac Amarú y las contradicciones del sistema colonial.* Lima: Instituto de Estudios Andinos, 1980.
Góngora, Mario. *Origen de los inquilinos de Chile central.* Santiago: Editorial Universitaria, 1960.
———. *Encomenderos y estancieros: Estudios acerca de la constitución social aristocrática de Chile después de la Conquista, 1580-1660.* Santiago: Editorial Universitaria, 1970.
———. *Studies in the Colonial History of Spanish America.* Cambridge: Cambridge University Press, 1975.
Goy, J., and E. LeRoy Ladurie, eds. *Les fluctuations du produit de la Dîme.* Paris: Mouton, 1972.
Grieshaber, Erwin P. "Survival of Indian Communities in Nine-

teenth-Century Bolivia." Ph.D. diss., University of North Carolina, 1977.
———. "Survival of Indian Communities in Nineteenth-Century Bolivia: A Regional Comparison." *Journal of Latin American Studies* 12 (1980): 223-269.

Guzmán, Augusto. *Cochabamba*. Cochabamba: Amigos del Libro, 1972.

Guzmán Arze, Humberto. *La realidad social de Cochabamba*. Cochabamba: Amigos del Libro, 1972.

Halperin, Rhoda, and James Dow, eds. *Peasant Livelihood: Studies in Economic Anthropology and Cultural Ecology*. New York: St. Martin's, 1977.

Hamilton, Earl J. *War and Prices in Spain, 1651-1800*. Cambridge: Harvard University Press, 1947.

Hamnett, Brian, "The Appropriation of Mexican Church Wealth by the Spanish Bourbon Government: The 'Consolidation of Vales Reales.' " *Journal of Latin American Studies* 1 (1969): 86-91.

Hanke, Lewis. *The Imperial City of Potosí*. The Hague: Nijhoff, 1956.

Harris, Olivia. "Kinship and the Vertical Economy of the Laymi Ayllu, Norte de Potosí." In *Actes du LXIIe Congrès International des Americanistes*, 4: 165-177. Paris: Société des Americanistes, 1976.

———. "Labor and Produce in an Ethnic Economy: Northern Potosí, Bolivia." In Lehmann, ed., *Ecology and Exchange*, 70-97.

———. "Ecological Duality and the Role of the Center: Northern Potosí." In Masuda, Shimada, and Morris, *Andean Ecology*, 311-336.

Harris, Olivia, and Xavier Albó. *Monteras y guardatojos: Campesinos y mineros en el norte de Potosí*. La Paz: Centro de Investigación y Promoción del Campesinado, 1975.

Harris, Olivia, Brooke Larson, and Enrique Tandeter, eds. *La participación indígena en los mercados surandinos: Estrategias y reproducción social, siglos XVI-XX*. La Paz: CERES, 1987.

Harris, Richard L. "Marxism and the Agrarian Question in Latin America." *Latin American Perspectives* 5 (1978): 2-26.

Heckscher, Eli. *Mercantilism*. 2 vols. New York: Macmillan, 1955.

Helmer, Marie. "Commerce et industrie au Pérou à la fin du XVIIIe siècle." *Revista de Indias*, no. 10 (1950): 519-526.

———. "Mineurs allemands à Potosí: L'expédition Nordenflycht (1788-1789)." *La minería hispana e iberoamericana* 1 (1978): 513-528.

Hemming, John. *The Conquest of the Incas.* London: Sphere, 1972.

Herr, Richard. *The Eighteenth-Century Revolution in Spain.* Princeton: Princeton University Press, 1958.

Hidalgo Lehuedé, Jorge. "Amarus y cataris: Aspectos mesiánicos de la rebelión indígena de 1781 en Cusco, Chayanta, La Paz, y Arica." *Revista Chungará,* no. 10 (1983): 117-138.

———. "Ecological Complementarity and Tribute in Atacama, 1683-1792." In Masuda, Shimada, and Morris, *Andean Ecology,* 161-184.

Hilton, Rodney. "Agrarian Class Structure and Economic Development in Pre-Industrial Europe: A Crisis of Feudalism." *Past and Present* 80 (1978): 3-19.

———, ed. *The Transition from Feudalism to Capitalism.* London: New Left Books, 1976.

Hobsbawm, Eric. "A Case of Neo-Feudalism: La Convención, Peru." *Journal of Latin American Studies* 1 (1969): 31-50.

Hutchins, Patricia C. "Rebellion and the Census of Cochabamba, 1730-1732." Ph.D. diss., Ohio State University, 1974.

Hyslop, John. "An Archeological Investigation of the Lupaqa Kingdom and Its Origins." Ph.D. diss., Columbia University, 1976.

Isbell, Billie Jean. *To Defend Ourselves: Ecology and Ritual in an Andean Village.* Austin: University of Texas Press, 1978.

Janvry, Alain de. *The Agrarian Question and Reformism in Latin America.* Baltimore: The Johns Hopkins University Press, 1981.

Janvry, Alain de, and L. A. Couch. "El debate sobre el campesinado: Teoría y significación política." *Estudios rurales latinoamericanos* 2 (1979): 282-295.

Jara, Alvaro. "Dans le Pérou du XVIe siècle: La courbe de production de mataux monnayables." *Annales E.S.C.* 22 (1967): 590-608.

Kamen, Henry. "El establecimiento de los intendentes en la administración española." *Hispania* 24 (1964): 368-395.

Kay, Cristobal. "Comparative Development of the European Manorial System and the Latin American Hacienda System: An Approach to a Theory of Agrarian Change for Chile." D.Phil. diss., University of Sussex, 1971.

———. "Comparative Development of the European Manorial System and the Latin American Hacienda System." *Journal of Peasant Studies* 2 (1974): 69-98.

Keith, Robert G. *Conquest and Agrarian Change: The Emergence of the Hacienda System on the Peruvian Coast.* Cambridge: Harvard University Press, 1976.

Klein, Herbert S. *Politics and Political Change in Bolivia.* Cambridge: Cambridge University Press, 1969.

———. "Structure and Profitability of Royal Finance in the Viceroyalty of the Río de la Plata in 1790." *Hispanic American Historical Review* 53 (1973): 440-469.

———. "Hacienda and Free Community in Eighteenth-Century Alto Perú: A Demographic Study of the Aymara Population of the Districts of Chulumani and Pacajes in 1786." *Journal of Latin American Studies* 7 (1975): 193-220.

———. *Bolivia: The Evolution of a Multi-Ethnic Society.* Oxford: Oxford University Press, 1982.

———. "Peasant Response to the Market and the Land Question in the 18th and 19th Centuries." *Nova Americana*, no. 5 (1982): 103-134.

Klein, Herbert S., and John J. TePaske. "The Seventeenth-Century Crisis in the Spanish Empire: Myth or Reality?" *Past and Present* 90 (1981): 116-135.

Kohl, James. "The Cliza and Ucureña War: Syndical Violence and National Revolution in Bolivia." *Hispanic American Historical Review* 62 (1982): 607-628.

Kubler, George. "The Quechua in the Colonial World." In *The Handbook of South American Indians*, 7 vols., edited by Julian Steward, 2: 334-340. Washington, D.C.: Smithsonian Institution, 1946.

———. *The Indian Caste of Peru, 1795-1940: A Population Study Based upon Tax Records and Census Reports.* Washington, D.C.: Smithsonian Institution, 1952.

Kula, Witold. *Problemas y métodos de la historia económica.* Barcelona: Península, 1973.

———. *An Economic Theory of the Feudal System.* London: New Left Books, 1976.

La Force, James C., Jr. *The Development of the Spanish Textile Industry, 1750-1800.* Berkeley and Los Angeles: University of California Press, 1965.

Langer, Erick. "Labor Strikes and Reciprocity on Chuquisaca Haciendas." *Hispanic American Historical Review* 65 (1985): 255-278.

Larson, Brooke. "Merchants and Economic Activity in Sixteenth-Century Potosí." Master's thesis, Columbia University, 1972.

———. "Caciques, Class Structure, and the Colonial State." *Nova Americana*, no. 2 (1978): 197-235.

———. "Economic Decline and Social Change in an Agrarian Hinterland: Cochabamba in the Late Colonial Period." Ph.D. diss., Columbia University, 1978.

———. "Rural Rhythms of Class Conflict in Eighteenth-Century Cochabamba." *Hispanic American Historical Review* 60 (1980): 407-430.

———. *Explotación agraria y resistencia campesina en Cochabamba*. Cochabamba: CERES, 1984.

Lehmann, David. "Introduction: Andean Societies and the Theory of Peasant Economy." In Lehmann, ed., *Ecology and Exchange*, 1-26.

———, ed. *Ecology and Exchange in the Andes*. Cambridge: Cambridge University Press, 1982.

Lenin, V. I. *The Rise of Capitalism in Russia*. Moscow: Progress, 1974.

Levene, Ricardo. *Vida y escritos de Victorián de Villava*. Buenos Aires: Peuser, 1946.

Levillier, Roberto. *Don Francisco de Toledo, supremo organizador del Perú: Su vida, su obra (1515-1582)*. 3 vols. Madrid: Espasa-Calpe, 1935-1942.

Lewin, Boleslao. *La rebelión de Túpac Amarú*. Buenos Aires: Hachette, n.d.

Lockhart, James. "Encomienda and Hacienda: The Evolution of the Great Estate in the Spanish Indies." *Hispanic American Historical Review* 49 (1969): 411-429.

Lofstrom, William Lee. *The Problem and Promise of Reform: Attempted Social and Economic Change in the First Years of Bolivian Independence*. Cornell University Dissertation Series, no. 33. Ithaca, N.Y., 1972.

Lohmann Villena, Guillermo. *El corregidor de Indios en el Perú bajo los Austrias*. Madrid: Ediciones Cultura Hispánica, 1957.

Long, Norman, and Bryan R. Robert. *Miners, Peasants, and Entrepreneurs: Regional Development in the Central Highlands of Peru*. Cambridge: Cambridge University Press, 1984.

———, eds. *Peasant Cooperation and Capitalist Expansion in Central Peru*. Austin: University of Texas Press, 1978.

Lumbreras, Luís G. *The Peoples and Cultures of Ancient Peru*. Washington, D.C.: Smithsonian Institution Press, 1974.

Lynch, John. *Spanish Colonial Administration, 1782-1810: The Intendant System in the Viceroyalty of the Río de la Plata*. London: Athlone, 1958.

———. *Spain under the Hapsburgs: Spain and America, 1598-1700*. 2 vols. New York: Oxford University Press, 1969.

Macedonio Urquidi, José. *El origen de la noble villa de Oropesa.* 2nd ed. Cochabamba: Municipalidad de Cochabamba, 1971.

Macera, Pablo, "Feudalismo colonial americano: El caso de las haciendas peruanas." In his *Trabajos de historia,* 4 vols. 3: 139-227. Lima: Instituto Nacional de Cultura, 1977.

Málaga Medina, Alejandro. "Las reducciones en el Perú (1532-1600)." *Historia y cultura* (Lima) 8 (1974): 155-167.

Mallon, Florencia. *The Defense of Community in Peru's Central Highlands: Peasant Struggle and Capitalist Transition, 1860-1940.* Princeton: Princeton University Press, 1983.

Mariluz Urquijo, José María. "Noticias sobre las industrias del virreinato del Río de la Plata en la época del Marquéz de Aviles (1799-1810)." *Revista de historia americana y argentina* 1 (1956-1957): 85-118.

Martínez Alier, Juan. "Relations of Production on Andean Haciendas." In *Land and Labor in Latin America: Essays on the Development of Agrarian Capitalism in the Nineteenth and Twentieth Centuries,* edited by Kenneth Duncan and Ian Rutledge, 141-164. Cambridge: Cambridge University Press, 1977.

Masuda, Shozo, Izumi Shimada, and Craig Morris, eds. *Andean Ecology and Civilization: An Interdisciplinary Perspective on Andean Ecological Complementarity.* Tokyo: University of Tokyo Press, 1985.

Meillassoux, Claude. *Femmes, greniers, et capitaux.* Paris: Maspero, 1975.

Mellafe, Rolando. "Frontera agraria: El caso del virreinato peruano en el siglo XVI." In *Tierras nuevas: Expansión territorial y ocupación del suelo en América (siglos xvi-xix),* edited by Alvaro Jara, 11-42. Mexico City: Colegio de México, 1969.

Mintz, Sidney. "Internal Market Systems As Mechanisms of Social Articulation." In *Proceedings of the 1959 Annual Spring Meeting of the American Ethnological Society,* edited by V. F. Ray, 20-30. Madison: University of Wisconsin Press, 1959.

———. "Caribbean Marketplaces and Caribbean History." *Radical History Review,* no. 27 (1983): 110-120.

Mitre, Antonio. *Los patriarcas de la plata: Estructura socioeconómica de la minería boliviana en el siglo XIX.* Lima: Instituto de Estudios Peruanos, 1981.

Moore, Barrington, Jr. *Social Origins of Dictatorship and Democracy: Lord and Peasant in the Making of the Modern World.* Boston: Beacon, 1966.

Moore, John Preston. *The Cabildo in Peru under the Hapsburgs: A*

Study in the Origins and Powers of the Town Council in the Viceroyalty of Peru, 1530-1700. Durham, N.C.: Duke University Press, 1954.

Moreno, Gabriel René. *Ultimos días coloniales en el Perú.* La Paz: Juventud, 1970.

Moreno Cebrián, Alfredo. *El corregidor de indios y la economía peruana en el siglo XVIII.* Madrid: Instituto Gonzalo Fernández de Oviedo, 1977.

Mörner, Magnus. "A Comparative Study of Tenant Labor in Parts of Europe, Africa, and Latin America, 1700-1900." *Latin American Research Review* 5 (1970): 3-15.

———. *La corona española y los foraneos en los pueblos de indios de América.* Stockholm: Almqvist and Wiksell, 1970.

———. "The Spanish American Hacienda: A Survey of Recent Research and Debate." *Hispanic American Historical Review* 53 (1973): 183-216.

———. "En torno a las haciendas de la región del Cuzco desde el siglo XVIII." In *Haciendas, latifundios, y plantaciones en América latina,* edited by Enrique Florescano, 346-374. Mexico City: Siglo XXI, 1975.

———. "Some Characteristics of Agrarian Structure in the Cuzco Region towards the End of the Colonial Period." *Boletín de estudios latinoamericanos y del Caribe* 18 (1975): 15-29.

———. *Perfil de la sociedad rural del Cuzco a fines de la colonia.* Lima: Universidad del Pacífico, 1978.

———. "Economic Factors and Social Stratification in Colonial Spanish America, with Special Regard to Elites." *Hispanic American Historical Review* 63 (1983): 335-370.

———. *The Andean Past: Land, Societies, and Conflict.* New York: Columbia University Press, 1985.

Moscoso, Maximiliano. "Apuntes para la historia de la industria textil en el Cuzco colonial." *Revista universitaria* 51-52 (1962-1963): 67-94.

Muñoz Pérez, J. "La publicación del reglamento de comercio libre de Indias de 1778." *Anuario de estudios americanos* 4 (1947): 615-664.

———. "Los proyectos sobre España e Indias en el siglo XVIII: El proyectismo como género." *Revista de estudios políticos,* no. 81 (1955): 169-185.

Murra, John V. "Rite and Crop in the Inca State." In *Culture in History,* edited by Stanley Diamond, 393-407. New York: Columbia University Press, 1960.

———. "On Inca Political Structure." In *Comparative Political Systems*, edited by Ronald Cohen and J. Middleton. New York: Natural History, 1967.

———. "An Aymara Kingdom in 1567." *Ethnohistory* 15 (1968): 115-151.

———. "El 'control vertical' de un máximo de pisos ecológicos en la economía de las sociedades andinas." In *Visita de la provincia de León de Huánuco en 1562*, 2 vols., edited by Iñigo Ortiz de Zúñiga, 2: 429-476 (Huánuco: Hermilio Valdizán, 1972), as reprinted in Murra, *Formaciones económicas y políticas*, 59-116.

———. *Formaciones económicas y políticas del mundo andino.* Lima: Instituto de Estudios Peruanos, 1975.

———. "Aymara Lords and Their European Agents at Potosí." *Nova Americana*, no. 1 (1978): 231-244.

———. "La guerre et les rébellions dans l'expansion de l'état inka." *Annales E.S.C.* 33 (1978): 927-935.

———. *La organización del estado inca*. Mexico City: Siglo XXI, 1978.

———. " 'El archipiélago vertical' Revisited." In Masuda, Shimada, and Morris, *Andean Ecology*, 3-14.

———. "The Limits and Limitations of the 'Vertical Archipelago' in the Andes." In Masuda, Shimada, and Morris, *Andean Ecology*, 15-20.

Nash, June. *We Eat the Mines and the Mines Eat Us: Dependency and Exploitation in Bolivian Tin Mines*. New York: Columbia University Press, 1979.

Olen, Leonard E. *Cantón Chullpas: A Socio-Economic Study of the Cochabamba Valley of Bolivia*. Washington, D.C.: Foreign Agricultural Reports, 1948.

O'Phelan Godoy, Scarlett. "La rebelión de Túpac Amarú: Organización interna, dirigencia, y alianzas." *Histórica* 3 (1979): 89-121.

———. "Tierras comunales y revuelta social: Perú y Bolivia en el siglo XVIII." *Allpanchis*, 13th year, vol. 19 (1983): 75-91.

———. *Rebellions and Revolts in Eighteenth-Century Peru and Upper Peru*. Cologne: Bohlau, 1985.

Orlove, Benjamin. "Inequality among Peasants: The Forms and Uses of Reciprocal Exchange in Andean Peru." In Halperin and Dow, *Peasant Livelihood*, 201-214.

Palacio Atard, Vicente. "Areche y Guirior: Observaciones sobre el fracaso de una visita al Perú." *Anuario de estudios americanos* 3 (1946): 269-376.

Parejas, Alcides. "Don Lázaro de Ribera, gobernador de la provincia de Moxos (1784-1792)." *Anuario de estudios americanos* 33 (1976): 949-962.

Parry, John. *The Sale of Public Offices in the Spanish Indies under the Hapsburgs.* Berkeley and Los Angeles: University of California Press, 1953.

Patch, Richard W. "Social Implications of the Bolivian Agrarian Reform." Ph.D. diss., University of Michigan, 1956.

Pearse, Andrew. "Peasants and Revolution: The case of Bolivia." *Society and Economy* 1 (1972): 255-279, 399-424.

Pease, Franklin. "The Formation of Tawantinsuyu: Mechanisms of Colonization and Relationship with Ethnic Groups." In Collier, Rosaldo, and Wirth, *The Inca and Aztec States,* 173-198.

Peñaloza, Luís. *Historia económica de Bolivia.* 2 vols. La Paz, 1953-1954.

Phelan, John L. "Authority and Flexibility in the Spanish Imperial Bureaucracy." *Administrative Science Quarterly* 5 (1960): 47-65.

Pike, Frederick B. "Aspects of Cabildo Economic Regulation in Spanish America under the Hapsburgs." *Inter-American Economic Affairs* 13 (1960): 67-86.

Pilar Chao, María del. "La población de Potosí en 1779." *Anuario del Instituto de Investigaciones Históricas* no. 8 (1965): 171-180.

Platt, Tristan. "Acerca del sistema tributario pre-Toledano en el Alto Perú." *Avances,* no. 1 (1978): 33-44.

———. "Espejos y maíz: El concepto de yanatín entre los Macha de Bolivia." In *Parentesco y matrimonio en los Andes,* edited by E. Mayer and R. Bolton, 139-182. Lima: Universidad Católica, 1980.

———. "The Ayllus of Lipez in the Nineteenth Century." Paper presented at the Congress of Americanists, Manchester, England, Sept. 5-10, 1982.

———. *Estado boliviano y ayllu andino: Tierra y tributo en el Norte de Potosí.* Lima: Instituto de Estudios Peruanos, 1982.

———. "The Role of the Andean Ayllu in the Reproduction of the petty Commodity Regime in Northern Potosí (Bolivia)." In Lehmann, ed., *Ecology and Exchange,* 27-69.

———. "Liberalism and Ethnocide in the Southern Andes." *History Workshop,* no. 17 (1984): 3-18.

———. "Calendarios tributarios e intervención mercantil: La articulación estacional de los ayllus de Lipez con el mercado minero potosino (siglo XIX)." In Harris, Larson, and Tandeter, *Participación indígena,* 471-558.

Platt, Tristan, and Ramiro Molina Barrios. *Qollaruna: El origen social del proletariado del estaño*. Forthcoming.

Polanyi, Karl. *The Great Transformation: The Political and Economic Origins of Our Time*. Boston: Beacon, 1944.

———. "The Economy As Instituted Process." In *Trade and Market in the Early Empires*, edited by C. Arensberg, K. Polanyi, and H. Pearson, 243-270. New York: Free Press, 1957.

Postan, M. M., and John Hatcher. "Agrarian Class Structure and Economic Development in Pre-Industrial Europe: Population and Class Relations in Feudal Society." *Past and Present* 78 (1978): 24-37.

Rasnake, Roger. "The *Kurahkuna* of Yura: Indigenous Authorities of Colonial Charcas and Contemporary Bolivia." Ph.D. diss., Cornell University, 1982.

Rejas, Damian. *Tercer centenario de la fundación del Monasterio de Santa Clara (1648-1948)*. Cochabamba: Universal, 1948.

Reyeros, Rafael A. *El ponqueaje: La servidumbre de los indios bolivianos*. La Paz: Universo, 1949.

Rivera, Silvia. "La expansión del latifundio en el altiplano boliviano." *Avances*, no. 2 (1978): 95-118.

———. "El mallku y la sociedad colonial en el siglo XVII: El caso de Jesús de Machaca." *Avances*, no. 1 (1978): 7-27.

Rodríguez Ostría, Gustavo. "Expansión del latifundio o supervivencia de las comunidades indígenas? Cambios en la estructura agraria boliviana del siglo XIX." *Serie: Historia*, Instituto de Estudios Sociales y Económicos (IESE), Working Paper no. 1. Cochabamba: Universidad Mayor de San Simon, 1983.

Romano, Ruggiero. "Tra XVI e XVII sécolo: Una crisis económica, 1619-1622." *Revista storica italiana* 74 (1962): 480-531.

———. "Movimiento de los precios y desarrollo económico: El caso de Sudamérica en el siglo XVIII." *Desarrollo económico* 1-2 (1963): 31-43.

———. "Encore la crise de 1619-1622." *Annales E.S.C.* 19 (1964): 31-37.

Rowe, John H. "Inca Culture at the Time of the Spanish Conquest." In *The Handbook of South American Indians*, 7 vols., edited by J. Steward, 2:253-255. Washington, D.C.: Smithsonian Institution, 1946.

———. "The Incas under Spanish Colonial Institutions." *Hispanic American Historical Review* 35 (1957): 155-199.

Saignes, Thierry. "Une frontière fossile: La cordillère chiriguano au

XVIe siècle." 2 vols. 3rd cycle doctorate, University of Paris, 1974.

———. "El desenclavamiento de Charcas Oriental: Análisis de dos fracasos." *Historia y cultura* (La Paz) 2 (1976): 63-88.

———. "De la filiation à la résidence: Les ethnies dans les vallées de Larecaja." *Annales E.S.C.* 33 (1978): 1160-1181.

———. "Políticas étnicas en Bolivia colonial, siglos XVI-XIX." *Historia boliviana* 3 (1983): 1-30.

———. *Los Andes orientales: Historia de un olvido.* Cochabamba: CERES, 1985.

———. "Notes on the Regional Contribution to the Mita in Potosí in the Early Seventeenth Century." *Bulletin of Latin American Research* 4 (1985): 65-76.

———. "Ayllus, mercado, y coacción colonial: El reto de las migraciones internas en Charcas, siglo XVII." In Harris, Larson, and Tandeter, *Participación indígena*, 111-158.

Salamanca, Octavio. *La crisis en el departamento de Cochabamba.* Cochabamba: Ilustración, 1927.

———. *El socialismo en Bolivia.* Cochabamba: Bolívar, 1931.

Salomon, Frank. "Andean Ethnology in the 1970s: A Retrospective." *Latin American Research Review* 17 (1982): 75-128.

———. "The Dynamic Potential of the Complementarity Concept." In Masuda, Shimada, and Morris, *Andean Ecology*, 511-532.

Sánchez, Rodrigo. "The Model of Verticality in the Andean Economy: A Critical Reconsideration." *Actes du XLIIe Congrès International des Américanistes*, 4: 213-226. Paris: Société des Américanistes, 1977.

Sánchez-Albornoz, Nicolás. "La saca de mulas de Salta al Perú, 1778-1808." *Anuario del Instituto de Investigaciones Históricas*, no. 8 (1965): 261-312.

———. *The Population of Latin America.* Berkeley and Los Angeles: University of California Press, 1974.

———. *Indios y tributos en el Alto Perú.* Lima: Instituto de Estudios Peruanos, 1978.

———. "Migración rural en los Andes: Sipesipe (Cochabamba), 1645." *Revista de historia económica* 1 (1983): 13-36.

———. "Mita, migración, y pueblos: Variaciones en el espacio y en el tiempo, Alto Perú, 1573-1692." *Historia boliviana*, no. 3 (1983): 31-46.

Santamaría, Daniel. "La propriedad de la tierra y la condición social del indio en el Alto Perú, 1780-1810." *Desarrollo económico*, no 66 (1977): 253-271.

Santos Martínez, Pedro. *Historia económica de Mendoza durante el virreinato, 1776-1810.* Madrid: Universidad Nacional de Cuyo, 1961.

———. *Las industrias durante el virreinato, 1776-1810.* Buenos Aires: Editorial Universitaria de Buenos Aires, 1969.

Schoop, Wolfgang. "Los ciclos rotatorios de los comerciantes ambulantes en las ferias semanales de los valles de Cochabamba." *Arbeitspapiere* (Universität Bielefeld), no. 13 (1978).

Scott, James. *The Moral Economy of the Peasant.* New Haven: Yale University Press, 1976.

Semo, Enrique. *Historia del capitalismo en México: Los origenes, 1521-1763.* Mexico City: Era, 1973.

Shafer, Robert J. *The Economic Societies in the Spanish World, 1763-1821.* Syracuse: Syracuse University Press, 1958.

Slicher van Bath, B. H. *The Agrarian History of Western Europe, 800-1850.* London: Edward Arnold, 1963.

Spalding, Karen. "Social Climbers: Changing Patterns of Mobility among the Indians of Colonial Peru." *Hispanic American Historical Review* 50 (1970): 645-664.

———. "Tratos mercantiles del corregidor de indios y la formación de la hacienda serrana en el Perú." *América indígena* 3 (1970): 595-608.

———. "The Colonial Indian." *Latin American Research Review* 7 (1972): 47-76.

———. "Kurakas and Commerce: A Chapter in the Evolution of Andean Society." *Hispanic American Historical Review* 53 (1973): 581-599.

———. *De indio a campesino: Cambios en la estructura del Perú colonial.* Lima: Instituto de Estudios Peruanos, 1974.

———. "Hacienda-Village Relations in Andean Society to 1830." *Latin American Perspectives* 4 (1975): 107-121.

———. "Exploitation As an Economic System: The State and the Extraction of Surplus in Colonial Peru." In Collier, Rosaldo, and Wirth, *The Inca and Aztec States,* 321-342.

———. *Huarochirí: An Andean Society under Inca and Spanish Rule.* Stanford, Calif.: Stanford University Press, 1984.

———, ed. *Essays in the Political, Economic, and Social History of Colonial Latin America.* Newark: University of Delaware Press, 1982.

Stavenhagen, Rodolfo. *Social Classes in Agrarian Societies.* Garden City, N.Y.: Doubleday, 1975.

Stein, Stanley. "Reality in Microcosm: The Debate over Trade in America, 1785-1789." *Historia ibérica*, no. 1 (1976): 111-119.

Stein, Stanley, and Barbara Stein. *The Colonial Heritage of Latin America: Essays on Economic Dependence in Perspective*. New York: Oxford University Press, 1970.

Stern, Steve J. *Peru's Indian Peoples and the Challenge of the Spanish Conquest: Huamanga to 1640*. Madison: University of Wisconsin Press, 1982.

———. "The Struggle for Solidarity: Class, Culture, and Community in Highland Indian America." *Radical History Review*, no. 27 (1983): 21-48.

———. "The Age of Andean Insurrection, 1742-1782: A Reappraisal." Paper presented at the Social Science Research Council/University of Wisconsin conference on Resistance and Rebellion in the Andean World, 18th-20th Centuries, Madison, Wis., Apr. 26-28, 1984.

———. "New Directions in Andean Economic History: A Critical Dialogue with Carlos Sempat Assadourian." *Latin American Perspectives* 12 (1985): 133-148.

Tandeter, Enrique. "Rent As a Relation of Production and As a Relation of Distribution in Late Colonial Potosí." Paper presented at the Latin American Studies Association Meeting, Pittsburgh, April 15-17, 1979.

———. "Mita, Minga y Kajcha." Typescript. (Spanish version of chapter 3 of his "Rente comme rapport de production.")

———. "La rente comme rapport de production et comme rapport de distribution: Le cas de l'industrie minière de Potosí, 1750-1826." 3rd cycle doctorate, École des Hautes Études en Sciences Sociales, Paris, 1980.

———. "Forced and Free Labor in Late Colonial Potosí." *Past and Present* 93 (1981): 98-136.

———. "La producción como actividad popular: 'Ladrones de minas' en Potosí." *Nova Americana*, no. 4 (1981): 43-65.

Tandeter, Enrique, Vilma Milletich, María Ollier, and Beatriz Ruibal. "El mercado de Potosí a fines del siglo XVIII." In Harris, Larson, and Tandeter, *Participación indigena*, 379-424.

Tandeter, Enrique, and Nathan Wachtel. *Precios y producción agraria: Potosí y Charcas en el siglo XVIII*. Buenos Aires: Estudios CEDES, 1984.

Taylor, William. *Landlord and Peasant in Colonial Oaxaca*. Stanford, Calif.: Stanford University Press, 1972.

TePaske, John. "La crisis del siglo XVIII en el virreinato del Perú."

In B. García Martínez, ed., *Historia y sociedad en el mundo de habla española*, 263-280. Mexico City: Colegio de México, 1970.

———. "The Fiscal Structure of Upper Peru and the Financing of Empire." In Spalding, ed., *Essays*, 69-94.

Thirsk, Joan, ed. *The Agrarian History of England and Wales (1500-1640)*. 4 vols. Cambridge: Cambridge University Press, 1967.

Thomas, R. Brooke, and Bruce P. Winterhalder. "Physical and Biotic Environment of Southern Highland Peru." In P. Baker and M. Little, eds., *Man in the Andes*, 21-59. Stroudsburg, Pa.: Doudon, Hutchinson, and Ross, 1976.

Thompson, Edward P. "The Moral Economy of the English Crowd." *Past and Present* 50 (1971): 76-136.

Thomson, G.P.C. "Puebla between Mine and Metropolis: Three Cycles of Growth and Decline, 1532-1850." Paper presented at the Seminar on Economic Imperialism and Latin America, University of London, Nov. 5, 1979.

———. "The Cotton Textile Industry in Puebla during the 18th and 19th Centuries." In *The Economies of Mexico and Peru during the Late Colonial Period, 1760-1810*, edited by Nils Jacobsen and Hans-Jürgen Puhle, 169-202. Berlin: Colloquium, 1986.

Tord Nicolini, Javier. "El corregidor de indios del Perú: Comercio y tributos." *Historia y cultura* (Lima), no. 8 (1974): 173-214.

———. "Sociedad colonial y fiscalidad." *Apuntes* 4 (1977): 3-28.

Troll, Carl. "The Cordilleras of the Tropical Americas: Aspects of Climatic, Phytogeographical, and Agrarian Ecology." In Carl Troll, ed., *Geo-ecology of the Mountainous Regions of the Tropical Americas*. Bonn: University of Bonn Geographical Institute, 1968.

Tschopik, Harry, Jr. "The Aymaras." In *The Handbook of South American Indians*, 7 vols., edited by J. Steward, 2: 501-573. Reprint. New York: Cooper Square, 1963.

Urquidi, Guillermo. *Monografía del departamento de Cochabamba*. Cochabamba: Tunari, 1954.

Van Young, Eric. "Mexican Rural History since Chevalier: The Historiography of the Colonial Hacienda." *Latin American Research Review* 18 (1983): 5-61.

———. "Conflict and Solidarity in Indian Village Life: The Guadalajara Region in the Late Colonial Period." *Hispanic American Historical Review* 64 (1984) 55-79.

Vargas Ugarte, Rubén. *Historia del Perú*. 5 vols. Lima: Librería Stadium–Imprenta López, 1949-1958.

Vázquez, Mario C. *Hacienda, peonaje, y servidumbre en los Andes peruanos*. Lima: Estudios andinos, 1961.

Vicens Vives, Jaime. *An Economic History of Spain*. Princeton: Princeton University Press, 1969.

Vilar, Pierre. "Réflexions sur la 'crise de l'ancien type': 'Inegalité des récolte' et 'sous-développement'." In *Conjoncture économique, structures sociales: Hommage à Ernest Labrousse*, 37-58. Paris: Mouton, 1974.

Villalobos, Sergio. *El comercio y la crisis colonial*. Santiago: Ediciones de la Universidad de Chile, 1968.

Wachtel, Nathan. *Sociedad e ideología*. Lima: Instituto de Estudios Peruanos, 1973.

———. *The Vision of the Vanquished: The Spanish Conquest of Peru through Indian Eyes, 1530-1570*. New York: Harper and Row, 1977.

———. "The *Mitimas* of the Cochabamba Valley: The Colonization Policy of Huayna Capac." In Collier, Rosaldo, and Wirth, *The Inca and Aztec States*, 199-235. New York: Academic Press, 1982.

Wallerstein, Immanuel. *The Modern World-System: Capitalist Agriculture and the Origins of the European World Economy in the Sixteenth Century*. New York: Academic Press, 1974.

Wennergren, E. Boyd, and Morris D. Whitaker. *The Status of Bolivian Agriculture*. New York: Praeger, 1975.

Wittman, Tibor. "Sociedad y economía de Cochabamba: La 'Valencia del Perú' en 1793." *Revista de Indias*, no. 31 (1971): 367-376.

Wolf, Eric. "The Mexican Bajío in the 18th Century: An Analysis of Cultural Integration." In M. Edmundson, ed., *Synoptic Studies of Mexican Culture*, 181-197. New Orleans: Tulane University Press, 1957.

Wolf, Freda Y. "Parentesco aymara en el siglo XVI." In *Parentesco y matrimonio en los Andes*, edited by E. Mayer and R. Bolton, 115-136. Lima: Universidad Católica, 1980.

Zavala, Silvio. *El servicio personal de los indios en el Perú*. 3 vols. Mexico City: Colegio de México, 1978.

Zulawski, Ann. "Agricultural Labor and Social Change: Pilaya and Paspaya in the Eighteenth Century." Paper presented at the International Congress of Americanists, Universidad de los Andes, Bogotá, July 1-7, 1985.

———. "Labor and Migration in Seventeenth-Century Alto Perú." Ph.D. diss., Columbia University, 1985.

INDEX

Library of Congress Cataloging-in-Publication Data

Larson, Brooke.
Colonialism and agrarian transformation in Bolivia: Cochabamba, 1550-1900 / Brooke Larson.
p. cm.
Bibliography: p.
Includes index.
ISBN 0-691-07738-X (alk. paper) ISBN 0-691-10241-4 (pkb.)
1. Agriculture—Economic aspects—Bolivia—Cochabamba Region—History. 2. Peasantry—Bolivia—Cochabamba Region—History. 3. Mercantile system—Bolivia—Cochabamba Region—History. 4. Cochabamba Region (Bolivia)—Rural conditions. 5. Cochabamba Region (Bolivia)—Politics and government. I. Title.
HD1870.C62L37 1988

305.5′63—dc19 87-34463
CIP